CONTEMPORARY

SOUTHERN

EDITED BY

Richmond Croom Beatty

AND

William Perry Fidler

1940

D. C. HEATH AND COMPANY

BOSTON

PRINTED IN THE UNITED STATES OF AMERICA. 4 H 0

OFFICES: BOSTON NEW YORK CHICAGO
SAN FRANCISCO DALLAS ATLANTA LONDON

PREFACE

THIS volume of readings is an outgrowth of the opinion of its editors that Southerners interested in Southern life and letters should be afforded an opportunity to acquaint themselves with the best creative and critical thought of their region. The compilers of anthologies hitherto, for reasons of their own, appear to have given to the contemporary writers of the South only negligible attention. We are offering the present book by way of a corrective. Its contents are, of course, not inclusive, for the reason that a number of major Southern authors — Cabell, Glasgow, Heyward, Stribling, and others — are important primarily as novelists and obvious exigencies of length have precluded the use of valid specimens of their work. We believe, none the less, that a sizable and important representation is contained within these pages, and that a knowledge of that representation will prove of fundamental value to interested readers.

RICHMOND CROOM BEATTY, Vanderbilt University
WILLIAM PERRY FIDLER, University of Alabama

August, 1940

CONTENTS

The Essay

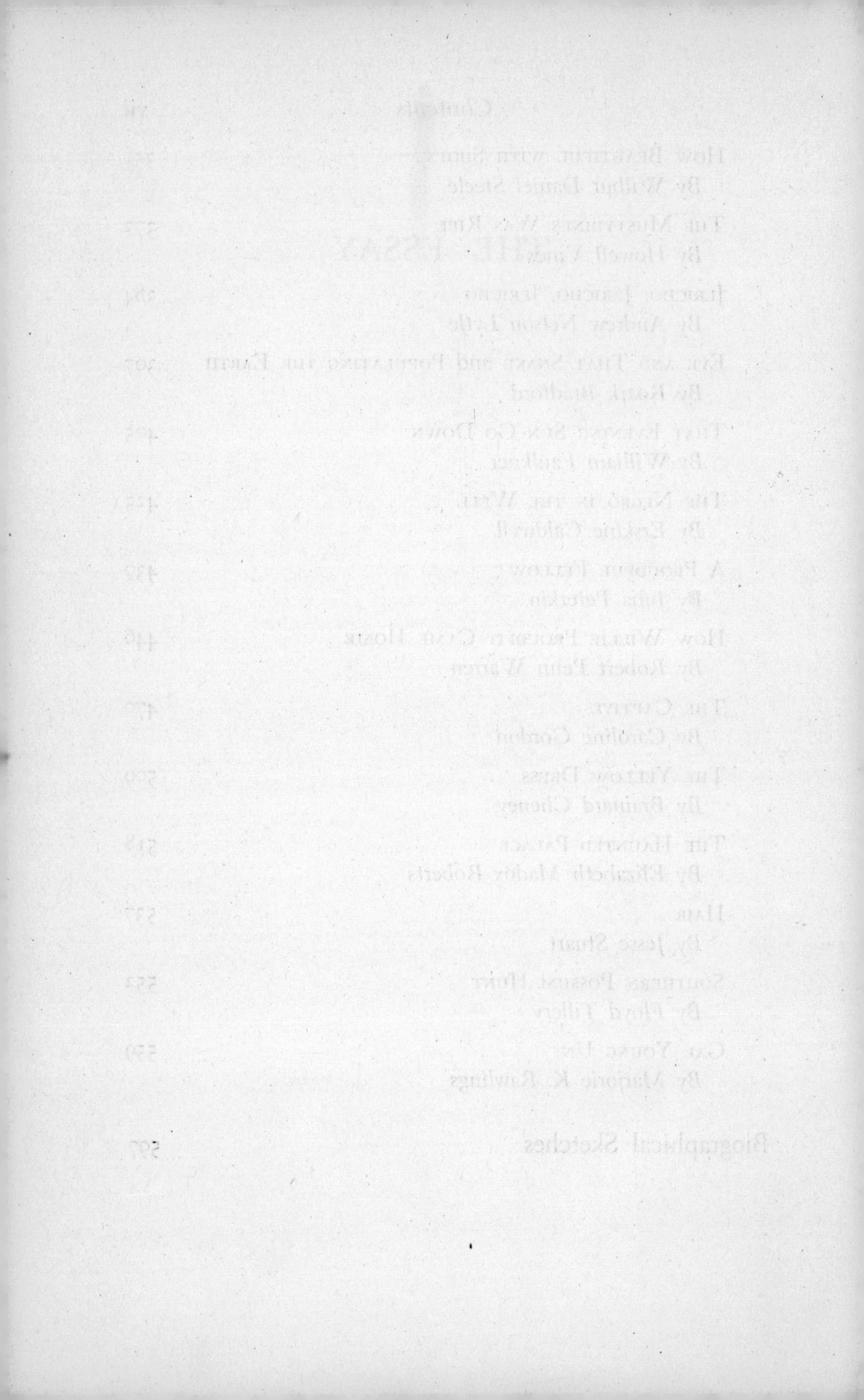

THE ESSAY

The Essay

THE MAJOR critical debate which the student is likely to notice in this collection of essays is one in no sense new. It has gone on in various ways continuously since 1865 and appears far from settled yet. To state the issue in its simplest terms would be to say that a remarkable number of our writers have addressed themselves to the question: What kind of South do we want? Should we wish this region to resemble, say, the industrial Northeast, with the advantages and the limitations that go with life in that section; or are there certain human values in that way of life once called " typically Southern " which are not yet wholly dead, and which are still altogether worth cherishing?

We have called this debate an old one. To name a few of the figures of the first decades after the war who found themselves preoccupied with it would be to cite Robert Lewis Dabney of Virginia; Albert Taylor Bledsoe, a Virginian in background, who set forth his views in his Baltimore magazine, the Southern Review; and Charles C. Jones, a Georgia historian. These men all deplored Appomattox and the change to their civilization which, they felt, was bound to follow it. It seemed to them most regrettable that the South was being made to accept a reconstruction ushered in with violence and dedicated to the worship of the twin gods of " Speed and Mass."

On the other hand, there were men like Henry W. Grady of Georgia, Walter Hines Page of North Carolina, and a host of others, who looked upon the Dabney point of view as hopelessly old-fashioned. Let the sections love one another, said Grady; let all the bloodshed and violence be forgotten. Let North Carolina, said Page, set up mills, pave her highways, modernize her schools, become as brisk and as progressive and as up-to-date as ever she can. If she does this, she will become rich; and after all, are not Riches and a State of Blessedness practically synonymous terms?

In recent years the debate has passed into a far more critical stage. Some Southern thinkers began to point out that although Lincoln had spoken of uniting the divided house, saying that one which remained divided "cannot stand," the grand unity he referred to seems still far from realized. These men have noticed, for instance, that unity implies a certain legislative impartiality between sections as the primary condition under which a state of harmony and fairness may exist. They have pointed out, further, that our national government has been dominated since 1865 almost continuously by industry. That the South, they continue, has inadequate libraries, impoverished farmers, and merchants victimized by unequal freight rates is mute testimony of the tribute it has had to pay to those who are industrially strong. Out of the encounters, oral and written, between those of the Dabney and the Grady persuasions has come some of the most stimulating prose in American literature.

Both groups have suggested plans for the South, ways in which, they contend, life may be lived here with greater completeness and satisfaction. The problems which they treat are, we believe, the most important which Southerners of today must face, for on the conclusions we reach with respect to them the future of the South depends.

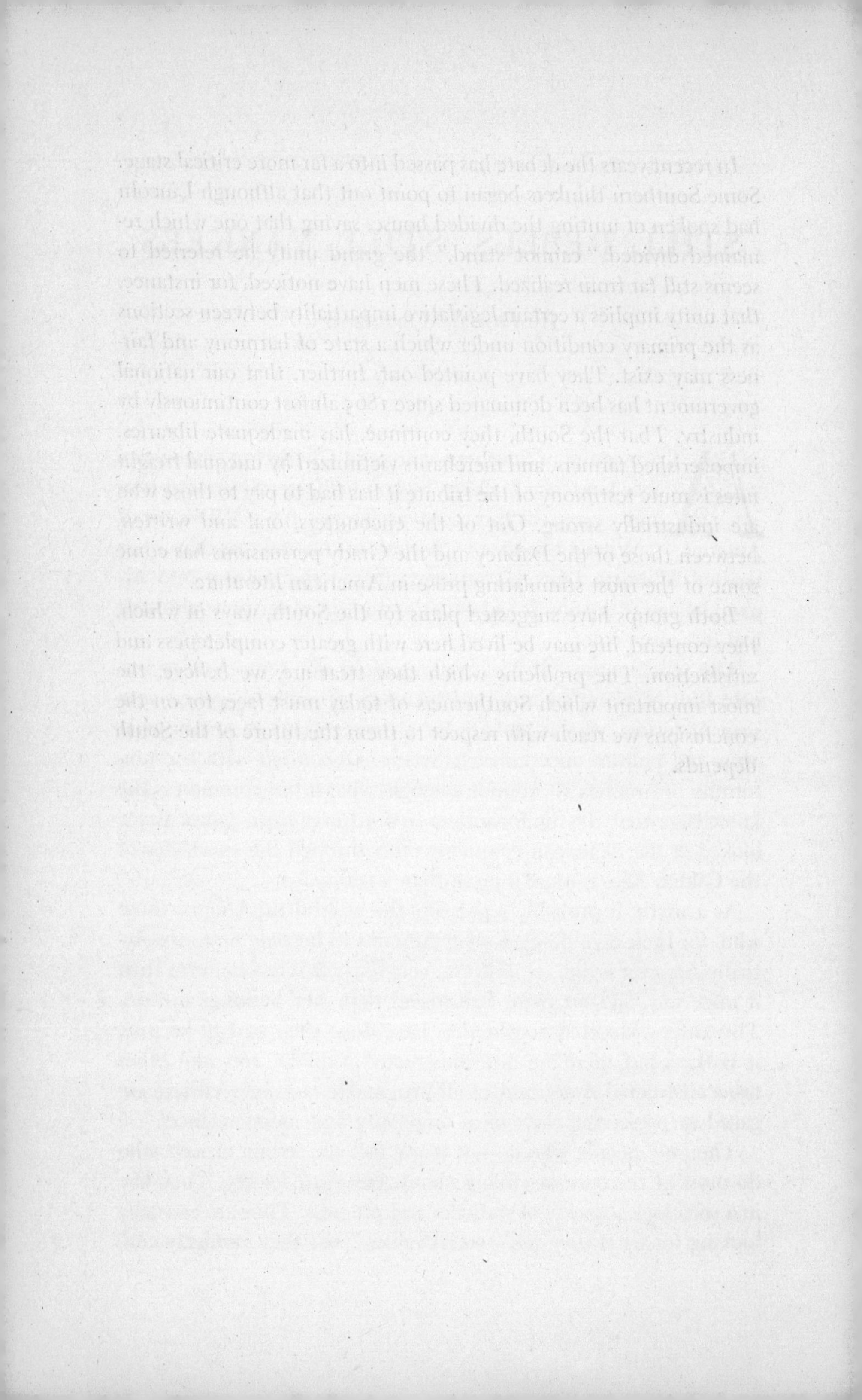

STILL REBELS, STILL YANKEES

By Donald Davidson

AT a meeting of Southern writers in Charleston some years ago, Laurence Stallings looked belligerently around him and expressed an ardent preference for a " Balkanized America." " What I like about Charleston," he said, " is that it has resisted Abraham Lincoln's attempts to put the country into Arrow Collars. If the South had won the war, the country would have had lots more color."

The rebelliousness of Mr. Stallings need not compel us to suspect him of being an unreconstructed Southerner disguised as a man of letters, who is looking for artistic reasons to justify what arms and politics once failed to secure. Discontent with the uniformity of America is common enough; what is not common is the knowledge that this uniformity, a byword ever since James Bryce looked at the American commonwealth through the spectacles of the Gilded Age, is more a myth than a reality.

As a myth, it probably represents the wishful thinking of those who, for their own designs, want America to become uniform. Actually America is not yet uniform; very likely it is less uniform than it once was, and far more Balkanized than Mr. Stallings dreams. The unreconstructed Southerners have done their part in keeping it Balkan; but there are unreconstructed Yankees, too, and other unreconstructed Americans of all imaginable sorts, everywhere engaged in preserving their local originality and independence.

The only people who do not know this are certain experts who do most of the current talking about American society. They live in a sociological pickle of statistics and progress. They are eternally looking for what they call " social values," but they strangely confine their research to libraries and graduate " projects " at the larger universities. They avoid the places where social values may be encountered in the flesh. If they stumble upon a living social value, walking visibly about some spot of earth and drawing its nutriment from a tradition embodied in the houses, speech, crafts, music, folklore, and wisdom of an actual people, their rule is to denounce it as an anachronism and to call for its extermination. For them, nothing must grow according to its nature, but things " develop " by laboratory formulae, which are obtained by inspecting the reactions of the most abnormal and depressed specimens of humankind, too weak to protest against sociological vivisection.

Those of us who still believe in the map of the United States know that it marks the residence of some diverse Americans who had better not go unacknowledged. In Vermont, for instance, are people who are still Yankees; and in Georgia, and elsewhere, there are still Rebels. I remember talking with a certain Virginian who watched a Vermont sunset with me, one summer evening. As the sun passed below the distant Adirondacks, we looked at the Green Mountains around us, and at the trim Vermont fields where all the weeds were flowers and all the grass was hay. In the clear detail of the afterglow we saw the forests of spruce and balsam and maple, and spoke of how the very wilderness, in this New England state, had uprightness and order. The woods were as snug and precise as a Yankee kitchen — no ragged edges, no sprawling, nothing out of place. In the clearings the farmhouses were all painted; and the barns were painted, too. The streams were orthodox streams, almost model streams, with water always translucent and stones rounded and picturesquely placed among moss and ferns. They were often called " brooks " — a word that for Southerners existed only on the printed page.

On this land, the Virginian said, the Yankees had looked so intimately and long that, like the man in Hawthorne's story of the Great Stone Face, they had become the image of what they contemplated. The Yankee genius of Vermont was upright, vertical, and no doubt Puritan. Where the landscape itself enforced consistency and order, how could the people concede much virtue to inconsistency and irregularity? The forebears of the Vermont Yankee had once failed to understand how Southerners could be devoted both to slavery and democracy. That old failure of understanding did not seem queer, or worth more than a passing sigh, to two Southerners who stood looking at sunset upon a land whose gentled wildness suggested the urgent possibility of a well-ordered universe, cut to a discreet Yankee pattern. But the human geography of America had now become a particolored thing, sprawling across the continent in a crazy-quilt of provinces, or sections, each with its private notion of a universe. No longer, as in the sixties, could the Yankee make bold to set up a general pattern for the entire Union. He had enough to do if he would defend and preserve what was peculiarly his own — his very own, surely, in upper New England. In such a purpose of preservation the two Southerners at last could make bold to sympathize, even to help if possible. But preservation could not be achieved without recognizing a principle of diversity in American life. Only by such means could one make any sense out of Lamar's famous epigram in his eulogy on Sumner, "My countrymen, know one another and you will love one another"; it ceased to have meaning if America was to be subjugated to the ideal of uniformity, or to the ideal universe that some one section might generate.

But how could the principle of diversity be inculcated? On the negative side, certain false images, the product of legend or propaganda, must somehow be counterbalanced. Regrettably enough, some of the fairest legends caused the greatest embarrassment. To the Virginian I recalled the horror of a good lady from the Middle West, who was motoring from Washington to Richmond. Mount Vernon was all right, she thought; there the legend was safely frozen. But beyond, on the road to Richmond, what had become of all the great mansions she had read about, the cotton fields with Negroes caroling, the old gentlemen in goatees and white vests, sipping mint juleps in the shade? They were not visible. There were only a few scattered shacks and tumbledown barns in miles of impenetrable wilderness that looked for all the world as it must have looked when John Smith first invaded it. If she could have encountered the legend, the lady would have been content. But not seeing it or knowing how to locate it, she was smitten with a housewifely desire to get at this ragged land with a good broom and whisk it into seemliness.

Other sojourners had been anxious to do a far more drastic tidying-up. The Harlan County visitors, the Scottsboro attorneys, the shock troops of Dayton and Gastonia asked no questions about the genius of place. Wherever they went on their missions of social justice, they carried with them a legend of the future, more dangerously abstract than the legend of the past, and sternly demanded that the local arrangements be made to correspond with it, at whatever cost. The local arrangements, indeed, might well bear some mending. And yet the only America that the visitors offered as a model was an overgrown urban America, forever in process of becoming one laboratory experiment after another.

What could be done about all this? Our answers were shrouded in darkness as we walked back to the log fires and good company of a New England inn. The Virginian, after the fashion of good Southerners who do not want to let anybody know the uncertainty of their minds under modern conditions, did not propose any answer. Instead, he told several good stories. They were his courteous and delightful way of saying that he was being pounded between his own unyielding loyalty and the howling respectability of the great world.

❦ ❦ ❦

If any answer is to be found, if anything positive is to be done, it must surely be through a laborious process of discovering America all over again. When one looks at America, not to see how it does or does not fit the synthetic ideals proposed for its future, but only with the modest purpose of detecting the realities — let us say the social values — that persist in local habitations, he soon realizes that comparisons are more fruitful than condemnations. More specifically, when one has the good fortune to go directly from a summer in Vermont to an autumn and winter in Middle Georgia, he forms a clear picture of sectional differences. This picture is not in the least favorable to the notion that the diverse America of the Rebels and Yankees is in any immediate danger of being submerged.

If on coming to Vermont I had consulted the modern legend of New England that vaguely haunted my mind, I would have received the iconoclastic shock which our advanced thinkers argue is the first step toward salvation. Had not a New England migrant to the South assured me that his ancestral acres were now inhabited by Montenegrins, who had turned them into a goat farm? Had not the sepulchral Eugene O'Neill and others told tales of the poverty and decadence of New England life? The farms were deserted, it was said; the immigrants and mill towns had come; the Yankees had left for parts unknown, or, remaining, had become degenerate. Even the loyalty of Robert Frost gave no comfortable assurance, if one accepted the New York aleck's criticism of *North of Boston;* though there were many wistful asides in which Frost put forth the guarded wisdom of a not yet daunted soul. The New England of Whittier and Webster was supposed to be extinct; it had been replaced by Puritan-baiters and F. Scott Fitzgeraldites who drank cocktails and read Proust when not conducting the insurance business of the United States.

But if the Vermont that I saw was in the least representative of New England, this composite picture was a wild detraction. In Vermont, if nowhere else, a New England like that of Whittier and Webster miraculously persisted, a reality capable of reducing a Southerner almost to despairing envy. I could understand what led Walter Hines Page, a quarter of a century ago, to disparage his native North Carolina and fall in love with New England. But the time was past when one needed to disparage or praise in the interest of the America Page dreamed about, for in the 1930's it seemed impossible of realization, or, where realized, already past saving. To one who did not accept Lincoln's quaint idea that the United States must become "all one thing or all the other," it seemed more than ever true that the unity of America must rest, first of all, on a decent respect for sectional differences.

If Vermont and Georgia could be taken in a broad way to stand for New England and the deep South, one could easily trace out the most general differences. The Vermont towns, like the Vermont landscape, were swept and garnished, as if the Day of Judgment might at any moment summon them into the presence of the celestial inspector. They looked as if Vermonters lived by the adage "Handsome is as handsome does," and one could reflect that this proverb might well have issued from some collaborative effort of Poor Richard and Jonathan Edwards. The most delightful of Southern towns was almost certain to mix a little squalor with its grandeurs. Here, what a Southerner most particularly noticed, was the neatly painted aspect of everything, the absence of ramshackle buildings and litter, the white steeples of churches, the shipshapeness of streets, yards, garages, barber shops, and public buildings. By some special benison of God and the New England conscience, not a billboard had been allowed to sprout between Bennington and the Canadian border. Perhaps by the same double grace, not a weed sprouted, either. All the weeds had turned into ferns and buttercups. Vermont farms were Currier and Ives prints of what good farms ought to look like, with orchards and brooks in exactly the right place and gates that did not need mending. In the background were lakes and mountains where one would put them if he were Aladdin or Wordsworth. It was not surprising to be told that hardly a poison snake, and no poison ivy, existed in the state of Vermont; or to find that there were excellent trails running the whole length of the Green Mountains, with fingerposts at every wilderness crossroads, and tin huts, with beds, firewood, and caretaker, atop of the highest peak. A few nagging irregularities of nature, like blackflies and mosquitoes, seemed really blasphemous in a land to which God had given a monopoly of all things good and precise. No wonder, with all this beneficence around them, that the Yankees remembered the *Mayflower* and forgot John Smith, honored Bunker Hill and neglected King's Mountain. If they could claim such priority in the benevolence of God, their proprietary feeling toward the Revolutionary War and their almost hereditary claim to the direction of the United States government were by comparison insignificant appurtenances, theirs as a matter of course and by general presumption.

Although I did not hold very devotedly to the economic determinism of modern historians, it was a temptation to say that the people were a great deal like the land. There was the climate, which put keenness into a Southerner's veins. Summer was short, and one had to make the most of it; winter was severe, and one had to keep shield and buckler perpetually ready against it — in that matter was God benevolent or ruthless? Short summers and cold winters made the Vermont Yankee frugal and careful. He must watch his corners. If he were caught napping, he would perish. So much and no more was the gift of his seasons; so much and no more was the rule of his nature. And one had to watch over his neighbor as well as work with him if the general security were not to be imperiled by some outrageous letting down of bars. Very likely, the New England civic conscience derived as much from the imperatives of climate as from the Puritan tradition; the one egged on the other.

No great check had ever been put upon the development of qualities that the Southerners recognized as ineradicably Yankee. History had been as kind to the Yankee as God had been kind. Since Revolutionary times no great sudden change had ever swept over these peaceful towns and this quiet landscape. Industrialism had come slowly and somewhat agreeably upon a people who had the ingenuity to use it and the moral force to make it behave. How could they who thought they knew how to tame the monster realize that he might walk unshackled and ravening elsewhere? The Yankees, indeed, had never tasted defeat. Since Burgoyne's expedition no invader had come upon them to ravage and destroy. They had freed the Negroes, replying " I can " to duty's " Thou must "; but they were fortunately exempt from the results of emancipation, for no Negroes lived among them to acquaint them with the disorder of unashamed and happy dirt. One knew that a slum in New England would be a well-managed slum, and that New Englanders would comprehend Secretary Perkins's horror at the lack of plumbing in unreformed America and her notion of saving the barefoot South by building shoe factories. For in New England humanitarianism was the natural flower of good sense. In a land where everything was so right, it was hard to imagine a perverse land where so much could be so wrong without disturbing either a people's composure or their happiness.

But in the plantation country of Middle Georgia the social values required a different yardstick. The genius of Georgia was stretched out, relaxed and easy, in keeping with the landscape, which required a large and horizontal view of mundane affairs. The Georgian assumed that God would have sense and heart enough to take into consideration, when Judgment Day came around, a good deal besides external and man-made appearances. God was a gentleman, indeed, who would certainly know, without being told, that one was a person, a somebody, doing his best among some rather amazing arrangements that had better not be talked about too much. The climate might or might not predispose the Georgia Rebel to laziness; the fact was, he worked and fretted more than the Yankee knew. But the Rebel idea was never to seem to work and fret. You must not let your work ride you, was the saying. In plain truth, you did not need to. The land was bountiful, and the Lord would provide, and in event of the Lord's failure or displeasure you could always fall back on your kinfolks.

Where the seasons were all mixed up, so that autumn merged into spring without any sharp demarcation, and you might have a dubious summer in the middle of winter, it became almost a point of honor not to worry too much about provision. There was no need to watch corners when something was growing all the time. Almost anything would grow in Middle Georgia, and almost everything did grow, including weeds whose invasions could not possibly be repelled from every roadside and ditch if they were to be kept out of cotton and corn.

The Georgia landscape had a serene repose that lulled a man out of all need of conscience. It was anything but swept and garnished. It could be mild or majestic or genial and savage depending on what view you got of pines against red earth, or Negro cabins underneath their chinaberry trees, or sedge grass running into gullies and thence to impenetrable swamps, or deserted mansions lost in oak groves and magnolias. Rivers were muddy and at times unrestrained; they got out of bounds, as all things natural did here. In the pine barrens you might get an impression of desolation and melancholy; but things could grow lushly too, with the overpowering vegetable passion that harrowed the Puritan soul of Amy Lowell when she visited the Magnolia Gardens at Charleston. But finally, it was a well-tilled country, where you were forever seeing the Negro and his mule against the far horizon, or the peach orchards bursting into an intoxicating pink.

The seasons were full of charms and intimidations. Spring, with its dogwood blossoms and soft airs, might deliver a tornado or a flood; summer, full of grown corn and harvest ease, might turn into dusty drouth. The woods that lured you to enter and gave nuts and flowers for the taking were full of hidden terrors. Sit on a mossy bank without precaution, and in a few hours you might be on fire with chigoe bites. Stoop to pick a flower, and you might find a rattlesnake. Indoors the housewife had to fight cockroaches and flies; outdoors were hawks, polecats, weasels, possums, coons, and other varmints to harry the henhouse. Precision, for the Georgian, must rank among the Utopian virtues. If New England encouraged man to believe in an ordered universe, Georgia — and a good deal of the South besides — compelled him to remember that there were snakes in Eden. Nature, so ingratiating and beautiful, which bound the Georgian to his land with a love both possessive and fearful, was a fair but dreadful mistress, unpredictable and uncontrollable as God. The New Englander knew exactly where to find nature yielding, and he could make his arrangements accordingly. But the Georgian never knew. His safest policy was to relax, and he readily developed a great degree of tolerance for irregularity in nature and man. At his lowest level, this quality made him lackadaisical and trifling. In this he differed from the New England Yankee, who became a perfectionist, and then at his worst might turn into zealot, strangely intolerant even while, as idealist, he argued for tolerance.

History, like God and nature, had been both generous and unkind to Georgia and the South. The Georgia Rebel must approach his early history through a bloody link of war and reconstruction that was hazy and bygone to the Vermont Yankee. Defeat had possessed him and had rubbed deep into his wounds. Around him were the visible reminders of destruction and humiliation. His land had been ravaged and rebuilt, and he had been told to forget. But he would not and could not forget, and was therefore torn between his loyalty and his awareness that the great world was bored with his not forgetting. He had been rebuked for being inept at administering a newfangled government that he did not understand or like any too well, and in which he had been allowed to participate only by a kind of negligent afterthought. Turning desperately to the industrial civilization against which he had once taken arms, he had played it as a hedge against the problematic future. Though agrarian at heart, he had been forced to wonder whether the ingenious Yankee might not be right after all.

Thus he remembered the faith and hankered after the fleshpots at the same time. But industrialism, declining to be treated as a mere hedge, began Sherman's march to the sea all over again. It piled ugliness upon wreckage and threw the old arrangements out of kilter. The United Daughters of the Confederacy and the Kiwanis Club flourished side by side. Mule wagon and automobile, fundamentalism and liberalism, education and illiteracy, aristocratic pride and backwoods independence disproved the axiom that two bodies cannot occupy the same space. Cities that preserved the finest flavor of the old régime had to be approached over brand-new roads where billboards, tourist camps, filling stations, and factories broke out in a modernistic rash among the water oaks and Spanish moss. And everywhere was the Negro, a cheerful grinning barnacle tucked away in all the tender spots of Southern life, not to be removed without pain, not to be cherished without tragedy. The Georgian, when reproached for his intolerance, told himself that actually nobody outdid him in fond tolerance of the Negro. Lynchings, the work of hotheads and roustabouts, were regrettable; but what did a few lynchings count in the balance against the continual forbearance and solicitude that the Georgian felt he exercised toward these amiable children of cannibals, whose skins by no conceivable act of Congress or educational program could be changed from black to white. The presence of the Negro, which had its advantages in agriculture and domestic service, made the Georgian's life both comfortable and ramshackle; it gave him devoted servants and social problems, cheap labor and hideous slums, an endless flow of folklore and anecdote, and eternal apprehension for the future. But in his own way the Georgian respected the Negro as another irregularity, taking a human and personal form, that had somehow to be lived with. He distrusted all ready-made prescriptions for bringing about regularity. In Georgia, life went along horizontally: you never crossed a bridge until you came to it — and maybe not then.

❦ ❦ ❦

But sociologists not only cross bridges; they build all imaginable kinds of new ones. The picture of America, as sociologically reformed, does not contemplate any great concessions to Yankee uprightness or Rebel relaxation. Indeed, the sociologist, armed with science, is ready to follow reformation with transformation. In the vast inevitable working of the social forces, sectional differences become irrelevant. With a cold smile the sociologist pronounces a death sentence upon Rebel and Yankee alike. Not that they matter very much — but they will have to yield!

When he talks like this, I am perversely compelled to remember the individuals I have seen, Brother Jonathan of Vermont and Cousin Roderick of Georgia, whom I cannot imagine as yielding to the puny weapons flourished by our social philosophers. They are local incarnations of the Old Adam. They are the immovable bodies that can furnish the irresistible social forces with an incalculable meeting. They are human beings, undebatably alive; and they are different.

Brother Jonathan lives in Yankeetown — for a place name is often a " town " in New England, and less often a " ville " or a " burg " as in the South. He is a wizened little chip of a man, with blue eyes and a bald head, and he looks frail enough for any northwest wind to blow away. But there is not a wind on this planet strong enough to blow Brother Jonathan off his mountain farm. If any wind contrived to do so, he would climb right back again in the matter-of-fact way that Robert Frost describes in *Brown's Descent* — he would " bow with grace to natural law, and then go round it on his feet."

Brother Jonathan is past seventy years, and his wife Priscilla is well over sixty, but between them they still manage to do most of the daily work, in house and field, for a two-hundred-acre farm, most of which is in woodland and meadow. Nathaniel, their adopted son, helps some now and then; but Nathaniel, who is carpenter, mechanic, cabinetmaker, mountain guide, and tax collector combined, is busy putting up the new house into which he and Sophronia, his wife, will soon move — they are building it extra large, to take in summer boarders. Sophronia helps Priscilla as much as she can, but she has her own small children to look after. Later on, Brother Jonathan hopes to get a twelve-year-old boy from the orphanage, who will do the chores for his keep. But now, Brother Jonathan must be up at daylight to start the kitchen fire and milk the cows. If it is haying time, he is out in the meadow early with the mowing machine, which he has sharpened and greased with his own hands or repaired at his own smithy if it needs repairing. The mower bumps and clicks through the rough meadow, tossing the little man to and fro as he warily skirts the outcrops of stone that will have to be circled with a scythe to get the last wisp of hay.

Later, he changes the patient old horses from mower to wagon and starts in with a pitchfork. It is a sight to see him navigating the loaded wagon from the upper field to the barn, past jutting boulders and through deep ruts. But his pace is easy; he keeps it up all day without undue perspiration or agony, and after supper cuts his wood and milks his cows again in unruffled calm. He does not seem tired or bored. As he milks, he philosophizes to the listening stranger. Yes, times are not what they were, but a man can get along if he will be careful and honest. Foolish people, of course, never know how to manage. The harm all comes from people of no character that do things without regard to common decency. The stars are shining when he takes the pails of milk into the kitchen. Under the hanging oil lamp he reads the Burlington *Free Press* or *The Pathfinder* until he begins to nod.

All the arrangements on Brother Jonathan's farm are neat and ingenious — the arrangements of a man who has had to depend largely on his own wits and strength. The barn is cleverly arranged in two stories, with a ramp entering the upper story for the convenience of Brother Jonathan and his hay wagons, and running water on the lower story, for the convenience of the animals. One well, near the barn, is operated by a windmill; it supplies the stock. Another well, higher up, supplies the house, for Brother Jonathan has a bathroom in the upper hall and faucets in the kitchen. He has no telephone or electric lights. A man can dig and pipe his own well, and they are finished; but telephone and electric lights, not being home contrivances, require a never ending tribute to Mammon. He has his own sawmill and his own workshop, where he can mend things without losing time and money on a trip to the village. His garage, occupied at present by Nathaniel's four-year-old car (which is not being used!), contains a carpenter's bench and a small gas engine rigged to do sawing and turning. There are pelts drying on the walls.

The house is built to economize space and retain heat. For all its modest proportions, it is convenient and comfortable. The kitchen is spacious and well equipped. The pantry and cellar are stored with vegetables, fruits, and meats that Priscilla has put up with her own hands. The dining-room, with its long table covered with spotless oilcloth, is eating-room, living-room, and children's playground combined. Here all gather after supper: the women with their tatting and embroidery; the lively dark-eyed boy from the village, with his homemade fiddle; a summer boarder or two, or a visiting relative; and always Brother Jonathan with his newspaper. In one corner is a reed organ, on which Brother Jonathan occasionally plays hymns. In another corner is a desk, filled with miscellaneous papers, books, and old magazines. On the walls hang a glass frame containing butterflies, the gift of a wandering entomologist; an 1876 engraving of General Washington being welcomed at New York, with the pictures of all the Presidents, up to Hayes, around the border; and a faded photograph of a more youthful Brother Jonathan with his fellow baggage-clerks, taken in the days when he went west and got a job in Chicago. Brother Jonathan talks of Chicago sometimes, but he never reveals why he, unlike many other Yankees, came back to Vermont.

The temper of the household is a subdued and even pleasantness which the loud alarms and excursions of the world do not penetrate very far. The progress of Nathaniel's new house; the next morning's arrangements for gathering vegetables and canning; what Brother Jonathan shall say in the speech he is to make at the approaching celebration of the Timothys' golden wedding — such topics take precedence over the epic contentions of Mr. Roosevelt. Priscilla may go so far as to marvel that anybody can doubt the goodness of Mr. Hoover. (She does not add, as she well might, that Mr. Roosevelt, as a "Yorker," inherits the distrust of Vermont.) Or Brother Jonathan may warm up to politics enough to announce his everlasting distrust for liquorish Al Smith and to confess that, out of firm disapproval for vice, he has once or twice bolted the Republican ticket and voted for the Prohibition party's candidate. But in the South, he supposes, he would be as good a Democrat as the next one. They are all curious about the South — about Negroes — and whether the Southern people still have hard feelings against the North (on this point they seem a little anxious and plaintive). But the talk soon shifts to the Green Mountain Boys, from one of whom Brother Jonathan is descended, or to stories of his childhood, when bears were as thick as porcupines are now — he tells of how seven bears were once killed in the same tree. In these stories Brother Jonathan may put in a dry quip or two, by way of garnishment. He has a store of homely jokes and extended metaphors, to which he frequently adds a humorous gloss to be sure the stranger gets the point. Then maybe there is a game of anagrams — or on another evening, a corn roast, with a few cronies and kinfolks from the village, who talk the clipped Yankee-talk that seems, to Southern ears, as pure an English as can be, with only a little of the twang that dialect stories have taught one to expect.

Brother Jonathan is not dogmatic to the point of testiness, but he is firmly rationalistic on many points. He declares it incredible, for instance, that Catholics can believe in transubstantiation — how can bread and wine *actually* turn into the blood and body of Jesus Christ? Yet oddly enough, Brother Jonathan is neither Congregationalist nor Unitarian, but Methodist, and does not mind repeating the Apostles' Creed, with its formidable references to the Trinity and the Resurrection. I am led to suspect that it is not the doctrine but the authority to which Brother Jonathan is temperamentally hostile. He is used to depending on himself; he does not like to be told things. And his independence is of a piece with the whole conduct of his life. Years ago, when a famous local character eccentrically bought up all the surrounding woodland and farm land and turned it into a forest reserve which he bequeathed to a neighboring college, Brother Jonathan did not sell out. He held on then, he holds on now, with a possessiveness that would be the despair of communists. He will continue to hold on, as long as trees yield maple syrup — which he will never, never basely dilute with cane syrup — and boarders return summer after summer.

For Brother Jonathan belongs in spirit to the old republic of independent farmers that Jefferson wanted to see flourish as the foundation of liberty in the United States. To conserve that liberty he has his own Yankee arrangements: the "town," which the Southerner had to learn consisted of a village and a great deal of contiguous territory up to the next "town line"; and the town meeting, at which Brother Jonathan could stand up and tell the government what he thought about it. Of the uses of town meetings Priscilla has something to say, which comes, I reflect, with a little feminine sauciness. A certain individual, she relates, was criticized for not painting the "community house," as he had been employed to do; and when he excused himself on the ground that paint was lacking, his own wife sprang up in the town meeting and cried: "Don't believe a word he says. That paint's setting in the cellar this minute!"

But the Southerner could reflect that such family intimacy might have civic advantages. Brother Jonathan's local government is composed of nobody more Olympic or corrupt than his own neighbors and relations. For him it is not something off yonder, and he visualizes the national government (though a little too innocently) as simply an enlarged town meeting, where good management ought to be a matter of course: it maintains a library, it looks after roads, it sees that taxes are paid and well spent. If the state government does not behave, Nathaniel himself will run for the legislature and see that it does behave.

In all this there was much for a Southerner to savor seriously and learn about — as he savored and learned about the strange food that appeared on Brother Jonathan's table: doughnuts for breakfast, maple syrup on pie and cereal, the New England boiled dinner, the roasting ears that were really roasted in the old Indian fashion. Just as Brother Jonathan's menu suited the soil and the people, so his tidiness and responsibility suited the unobtrusive integrity of his character. With emphasis, one could say: Vermont is upright, vertical, and, even yet, Puritan — why not?

❦ ❦ ❦

And almost two thousand miles away, with an unconcern about the state of the world that parallels but differs from Brother Jonathan's, Cousin Roderick of Rebelville is achieving another salvation somehow not recorded in the auguries of socialistic planning. Autumn is beginning, the scuppernongs are ripe, and he invites everybody to come over and join him in the scuppernong arbor. In the late afternoon a merry crew gather around the great vine, laughing and bantering as they pick the luscious grapes and crush them against their palates. Sister Caroline is there, with a figure as trim and a wit as lively at eighty as it must have been at twenty. Young Cousin Hector and his wife are there — they are " refugeeing " from the industrial calamity that overtook them in a Northern city. And there are numerous other vague cousins and sisters and children, all munching and passing family gossip back and forth between bites. Cousin Roderick's own Dionysian laughter goes up heartiest of all among the leaves, as he moves to and fro, rapidly gathering grapes and pressing them upon the visitors. " Oh, you are not going to quit on us," he says. " You must eat more than *that*. Scuppernongs never hurt a soul." The scuppernong vine, he declares, is a hundred years old and nearly always fruitful. But not so old, never so fruitful, puts in Sister Caroline, as the scuppernong vine at the old place, that as barefoot children they used to clamber over.

Then the meeting is adjourned to Cousin Roderick's great front porch, where one looks out between white columns at sunset clouds piling up into the deep blues and yellows of a Maxfield Parrish sky. Down the long street of Rebelville, between the mighty water oaks set out by Cousin Roderick's kin after the Confederate War, the cotton wagons are passing, heaped high with the white mass of cotton and a Negro or two atop, and the talk goes on, to the jingle of trace chains and the clop of mule hoofs on the almost brand-new state highway, which is so much better for rubber tires than mule hoofs. Over yonder lives Cousin Roderick's Aunt Cecily, a widow, the single indomitable inhabitant of a stately mansion where economics has not yet prevailed against sentiment. Next door is Uncle Burke Roderick, a Confederate veteran who at ninety still drives his horse and buggy to the plantation each morning; he is the last survivor of three brothers who were named Pitt, Fox, and Burke, after their father's eighteenth century heroes. All around, indeed, are the Roderick kin, for Cousin Roderick, whose mother married a Bertram, bears the family name of his mother's people, a numerous clan who, by dint of sundry alliances and ancient understandings, attend to whatever little matters need attention in the community affairs of Rebelville, where Jefferson's " least government " principle is a matter of course. Before supper, or after, some of the kinfolks may drop in, for there is always a vast deal of coming and going and dropping in at Cousin Roderick's.

As he takes his ease on the porch, Cousin Roderick looks to be neither the elegant dandy nor the out-at-elbows dribbler of tobacco juice that partisans have accredited to the Southern tradition. He is a fairly tall, vigorous man, plainly dressed, with the ruddiness of Georgia sun and good living on his face. His eyes are a-wrinkle at the corners, ready to catch the humor of whatever is abroad. His hand fumbles his pipe as he tells one anecdote after another in the country drawl that has about as much of Mark Twain and Sut Lovengood in it as it has of the elisions and flattenings supposed to belong to Southern patrician speech. In fact, though he is really patrician (as the female members of his family can assure you) he does not look anything like the Old Colonel of legend, and in spirit he, too, belongs to the Jeffersonian constituency. He has some of the bearing of an English squire, and a good deal of the frontier heartiness that Augustus Baldwin Longstreet depicted in *Georgia Scenes*. He assumes that the world is good-humored and friendly until it proves itself otherwise. If it does prove otherwise, there is a glint in his eye that tells you he will fight.

Cousin Roderick is the opposite of Chaucer's Man of Law, who ever seemed busier than he was. Cousin Roderick is busier than he seems. His air of negligence, like his good humor, is a philosophical defense against the dangerous surprises that life may turn up. Really, he is not negligent. He does not work with his own hands, like Brother Jonathan, or his Southern brothers of upcountry and bluegrass; but in the past he has worked aplenty with his hands and knows how it should be done. On his several tracts of land, the gatherings of inheritance and purchase, are some one hundred and fifty Negroes whom he furnishes housing, food, and a little money; they do his labor — men, women, children together — they are his "hands." He is expected to call them by name, to get them out of jail, to doctor them, even sometimes to bury them when "lodge dues" may have lapsed. They are no longer his slaves; but though they do not now utter the word, they do not allow him to forget that he has the obligations of a master.

As Cousin Roderick makes the "rounds" of his fields — no more on horseback, as of old, but in a battered Chevrolet — he sets forth his notions of economy. As for the depression, that is no new thing in Rebelville. People here have got used to ruination. After the Confederate War came Reconstruction, Tom Watson, and the Populist turmoil of the nineties; a while later, the peach boom and its collapse; then the Florida boom with its devastations; and now, this new depression. Like most of his kin, Cousin Roderick has simply retreated into the plantation economy. He tells how, when he was a young fellow just beginning to take charge, his father came out to the plantation one day and asked for a ham. Cousin Roderick explained that hogs were up to a good price; he had sold the entire lot, on the hoof, and had good money in the bank. "Sir," said the old man, "let me never again catch you without hams in your smokehouse and corn in your crib. You've got to make this land take care of itself." "And that," says Cousin Roderick, "is what I aim to do." From the land he feeds his own family, the hundred and fifty Negroes, and the stock. Whatever is left, when taxes and upkeep are deducted, is the profit. Anything that grows, he will plant: asparagus, peaches, pecans, onions, peppers, tomatoes, and of course the great staple crops, grain, hay, and cotton. Especially cotton, for no matter how low the price, cotton is money. It is ridiculous, he thinks, to talk of getting people who are hard-up for money to reduce cotton acreage. For his part, Cousin Roderick intends to make every bale his land will produce. But if cotton fails, he still can sell cattle, or cabbage, or timber from his baronial holdings. Land is the only abiding thing, the only assurance of happiness and comfort. He wants more land, not less.

One suspects that Cousin Roderick, however hard-pressed he may be at the bank, is fundamentally right. If he is not right, how does he manage, in these times, to send a daughter to college, and entertain his friends, and keep a cheerful face before the world? The portraits of his ancestors, looking down from their frames above great-grandfather's sideboard or his wife's new grand piano, eternally assure Cousin Roderick that he is right. They won this Eden of sandy earth and red clay, where all things grow with a vigor that neither winter nor drouth can abate. Not soon, not soon will their son give it up.

To the designs of experts who want to plan people's lives for them, Cousin Roderick gives no more than the indulgent attention of a naturally kindhearted man. He reads the anxious thunderings of the young men who reproduce, in the Macon *Telegraph*, the remote dynamitical poppings of the *New Republic*, and is unmoved; the young men are like the mockingbird who sat on the cupola of the courthouse while court was in session and so learned to sing: *Prisoner-look-upon-the-jury! Jury-look-upon-the-prisoner!* GUILTY! GUILTY! GUILTY! It is a little incredible that so much planning should need to be done. Don't people know how they want to live? As for politics, long since it became tawdry and uncertain. Politics is for lawyers. Cousin Roderick would no more think of running for the legislature than he would think of moving to China. In that, perhaps, he lamentably differs from his ancestors. But in Rebelville political action is generally no more than a confirmation of what has been talked around among the clans. If you really want things done, you speak quietly to Cousin So-and-So and others that pass the word to everybody that counts. And then something is done.

In Rebelville the politics and economics of the bustling world become a faint whisper. All that matters is to see one's friends and relatives and pass from house to house, from field to field, under Georgia skies; to gather at a simple family dinner where only three kinds of bread and four kinds of meat are flanked by collards, sweet potatoes, corn, pickles, fruits, salads, jams, and cakes; or at a barbecue for fifty or more, for which whole animals are slaughtered and, it would seem, entire pantries and gardens desolated; or to sit with the wise men in front of the store, swapping jokes and telling tales hour after hour; or to hunt for fox, possum, coon, and quail, in swamp and field; or (for the ladies) to attend meetings of U.D.C.'s, and missionary societies; or church service, or district conference or the tender ceremonies of Confederate Memorial Day, or the high school entertainment; or to hear the voices of Negroes, sifting through the dusk, or the mockingbird in moonlight; or to see the dark pines against sunset, and the old house lifting its columns far away, calling the wanderer home. The scuppernongs are gone, and cotton is picked. But already the pecans are falling. And planting begins again while late roses and chrysanthemums are showing and, even in the first frosts, the camellias are budding, against their December flowering. What though newspapers be loud and wars and rumors threaten — it is only an academic buzzing, that one must yet tolerate for manners' sake. Sowing and harvest go together, and summer runs into winter, and in Georgia one is persuaded to take the horizontal view.

By some it may be said that dark clouds hang over Yankeetown and Rebelville — and clouds of menace, maybe of destruction. I do not deny their presence, but my story is not of such clouds. In this strange modern world it may be observed that men talk continually of the good life without producing a specimen of it, to convince an inquirer. Brother Jonathan and Cousin Roderick do not talk about the good life. They lead it. If government is intended to serve human interests, what does it propose to do about them? I cannot believe that a government or a science which ignores or depreciates them is very trustworthy. I believe that government and science will fail unless they are taken into account. They, and others, are the incarnations of the principle of diversity through which the United States have become something better than Balkan, and without which the phrase " my country " is but a sorry and almost meaningless abstraction.

— From *The Attack on Leviathan*, University of North Carolina Press, 1938. Reprinted by permission.

IT NEVER SNOWS

By Clarence Cason

JAMES J. HILL, the railroad builder, studiously governed his investments in accordance with his business maxim that no man upon whom the snow does not fall is ever worth a tinker's dam. Such a conception implies no recommendation for the southern part of the United States. I can remember that during my boyhood in the deep South we used to be able to make snow ice cream once or twice a year. With a large kitchen spoon we would scoop the fresh snow from where it lay banked lightly on a railing of the garden fence and mix it in a bowl with cream, sugar, and vanilla extract. It made our palates tingle with exoticism. Our feeling was that little Rollo, whose fun at ice skating was described in our third-grade reader, would virtually subsist on snow ice cream should he take advantage of his opportunities in the cold North where he lived. But it has been snowing less and less in the South during the past thirty years, and as a consequence the country has no doubt gone to the dogs long since — from the point of view of Mr. Hill's philosophy.

Their English heritage restrains most Americans from thinking of geography except in terms of investments. Even so, there is one respect in which all must agree that the change in Southern climate is not a calamity. A certain kind of Southerner can, by nature, be happy with a hole in his pants. Other Southerners have been forced by necessity to cultivate the faculty. So it may be just as well that the climate has been moderating. This lack of concern for frayed trousers is in itself a conspicuous element in Southern solidarity. Whether it constitutes a regional virtue is another question, for, as

Gertrude Stein says, one may like a view and still prefer to sit with his back to it.

Such a conception inevitably raises the disturbing possibility that Southern complacency (another aspect of the regional solidarity) may contain large doses of wishful thinking. A poet from another part of the country, who once surrounded himself with camellias and wistaria in a Southern town, was amazed when a native gentleman of parts frankly advised him, for the sake of his career, to get away before it was too late. Southern persons who in their youth have cherished special aspirations experience no difficulty in understanding this advice. Do such persons, after having realized that it is too late for them to take their places in creative activities of the outside world, simply try to compensate in the manner of spinsters who scoff at marriage, or in the vein of the members of the Sew-We-Do Club who are saddened at the immoralities of the Society set, or in the manner of the unsuccessful speculators who attempt to heap scorn upon Wall Street? But that disturbing possibility must be admitted only parenthetically. Too much analysis of it would leave one mentally unbuttoned.

If snow falls infrequently on the Southern land, the sun displays no such niggardly tendencies. In Mississippi there is justification for the old saying that only mules and black men can face the sun in July. Summer heat along the Middle Atlantic coast and on the Middle Western plains causes more human prostrations than it does in the South. The difference lies partially in the regularity of high summer temperatures in the South but mainly in the way the Southerner takes the heat. A Georgian takes the heat relaxed in a hammock or reclining on the bank of a shaded stream, wherein he has cast a hook for catfish, rather hoping that they will not disturb him too much. Golf in Georgia, Bobby Jones to the contrary notwithstanding, will never become more than measurably popular. It has the defect of not taking enough time. Fishing and hunting are better adapted to the native temperament. The most typical Southern businessman of my acquaintance is inclined to welcome rainy days because they enable him to get things in order at his real estate office. While the New Yorker or the Chicagoan rushes out into the heat of July and has a sunstroke, the Southerner's discretion, which often persists throughout the winter, constitutes one of the conditioning elements of his unified culture.

2

There is no escaping the conviction that fishing in the South is pursued for its own sake, and not as a means of recuperation between business deals. No one is shocked because most of the cockroaches used for bait are obtained from grocery stores. Instead of being filled with alarm at the unsanitary conditions suggested by that fact, representative Southerners would hardly demand a more noble service from grocery stores than the furnishing of cockroaches well bred with respect to size and degree of toughness. (They should be just large and tough enough to stay on a hook without being large and tough enough to prove formidable when handled.)

Although I know that it is heresy to suggest such an idea in the midst of an age of progress, it may be that ultimate truth lies in the spiritual attitude of the Southerners who are always going fishing. A person who has achieved an immunity from the everlasting inner demand that he improve upon his earthly position must possess an unusual degree of cosmic equilibrium. He must have learned in some way that composure of the human spirit is all that actually matters. He has attained, without conscious effort, the serenity for which all men strive.

Activity, as he perhaps knows through some instinctive realization, is but a confession that peace is unendurable. It is in search of peace that all activity is directed. A parallel may be drawn from music. After a symphony of Brahms, it is the ensuing moment of silence into which the spiritual satisfaction of the hearer is mainly concentrated. One has the impression that all the sounds of the music were contrived in order to produce that single ecstatic moment of profound and complete satisfaction. If this analysis is sensible, one must feel occasionally that the sounds of music are arranged in such a way as to compose the soul and mind for the concentrated joy of a moment of silence, a vacant interval in time made perfectly endurable for the restless spirit of man.

It is much the same way with physical and mental activity. We build a fire in the grate in order that we may sit before it in comfort and ease. The fire in the grate is not the thing we want; it is the comfort and ease. Similarly, the principal joy of intellectual activity is involved in the attainment of a satisfactory conclusion, a moment in which the intellectual struggle gives way to a brief interval of serene comfort of the mind.

What shall we say of the person who is not influenced by the driving force which impels his fellows to improve upon the conditions about them? Shall we say that he is decadent or that he is the possessor of wisdom? Whatever the correct answer may be, the fact remains that no great consciousness of dissatisfaction can be in the minds of Southerners who are forever going fishing. Without being under the necessity of forcing themselves through rounds of accomplishment, they can endure peace. Without having the refractory sounds of the universe resolved into a harmony for them, they can endure silence. No one should miss the significance of the fact that the old houses of Charleston have their blind sides turned towards the street.

At any rate, all men and women of consequence in the eastern part of the United States sail for Europe if they can as soon as the summer heat begins. In the South, however, the foreign tourist agencies know that their summer prospects lie chiefly with the schoolteachers. Persons of consequence in the South are satisfied to go fishing.

3

Upon the ethnic structure of the South the sparsity of snow has exerted a tremendous influence. It brought the Negro and has kept the Scandinavian away. When the first slave ships came three hundred years ago, it was natural for them to drop their African cargoes upon the warm soil of the cotton and rice plantations. During the three centuries of his residence in the Southern states the Negro has had almost as much as the sunshine to do with conditioning the lives of the white people of the region. Like the heat of the sun, the Negro has delimited activity among the whites; like the sun, he has given his energy to the growing of crops for the white man. The floods of immigration which overwhelmed most of the

United States for a generation after 1890 made little headway in the South, where the native populations, which had not completely succumbed to the doctrine of bigger towns at any cost, insisted that the South already had as many people as the Negroes could support.

When the presence of plenty of slaves allowed Southerners to have a decent respect for the summer heat in building their residences, the characteristic form of regional architecture was developed. Wide hallways and high ceilings insured ample ventilation, and the custom of setting the kitchen off at one side relieved the drawing-room guests from the malodorous fumes of boiling cabbage and frying red snapper in August. With the passing of slavery and the arrival of the Spanish bungalow, however, the Southerner more than ever began to feel under the compulsion to seek fresh air on the outside. It used to be said that travelers could always tell when they were in Virginia by the accumulation of dust under the hotel beds. Having recently spent a night at one of the immaculate hostelries of Richmond, I am sure that such a statement would be an arrant libel today. But it is true that the genuine Southerner harbors a greater concern for his garden than for the inside of his house. It must be agonizing for Southern publishers to realize that books cannot be read beside a cape jessamine bush in the moonlight. The New England fireside chair — from which one looks through the window upon the snow and ice of a long winter, and then takes down another volume from the bookshelves — has no counterpart below the Potomac. The Southerner reads the morning newspaper because he wants to know about the Society events and the election campaigns, which he regards in somewhat the same light; but he thinks books are suitable only for invalids.

Nor is too much to be expected of air-cooling machines in the way of keeping Southerners from spending most of their time out of doors. Air conditioning cannot be a grand success in the South for the reason that the honest natives of the region recognize the natural summer heat as a welcome ally in that it makes the inside of houses and offices agreeably uninviting, if not actually prohibited territory.

Although it is true that the Southern states are remarkable for the high percentage of their native-born population, no one should make the mistake of thinking that the social structure of the South as a whole is homogeneous. In no other part of the United States are class lines so rigidly drawn. One of the delights of my four years of residence in Wisconsin was the custom of going on numerous picnics in the late spring and early summer. Crossing the beautiful pasture lands of that state, we used to notice that the cows invariably faced in the same direction. It became a sort of byword with us. "All facing the same way," we would say to each other every time we sighted a herd of Guernseys. The farmers of that fine state, where the heavy snowfall brings the grass forth in succulent abundance every spring, also give the impression of going in the same direction on a basis closely approaching equality. But in the South it is a scientific fact, if a continuous observation of the phenomenon can be accepted as scientific evidence, that cows in the pasture do not face the same way; and it is an economic fact, so well established as to need no proof, that the farmers themselves are by no means going in the same direction.

The heavy snows of Wisconsin are influential in giving the farmers the kind of ambition which comes from physical vigor; also the snow plays a part in giving the cows plenty of grass to eat, and this results in their having a definite and obvious way of spending their time in the pasture. On the other hand, the long assault of the summer heat in the South is more effectual in baking the grass than the scarce winter snow can be in reviving it. As a consequence, the cows, mulling over the meadows, feel themselves at a loss, and stand aimlessly about, facing in all directions. The weather also affects the farmers of the South in a similar manner. Enervated by the summer heat, they cannot muster a sufficient amount of vitality to pull the weeds from their cotton and demand the rights of freeborn American citizens at the same time. They become easy prey for the tenant bosses, the land sharks, and the moneylenders. The July sun, in other words, has been exerting an influence for generations in determining social and economic classes in the South. One's social status can be loosely measured in terms of the inverse ratio of the number of hours spent at the mercy of the July sun.

4

It remains true, however, that the same Southern weather which tends to stratify the population also draws the classes together again in a cohesion of interests in the fortunes of King Cotton. This consuming passion, together with a lamentable common interest in King Cawn (which probably did not decrease with prohibition), is strong enough as a force in Southern solidarity to offset whatever influences the lack of snow may exert in direct opposition. Especially since the promulgation of President Roosevelt's New Deal, the South has come to recognize more and more its community of interest in the fortunes of cotton as a world commodity. Not even the bearing of General Johnson's industrial codes upon the South, particularly with respect to the wage differentials, has given Southerners as much of a feeling of regional consciousness as have the various federal programs relating to cotton.

The climate of the South also has an effect upon the nervous systems of the inhabitants. They like pepper in their food, strong coffee, and the excitement of fights. These tastes are reflected at the dinner table, at lynching bees, and in political campaigns. The Southerner, his nerves irritated by the heat, is far more interested in elections than in government; far more concerned over the sporadic eruptions of Red propaganda than over racial or social questions in their broader aspects. At first glance, the transitory and shifting nature of immediate interests in the South appears to be at variance with the region's reputation for traditionalism. But this conflict is only on the surface. Fundamentally the shifting of Southern interests — within certain well-defined orbits — is in itself one of the most solidly established traditions. In Alabama there is a statue inscribed to "The Man Who Killed Old Abe Lincoln in 1865," and another dedicated to the Boll Weevil in celebration of its contribution to raising the price of cotton by reducing the yield in 1927.

Passing note must also be made of the effect of indigenous diseases in building up a coherent structure of shared experiences in the South. Although malaria is sometimes classified by the natives as being like hookworm and pellagra in implying an unacceptable social status, most Southerners in moments of close confidence will admit that they at some time or another have had a touch of malaria, or that they have friends who have had malaria, or at least they know what a mosquito is like. These experiences, especially when they are treated confidentially, have a way of drawing the people of a region together in a most effective manner. In fact, it might be argued (though not by me) that malaria in the South is almost as potent a factor in the regional solidarity as is the universally shared indignation against the Yankee.

Yet, in final analysis, excellent as are the reasons for Southern languor, pleasant as are the relaxations offered by the fields and the streams to the Southern mind — sublime as it may be for one to go fishing and invite his soul to search for the secret of the gods in dreamy contemplation — there is much work that ought to be done below the Potomac. The consciences of the Southern Bourbons, however, have never held work to be a solemn duty, so far as they themselves have been concerned. Southerners of a less elevated class do labor, of course; they labor hard and long, and, even during the era of the National Recovery Administration, perhaps for fewer cents per unit of energy than do most persons elsewhere in the United States. Nor can one overlook the assiduous application of other Southerners, many of whom do not fare so badly in securing adequate returns for their efforts. Among these are the promoters (for their own profit) of such slogans as "Unlimited Natural Resources" and "Cheap Anglo-Saxon Labor." The activities of these gentry — even now, as well as in the 1920's and before that decade — are sufficient, it must be admitted, to threaten the validity of all that I have ever said with reference to Southern languor.

But the patterns of the plantation days of long ago still survive in the habits of the privileged classes. Even the operators of gasoline filling stations invariably have black assistants to turn cranks, inflate tires, fill radiators, polish windshields, and perform all the other duties of the establishment — except that of accepting the customers' money. As of old, the climate and the presence of the Negro are the main conditioning elements in Southern culture.

— From 90° *in the Shade*, University of North Carolina Press, 1935. Reprinted by permission.

ENCAUSTICS FOR SOUTHERNERS

By Stark Young

Sette Frati

The Countess N—— comes from one of the richest and — it is pleasant to report — best bred families in New York; she is also discreet, Junior League, and educated. All this, of course, makes her reactions important. She looks in a curious way futile and mashed (I do not mean spiritually mashed). She is mashed, too, in the Pullman sense; which is to say that the artificial flowers on her abandoned, *de rigueur*, proper-shop gown look as if she had slept upon them. I do not say that, quite; for she looks really as if she had never slept with anything but meditations, analytical preoccupations, and laxatives.

Curiously enough, nevertheless, this mashed look extends to the impression that one gets of her whole nature. Life has wronged her (not to speak of the heinous glands) so that her whole aspect, face, arms, hands, back, and bosom — which are the parts her fashionable dressmaker decided on for exhibition — seems to announce already an inner constriction, and to promise a sallow withering very soon. She speaks firmly, shyly, and with a certain egotism that is sometimes characteristic of a person who is essentially solitary, no matter what husband or friends may do. One who was brought up so rich is likely to be spoiled, naturally; and being spoiled may well lead to some inner solitude.

She is married to a count with a great name, whose family seat is in the central part of Italy, not far from the village of Sette Frati, " Seven Brothers " — I'll wager she has dwelt upon that name; we shall see why later, perhaps — and in sight of cerulean lakes and private domains highly vegetous, to use Ben Jonson's word for it. In the winter they live in Rome.

I met the countess for the third time not long ago at dinner on Park Avenue in the same creases but a different dress, as if she slept the same way regardless of modistes — in other words, though a countess with one of the highest names in Europe, she has a democratic equality among the perpetually disheveled of this world. After dinner (one of those careful affairs in which the young hostess gets her hints for new dishes out of the recipes by celebrated chefs printed in the Sunday magazine sections) the countess found herself near me, and we began to talk of her life in Italy, ten years of it. That joyless, sallow expression makes me by contrast think of oleanders, wine, and a bright moon. It seems that to the count's beautiful estate in the country his family, which means also his mother and various nieces, nephews, visiting cousins, and so on, are wont to come during the summer season and presently to settle down. The count's family, in sum, spend months at the country place near Sette Frati.

One of the things that Teutonic foreigners never quite know of Italians is that they love the life *in campagna — in villeggiatura*, as they sometimes call it. It is true that Italian poetry — since the Renaissance of shepherdesses and rills — is sadly lacking in the appreciation of nature. Their poets seem to have neglected to observe the primrose in its full fertility of human illustration. They have not sufficiently noted the hare, as the fine mist rises in his tracks behind him traversing the heather; nor have they exactly noted the passions of ashbuds during their blackness in the front of some month or other (Tennyson says March). The Italians have, alas, a tendency to condense nature or some natural effect to a phrase; which only shows their lack of profundity. They fire some notation of the natural world with passionate humanity; which only shows their classicism, their lack of botany, profundity, pantheism, and rapture. The poor things have noted the snail on the thorn, but failed to deduce from it that all's right with the world.

We must return, however, to the main fact of these summer stretches among the cypresses, lakes, peasants, and consanguinity, as the countess describes them to me.

From her accounts I gather that it is indeed a gloomy time for her. You are apt to have an aunt visiting, an uncle, a grandmother, cousins, with respected little cousins, and in the front portico people sitting long evenings, some of the peasants coming up perhaps, music sometimes (not very chic but, of course, the countess doesn't mind that); and then there are country visits, with simple diversions. I put all these things in one sentence because they remained in the countess's mind as a stream. Plainly, her summers *in villeggiatura* are duller than, dreaming of princes and palaces, she grew up to expect. I suppose to her it all seems to be a great to-do about nothing.

I do not mean to give a false impression of this very pleasant, slightly neurotic, unconsciously spoiled daughter of a high millionaire New York family of at least three generations in tradition (though I should add that their wealth enabled them to generate early) who is married thus into an ancient Italian life. But I must set down, before I leave her situation, my reflections on it in one simple Southern respect. The count should have married one of my cousins from the South.

Such a marriage would have been impossible, of course, because she would not have anything like a million, or even a quarter of a million. The count's family would have been devoted to her; I can see her now throwing her arms around some of those old aunts or uncles and grandmothers, and recognizing in them not a few of the same traditions on which she herself had been brought up. And as for sitting in the portico — which she would have called the gallery — she could have done that with the best of them. She would not constantly have asked herself what was there to do; she could even have lived without tennis. She would not have needed to dash in a motorcar across country for luncheon. She would have understood, lying in bed at night, with the scent of the petunias rising from the garden below, that life, if it is to last, has a social scheme, has certain hard restrictions and finalities and orders, within which flourish all those affections, family loyalties, and uneventful times together that Southern people know the value of.

Yes, it is a pity that circumstances in this world did not allow the count to marry an American from the South. The poor countess bought what she wanted, but what was in what she bought she did not want. I can see the old Italian ladies thinking of how active their American countess was; not active in order to do anything really, but stirred to her center by the absence of anything to do. She had brought, however, a good dowry — *pazienza* — one cannot have everything!

What shall we do? is plainly the countess's motto — not that she knows it. In Italian it is *che faró*, but, of course, to an Italian that suggests *che faró senza Euridice?* What shall I do without Eurydice — that celebrated aria from Gluck's opera; or at least *che faró senza* something? I trust the difference is clear — what shall I do without something beloved, signifying an objective that feeds life. Which is quite another matter from "What shall I do?"

I can see one of my cousins now, if the Southern fortunes had remained so that the count could have afforded to marry her, sitting on the gallery, or terrace, of that Sette Frati villa, any afternoon or evening, and fitting exactly into the life and scene.

Culture in the Dirt Road

I have just been talking with Mrs. M——, and she reports to me the conversation of X, an acquaintance we both have in literary criticism — a great master, in fact, of stirring conclusions. The gist of it is that he has lately been on a visit to Nashville, and on his return has announced that, from what he had seen, he is about to decide that there never has been any culture in the South. About to decide.

Instead of leaping, as I doubtless should, to some endeavor that might head off an unfavorable decision on his part (a decision that would be offensive to the Chamber of Commerce), I find myself thinking of X's presence. A face, as it were, cumulous, with something both sullen and haughty about it that reminds you of a boil that has come to a head but refuses to burst, and a sound in his speech as if his nose were full of cotton seed. These, doubtless, are unfriendly comparisons, perhaps not even cultured save in a homely sense. What puzzles me is that X has assumed that the whole town of Nashville culled whatever were its loveliest aspects and laid them at his feet. Or does he think culture is waiting in the middle of, as we call it, the dirt road?

On the other hand, there is Z, who writes for a paper in one of the border states, half Northern, half Southern. He, it seems, has read some of my remarks on the city of Natchez. Now this culture and these fine people that I pretend existed in Natchez he doubts very much. He was in Natchez once, he says, for his newspaper, sent there to report a lynching. He must say he didn't see any of these fine people.

This is a most unfortunate moment for me socially; I cannot say to Z, "You should have let them know you were coming."

Return of the Native

Claribel grew up in Tennessee, an orphan under the roof of an aunt and uncle who fought like cats and dogs. We need not dwell on these unhappy years except to say that Claribel at twenty came to New York, began — somehow — her bookshop, was admired all up and down Park Avenue, seemed wistful to authors, and strove earnestly to forget her entire beginnings, which I suppose was natural.

Of late years, however, she has had a great number of rich friends who are buying plantations in South Carolina and Virginia, or living like lords (on the Riviera) in Florida, and they have often invited her down to these splendid demonstrations of estates and one-generation patriarchy. Furthermore she has heard of much biography, of fiction and of other matters in travel magazines, all dealing with the Southern material (every early fan window in Massachusetts having already been photographed). Going South has become very smart. How et cetera, et cetera, it all is! And how cheap it is! Restore the plantation great houses! C——, of the well-known soups, has opened up Belle Chasse, in the tidewater country. Claribel hears this at dinner parties.

"I'm all for the South," she has begun to say.

Richmond Lady Reading of Sad New York Lady

I watch Mrs. T—— as she reads the notice that Mrs. K—— is going to be obliged to have an auction, and that two of her houses in the country have been closed. Mrs. T—— is sad not from the house-closings, but because a circle of New York friends sitting there with her have been saying how hard it was for Mrs. K——, poor dear, no stables this summer, and so many responsibilities! Such a hard situation!

As I watch this scene I can hardly believe my eyes. Is it possible that little Mrs. T——, who is none too rich now, has completely forgotten her mother, in the days when they all made their lawn dresses, baked the cakes, and thought themselves lucky that they were not obliged even to do the washing? Her grandmother, after the Civil War, had to plow the field sometimes or else see her children starve — after, that is, she had sold what silver had been left from a handsome interment that baffled the general's men.

Still it is sad that Mrs. K—— will not be able to take out her hunters this season, and comparisons would be ungracious. It is better, as she herself recently explained to me, that she and her daughter go to Europe this summer. To have the horses, et cetera, would cost $20,000 at least, she says, whereas the two of them can spend July and August in Europe for $10,000. I quote this to Mrs T—— (my own grandfather was glad for a long time to take in $700 a year from his plantation) and like two fool Southerners we sit looking sadly at each other over Mrs. K——.

Sweet Defense

Miss Flora comes from the Charleston country; and, though she circulates in New York at a considerable rate, I am often struck by her helplessness. Far back in her spirit, sweet and most arrogant. A face gentle and ingratiating; an education floral and uncertain. And, I believe, a rather bad ear for sound.

At any rate, the other day at a fashionable New York club made up half of ladies and half of good addresses, I sat at the tea table listening to a gracious but grilling banter addressed to Miss Flora. She hearkened, blushed, smiled, poured more tea, and finally made a little speech which sounded like a quotation from a worn oration, though it was something about Southern aristocracy — bless her heart!

Now I should have advised something very different for Miss Flora, a bit of policy and a hint at sweet defense. First I should have said that our entire South has been filled up with somewhat frightened schoolteachers who learned to pronounce things out of books. Then I should have said, arm yourself, dear Miss Flora, with some international or historical illustrations. For example, there are scores of members of the English aristocracy who say *it don't, it ain't,* and so on, not to speak of a pronunciation of *girl* which amounts practically to " gal." When Miss Flora, following her own uncle, the old judge, says " jine " for *join,* " hyst " for *hoist,* " pint " for *point,* and so forth and so on — she's almost eighty and will likely be the last of her race to do these things — I should like her to be able to add that these are merely good Queen Anne pronunciations of such words, just as the word *roil* is still given the Queen Anne pronunciation, though people who don't know the difference have begun to spell it *rile.*

And for another example, I should like to hint to her, when she says " cha'acter " or " Pa'is," that Byron, Lord Byron, and various members of his family always pronounced the name " Bi'on."

Nothing checks the newly learned bourgeois like tradition handed on, not read. Nothing snubs like snobbery. Once we got that in Miss Flora's head, she could execute the scheme with the most amiable malice, along with that violet smile that she has not yet lost.

Incarnation

H—— is a fine chap, sweet-tempered, good-hearted, and anxious not to be laughed at. He was, it seems, bright as a little child, very bright, so that you might have thought he would represent his family education. But now, with lazy time and scattered habitats in commercial towns North, his family education has to represent him.

I have lately observed H—— with a common friend of his and mine, a man that reviews books for a leading daily. A novel, it appears, has come out in which the author portrays a Virginia town with an assortment of backward citizens, a colonel, provincialism, old ideals, and the bunk, so the book seems to say, the bunk. The writer, I gathered from my reviewer friend — who had of course said this in print, there is no time to waste your stuff — showed in a fine, satirical manner, not uncommon in various pleasing Southern authors, that these fools in this Virginia town lived on lies. The proof of that lay chiefly in the fact that the old colonel was admired by the citizens as the embodiment of all that is chivalrous, honorable, and Southerngentleman — I make it one word in this case; but was, as a matter of fact, merely a pious fraud, none too anything of these high and boasted qualities attributed to him. The colonel (plus all the ideals grouped with him) was, therefore, the bunk. Proved.

I watched H——'s face, and have often thought since then of what may happen when you have neglected to think out your inheritance. What we could say to the reviewer is easy. His novel and his review prove nothing at all. I feel in fact like saying to him that plenty of babies kick in the womb before they are born; there is nothing intellectual or debunking about that.

The rebuttal of the novel's argument should be simple to H—— or to any Southern person who will take the trouble to dwell on his own things:

It is of only *incidental* consequence that these admirers of the colonel in the Virginia town, these believers in his embodiment of their ideals, were deluded in him. On that basis the novel is only finding out about Santa Claus. The point is not that the colonel did not truly represent these ideals. The significant point is what the ideals were, for which these townspeople sought an embodiment.

Aged Aunt and the Devil

My dear aunt, Miss R——, is at present confronted with a niece, Lola, who is very pretty, who has just married unhappily — some months ago, it was — and who is busily explaining the unhappiness of her situation and the egotistic convolutions of her selfhood by quoting and explaining considerable sections of modern thought with which she has become acquainted.

"Goodness knows, I didn't bring up Lola," my aunt says of her dear niece, in a tone which implies you didn't get the ringworm from me, my dear.

The fact is that Lola was brought up by her uncle, her father's brother, who regarded all women, except the ugly ones, as sugar-coated fools from which male gallantry is to remove the sugar. As I remember, Lola says her uncle used to make her cut his nails, but I know little about that. At any rate, she says that, considering her early years, she has done the best she could. She will then give you a vast sketch of all the complexes, the inferiority complex and otherwise, that she suffers from because of her earlier life.

There are moments in the discussion when Lola quite embarrasses her aunt and a good many other people. On the other hand, certain more modern and sophisticated neighbors listen to her with attention. The truth is, as I have observed, however, they are not so much surprised at her knowledge of the science of psychology as they are at her knowledge of her early years. In sum, one may doubtless know all science, but how does one remember all these minutiae of the far and scattered past? How few could do that! I have talked with our aunt about Lola's explanations and condonements of herself; and we have agreed on one thing, which is that, pragmatically, it would be a great deal better for such people as Lola if they thought in terms of the old morality. In a word, though it might be less subtle, it would be a good thing if Lola stopped explaining all her tedious qualities, touchiness and egotism, by her adolescent history and adolescent brunts, and began to explain merely that she was full of the devil. If she said to me, I have a certain aroma because I have a piece of Limburger cheese in my pocket, I really do not believe that I should find it poignant. I am afraid I should say, " Take it out." I can scarcely — as I might with Limburger — ask Cousin Lola to remove all the early section of her life in this world. I could say, perhaps, since she knows these things so thoroughly, why not neglect various sections? But if she said she was full of the devil, I should have some hell-fire phraseology to hand, by inherited quotation. Full of the devil — that is old theology. The only devil I and my friends know is on the bottle of pepper sauce, a forked tail and so on. But, of course, the point for Lola is that old kirk devil.

If Lola should put her shortcomings — for which, so long as we are being archaic, we may as well say she should be lynched — down to the devil, it would be, of course, better practically, but far less intellectual perhaps. Good and useful nevertheless. Full as Lola is of modern thought, it will do no harm to remember that when we convert Lola to modern thought we convert modern thought to Lola. Unlucky old aunt!

However, Lola goes on, letting herself out with isms and complexes (Germanic origins). And those who know (and, by perplexity, pseudo-popular analyses, and natural kindness, admire) her say, " Such psychology! Such psychology! "

It reminds me of that little book of Sicilian travels where we read of the shrine with the Virgin's history depicted in it. In one scene the neighbors are gathered; St. Anna, the author tells us, has been prophesying all the morning and everybody says they never heard such prophecy in all their lives!

Loving Owner

She is a gentle little lady, with a proud nose. Once long ago her family was more than common rich, there in their South Carolina home. The plantations paid, and the city house that her grandfather built showed many luxurious furnishings, silver, portraits, and other tokens of good living and refinement. Of late years since nice people, even, have taken to opening their houses to touring strangers, thanks to gasoline and journalism, this lady has conducted many a visitor through —— ; I must not mention the name, but the stairs are graceful, the sofas with their damask are the originals; the inlaid papier-mâché, the rosewood with its roses carved on it, the silver, are still there, in part at least. There are also some porcelain figurines, chandeliers with crystal, gilt silver cake-baskets, and so on.

At first, when my friend showed people through the house — not quite all of it, including her own bedroom, where she has a basket in which sick and crippled chicks and goslings may sleep, a vase of peacock feathers, a puffed crazy-quilt and other items that, as a matter of fact, give the room a human vagary and charm such as no other part of the house presents — at first, when she showed the house, she spoke of *its age*. It was ancient, full of antiques. From that antique exclusiveness and that anemic phrase " Old Southern Home," she passed to the idea of fine, and then even to palatial. And so on from bad to worse. It was a sort of map, or tracing, of that method by which certain authors through certain decades built up a set of assumptions and élite nonsensicalities that almost made us Southerners ridiculous. And such bombast helped to provide a better market for books by Southern authors depicting us as degenerate, faking, and chivalry-fools, living on what is popularly called old stuff and bluff. This has become matter that raised eyebrows are not enough to dispose of, nor aristocratic scorn enough to dismiss.

Now I should like to advise my friend, there in her old house. She shows it graciously but is on the way to a certain pride of flesh, so to speak, a certain turning of the house's claims into her own private heraldries. I should like to say to her things like the following:

Dear friend and dear lady, you are not a Braganza, a Montmorency, a Hapsburg, Colonna, and so forth and so on; not immediately so at least. You are the descendant of a good line of fine people, related to the land, with a sense of responsibility to the society of which they make a part and which they intend to take a hand in ruling. For this class in the South, the life of the affections was believed in and followed; the family idea had meaning. My dear lady, I daresay you are aware (I know you are not, but wish to be courteous) that certain city writers have said we were merely Chinese in this. I hope you know that such writers (if you had ever heard of them) know just about as much about us as about China, which means they know nothing, but merely make of this their magazine copy or gin talk. I hope you know that Southern culture meant, not speaking Greek for the gentlemen and ladies and committing to memory the history of literature, but a certain sense of refinement in feeling, a desire for civilization and continuation, a wish to please, to harmonize human relationships and living, and perhaps we must admit, a determination to believe that for certain gentle results a little time (and even place in certain cases) must be added to money and push.

Now, what I want to say to you, my dear lady, is that your house is not a palace, not even important architecture. It shines mostly by the ensemble, the house plus the trees, the grounds, the Southern sky, and, may I say? such graces of its intrinsic life as you yourself are.

May I say, too, that most of these things of yours, these articles, bits of china, silver, and so on, can be bought on Third Avenue in New York, in the Victorian antique shops; and are, besides, not confined by any means to the South? In Europe there are miles of this very furniture that you possess, even to the inlaid tables, crystal-lustres, and vases. The whole supplication that I lay at your feet is for the purification of the vain human heart, and for the avoidance of our seeming a trifle innocent, or ridiculous, to outsiders. It can be expressed in a simple rearrangement of statement:

When you lead your visitor toward an object, please say, at best, "This is a thing we've always loved," which reverts to your own persuasion, instead of, "This is a fine —, etc.," which invites what is called expertizing. Or say, "This is a piece of Sèvres of the First Empire." Or, if you wish to soar: "These my great-grandfather used to amuse himself having over from London." (Or Paris or Rome, according to taste.)

By this means two things may be accomplished: (1) A visitor from a nearby little town will not go away more ignorant and mixed up than ever over what is antique, what is distinguished or rare, what is a thing loved rather than a priceless thing. (2) People from sophisticated centers cannot go away smiling indulgently at us Southerners and our claims. (I am acquainted with plenty of people here in New York whom I should much prefer to have think my great-grandfather used to beat up Dresden cups when he had drunk too much Bourbon, than to have them think his great-grandson believes the three or four Dresden cups still left us to be unique in the world.)

At bottom this is most serious advice to my friend in her old house. I am asking her only to feature — as the journals and the films put it — her love of these old things for love's sake. For this is the way she has thought of them during most of her life. In fact, this is the way she really thinks of them now. She thinks thus now, despite our national money clichés that batter her brain, despite our advertising, our touristic movements that send endless riff-raff into places they neither understand nor belong to.

In this lady's case, the joke is — and the tears of things too — that what she really wants is that the moment should go off, should be entertaining. (And, perhaps, a little to be the heroine of it, which is natural.) To make the moment go off, her instinct tells her that for most visitors nowadays the terms "rare" and "priceless" are the only terms that speak, that give the thrill.

The point of all this is that I want my friend to believe in her own spirit (apart from words). It is this in her that will convince, or at least touch, many of the poor visiting creatures from American cities, touring, rich and lost, defeated by their own smart adequacy in a world they have made empty for themselves of almost everything but the priceless.

If none of the above soulful arguments should stir this lady, then I hope she will heed me when I say that, if we can prevent it, nobody who is an outsider must go away feeling indulgent to "the poor creature's pride in her old things." She owes it to her South to see to it that they go away at least baffled, so to speak; wondering, for instance, if the last car they have bought — newest model — is quite enough.

Backward South

Not far from Baton Rouge, I have been talking to a man at a gasoline station, one of those sons of a Southern judge who are reduced to picking up what living they can. He gives me a discussion of communism as it appears here and there in our capitalistic North.

Some of those people, they tell him, he says, want to divide everything. What is there to divide? Does anybody want to pay our taxes?

I go home to dinner with him, and he begins to tell me how in his house they live, and him gettin' only a tiny bank salary.

Well, he says, you see they have a little land which pays its taxes and, now that the government bribes them not to farm it, provides also a bit of income. His wife is dead, but her mother takes care of the children. Then, too, the garden. The garden grows in great abundance, and so they send things up and down the street anyhow. "Now," he says, "I reckon if everybody owned the garden they would all work it — but would they?" At this he cackles. I explain that it is very fine to travel in Russia now, that everybody has work there, and that tourists, carefully steered, on a two weeks' orbit, see, besides museums and other distinguished matters, apartment houses with water taps in the halls, and are shown poor people wearing shoes. You don't mean it! he says. Now Celie, their cook, has got some shoes, but she won't wear them when she's at home. What she wants is her three dollars a week, and then she just plays with the children after dinner; they all ride the calf.

I try to make it all seem quite wrong and it keeps turning out quite right. Even the calf's sufferings fail me; it seems the calf's mighty fat. It must be that I cannot put the argument as it should be put.

From what they tell her, the grandmother says, some of those people up there must be going crazy.

"I read how one man said he didn't like his mother and all that. I reckon some mothers are bad, some sons too — my mother used to tell of a woman in Carolina who had a child so bad she used to ring a bell when they went through the streets." The two children propped at either side of their grandma now roar with laughter.

" I remember," she says, " my own dear son was no angel. Once in particular, he certainly was not. So I said, 'You just come on in this house and sit here with me; we're going to talk this thing out.' Of course we had some peach ice cream in the icebox and we ate that, though I said, 'We're going to talk this thing out.' "

The beginning of a solution for this household, I decide, would be to stop the grandmother and the father loving these children. If no mere Five-Year Plan could do that, well, the father and grandmother will in time die off.

It may very well be, of course, that we must plan for more than five years in order to make these children quit loving these older people.

" My children don't tell me any lies," their father says, " and we have a guitar, a banjo, a mandolin, and an accordion, and sit here on the porch when it's warm weather, you know — it's a regular band almost — and play. I've got good children."

It is not easy, I suppose, to resist such blandishments and simple, open confidence, even from a parent. I can scarcely shine against it. And so it looks as if the children might grow up benighted. I might find it hard to convince them how much better it would be to climb up on the state's lap and play tunes with comrades, citizens and citizenesses, on community-tuned guitars.

This is at least one thing that is meant by the Backward South.

Summer Night

S—— is a plumpish young man of twenty-five, regarded here in New York as of an amiable disposition. He comes from Louisiana, and the gallery of his father's house is in the shade of water oaks, old, wide, black-green, hanging with moss. I have seen his mother's picture on his desk; such a lovely, delicate, and possessive face! Beyond her, as she stands there in the photograph, is a rose garden, flower after flower; it must have been full summer in that place.

Two or three times I have heard S—— trying manfully and loyally to explain to his friends here a strange, close longing that he has for this country of his. He talks about the climate, the peace, the fresh fruit, everything, including the easy living with so many servants about and so few engagements.

I have long wanted to ask him why he does not merely say flatly that, though the day may be beautiful and not too brief there at home, the wonder of that Southern country is the evening and the nights. Something about those breathless summer nights, the leaves moving softly, the voices on the porch of those who love you. Nights soft and passionately repeated like a beloved name. Walks along the dusk of the streets in the little town, garden fragrancies, near stars, shadows, dogs at a distance barking, voices, and the knowledge that you are loved.

Lately I heard S—— say some of this, at least, to his blond roommate, who takes so much exercise that he is always exhausted and sleepy: " By God, I've written them that in June I'm comin' home! "

Days not too brief. Breathless summer nights.

—From the *Virginia Quarterly Review*, April, 1935.
Reprinted by permission.

THE ENGLISH LANGUAGE IN THE SOUTH

By Cleanth Brooks, Jr.

One of the prices of democracy and democratic education is that you want to speak like everybody else. And one of the ills of isolation — one, if you like, of the limitations of the provincial — is that you are nervous, or may become so, as to what is done in the great world outside. It follows, therefore, with regard to the South and Southern people, that sometimes they are not sure of themselves, that they abandon too readily their own guns, and are apt to be defenseless before accusations that are mainly limited, if not even ignorant. It is not necessary to speak a language that is archaic and out of tone with our present world. But, on the other hand, we are not obliged to be exactly like the general mass spread over the entire United States; nor must we, on a lower plane, seek that generalization of speech that represents everybody who is not anybody. Within limits, it is a good thing to speak your own way, the way of your own part of the world. It follows, therefore, that it is not a bad idea to look into the background of your inherited speech, with the mingled purposes of justification, defense, and, if need be, compromise. Tone of voice is one thing and so is rhythm. The present article is about the language spoken.

A Southern pronunciation — lumping it all together, despite the fact that in the South there are many different ways of speaking — is usually thought to have emanated from the Negro; on the lips of a Virginia girl, pleasantly quaint, like other relics of the influence of the Negro mammy, but corrupt English after all. This popular belief has from time to time acquired the dignity of publication. Dr. Embree, for example, in his *Brown America* unhesitatingly attributes the Virginia lady's accent to the influence of the Negro. The origins of Southern speech, however, cannot be accounted for under a theory of Negro influence. Moreover, Southern English is not a corrupt form of " standard English." To make this point is to raise a number of questions with regard to the criterion of correct English — questions which divers people with their dogmatic assumptions on the subject never take into account.

In the first place, the speech of the Southern states represents an older form of English than that which is found in standard British English today. Indeed, it conforms rather closely to the description which A. J. Ellis gave in the last century of the behavior of the speech of a colony. The speech of a colony is conservative. It is in the language of the mother country that innovations are made. For example, few people other than professional students of the language know that the so-called broad *a*, heard in the British pronunciation of words like *path, staff, last,* and *dance,* is a later form than the vowel that is usually met with in these words in America. The broad *a*, most scholars agree, did not become fashionable in England until late in the eighteenth century. The settlement of America by Englishmen began early in the seventeenth. Obviously, the form used by Englishmen today could not have been the pronunciation carried over by the seventeenth century colonists.

It can be said that a large part of the United States is capable of making criticisms of Southern speech that are merely refined criticism; for the speech of other sections of this country is in its origins also seventeenth century English. Such criticisms are usually based on a hazy assumption that present " standard British " (the speech of the educated classes in London) is " correct," and that the nearer American speech approximates this, the more nearly correct it is. The assumption is not necessarily true, and only ignorance and fear can make us think so. What we can say, however, is that if American English is based originally on seventeenth century English, the South has clung more tenaciously to these original forms than have other parts of the country. Indeed, many of the pronunciations which are usually regarded as specifically " Negro " represent nothing more than older native English forms. The pronunciation, for example, of *get* as " git," so widespread in America and certainly not confined to the Negro, was the standard English form in the eighteenth century; and the pronunciation of *yellow* as " yal-uh " was also the polite eighteenth century pronunciation. Examples could be multiplied. To give only a few: *boil* pronounced as " bile "; *oblige* as " obleege "; *china* as " chainy." One remembers that Boswell remarks on Dr. Johnson's pronunciation of *heard* with the vowel of *hear*, and that Noah Webster prefers the pronunciation *hierd*, taking *heard* as merely an affectation that he has heard since the Revolution. In Anglo-Saxon it was *hierde* and often enough in Middle English. The so-called dropping of the g in final *-ing* as in " darlin' " for *darling* was perfectly correct in England itself in the eighteenth century, not to mention its practice nowadays by the British upper classes. Many a lord says " it don't." Matthew Arnold said " fascinatin'," not *fascinating*.

You will hear pronunciations in the South, however, which do not go back to any pronunciation in earlier *standard* English. This does not mean that they originated on our side of the Atlantic. They represent forms from the provincial dialects — pronunciations which occurred in the dialects of certain parts of England but which did not, as such dialectal forms occasionally did, obtain a footing in the standard language. These dialect forms are of great importance because they offer a possible means for determining the regions in England from which came the colonists who set the speech pattern of the South. Joel Chandler Harris has Uncle Remus pronounce *until*, *unsettle*, etc., as " awn-til," " awn-settle," etc. *Un-* is still pronounced " awn " by dialect speakers in Devon. Uncle Remus pronounces *corner* as " cawnduh," inserting a *d* in it. The living dialects of Somerset and Devon give the same form. When Uncle Remus pronounces *whether*, he leaves out the *th*, but so do the dialects of Wiltshire, Dorset, Somerset, and Devon. Again, the word *seven* is frequently heard in the South as " sebn," but the same form occurs in a number of dialects of England, including those of the southwest. In the southwest of England, " gwine " occurs for *going*. Even the dropping of a final *d* as in *told*, " tole," or in *hand*, " han'," or of a final *t* as in *last*, " las'," is not a corruption. If it is a corruption at all, it is one which probably came into this country by passage across the Atlantic. Such forms are the regular developments in many of the living dialects of Great Britain.

As a matter of fact, a number of words in the South which appear to be new words entirely, represent in their origin merely dialectal forms of standard English: *roil* is a purely literary word, but "rile," which is related to it in the same way as "bile" to *boil*, is common. "Ingun" is a variant of *onion*, still to be found in many of the counties of England and Scotland. The word "frail," used in the South in the sense of a severe beating ("I'm going to *frail* the life out of him") has no relation to *frail* in the sense of "fragile." It is a development of *flail* which has occurred in many of the provincial dialects of Great Britain. The word "rare" as used in the phrase "rarin' to go" is related to the word *rear* in the same way that "quare" is related to *queer*. Both "rare" and "quare" are widely distributed through the dialects of Great Britain. "Peart" is a development of *pert* and must have been brought across the Atlantic by the early settlers, for it still exists in a number of English counties.

In this connection one may point out that the Southern *r* is connected with the south of England as well as with the Southern states of America. In this part of England the consonant *r* was lost very early, before consonants and at the end of words. From the seventeenth century onward this development had penetrated the standard language, and this treatment of *r*, far from being a slurring or a corruption, is the treatment standard in British English today. It is the normal treatment also in some other parts of America— eastern New England, for example. On the western edges of the Southern states, Midwestern influence has come in bringing the *r* with it; in the mountain regions of the South also (under Scotch-Irish influence?) the *r* is preserved.

As one instance after another of Southern speech traces itself back to England, either to earlier standard English or to provincialisms of the south and southwest counties, it rapidly becomes apparent that any theory of Negro influence must be abandoned. The Negro learned his speech from the colonists, who must have come predominantly from the English southwest. The Negro has then preserved many of these original forms, even after most of the whites have discarded them. This is not to state, of course, that Uncle Remus speaks the dialect of Hardy's peasants. But the fact that his dialect, wherever it deviates from modern British English, differs together along *with* the dialects of the southwest counties indicates that Southern speech has been colored by the English southwest.

The only alternative to this theory is to accept what amounts to a staggering coincidence. The magnitude of the coincidence will be made more vivid by consideration of a few more specific cases. Take the Southern variants of *muskmelon,* for instance. *Melon* is often heard as " million " in the South, especially among Negroes; and *muskmelon* is frequently, even among whites, pronounced " mushmelon." The form " mushmillion," which Harris has Uncle Remus use, and which may still be heard among old people in the South in country districts, would accordingly be considered by most people as about as thoroughly " Negro " as a word could be. The form seems obviously to be a corruption. But one holding such a view will be disconcerted to find in the Oxford Dictionary precisely this form occurring in a passage written by one Jerome Horsey in 1591. . . .

The interpretation of the origin of Southern speech given above raises questions with regard to the origin of the speech used in other parts of the country. If the speech of the Southern states shows forms from seventeenth and eighteenth century standards and from the provincial dialects of England, why do not such forms appear in the states of the North? The answer, of course, is that they do. In James Russell Lowell's *Biglow Papers,* written in the New England rustic dialect, occur many spellings which indicate such pronunciations. We find even more parallelisms with Southern forms when we consult early New England records with their occasional spellings which indicate dialectal pronunciations, or else the remarks on pronunciation made by the early grammarians of this section. To take only a few examples collected by the late George Phillip Krapp in his *English Language in America,* " skase " for *scarce* must have occurred frequently in the earlier speech of this country, in the North as well as in the South. It probably derives from the southern part of England, where the *r* was lost early before consonants and at the end of words. *Itch* is pronounced

" each " by Uncle Remus, but formerly it was so pronounced in parts of the North. " Drap " for *drop* and " crap " for *crop* are still frequently heard in the South, but such forms were once found in New England also; and in the case of both sections, their ultimate origin was probably in the dialects of the southwest of England.

Most scholars who have worked on the subject believe that the New England coast was predominantly influenced by the south and east counties of England. Pronunciations from the eastern counties, Norfolk, Suffolk, and Essex, are to be found there: for example, the pronunciation of *whole* as something resembling " hull," *stone* resembling " stun," etc. The evidence would seem to indicate, however, in my opinion, considerable influence from the counties of the southwest as well. The influence of the southwest, as has been pointed out, seems dominant in the South, though some forms occurring in Virginia seem to point back to the eastern counties, and other influences may be present in other parts of the South. At any rate, the language of both New England and the South — whatever differences existed between them — in the eighteenth century must have differed very considerably from the British English of today. The marked difference between eastern New England and the South did not exist at this period. These differences came later, and came, not with laziness and corruption in the South, but with innovation in New England through the influence of spelling, the elocution book, and the diligence of the New England schoolma'am. Probably no other part of the English-speaking world in any one period has produced so many spelling books and dictionaries as New England produced in the early nineteenth century.

There is also evidence to indicate that New England has consciously imitated British pronunciation by taking over from it later developments of the qualities of certain vowel sounds, and imposing them in whole classes of words like *corn, morning, short, thorn,* etc., which were distinguished in pronunciation from words like *divorce, store, pork, fort,* etc. The first group had an *aw* vowel, the second a long o. Today in British pronunciation, both groups have *aw*, but this development did not take place in England until the nineteenth century. Consequently, the appearance of examples of the present-day British pronunciation in New England (or elsewhere in America) suggests a late imitation of British English.

This difference in attitude toward speech in New England on the one hand and the South on the other is an indication of more fundamental cultural differences. The desire to cultivate " correctness " of speech, the reliance on spelling, the diligence of the New England schoolma'am, may, if you choose to do so, be interpreted as marks of the cultural continuity existing between the New England and the Old. They are susceptible, however, of another account, not quite so favorable, perhaps; they may be interpreted as symptoms of a feeling of cultural inferiority — of anxiety, that is, as to status. But it might be more graceful to let a New Englander speak in this matter of New England's dependence on the mother land. Henry Adams, writing of the mid-nineteenth century, says: " The tone of Boston society was colonial. The true Bostonian always knelt in self-abasement before the majesty of English standards; far from concealing it as a weakness, he was proud of it as his strength."

The attitude of the South (again speaking in relative terms) was quite different. The South never had quite the reverence for the written word which prevailed in New England. Like England itself, especially among country families and the aristocracy in general, it was content to rest the criterion of speech on a living oral tradition. Unconsciously at least and by its very lack of extreme self-consciousness, the South ceased to be a colony. Whatever general conclusion one may wish to draw, it would be hard to deny that the attitude toward speech in the South exhibits a culture in a very healthy state. The continuity between class and class and even between race and race was not severed by that artificial and irritating barrier, a *class* dialect.

The influence of spelling has, of course, exerted itself on Southern speech, but less than it has on that of most other sections of the country. Otherwise, there has been little or no attempt to keep up with the later developments of British English. Many Southerners, educated persons as well as the uneducated, consistently pronounce *better* as " bedduh," *bottle* as " boddle," etc., thus carrying on regularly in their speech a development largely to be found in the dialects of the English southwest. " Taripin " is the almost universal pronunciation of *terrapin,* for few allow themselves to be browbeaten by the spelling. As a matter of fact, *terrapin* is in origin an Algonquin Indian word, and the earliest form seems to have had an *a* rather than an *e.*

The student of language is supposed to be completely objective — to describe conditions rather than to prescribe standards. But perhaps he may be allowed to affect standards, at least in one regard: by giving a true description when a false description is being made the basis for prescriptions. On one fact, scholars are agreed: that the standard of speech for a country is that of the " best " speakers, the educated speakers, of that country. British English is undoubtedly correct for the modern Englishman. It is not correct, by virtue of that reason at least, for the Virginian or Tennessean. Moreover, in trying to find a standard for modern America, the best authorities are agreed that there is no virtue in trying to impose an artificial and synthetic criterion. If the Virginian is not to be forced into imitation of the Oxford don, there is logically no reason for him to be forced into imitation of Boston — or, for that matter, of Chicago or Hollywood.

If the South — or, for that matter, any other sections of the country — under the influence of the radio, the talking pictures, or other " cultural " forces, cares to abandon its characteristic speech, the pronunciation then adopted by the educated speakers of the region will, of course, then be the standard. But that adoption need not be made under the delusion that something poor is being abandoned for something " better." Certainly the heritage the South possesses is not one to be ashamed of — neither the seventeenth century standard forms, nor the coloring of Devon, Somerset, and Dorset. The men of the west country were active in the conquest and settlement of America. One of the most prominent of them, Sir Walter Raleigh, was not ashamed of his provincial accent, even at Elizabeth's court. John Aubrey, the gossipy biographer of the seventeenth century, tells us that he heard one of Raleigh's contemporaries say that " notwithstanding his so great mastership in style and his conversation with the learnedest and politest persons, yet he spake broad Devonshire to dying day." It would be odd, indeed, if Raleigh's fellow countrymen, mariners, adventurers, and colonists, not courtiers at all, had not bequeathed forms of their sturdy speech to their descendants in the New World.

Gy pronounced *gj* in such a word as *garden*, found in Virginia and sometimes in other eastern parts of the South, is traced back to Leicester, northwest Oxford, Hereford, north Derby; *ky* pronounced *kj* in *card* — found also in Maine as well as the South — goes back to west Somerset, Aberdeen, and north Derby.

"Through the South and New England, in the colloquial speech of educated and cultivated people the suffix *-ing* as in *going* is commonly *-in'*. . . . This characteristic of eighteenth century speech is not quite so evident in the South generally as it is on the Eastern Shore of Virginia and on the New England coast, where the syllable containing *-in'* has a stronger stress. For example, *pudding*, which generally becomes 'pudn' colloquially, is on the Eastern Shore and in New England 'pudin.' In *going* ('goin') the second syllable is not obscured. In the South generally, this 'loss of g' may seem slovenly; on the Eastern Shore and in New England the g is lost precisely ('puddin,' for example, instead of the Southern 'pudn').

"No one should feel ashamed of this ancient and honorable pronunciation." (William Cabell Greet, "Southern Speech" in *Culture in the South*, p. 609.)

— From *A Southern Treasury of Life and Literature*, Charles Scribner's Sons, 1937. Reprinted by permission.

A PLEA TO THE PROTESTANT CHURCHES

By Cleanth Brooks, Jr.

THE WAR between science and Protestantism is over. Perhaps it was an unnecessary war — perhaps it need never have been fought. In any case, the proponents of Protestantism have been defeated; they have been worse than defeated: they have been converted.

In saying this, I am not underestimating the present strength of Fundamentalism. It is impressive. But its strength is chiefly in rural areas and is bound up with an older generation. The intellectual leaders of Protestantism, almost to a man, are not Fundamentalists; and Fundamentalism deprived of leaders, it is safe to predict, will not be able to survive the present intellectual climate.

One can be, or perhaps should be, thoroughly sympathetic with the Liberal Protestant in his unconscious capitulation to the enemy. As a man and as a citizen, he has coveted intercourse with other intellectuals. He has naturally found the cruder aspects of Fundamentalism repugnant. Moreover, he has become acutely conscious of the hiatus existing between the dominant interests of modern America and specifically religious interests. At his best, therefore, he has repudiated the close alliance between the church and the status quo. I am not forgetting that many of his brother Protestants still repose in a sturdy unconsciousness of any discrepancies existing between a Christian civilization and the Liberty League's enlightened American capitalism. But the number of Protestant leaders who have broken with the status quo is much larger than most people believe. And it is growing larger. And it is with this group — a group which contains not only the intellectuals but many of the most sincere spirits — that the future of American Protestantism rests.

The Liberal Protestant's repudiation of Fundamentalism on the one hand and of our unchristian society on the other ought to allow us to see his religion itself in some purity, naked and unencumbered. But what one sees immediately raises the question: Can Protestantism possibly survive another reformation without becoming reformed out of existence — that is, reformed out of existence as a religion? This last reformation has indeed come very close to leaving the Liberal Protestant up in the air. His position has thus far been primarily negative: in theology, emphasis on accommodating religion to science; in ethics, emphasis on a radical criticism of the present-day economic system. And as between the two, morals have been much more heavily emphasized than theology. Sermons and articles are full of this sort of thing: " Some other set of economic ideals which will be more Christian "; " If necessary, capitalism must be radically modified "; " Is communism consonant with Christianity? "

As the position becomes more positive, it tends toward a Christian socialism or communism, though here again it is vague. And it is the *religious* element that is vague — the relation of Christianity to the secular and temporal political program. If pressure is applied, one may predict that the Christian element will have to make room for the communistic. The sociological aspect of Christianity may seem to fit rather easily into the communistic scheme. But Christianity has historically included much more than a sociology. And if Christianity and communism seem to square easily with each other in their concern for the oppressed and exploited, an examination of the pronouncements of Liberal Protestantism will reveal very frail defenses against non-Christian attitudes on other relationships. For present-day Protestantism is already so far secularized that under pressure it might easily be forced to sell the pass completely. One may sum up as follows: In Protestantism's emphasis on the social gospel, in its regenerated zeal and concern for the conditions in which men live, is it proposing to carry out a Christian program? Or has it, under the influence of our contemporary scientific climate, become merely a socio-political program? The question is a serious one and it is asked seriously out of a great deal of respect for the sincerity of those religious leaders who have had to brave the disfavor of their wealthy, Big Business parishioners.

An answer to this question involves, of course, a definition of religion and implies a particular position on the relation of religion to science. Perhaps it is best to indicate briefly and rapidly what the writer's position on that question is; for, however obvious the following propositions may be, Liberal Protestantism is not acting upon a realization of them.

In the first place, science cannot prove its underlying assumptions. They must be, literally, *assumed.* And in the second place, science has nothing to say about values. Science always prefaces its prescriptions with an *if: if* you want this result, then take this means. Science is quite properly technician-in-chief to civilization: it defines the means to be employed for attainment of various objectives. But it cannot be the pilot. It cannot — as science — name the objectives. That is the function of religion, if religion is to have any function at all. And religion may be roughly defined as that system of basic values which underlies a civilization.

Liberal Protestantism, however, in its anxiety to live amicably with science, has schooled itself upon a scientific discipline almost exclusively. The discipline of the means is ultimately irrelevant to religion, which is a discipline of objectives, and has worked it much positive injury. That injury can perhaps be most clearly displayed by contrasting the scientific discipline with the discipline of art, a discipline to which Protestantism is historically antipathetic, and which the typical Liberal Protestant pastor noticeably lacks.

I prefer, for a particular reason, to contrast art with science, rather than religion with science. The qualities which art shares with religion are just those which Liberal Protestantism through its imitation of science has lost. For the Protestant reader, a contrast between religion and science may be neither clear nor emphatic. To say that Protestantism has so far lost its conception of religion that it is difficult to make it understand what it has lost is perhaps the most cruel thing that one could say about it. But I am availing myself of the privileges of a Protestant (perhaps to the limit) in speaking out on these matters; and I am serious; and I want to be understood.

In using the term *art*, I am perhaps inviting misconceptions. I obviously do not mean by *art* empty and frivolous decoration. My criticism of Protestantism is not that it lacks a properly restful ritual or a tasteful church architecture. I am using *art* in the sense of a description of experience which is concrete where that of science is abstract; many-sided where that of science is necessarily one-sided; and which involves the whole personality where science only involves one part, the intellect. These are qualities which are essential to worship, and a religion without worship is an anomaly. It deserves — if only to keep the issues clear — another name. Religion is obviously more than art. A religion is anchored to certain supreme values, values which it affirms are eternal, not merely to be accepted for the moment through a " willing suspension of disbelief." But a religion which lacks the element of art is hardly a religion at all.

The injury done by the prevailing scientific discipline reveals itself ominously in many a liberal sermon. In the first place, science attempts an intellectual exposition. This can never be purely intellectual, of course, but complete purity is its goal. The argument is convincing in so far as the scientist can clear himself of all emotional factors, all considerations of value, all that might make the conclusion arrived at personally attractive to him. The sermon cannot properly avail itself of such conditions, and yet the liberal sermon often forces itself into just such a structure. It amounts to a lecture. It exposes a religion truncated in the direction of science.

In the second place, science attempts to conquer new areas for truth, consolidate its gains, and then move on to the conquest of further areas. Science is not only abstract but progressive. But if the Christian affirmations are in any sense eternal (qualify the term as you will), they are not points to be abandoned in favor of new truth, new discoveries. " The Search for God " is all very well for a party of religious explorers; it hardly does for a religion which maintains that it has found Him.

If there is to be a search at all, it will have to be a search in something of the sense in which the poet explores himself in relation to the truth, pondering over it, relating it to various sets of conditions, but returning to it and working back to it as to a center rather than regarding it as a point on a line along which he continually advances. Here again Liberal Protestantism finds itself in a quandary. Granting acceptance of the truth, what does it have to give? For the sinner, one may assume that it does have something. To the average congregation of "converted," it often finds itself with nothing further to offer. And this is perhaps the explanation for the Liberal Protestant pastor's offering book reviews, current events, sociology, etc. — more often than you would think — in lieu of worship.

In the third place, and of course most important, science is man-centered and "practical." Bertrand Russell is right, ultimately, in calling science "power-knowledge." And it is power-knowledge, of course, because it has man as its point of reference. It puts the handle into his hands so that he can *use* its information. If religion is a knowing also, a body of knowledge, it is hardly knowledge in this sense. It cannot be put to use — not in the sense in which science can be. And religion, again like art, is not man-centered in the same sense in which science is. To illustrate from art, the artist attempts something of a *rapprochement* with the universe outside him. Laying aside the practical motive, he tries to bring his interests into terms with larger, more universal interests.

Liberal Protestantism, on the basis of the books and articles which its leaders produce and the sermons which they preach, is pretty thoroughly man-centered, as a matter of emphasis at least. The fatherhood of God, one feels, is no longer the correlative of the brotherhood of man. The brotherhood of man tends to become an exclusive end in itself. There is little wonder that the most positive affirmation which Liberal Protestantism can make is apt to be some form of socialism.

One may illustrate this matter from the *Christian Century*, again expressing all sympathy for it and a good deal of thoroughly well-deserved praise. It is the strongest and most admirable of the Liberal Protestant publications; but because it is the strongest, it sets forth in itself most cruelly the fundamental weakness of the group it represents.

Its views on economics, politics, and related matters are honest, forthright, and full. On these topics it resembles, and compares very favorably with, the *New Republic* and the *Nation*. It refuses to be lulled into a belief that the prevailing order is Christian in any but a nominal sense, and it criticizes affairs, domestic and foreign, vigorously and fearlessly. Yet the reader of this religious paper is aware of a sad weakness in its theology.

I am not trying to force a choice of extremes here. I am not asking that Protestantism devote itself to nothing but theology. I am simply pointing out that in so far as the *Christian Century* mirrors a group, that group is already far along the road to secularization. Where one's interests lie, to paraphrase the Scriptures, there lies one's heart also. And judged by the *Christian Century*, the hearts of the leaders of Liberal Protestantism lie in the realm of temporal affairs.

This is, of course, the fundamental explanation of the rise of the liturgical religions in the last decades. After discounting the cases of snobbery and the cases of those who wish a retreat from a disagreeable world into the peace of a beautiful aestheticism, the liturgical religions have something to give which advanced Protestantism would do well to cultivate if it expects to remain a religion at all.

Communism sets out to provide handsome creature comforts, luxuries, and, more than that, leisure in which man may presumably develop his mind and aesthetic faculties. It provides them at a price, of course. But in proportion as Protestantism becomes a mere humanitarianism (or by emphasis a humanitarianism) it will have less and less to disagree with in the communist program, less and less to offer in addition to such a program; and even if it maintains its reservations, in a time of crisis, those scruples will be entirely too flimsy to stand. To repeat what has been said earlier in this essay, the real issue comes down to this: If the Christian values are *true*, if they are worth adhering to, shall they determine the civilization; or shall the economic order into which we drift determine our values by allowing to us whatever values such an economic order will permit?

Obviously, the modern world of finance capitalism does not represent a Christian civilization; but is the movement to the left the only alternative? And if the church has in the past compromised often and shamefully, does not a *rapprochement* with the left involve its compromises too? This last question may be given point by quoting from the conclusion of a recent article in the *Christian Century* entitled "Must Christains Reject Communism?" The author there outlines "the foundations of a social philosophy" on which communism and Christianity might agree:

1. The only forces which work any real change in politics or economics are the result of organizing the interests of some group and making them effective.
2. The change we want — a reintegration of society on a higher level — can be accomplished only by organizing the interests of a majority group.
3. The issue as to whether this can be done effectively rests with man — or rather with God — that curious power which only man seems to possess, of consciously realizing his situation and molding it nearer to his desire.

The last sentence is particularly revealing. That curious power of molding situations to man's desire would seem to be science, not the Christian God, though perhaps the communist God. The author concludes by stating that the Christian in accepting communism "need not sacrifice his Christianity, for that in its pure form has always promised that one day the lowly will be exalted and the proud and powerful brought down."

The phrase, "in its pure form," obviously begs the question. The pure form is arrived at by a selection which involves disregarding among other things the statement that "My kingdom is not of this world." The old, troubled questioning, Why did God make man capable of sin and evil? returns here, not in the form of anguished complaint, but as an affirmation: now that we have the technical power, we will make sin impossible.

The article is a rather extreme but representative enough example of Protestantism secularizing itself out of existence — becoming conformed to this world. If the Christian assumptions are valid, then the Christian theologian and pastor, whatever the world may think, can hardly have a more important vocation. If, on the other hand, the Protestant Liberals are merely humanitarians in search of a social program, then they are perhaps right, but they are hardly Christian in any historical sense of the term, and intellectual honesty calls for the admission of the fact to themselves as well as to others.

The tendency to the left is apparently honest and courageous. I do not propose to inveigh against it on either of these grounds. But I do not believe that it holds the hope of a *Christian* civilization. It is all very well for Protestantism to become commendably zealous in rendering unto Caesar the things that are Caesar's; but in its zeal it has come very close to slighting God. And the Liberal Protestant perhaps needs to be reminded that the followers of Marx will be quite as jealous in claiming their dues as Caesar himself.

Unless Liberal Protestantism is prepared to be a religion, it is a superfluity, and it had better allow itself to be absorbed into one of the movements which put the material well-being of man first, willing to implement this through collectivization, the liquidation of certain classes, and whatever else may be necessary. But a religion may be necessary and inevitable after all. Civilizations are founded, not on ethical societies, but on religions. Communism itself is in this sense a religion, though one of the materialistic religions and one of the religions of man, burdened with his infirmities. The promise of communism to realize itself in practice rests, indeed, on the fact that it is a religion; that is, that it makes a claim to authority, that it can claim emotional allegiance, and that it has a world view. Christians who hope to short-cut to the promised land via communism will find themselves badly fooled. Without its non-Christian elements, communism would carry as little hope for practical and early fulfillment of its promises as does Liberal Christianity.

It would be a heartening sign if Liberal Protestantism could get over its sense of inferiority, could abandon its effort to keep up with the Millikans and Jeanses and Marxes, and could attempt to realize its basic function, that of a religion. This would not necessitate a return to the *crudities* of Fundamentalism, unless one believes, in an age of relativities, that belief in an absolute is crude. It would not necessitate the suppression of the social gospel, though it would involve deciding what sort of social gospel is Christian and what is not. It would not demand cessation of a radical criticism of the present economic order, though it would involve relating that criticism to a positive conception of a Christian society.

I am not certain that Protestantism has such a rally as this left in it. If it has, probably the greatest obstacle it will have to overcome is the all-pervading economic determinism embedded in such a phrase as "You can't turn back the clock." For the movements which seem to me to have most hope for realizing a Christian order will probably bear this stigma. They involve, on the political and economic side, giving meaning to the sacredness of human personality and to the freedom of the will by restoring property. The proposal may sound quixotic to the modern mind. But this is a measure of the seriousness of the problem. If Liberal Protestantism has so much acquired the modern mind, if it has become so much infected with economic determinism, that it has lost its belief in the freedom of the will, then the case is hopeless indeed. For the freedom of the will implies, among other human privileges, a genius for defining objectives — not a surrender to the tyranny of the means.

— From *Who Owns America?* Houghton Mifflin Company, 1936. Reprinted by permission.

THE EMANCIPATION OF WOMAN

By Virginius Dabney

UNTIL COMPARATIVELY recent times, woman's position in society was almost invariably subordinate to that of man. Under the Mosaic law, for example, she enjoyed scarcely any legal rights, and under the Roman law her situation at first was similar, although her disabilities were subsequently lightened and indeed virtually abolished by the Christian emperors. The early Christian fathers, on the other hand, seem to have looked upon the ladies with a decidedly jaundiced eye. St. Chrysostom is suspected of having expressed more than his own individual opinion when he pronounced woman " a necessary evil, a natural temptation, a desirable calamity, a domestic peril, a deadly fascination, and a painted ill," for one of his clerical compatriots was so ungallant as to describe her as " the door of hell."

With the advent of the Renaissance, however, woman's status underwent a marked improvement, and this improvement was manifest over a considerable period. Later there was a gradual decline in her position. In eighteenth century England, for example, she sank to a level not greatly superior to that which she had occupied five hundred years earlier. The disesteem in which she was held is sufficiently evidenced by the attitude of the essayist Addison, who advised her to " content herself with her natural talents, play at cards, make tea and visits, talk to her dog often, and to her company but sometimes."

Prevailing theories as to masculine supremacy were sharply challenged by Mary Wollstonecraft in 1792 with the publication of her *Vindication of the Rights of Woman,* a plea for equality of educational opportunity. But it was to be many years before her plea was granted, either in England or America.

The ante-bellum South placed woman on a lofty pedestal, and Southern chivalry worshiped at her feet. Southern gentlemen never wearied of hymning the glories of Southern womanhood. When, for example, a celebration of the one hundredth anniversary of the founding of Georgia was held at Athens in the early 1830's, numerous toasts were drunk, but the one which brought twenty rousing cheers, nearly twice the number accorded any of the others, was to " Woman!!! The center and circumference, diameter and periphery, sine, tangent, and secant of all our affections! "

In the Old South there were no women's " rights," as these are known today. George W. Bagby, the Virginia writer, described the status of woman at the period in the following words: " To feed, to clothe, to teach, to guide, to comfort, to nurse, to provide for and to watch over a great household and keep its complex machinery in noiseless order — these were the woman's rights which she asserted, and there was no one to dispute; this was her mission, and none ever dared to question it."

Miss Ellen Glasgow comments in more acidulous vein in her novel *Virginia* upon the rôle occupied by Southern womanhood before the war. The heroine's education, Miss Glasgow wrote, was " founded on the simple theory that the less a girl knew about life, the better prepared she would be to contend with it," and was designed " to paralyze her reasoning faculties so completely that all danger of mental ' unsettling ' or even movement was eliminated."

Such was the situation in Dixie under the beneficent régime of chivalry. So chivalrous, indeed, was the ante-bellum South that its women were granted scarcely any rights at all. Everywhere they were subjected to political, legal, educational, social, and economic restrictions. They took no part in governmental affairs, were without legal rights over their property or the guardianship of their children, were denied adequate educational facilities, and were excluded from business and the professions.

This is not to say, however, that the women of " before the war " were lacking in capabilities of a high order. For if they were not always learned in books, they often exhibited executive and administrative ability in the management of large households. It is quite likely, too, that those who did possess a measure of "book learning" were frequently reluctant to disclose the fact, lest they be accused of indulgence in intellectual exercises unbecoming a Southern gentlewoman.

When Frances Wright of Scotland came to America in 1820, the agitation for the emancipation of woman in this country began. Then about a decade later the antislavery movement got under way, and the two causes were in large measure joined. Many who objected to slavery also felt that the subordinate position of woman could never be justified on logical grounds. In 1840 the temperance movement was launched in earnest, and a third group of agitators sprang up, a group which included numbers of those who also were working against slavery and for woman's rights. Thus by the middle years of the century these three mutually coöperative crusades were well under way, each led by women of great determination.

Two of the principal reformers were the Grimké sisters of Charleston, South Carolina, who had left their native state in 1819 in protest against the slave system, and had become active anti-slavery workers in the North. Angelina Grimké's marvelous oratorical powers have been noted in an earlier chapter. The novel spectacle of a Southern gentlewoman speaking to immense throngs on political topics and swaying them with her eloquence did much to undermine the theory that the arena of public affairs should be reserved exclusively for men. The Grimkés were attacked in the North by the General Association of Congregational Ministers, which charged them with seeking to entice "women from their proper sphere and loosening the foundations of the family." This brought forth a vigorous defense of the sisters from John G. Whittier in his poem "The Pastoral Letter."

But while there was opposition throughout the country to the efforts of the feminists, that opposition was strongest in the Southland. There the twin institutions of chivalry and slavery combined to thwart the equal rights movement at every turn. Miss Nell Battle Lewis has pointed out in a discriminating series of articles in the Raleigh *News and Observer*[1] that slavery operated in various ways to prevent the liberation of Southern womanhood. Miss Lewis

[1] April 19 and 26, May 3, 10, 17, and 24, 1925.

calls attention to the fact that the close relationship between the feminist movement and the antislavery movement was severely prejudicial to the cause of equal rights in the South. At the same time, she says, the argument was advanced that if the franchise were granted to women, Negro women might get the vote and there would also be danger of "social equality." She also advances the contention that the very presence of the institution of slavery "acted to dull the South's conception of individual liberty as the greatest boon of all mankind and made the lack of such liberty in the case of women seem less important and less deplorable than it otherwise might have appeared."

When Harriet Martineau visited this country in the middle thirties, she found only seven occupations open to women; namely, teaching, needlework, keeping boarders, working in cotton mills and in book binderies, typesetting, and household service. These forms of employment were available in the United States as a whole to women of all classes, but the last four on the list and perhaps others were not regarded as suitable for women of the Southern aristocracy. These gentlewomen conducted numerous private schools, and in the late forties and the fifties they held positions in the public schools, notably in North Carolina, where Superintendent Calvin H. Wiley succeeded in procuring for female teachers with certificates the highest salaries in the nation. In addition, women of the upper class sometimes wrote for the magazines or the newspapers, and occasionally there was a woman novelist, although Miss Martineau displayed no awareness of this fact. Publications which were especially hospitable to feminine contributors during the two decades immediately preceding the war include the *Southern Literary Messenger*, the Charleston *Literary Gazette*, and the Louisville *Courier*.

There were practically no facilities for the higher education of women at the opening of the nineteenth century, either in this country or in England. Even in Boston girls were barred from all public school grades above the primary, and they were not permitted to receive primary instruction except from April to October, a situation which obtained until 1825.

The Old South was unable to boast of a worker in the field of women's education to rank with Emma Willard or Mary Lyon in the North, but the educational facilities offered to women below the Potomac were not greatly inferior to those provided contemporaneously in other sections. Genuine collegiate work was not available to "females" anywhere in the United States until the founding of Vassar College in 1865. Most of the so-called institutions of higher learning for women in the pre-war era were seminaries offering courses in music, art, etiquette, and English literature, with an occasional excursion into French and the classics.

Outstanding among the earliest of these schools to be established in the Southern states was Salem Female Academy, founded by the Moravians at Salem, North Carolina, in 1802. Four years later the Rev. John Lyle, a Presbyterian divine, opened the first female seminary in what was then the West, at Paris, Kentucky. He was able to build up an enrollment of two hundred or more, but in 1809 or 1810 he closed the school permanently because certain of its officials objected to the public reading of the Bible there.

The need for better educational facilities for women was recognized in Mississippi earlier than in many of the other states. Elizabeth Female Academy was founded in 1818 at Washington, and twelve years later Mississippi College, a coeducational institution, was opened at Clinton. Through the efforts of Miss Sallie E. Reneau and Governor John J. McRae the state legislature voted the establishment of a State Female College in 1856; but as no endowment was provided, this gesture was rather futile. It is obvious, however, that the attitude of a substantial element in Mississippi toward woman's position in society was decidedly advanced for the period. When in 1839 Mississippi granted to married women the control over their own property, it was the first state in the Union to do so.

Alabama, too, displayed an awareness of the need for higher learning for women rarely found in the first quarter of the nineteenth century. As early as 1820 the Alabama legislature, in establishing the state university, provided for a branch which would offer "female education." Two years later the number of such branches was increased to three. Unfortunately this broadly comprehensive plan was never put into operation, probably owing to lack of adequate finances.

Duncan G. Campbell was the pioneer agitator for better educational facilities for women in Georgia. After his death, Daniel Chandler took up the cudgels, and it was largely through his efforts that the Georgia Female College at Macon was chartered by the state in 1836. This institution, now known as Wesleyan College, claims to have been the first college for women in the country to give the B.A. degree. The difficulties under which it labored in the early years of its existence may be at least partially envisioned in the answer given by " a gentleman of large means and liberal views " when asked to contribute to its support.

" No, I will not give you a dollar," this liberal gentleman declared. " All that a woman needs to know is how to read the New Testament, and to spin and weave clothing for her family."

A Vermonter named Zelotes C. Graves was the guiding spirit behind the establishment in 1850 of the Mary Sharp College at Winchester, Tennessee, originally known as the Tennessee and Alabama Female Institute. Graves sought to provide as thorough collegiate training for women of Tennessee as was available to the men. He claimed that Mary Sharp was the first college for women in America to require both Latin and Greek for the B.A. degree, and the claim appears to have been well founded if one excludes coeducational institutions from the category of " colleges for women." The educational work done by Graves in the antebellum South was genuinely significant, and it is unfortunate that his college fell upon evil days in the eighties and was forced to suspend operations not long afterward.

Almost simultaneously with the establishment of Mary Sharp College in Tennessee, Charles Lewis Cocke, who at nineteen years of age had expressed a fixed intention to devote his life to the cause of higher education for women, took charge of Hollins Female Institute near Roanoke, Virginia, the first chartered institution for girls in the Old Dominion, now Hollins College. The opening of this school in 1852 doubtless was in some measure the result of the agitation for better educational opportunities for women begun years before by Thomas Ritchie in the columns of the Richmond *Enquirer*.

While there were other colleges for women in the Old South, those which have been mentioned are perhaps the most important. But if there was an appreciable amount of sentiment below the Potomac for equal educational facilities for women, there was practically none for equal political rights. The activities of Susan B. Anthony, Elizabeth Cady Stanton, and their fellow workers in the North on behalf of the enfranchisement of their sex were frequently greeted with hoots and jeers and sometimes with insults and physical violence. It appears certain that these ladies would have been given an equally inhospitable reception if they had extended their operations to the slave states, for both of them were as strongly hostile to slavery as they were favorable to women's rights, and Miss Stanton had been active in the antislavery crusade.

After Appomattox the militant suffragettes of the North were indignant at the enfranchisement of the illiterate freedmen in the former Confederacy by a government which had steadfastly turned a deaf ear to their own pleas for the ballot. But there was still little or no interest on the part of Southern women in the vote, and several decades were to elapse before any such interest could be aroused.

Meanwhile the women of the South were manifesting no little concern for the progress of educational movements, whether designed for the exclusive benefit of their own sex or not. So marked had this interest become, in fact, by the early nineties, that the Rev. A. D. Mayo, a New Englander who spent twelve years in educational work in the Southern states after the war, declared that the greatest single educational force in the area was to be found in its womanhood.

As in the case of the men's colleges, however, too much emphasis was placed upon the number in institutions. Many were led to believe that because there were more women's colleges below the Potomac than were to be found above it, the facilities for educating Southern women were superior to those provided for Northern women. In the early eighties no fewer than 111 of the 142 "higher institutions for women" in the country were in the Southern and South Central states; and of 904 degrees conferred on women in 1882, a total of 684 were conferred in those states. It need hardly be said, however, that the type of training provided at such colleges as Vassar, Wellesley, and Smith was far superior to anything offered at the period in the South.

Men like Governor W. Y. Atkinson of Georgia and Charles D. McIver of North Carolina were active in their respective states on behalf of improved educational opportunities for women, while J. L. M. Curry was zealous in the cause throughout the South. Atkinson, as a member of the State Normal and Industrial College for Girls at Athens, and after he entered the governor's chair, appointed a board composed entirely of women for the school. McIver was the greatest advocate of improved education for women in North Carolina. One of his favorite sayings was: "When you educate a woman, you educate an entire family." McIver devoted most of his adult life to this crusade, and he was chiefly instrumental in founding the State Normal and Industrial College at Greensboro.

Walter Hines Page jolted many citizens of North Carolina and other Southern states out of the *laissez faire* state of mind which had characterized their attitude on this question with his address on "The Forgotten Man" at the Greensboro college in 1897.

"I have thus far spoken only of the forgotten man," Page declared on that occasion, "but what I have come to speak about is the forgotten woman. . . . Let any man whose mind is not hardened by some worn-out theory of politics or of ecclesiasticism go to the country in almost any part of the state and make a study of the life there, especially of the life of the women. He will see them thin and wrinkled in youth from ill-prepared food, clad without warmth or grace, living in untidy houses, working from daylight till bedtime at the dull round of weary duties, and the slaves of men of equal slovenliness, the mothers of joyless children — all uneducated, if not illiterate. Yet even their condition were endurable if there were any hope, but this type of woman is encrusted in a shell of dull content with her lot."

In Mississippi the prolonged campaign of Miss Sallie E. Reneau both before and after the Civil War for the establishment of a state female college was unsuccessful, and Miss Reneau finally removed to Tennessee. Mrs. Annie C. Peyton then took charge of the movement. Largely as a result of her efforts, extending over a considerable period, the Mississippi Industrial Institute and College, the first school of its kind in the country, opened its doors in 1885 with nearly 350 students.

But if Mississippi was willing to make this concession to its feminine population, it was by no means ready to entertain newfangled theories having to do with "women's rights." President Richard W. Jones of the State Industrial Institute and College made this plain when he declared shortly after his inauguration:

"We are not teaching woman to demand the 'rights' of men nor to invade the sphere of men. The conditions are supplied here for that high training of the mind, of the sensibilities, of her aesthetic faculties, of the moral and religious parts of her being which fits her for the ways of modest usefulness, for works of true benevolence, and which invests her with that true womanly character and those beautiful Christian graces that constitute her the charm of social life and the queen of home."

By 1892 the state universities of Arkansas, Kentucky, Texas, and Mississippi admitted women on the same basis as men, but the movement for equal political rights was barely under way in the region. Long-cherished ideas concerning Southern chivalry made the average male living below the Potomac and the Ohio instinctively hostile to the equal rights program. Evidence of the strong hold of the chivalric tradition upon the young men of the South in the elegant nineties may be seen in the flamboyant dedication of the University of Virginia annual for 1895:

TO
SOUTHERN WOMANHOOD,
EVER THE INSPIRATION AND SUPPORT OF SOUTHERN
CHIVALRY, THIS VOLUME IS DEDICATED
WITH PRIDE IN HER PATRIOTISM,
REVERENCE FOR HER PURITY,
LOVE FOR HER MATCHLESS TENDERNESS,
AND TRUST IN HER UNFADING TRUTH

Such lofty sentiments were not entertained beyond the Mississippi, however, and four Far Western states gave the ballot to the ladies before the turn of the century.

Below Mason and Dixon's Line suffragists not only had to contend with the widespread beatification of woman, but they found it necessary at the same time to combat powerful groups with selfish interests to serve. These included exploiters of women and children in industry and men with money invested in the liquor business, elements which feared that an aroused and enfranchised womanhood would quickly force them to the wall. But if the brewers and distillers sought to thwart the movement, workers for equal rights found a valuable ally in the Woman's Christian Temperance Union, an organization enjoying particular puissance in the former Confederacy.

By 1915, eleven states, all west of the Mississippi River, had granted full suffrage to women, while Illinois had conferred upon its feminine population the right to vote in presidential elections. Advocates of enfranchisement were able to point to the accomplishments of women voters in the West in securing the passage of much liberal legislation, including laws having to do with factory inspection and child labor, juvenile courts, institutions for delinquents, improved educational facilities, and so on.

The movement made such progress that Woodrow Wilson endorsed suffrage for women in principle in 1916, provided it was conferred upon them through action of the individual states, and Charles E. Hughes, his opponent in the presidential campaign of that year, placed the stamp of his approval upon the proposed federal amendment. Two years later President Wilson urged the Congress to pass the suffrage amendment to the Constitution as a measure "vital to the winning of the war," and this was done in June, 1919. The amendment was then submitted to the states for ratification.

The suffragist drive had gathered such momentum in the years immediately preceding that Arkansas and Texas had granted the ballot to their womenfolk on virtually the same terms as their menfolk before the amendment was submitted, while Tennessee had done likewise, in so far as presidential and municipal elections were concerned. Arkansas had led the way in 1917 by passing a law permitting women to participate in Democratic primaries on the same basis as men, an enactment which was practically tantamount to complete enfranchisement, since the Democratic party is almost always overwhelmingly dominant in that state. Texas adopted similar legislation the following year, and then in 1919 Tennessee conferred the ballot on women desiring to participate in presidential and municipal contests.

Shortly thereafter the federal amendment was submitted to the states, and ratification began. One legislature after another fell into line, until thirty-five had done so. Only one more was needed when the Tennessee assembly convened in 1920. Realizing the crucial importance of capturing the Volunteer State, each side marshaled all the forces at its command. Nationally known suffrage leaders joined in the fight at Nashville and urged the legislature to complete the political emancipation of American womanhood by ratifying the amendment. Leading opponents invoked the ancient chivalric shibboleths and proclaimed that the supremacy of the white race would be jeopardized and the pillars of the social edifice undermined if women were given the ballot. After an epic struggle, the Tennessee assembly approved the amendment by a narrow margin, and the nineteenth amendment became a part of the organic law of the nation. The rockribbed conservatism of much of the South is evidenced, however, by the fact that the amendment was never ratified by the legislatures of Virginia, the Carolinas, Georgia, Florida, Mississippi, or Louisiana. This is of course attributable in some measure to the opposition of large numbers of prominent Southern women to the enfranchisement of their sex.

The result in Tennessee was due in part to strong journalistic support from Luke Lea's Nashville *Tennessean,* George Fort Milton's Chattanooga *News,* and other leading dailies. In the neighboring state of Kentucky, the Lexington *Herald,* owned and edited by Desha Breckinridge, supported the suffrage cause from the opening of the twentieth century and partially offset the fulminations of "Marse Henry" Watterson's Louisville *Courier-Journal* against those whom he contemptuously termed "silly Sallies and crazy Janes." W. T. Anderson's Macon *Telegraph,* usually conspicuously liberal, was the only important paper in Georgia which fought the suffragists. In Mississippi the Jackson *Daily News,* edited by Frederick Sullens, was as vigorously favorable to the enfranchisement of women as the Macon *Telegraph* was opposed to it.

Pro-suffragist editors in the South enjoyed the assistance and co-operation of many remarkably able women in the fight for enfranchisement. Some of these women were at the same time staunch advocates of other important liberal causes. For example, Mrs Madeline McDowell Breckenridge of Kentucky not only devoted a large part of her attention to furthering the suffragist movement, but her activities also extended into the fields of child labor and compulsory school attendance legislation and into public health and family welfare work. In Virginia Mrs. Lila Meade Valentine was a pioneer worker on behalf of better public welfare and public education, as well as an ardent advocate of votes for women, and she was ably assisted in her feminist endeavors by Miss Mary Johnston, who sought in her novel *Hagar* to further the emancipation of Southern womanhood, and who worked indefatigably in various ways for the cause. Other important suffragist leaders include Mrs. Minnie Fisher Cunningham of Texas, Mrs. Ella C. Chamberlain of Florida, Mrs. Elizabeth Lyle Saxon, Mrs. Caroline E. Merrick, and Miss Kate M. Gordon of Louisiana, Mrs. Mary Latimer McLendon of Georgia, and Mrs. T. Palmer Jerman of North Carolina. Occasionally, too, an intrepid male stood up and fought to give the opposite sex the ballot, braving the criticism and ridicule which was sure to be visited upon anyone who was conspicuous in the movement. Several journalists who did so have already been mentioned, but no list of the men who gave their time, their money, and their influence to the effort for enfranchisement would be complete without a reference to Chief Justice Walter Clark of North Carolina. The devotion of this eminent jurist to the suffragist cause is all the more striking when it is recalled that he was a Confederate veteran steeped in the traditions of the Old South.

We have noted the activities of Southern women in the educational field both in the ante-bellum and the post-bellum eras. While their influence was especially pronounced in the decades following the Civil War, the valuable services of the women of the former Confederacy to education in the early years of the twentieth century should under no conditions be overlooked. Women were active in the long series of annual Conferences for Southern Education which had their inception at Capon Springs, West Virginia, in 1898. In addition they were almost wholly instrumental in the formation of School Improvement Leagues throughout the South. These organizations, which were designed to promote the common schools, originated in Virginia, largely through the efforts of Mrs. Beverley B. Munford of Richmond and other leaders in the Coöperative Education Association of Virginia. Mrs. Munford has been the ablest and most conspicuous advocate of better educational facilities for the women of the Old Dominion, and her influence on behalf of this and other liberal causes has extended far beyond the borders of that commonwealth.

Another woman who has been widely influential in the South is Dr. Orie Lathem Hatcher, founder and executive head of the Southern Woman's Educational Alliance, an organization which is doing a pioneer work in providing vocational and educational training for Southern women, particularly in rural areas.

Many other women throughout the South have been prominent since 1900 in efforts looking toward the improvement of educational opportunities for their sex, particularly in the field of the higher learning. There is among them, however, a growing awareness that equality of opportunity does not necessarily imply absolute identity of courses and curricula. Now that they have won the right almost everywhere to the same grade of education as is enjoyed by members of the opposite sex, they are viewing the matter more objectively and are coming to a realization that the educational requirements of men and women are at times somewhat divergent. Yet the fact remains that while educational facilities have been tremendously broadened in the Southern states during the past three decades, those states are still the most laggard of all in providing collegiate instruction for women.

Virginia was the last state in the Union to provide such instruction. College doors were first thrown open to women by that commonwealth in 1918, when the College of William and Mary became coeducational. Two years later the University of Virginia amended its regulations sufficiently to permit women who are over twenty years of age and who have had two years of collegiate training to enter the graduate and professional schools and the department of education.

Although women were not made eligible for matriculation in the University of Georgia until 1918, several women's colleges had been operated by the state of Georgia for many years prior to that time. Consequently Georgia was well ahead of Virginia in providing educational facilities for its womanhood.

In this connection it is interesting to note that the University of Florida was the last state university in America to admit women. It did not do so until 1925, at which time it allowed them to enter subject to much severer requirements than were provided for male students. On the other hand, we should bear in mind that Florida has had a State College for Women since 1905.

One of the major interests of Southern women is in the work of women's clubs and similar organizations. Outstanding among club women below Mason and Dixon's Line may be mentioned Mrs. Percy V. Pennybacker of Austin, Texas, and Mrs. Samuel M. Inman of Atlanta, both of whom are known and respected over a wide area. During the past decade, however, and especially during the past five years, the typical women's clubs have given way in the South, as elsewhere, to societies, associations, or clubs of a more specialized and more selective nature. These include Business and Professional Women's Clubs, the various Leagues of Women Voters, study groups of one sort or another, alumnae groups, and so on.

There are numerous ways in which the Southern woman can earn a livelihood, but the South is still reluctant to accept her in such professions as law or medicine. In fact she must be equipped in the highest degree with respect to both training and personality to succeed in either of these callings. Her chances are considerably better in such comparatively new occupations as social service, public health, or library work, or in home economics or business. In industry, as has been pointed out in an earlier chapter, she is frequently exploited.

It should be stated that present-day Southern men appear to be a bit more alive to human values, and a bit less willing to surrender completely to the pull of professional ambition at the expense of the amenities of life, than those who achieve careers in the North or West.

Members of the various Southern women's clubs and other related groups are often active in promoting such liberal causes as better international relationships, improved public health, more humane systems of penology, and a more balanced attitude toward labor. They are particularly zealous in the sphere of interracial endeavor, where the work of Mrs. Jessie Daniel Ames of Atlanta, Miss Louise Young of Scarritt College, Nashville, and Mrs. W. A. Newell of Greensboro is deserving of high praise.

In conclusion it may be said that the liberal leadership which the women of the former Confederacy are exhibiting today in a number of important fields is one of the most significant phenomena of the Southern scene. These women who are scarcely a generation removed from the chivalric era, and who have emerged only recently from the penumbra of sanctity which previously enveloped them, are unquestionably among the most substantial liberalizing forces in the Southern states.

— From *Liberalism in the South,* University of North Carolina Press, 1932. Reprinted by permission.

MA'AME ETIENNE AND MAX

By Ward Allison Dorrance

My family was not native to this state, and though between the Missouri River and the house where I was born there stood the slope of one hill only, it was long before I thought myself a Missourian. Our people had entered South Carolina in the first of the seventeen hundreds. Long seasons had put habit on their ways and set a stamp upon their thought, a rhythm in the blood which they gave me. . . . Exiled Southerners rarely mention the South to strangers, as before Baptists Catholics prefer not to discuss the Blessed Virgin. For reasons, then, which do not concern you, I am yet a Southerner — come into the world like a buffalo calf born on the fringe of a herd in migration.

This, however, was the cause that in my heart there should be a love of land, and not of car loadings or of compound interest. There were too many generations in the mirrorlike recession of men behind me. I could not escape their ways. I could not live rightly cut off from earth, with soil and men flattened to symbols exchanged in the markets. I had to see boats and hear water, to feel differences of terrain beneath my feet. I had to watch men reaping and chopping, breaking horses and castrating hogs, with gestures inherited from God knows what ancestral past. If you call this *escapism,* then permit me not to care a hoot for your opinion. I was not thinking of what you'd say when I made my choice. I was trusting the magnet-needle lurch in the left side of my chest. By it I found true north.

There were stemming from me, even in childhood, yearnings, desire for a land to spend my love on. It is my good fortune that these yearnings have come down — like the gummed toes of vine tendrils — on the broad back of the state of Missouri. As it sometimes happens that one falls in love, seemingly all at once, with a human being, I know the year and the month when I "discovered" Missouri. I can almost name the night. An April night when I was landed from a packet.

Dusk had been rank with mist. We had passed the steamer *Iowa*, clucking to her barges, and had blown her a salute. The beam of her light came down on us like something solid. An answering blast . . . the rock of the wake. And dusk closed in again. Along the banks among the dogwood blossoms rode the Mississippi fireflies.

I stepped off at Little Rock — a place, not a town — which now, thanks long since to a change in the river, is the landing point for Sainte Genevieve. The packet churned away, and her lights were such that I remembered how on summer nights my mammy would let me have a mason jar to fill with "lightning bugs" . . . the dew-covered grass sharp on my ankles as I ran, clover heads round under my naked instep.

Then dark. I knew that I was in the heart of the land to which the French had given a magic name — *le pays des Illinois*. I did not know that directly opposite the point where I stood lay the ruined walls of the Fort de Chartres, the largest military stronghold of France between Quebec and New Orleans. I did not know anything then, in fact, except that I smelled the river and sensed its width, and that the night wind was in my hair as in the reeds of the bank.

Probably books ought not to be begun on a shore at midnight. In the grip beside me, nonetheless, was the *Dictionnaire Général de la Langue Française*, and plans for work which would treat of the descendants in Missouri of the French colonials, their language, their music, their folklore. To make matters worse, I had lately come from France, from the bright order of Paris. Now behind me lay Saint-Louis-en-Missouri, and before me a beautiful town with a beautiful name — Sainte Geneviève des Illinois. It did not matter that there was nowhere any light. How could morning clear this tangle of lands and time?

But much good came of it all — among other things this, that I came to love Missouri. Not in cities, but where I was fitted to love her (in the beginnings of her history).

In the village of Sainte Genevieve I made a friend, an elderly priest of a sort rarely seen in this country — the provincial cleric inhabiting farm land by choice (though he knew the libraries of Louvain, the villas of Fiesole), honest, industrious, by no means unintelligent, and, within gentlemanly limits, a delicate epicure. With him (in biretta and gown) I walked the streets. This house dates from 1785, that from 1790, from 1793, from 1808 or 1812. Here was once a house; one sees the slave quarters yet and the stable. Yonder was another, but nothing now remains. That kind of postern gate I see, by it one entered a trading post. This street was called in French the Rue Royale. North and south of the town it continued as the Chemin du Roi, the King's Highroad. It ran the length of a ridge that had carried an Indian trace — before that, a buffalo trail. The Americans planted poles and called it the Telegraph Road.

The charm of the architecture, the mold of age, visible no doubt even in the dead of winter, was very great now as we stood in the shade of the pecan trees; now that we stepped knee-deep in tulips; now that we stooped beneath arbors of wisteria and rose. And the charm was livelier still for me that I had the comments of the father in French — a French more sweetly Creole than he knew.

In the Deanery, Place du Bourg, we discussed the fate of the French colonial. Those of them who, at the time of the Purchase, had money, influence, position — these were able to become Americans. The new government courted them. But what of the commonality, the greater number? Those who had come down the Wisconsin, the Illinois, in 1690? in 1700? in 1710? Some of them are yet about Sainte Genevieve. The church kept services in French for them until 1893. There are to this day old ladies in the country around who must confess in French for the reason that they know no English. But most have been drawn to the city, or to towns like Festus and Crystal City where they labor in the glass " works "; to Flat River where they dig in mines.

" Mais t'nez, mon fils . . ." My friend has remembered a place where I may study the Missouri Creole isolated, untouched, or nearly so, by modern industry.

In a parish west of Sainte Genevieve, at La Vieille Mine (Old

Mines in English), near La Mine à Breton (Potose), is a congregation of some six hundred families. Of these roughly ninety per cent speak French as their mother tongue. All of them live approximately as they did at the time of the Purchase. The men make a living (but only when and as provisions are required) by modest garden patches and hill fields; by keeping a cow and a pig; by digging ore in shallow surface pits, as they did in colonial times.

❦ ❦ ❦

In this place I had the good luck to be quartered in the house of an extraordinary woman, Madame Etienne. She was generous-bosomed, with unruly black hair, with large and merry black eyes. She wore loose slippers from which her toes burst. And she would explain: " It's the nigger in me." She was the kind of great soul, the good wife who, as one says in French, exterminates herself for her family. . . . Not alone for them. For me. For any of the countryside that dropped in. From none did she exact even gratitude. Up at dawn, she cleaned and baked and fried — pans of *gâteaux sauvages* (which she pronounced *chouages*), green-grape pies, and *croquecignoles*. The side gallery was dotted at no matter what hour with buckets of potatoes to peel, peas to hull, corn to shuck. From the stove she would rush out under the apple trees to ring a bell, to settle a swarm of bees; to shoo in with her apron a turkey hen with her brood; to get butter from the spring house across the road, down a path through the mint and wild iris — a log building chill with flowing water, sweet with milk, where now and then a snake would uncoil from a dank corner. A whole day was not too long to stand over the barbecue pit at the picnic of Saint Joachim, she pushing back the hair that stuck to her face, bending over the coals while the others ate. If a hand was needed at the millet, cut but threatened with rain, there was Ma'ame Etienne who got the wagon into the barn — " et plus vite que ça voyons, les gars! "; who sent a man to the loft while she pitched from below. The man was English. He whispered to me later: " Thet woman purt nigh kilt me in yon hot loft."

If her sons skipped out to town without milking when the cows were late, then it was Ma'ame Etienne whom I found under the sycamores by moonlight pushing her head into a white cow's flank, the milk "talking" at the bucket.

On wash days it was she who showed me how to make fires as the Indians made them, placing the logs tip to tip beneath the cauldron, so the heat was where it was needed — all in the middle.

Ma'ame Etienne was gay. Only injustice made her angry. And she was a natural actress. Effortlessly she would imitate a pickaninny whose nose needed wiping; an old uncle caught stealing corn; a Negress talking to herself as she ironed; and (though here she crossed herself, asking pardon for the irreverence) a "drinking priest" whom she had known.

Ma'ame Etienne was my ally, my aid. She was one of the few of her generation who had been "out" — that is, who had traveled beyond the neighboring villages. She had indeed been "out" where few of us will ever be. She had once been cook on a construction boat. Therefore I was able to explain to her my mission. Without understanding quite the words she nevertheless, intuitively, got nicely to the root of the matter. As she went to the millet field with a fork, so she went after me.

And she purt nigh kilt me.

She pointed out that as an outlander and urbanite I could not immediately approach the hill-country colonials. They were ashamed, bashful, resentful. They were puzzled because I was not a Catholic, and suspected (because of my books and papers) that I was some sort of unfrocked priest. Or maybe a revenue officer. Above all, they had not the habit of academic discussion and were unable to answer a question asked directly. The way to go about it, Ma'ame Etienne thought, was to do just what they did. All day long. When they saw that I was not proud, when my presence had begun to blend with custom, they would talk as if I were not there. I could hear what I wanted on the spot. Then come home and put it down.

What Ma'ame Etienne did not say (though doubtless she thought it) was this: when the men and boys saw that I could not stick long on a half-tamed stallion; that for only half a morning (and not for three days) could I lift wheat sacks; that I was badly kicked by the sheep which I tried to shear; when I let them see that learning didn't really get a man anywhere; when, in short, I permitted them a superiority over me — then they would like me.

And so it came to pass. I was pitched by the stallion, kicked by the sheep, and almost fainted under wheat sacks that weighed more than I did. I won my place. I was invited to help "sprout off" corn, to go a-berrying, to bathe in the swimming hole, to ride after cattle, to drink wine under the arbors at night, to make change in a booth at the fair of Saint Joachim.

My card catalogue was grotesque against the whitewashed wall beneath the crucifix. But gradually it grew fat. These were my conclusions concerning the language of the Creole. French peasants, coming to Canada from various parts of western France in the seventeenth century, mingled their various related *patois* (with such academic French as had been brought among them) to make a Canadian French. This language was transported over the lakes, down the rivers, to Missouri (or to what was called "the Illinois country") there to acquire a few Spanish and Indian terms, there to be warped and eroded by folk ignorant of the written word. Part of it is very hard on the ear; part is strong and good; and part is maddeningly funny.

That task well on its way, I could turn to music and folklore — a diversion which brought me into contact with a remarkable man, Maxmilien Montmireil. The name is so nobly sonorous that one must resist with effort the inclination to say Maxmilien de Montmireil. But viewed from no angle could Max be made to look like a duke. I don't even think he would want to be one.

Max was cut from whole cloth, from wool strong and wide. His arms hung so far toward his knees as to suggest skill in swinging from branches. His fist could fell a horse. And as you'd expect, Max was very, very gentle. Only once did I see him when he was "mean." That was when he stood over a drunk who had jostled me: "Grouille-touè pas, grand fils de garce, ou ma t' cogner à terre!" (Try your hand at that, you who read French!) . . . His eyes were large and brown. They peered at you from out the hair that fell over his brow. Then suddenly, like a spaniel's, they would be full of affection.

From my point of view this was very important. Max thought

that the mold in which I was cast had certainly been broken. I had for him the appeal of an odd and fragile mechanical toy. He was sure that I belonged to the quality of some distant place. When I was in Europe, did the King have me in?

But Max, since years already there is no King in France!

Max shook his head.

I was the gosh durndest thing ever seen. I could make anybody believe anything. I was a *grand charreur* (a great talker; a windbag).

Perhaps it was this very capacity for wonder that made Max sensitive, in some curious oblique way, to the songs and lore of his people. To every *conteur* of tales, to every fiddler and singer, he took me before the summer ran out. Frequently he led me where, without him, I should certainly have been pitched neck and crop from the door.

Up mountainous side roads mottled with moonlight I picked my way beside him, answering his questions about the world outside. How much money must a man have to get married? Why, personally, I should not dare with less than three or four hundred. Then why am I not married? But Max, I haven't four hundred dollars a month. A month did I mean? And *cash*, Mother of Angels! Max didn't always have that in a year. But he had a wife and a baby and a cow and a pig and eighteen hens (three setting) and a garden and a rifle and a new kitchen cabinet. Max thought things must be pretty rotten out toward Saint Louis.

Much closer than that, Max. Closer much. The priest is right, Max. Stick by your wife and your pig. Don't go near the factories. Keep your rifle. Hunt squirrels when you feel like it. Stay where you may wash your feet in the Ruisseau aux Vieilles Mines, where you may swim and " make the moon rise " in the Rivière à Saint Joachim.

Over foot-logs beneath which streams stepped out musically in the dark, through timber where he turned when I fell, where he lit a match to find the book I dropped and took me by the hand . . . we'd come to a cabin. Here by a lamp would be sitting an old woman, expressionless, half blind. Over her Max would bend: " But don't you remember the song about the boy who went off to the wars? Don't you, no? But yes, little mama. You do remember. He came back home he did and he had jewels in a bag, isn't it? And his mother didn't know him? She killed him for the diamonds, for the rubies that shone in the moon? Then, when she found what she'd done, she hanged herself? No? No? Like that? But of course?"

The poor crone would not speak. No sign that she had heard. She bent her head, examining her ring. It might have been something from a peddler's pack. Something she might buy if it took her fancy.

Without warning she threw back her head. The accent, the cracked voice, if they were not witheringly pathetic, might be funny:

> "C'est un garçon, vive la jouè!
> Qu'est partsi pour la ghieurre . . ."

Max and the family stepped back beaming, as if in an attic they had started a music box or patched a walking doll. They were puzzled to know why my eyes were wet. I could not tell them that Granny's song is older than the sixteenth century, that its persistence through years of cordelling boats, sweating in the portages, fighting Indians, until the night it came out on air again from the old throat — I could not tell them that this moved me more than the ruins of Herculaneum and Karnak.

Sometimes we'd find a group of men around a table playing cards. They were glad to stop if the Uncle would tell them tales. The Uncle was a *conteur*. Of them all he remembered the folklore best. He alone got each of the tricky words just right. It was he who knew how to make silences eloquent, how to sadden with a glance, how to convulse with a wink or nod. And he was very touchy about the whole matter. One had to approach him as one sets about photographing wild life. Once laugh, once show irreverence — bah! As well try to lure back the deer frightened by the camera flash at night.

When the cards were pushed back, the Uncle would clear his throat. There would be an instant when we heard the moths thud at the lamp, the creek purling about its rocks beneath the window. Then we would hear of the prince whose magic key was swallowed by a fish, and the princess who roamed the golden wheat on the far side of the moon; of Johnny Greenpea; of the Prince White Pig and the Prince Green Snake; of how the rascal Beausoleil tricked the priest and how Madame the Vulture got a bald head. Or else we had swift, salacious little tales which certainly must have had common origin with those of Boccaccio.

When I could let my attention wander from the talk, the men around me kept me still alert. Here were heavy workmen, thick and hard, with hairy throats, with big hands limp in their laps. By nursery tales these same strong men were held entranced. No sign of guile or mockery in their eyes. When the heroine was getting the worst of it they were restless and concerned. When the villain began to catch it they were jubilant; they spat in their hands. When the priest was taken in by the tricks of Beausoleil they slapped their thighs and stamped, hilarious.

And I looked on, moved once more. Obviously I was not only hearing folklore. I was seeing the locale in which it is made. Ancestors of these men invented the fairies, the *little folk*. They heard the bells of the *Cathédrale Engloutie*, and at low tide saw the spires. . . .

Home Max and I would walk when the moon was high. And one night when the grain was ripe, when it was still warm with the day's sun and moved with a satin sound, I walked quite out of Max's country and came home with a book to which its friends were kind enough.

But it wasn't the sort I wanted to write. I wanted to say how I knew now a Missouri I could love; that the atoms of my body were so disposed as to receive tremor and send back echo from a land so venerable and so sweet.

Times of discovery like this take possession of the memory, and recollection is more alive than present life. . . . Once when I was offering to Ma'ame Etienne's pet lamb the nipple of a bottle, it got my index finger instead. For me the whole summer is in that greedy suck and pull. . . .

— From *We're from Missouri*, Missouri Press, 1938. Reprinted by permission.

THE PROFESSION OF LETTERS IN THE SOUTH

By Allen Tate

THE PROFESSION of letters in France dates, I believe, from the famous manifesto of Du Bellay and the Pléiade in 1549. It is a French habit to assume that France has supported a profession of letters ever since. There is no other country where the author is so much honored as in France, no other people in western culture who understand so well as the French the value of literature to the state. The national respect for letters begins far down in society. In a small French town where I was absolutely unknown I was able to use a letter of credit without identification upon my word that I was a man of letters. The French writers are respectable. The generation of Rimbaud and Verlaine was notoriously dissolute. French letters are a profession, as law, medicine, and the army are professions. Good writers starve and lead sordid lives in France as elsewhere; yet the audience for high literature is larger in France than in any other country; and a sufficient number of the best writers find a large enough public to sustain them as a class.

It goes somewhat differently with us. The public respects the writer according to his income. And, alas, writers themselves respect chiefly and fear only their competitors' sales. A big sale is a "success." How could it be otherwise? Our books are sold on a competitive market; it is a book market, but it is a luxury market; and luxury markets must be fiercely competitive. It is not that the natural depravity of the writer as fallen man betrays him into imitating the tone and standards of his market; actually he cannot find a public at all, even for that most lost of lost causes, the succès *d'estime*, unless he is willing to enter the competitive racket of publishing. This racket, our society being what it is, is a purely *economic* process, and literary opinion is necessarily manufactured for its needs. Its prime need is shoddy goods, because it must have a big, quick turnover. The overhead in the system is so high that the author gets only ten to fifteen per cent of the gross. It is the smallest return that any producer gets in our whole economic system. To live even frugally, a novelist, if he does not do odd jobs on the side, must have a sale of about thirty thousand copies every two years. His turnover, too, must be quick. He has his own self-sweat shop. One must agree with Mr. Herbert Read, in the February *London Mercury*, that authors under modern capitalism are a sweated class.

Poetry — as Mr. John Peale Bishop has said of the colored race — has an ancient and complicated culture of its own. I hesitate to speak of the poets. I do not hesitate to say that " Conquistador " is a better poem than " The Bride of Abydos "; yet Mr. MacLeish received for his poem, including the Pulitzer prize-money, less than one tenth of the proceeds from a performance particularly slipshod even for Byron.

We have heard for years, we began hearing it as early as Jeffrey's review of the first " Hyperion," that science is driving poetry to cover; I suppose it is; and we have the weight of Mr. I. A. Richards' arguments to prove it, and Mr. Max Eastman's weight, which is fairly light. Nineteenth century science produced a race of " problem " critics and novelists. The new " social " point of view has multiplied the race. Literature needs no depth of background or experience to deal with problems; it needs chiefly the statistical survey and the conviction that society lives by formula, if not by bread alone. The nineteenth century began this *genre*, which has become the standard mode. I confess that I cannot decide whether " science " or the mass production of books, or the Spirit that made them both, has given us shoddy in literature. We were given, for example, Bennett and Wells; Millay and Masefield. And I surmise that not pure science but shoddy has driven poetry to the corner, where, according to Eastman, the poets are " talking to themselves."

I shall not multiply instances. The trouble ultimately goes back to the beginnings of finance capitalism and its creature, machine production. The writer's loss of professional standing, however, set in before the machine, as we know it, appeared. It began with the rise of aristocracy, and the total loss of professionalism in letters may be seen in our age — an age that remembers the extinction of aristocracy and witnesses the triumph of a more inimical plutocratic society.

If my history is not wholly incorrect, it must follow that our unlimited pioneering, the pretext of the newness of the country, and our low standards of education do not explain the decline of the professional author. Pioneering became our way of industrial expansion, a method of production not special to us; we are a new country in so far as our industrialism gave the latent vices of the European mind a new opportunity; and our standards of education get lower with the increasing amount of money spent upon them. For my purposes, then, it is sufficient that we should look at the history of professionalism in letters in terms of the kinds of rule that European society, which includes American society, has had.

In the South we once had aristocratic rule; so, by glancing at the South, we shall see in our own history an important phase of the decline of the literary profession. There was, perhaps, in and around Boston, for a brief period, a group of professional writers, but not all of them, not even the majority, made their livings by writing. Even if they had, we should still have to explain why they were second-rate, and why the greatest of the New Englanders, Hawthorne, Melville, Dickinson, had nothing to do with them or with the rising plutocracy of the East. But it is a sadder story still in the South. We had no Hawthorne, no Melville, no Emily Dickinson. We had William Gilmore Simms. We made it impossible for Poe to live south of the Potomac. Aristocracy drove him out. Plutocracy, in the East, starved him to death. I prefer the procedure of the South; it knew its own mind, knew what kind of society it wanted. The East, bent upon making money, could tolerate, as it still tolerates, any kind of disorder on the fringe of society as long as the disorder does not interfere with money-making. It did not know its own social mind; it was, and still is, plutocracy.

But let us look a little at the backgrounds of Southern literature. I say backgrounds; for the South is an immensely complicated region. It begins in the northeast with southern Maryland; it ends with eastern Texas; it includes to the north even a little of Missouri. But that the people in this vast expanse of country have enough in common to bind them in a single culture cannot be denied. They often deny it themselves — writers who want to have something to jabber about, or other writers who want to offset the commercial handicap of being Southern; or just plain newly rich persons in the cities who would rather be like Pittsburgh than like New Orleans. It must be confessed that the Southern tradition has left no cultural landmark so conspicuous that the people may be reminded by it constantly of what they are. We lack a tradition in the arts; more to the point, we lack a literary tradition. We lack even a literature. We have just enough literary remains from the old régime to prove to us that, had a great literature risen, it would have been unique in modern times.

The South was settled by the same European strains as originally settled the North. Yet, in spite of war, reconstruction, and industrialism, the South to this day finds its most perfect contrast in the society of the North. In religious and social feeling I should stake everything on the greater resemblance to France. The South clings blindly to forms of European feeling and conduct that were crushed by the French Revolution and that, in England at any rate, are barely memories. How many Englishmen have told us that we still have the eighteenth century amiability and consideration of manners, supplanted in their country by middle-class reticence and suspicion? And where, outside the South, is there a society that believes even covertly in the Code of Honor? This is not idle talk; we are assured of it by Professor H. C. Brearley, who, I believe, is one of the most detached students of Southern life. Where else in the modern world is the patriarchal family still innocent of the rise and power of other forms of society? Possibly in France; probably in the peasant countries of the Balkans and of central Europe. Yet the " orientation " — let us concede the word to the University of North Carolina — the rise of new Southern points of view, even now in the towns, is tied still to the image of the family on the land. Where else does so much of the reality of the ancient land-society endure, along with the infatuated avowal of beliefs that are hostile to it? Where in the world today is there a more supine enthusiasm for being amiable to forces undermining the life that supports the amiability? The anomalous structure of the South is, I think, finally witnessed by its religion. Doctor Poteat of South Carolina deplores a fact which he does not question, that only in the South does one find a convinced supernaturalism: it is nearer to Aquinas than to Calvin, Wesley, or Knox.

The key to unlock the Southern mind is, fortunately, like Bluebeard's, bloody and perilous; we have not the easy sesame to the cavern of gaping success. We have had reverses that permit us to imagine what we might have been. (And only thus can people discover what they *are*.) Given the one great fact of the expanding plantation system at the dawn of the last century, which voice should we have listened to? Jefferson, or Marshall, or Calhoun? I mean, which voice had the deepest moral and spiritual implications for the permanence of Southern civilization? There was not time to listen to any voice very long. The great Southern ideas were strangled in the cradle, either by the South herself (for example, by too much quick cotton money in the Southwest) or by the Union armies. Whether or not we visit the bottom of the monstrous world, it is plain to modern historians of culture that peoples do not make, much less buy, a culture overnight; it takes time. Which view would have given the South a unified sense of its own destiny? Our modern " standard of living " is not a point of view, and it is necessary that a people should gather its experience round some seasoned point of view before it may boast a high culture. It must be able to illuminate from a fixed position all its experience; it must bring to full realization the high forms as well as the contradictions and miseries inherent in human society.

Where, as in the Old South, no such deep realization of the spirit was achieved, we must ask questions. (The right questions: not why the South refused to believe in Progress, or why it did not experiment with " ideas.") Was the structure of society favorable to a great literature? Suppose it to have been favorable: Was there something wrong with the intellectual life that cannot be blamed upon the social order?

The answer is both yes and no to the first question. It is emphatically yes and no to the second. So our answers are confused. At a glance one would expect the rich leisured class, highly educated as the Southern aristocracy was — for the South of the fifties had proportionately a larger educated minority than Massachusetts — to devote a great part of its vitality to the arts, the high and conscious arts; for even peasant societies achieve the less conscious arts — manners, ritual, charming domestic architecture. Assuming, as I do not think I am allowed to assume very confidently, that this society was a good soil for the high arts, there was yet a grave fault in the intellectual life. It was hagridden with politics. We like to think that Archimago sent the nightmare down from the North. He did. But it was partly rooted in the kind of rule that the South had, which was aristocratic rule. All aristocracies are obsessed politically. (Witness *Henry IV*, Parts One and Two; *Henry* V.) The best intellectual energy goes into politics and goes of necessity; aristocracy is class rule; and the class must fight for interest and power. Under the special conditions of the nineteenth century, the South had less excess of vitality for the disinterested arts of literature than it might have had ordinarily. There are no simple answers to the questions that I have asked. The South was a fairly good place for the arts, as good possibly as any other aristocratic country; only its inherent passion for politics was inflamed by the furious contentions that threatened its life. Every gifted person went into politics, not merely the majority.

The furious contentions themselves provided later answers to the problem of the arts in the South. At the end of the century one of the popular answers was that of the distinguished William Peterfield Trent, who laid bare all the Southern defects with the black magical talisman, Slavery. The defects could be whisked away, he argued in his life of Simms, with " essential faith in American democracy." The Northern people, at that time, may be forgiven this faith; it was the stuffed shirt of plutocracy and it was making them money; they had a right to believe in it. I cannot decide between credulity and venality as the reason for its being believed in the South. I am certain that in Trent's case it was credulity. If slavery was the cause of war, then slavery explained the political mania of the Old South; and the political mania stunted the arts. Partly true; partly false. Such an answer is more dangerous than an answer wholly false. In this instance it led the people to believe that their sole obstacle to perfection, slavery, had been removed. There was no need to be critical of anything else, least of all of the society that had come down and removed the blight; a society that by some syllogistic process unknown to me was accepted as perfect by the new Southern Liberals.

But the abolition of slavery has not made for a distinctively Southern literature. We must seek the cause of our limitations elsewhere. It is worth remarking, for the sake of argument, that chattel slavery is not demonstrably a worse form of slavery than any other upon which an aristocracy may base its power and wealth. That *African* chattel slavery was the worst groundwork conceivable for the growth of a great culture of European pattern is scarcely at this day arguable. Still, as a favorable " cultural situation " it was probably worse than white chattel, agricultural slavery only in degree. The distance between white master and black slave was unalterably greater than that between white master and white serf after the destruction of feudalism. The peasant is the soil. The Negro slave was a barrier between the ruling class and the soil. If we look at aristocracies in Europe, say in eighteenth century England, we find at least genuine social classes, each carrying on a different level of the common culture. But in the Old South, and under the worse form of slavery that afflicts both races today, genuine social classes do not exist. The enormous " difference " of the Negro doomed him from the beginning to an economic status purely: he has had much the same thinning influence upon the class above him as the anonymous city proletariat has had upon the culture of industrial capitalism.

All great cultures have been rooted in peasantries — in free peasantries, I believe, such as the English yeomanry before the fourteenth century: they have been the growth of the soil. What the Southern system might have accomplished we do not know: it would have been, as I have said, something new. Of course, the absence of genuine cultural capitals in the South has been cited as a cause of lassitude in the arts; perhaps it was a cause, as it is today. But it does not wholly explain the vague and feeble literature that was produced. The white man got nothing from the Negro, no profound image of himself in terms of the soil. He remained a Colonial. The Negro, who has long been described as a responsibility, got everything from the white man. The history of French culture, I suppose, has been quite different. The high arts have been grafted upon the peasant stock. We could graft no new life upon the Negro; he was too different, too alien.

Doubtless the confirmed if genteel romanticism of the old Southern imaginative literature (I make exception for the political writers of South Carolina — Hammond, Harper, Calhoun: they are classical and realistic) was in the general stream of romanticism; yet the special qualities that it produced, the unreal union of formless revery and correct sentiment, the inflated oratory of even private correspondence, witness a feeble hold upon place and time. The roots were not deep enough in the soil. Professor Trent was partly right: but for the wrong reason. It was not that slavery was corrupt "morally." It is amazing how much corruption societies can bear and still produce high cultures. Black slavery could not nurture the white man in his own image.

Although the Southern system, in spite of the Negro, was closer to the soil than the mercantile-manufacturing system of the Middle and New England states, its deficiencies in spiritual soil were more serious even than those of the debased feudal society of eighteenth century rural England. With this society the ante-bellum South had much in common.

The South came from eighteenth century England, its agricultural half; there were not enough large towns in the South to complete the picture of an England reproduced. The Virginian and the Carolinian, however, felt like English squires. They held their land, like their British compeers, in absolute, that is to say unfeudal, ownership, as a result of the destruction, first under Henry VIII and then under Cromwell, of the feudal system of land tenure. The landlord might be humane, but he owed no legal obligation to his land (he could wear it out) or to his labor (he could turn it off: called "enclosure" in England, "selling" under Negro slavery). A pure aristocracy, or the benevolent rule of a landed class in the interest of its own wealth and power, had superseded royalty which, in theory at any rate, and often in practice, had tried to balance class interests under protection of the Crown.

It should be borne in mind, against modern democratic and Marxian superstition, that royalty and aristocracy are fundamentally opposed systems of rule; that plutocracy, the offspring of democracy, and that Marxism, the child of plutocracy, are essentially of the aristocratic political mode; they all mean class rule. Virginia took the lead in the American Revolution, not to set up democracy, as Jefferson tried to believe, but to increase the power of the tobacco-exporting aristocracy. The planters wished to throw off the yoke of the British merchant and to get access to the free world market.

But the Southern man of letters cannot permit himself to look upon the old system from a purely social point of view, or from the economic view; to him it must seem better than the system that destroyed it; better, too, than any system with which the modern planners, Marxian or other color, wish to replace the present order. Yet the very merits of the Old South tend to confuse the issue; its comparative stability, its realistic limitation of the acquisitive impulse, its preference for human relations and not economic relations, tempt the historian to defend the poor literature because he feels that the old society was a better place to live in than the new. It is a great temptation — if you do not read the literature.

There is, I believe, a nice object lesson to be drawn from the changed relation of the English writer to society in the eighteenth century; it is a lesson that bears directly upon the attitude of the Old South towards the profession of letters. In the seventeenth century, in the year 1634, I believe, a young, finical man, then in seclusion at Horton after having taken his degrees at Cambridge, and till then unknown, was invited by the Earl of Bridgewater to write a masque for certain revels to be celebrated at Ludlow Castle. The masque was *Comus*, and the revels were in the feudal tradition. The whole celebration was "at home"; it was a part of the community life, the common people were present, and the poet was a spiritual member of the society gathered there. He might not be a gentleman: had Milton become a member of Egerton's "household" he would have been a sort of upper servant. But he would have been a member of the social and spiritual community.

Now examine the affair between Johnson and the Earl of Chesterfield: it is the eighteenth century. It was conducted in the new "aristocratic" style. For the flattery of a dedication the nobleman was loftily willing to give his patronage, a certain amount of money, to an author who had already completed the work, an author who had faced starvation in isolation from society. There is no great publishing system in question here; there were only booksellers. But there is already the cash nexus between the writer and society. The Earl of Chesterfield was a capitalist, not a feudal noble as Egerton to some extent still was: Chesterfield had lost the spiritual community; he required of the arts a compliment to the power of his class. He was the forerunner of the modern plutocrat who thinks that the arts are thriving so long as he can buy Italian paintings, or the sales sheets of the publishers show a large volume of "business," or so long as he creates "foundations" for the arts. The arts under plutocracy are a pleasant purchase.

Is there anything in common between the Earl of Chesterfield and a dour Scots merchant building a fortune and a place in the society of Richmond, Virginia, in the first third of the nineteenth century? I think that they have something in common. It was not John Allan who drove Poe out of Virginia. It was Virginia that drove Poe out of Virginia. The foreigner, trying to better himself, always knows the practical instincts of a society more shrewdly than the society knows them. Allan was, for once, the spokesman of Virginia, of the plantation South. There was no place for Poe in the spiritual community of Virginia; there was no class of professional writers that Poe could join in dedicating his works to the aristocracy under the system of the cash nexus. The promising young men were all in politics bent upon more desperate emergencies. It was obvious, even to John Allan, I suppose, that here was no dabbler who would write pleasant, genteel poems and stories for magazines where other dabbling gentlemen printed their pleasant, genteel stories and poems. Anybody could have looked at Poe and known that he meant business.

And until the desperate men today who mean business can become an independent class, there will be no profession of letters anywhere in America. It remains only to add to the brief history adumbrated in this essay some comment on the present situation of the desperate men of the South in particular. There are too many ladies and gentlemen, too many Congreves whose coxcombry a visit from Voltaire would do a great deal of good: the genteel tradition has never done anything for letters in the South, yet the Southern writers who are too gentlemanly to become conscious of their profession have not refused to write best sellers when they could, and to profit by a cash nexus with New York. I would fain believe that matters are otherwise than so: but they are so. If there is such a person as a Southern writer, if there could be such a profession as letters in the South, the profession would require the speaking of unpleasant words and the violation of good literary manners.

I wish this were the whole story: only cranks and talents of the quiet, first order maintain themselves against fashion and prosperity. But even these desperate persons must live, and they cannot live in the South without an " independent income." We must respect the source of our income, that fear it. This kind of writer is not luckier than his penniless fellow. (The only man I know who devotes a large income to undermining the system that produced it is a New Yorker.) Because there is no city in the South where writers may gather, write, and live, and no Southern publisher to print their books, the Southern writer, of my generation at least, went to New York. There he was influenced not only by the necessity to live but by theories and movements drifting over from Europe.

It was, possibly, a dangerous situation. Mr. John Crowe Ransom, whose distinguished contribution to this number of the *Virginia Quarterly Review* I have been privileged to see, points out all the implications of that danger. The Southern writer was perilously near to losing his identity, becoming merely a " modern " writer. He lost the Southern feeling which in the case of Mr. Young informs the Southern style: he might retain a Southern subject and write about it as an outsider, with some novelty of technique and in smart, superior detachment. These bad features of the last decade may be deplored, I hope, without asking the Southerner to stay at home and starve. That, it seems to me, is what Mr. Ransom asks, and it is likely to be asked by all our academic writers, for whom the idea of a profession of letters has little significance. It was not a foot-loose modern, but the classical Milton who remarked, " Wherever we do well is home "; wherever we are allowed best to realize our natures — a realization that, for an artist, presupposes permission to practice his craft — is the proper place to live. The Southern writer should if possible be a Southerner in the South. The sole condition that would make that possible is a profession of letters.

But the arts everywhere spring from a mysterious union of indigenous materials and foreign influences: there is no great art or literature that does not bear the marks of this fusion. So I cannot assume, as Mr. Ransom seems to do, that exposure to the world of modernism (Petrarchism was modernism in the England of 1540) was of itself a demoralizing experience. Isn't it rather that the Southerner before he left home had grown weak in his native allegiance? That his political and social history, and his domestic life, had been severely adulterated no less by his fellow Southerners than by the people in the North to whom he fled? Apart from this menace abroad, who cannot bring himself to wish that Miss Glasgow had studied James and Flaubert in her apprenticeship, and spared herself and us her first three or four novels? Could Mr. Young have written his fiction, to say nothing of his plays and criticism, had he read only Cable and Page? And, lastly, what shall we say of Mr. Ransom's own distinguished and very modern poetry?

Is not Mr. Ransom really deploring the absence, as I deplore it, of a professional spirit and professional opportunities in Southern literature? There is no reason why the Southern writer should not address a large public, but if he does he will learn sooner or later that — but for happy accidents — the market, with what the market implies, dictates the style. To create a profession of literature in the South we should require first an independent machinery of publication. Given that, we should need a Southern criticism that in its infancy would have to cry very loud. Criticism in its more immediate effects is — I must return to a disagreeable point — ill-mannered. Then we should need a native reading public.

We have exchanged the reasoned indifference of aristocracy for the piratical commercialism of plutocracy. Repudiating the later master, the new profession in the South would have to tell New York, where it had hitherto hawked its wares, that no more wares of the prescribed kind would be produced. For the prescribed ware is the ware that the Southerner also must produce, and it is not heartening to observe that his own Southern public waits for the New York journals to prescribe the kind, before he can get a hearing at home. Can there be a profession of letters in the South? Our best critical writing — and we have critical writing of distinction — can never constitute a Southern criticism so long as it must be trimmed and scattered in Northern magazines, or published in books that will be read curiously as travel literature by Northern people alone.

The Southerner, therefore, I think, has every disadvantage of the more generalized American, and a few special difficulties as well. There is constant pressure upon him from the changing fashions of the East. He must write about the South, if he is a novelist, as the most advanced school of opinion in New York directs him to write. Before 1929 he was told to contemn the South because there were not enough bathtubs below the Line; now he is told to contemn the South because there are too many. There are now the abuses of capitalism where before there were glories. We have never really taken any stock in either the abuses or the glories; we think that both are contemptible. I suppose it needed the genius of Mr. Stark Young to put this into a novel and get it read by thousands in the region where these fashionable opinions hold.

The considerable achievement of Southerners in modern American letters must not beguile us into too much hope for the future. The Southern novelist has left his mark upon the age; but it is of the age. From the peculiarly historical consciousness of the Southern writer has come good work of a special order; but this consciousness is quite temporary. It is that curious burst of intelligence that we get at a crossing of the ways, not unlike, on an infinitesimal scale, the outburst of poetic genius at the end of the sixteenth century when commercial England had already begun to crush feudal England. The Histories and Tragedies of Shakespeare record the death of the old régime, and Doctor Faustus gives up feudal order for world power.

The prevailing economic passion of the age once more tempts, even commands, the Southern writer to go into politics. Our neo-Communism is the new form in which the writer from all sections is to be dominated by capitalism, or "economic society." It is the new political mania. And there is no escape from it. The political mind always finds itself in an emergency. The emergency, real enough, becomes a pretext for ignoring the arts. It is such an age as Abraham Cowley complained of — a good age to write about but a poor age to write in.

The political future of America will decide whether there is to be an American profession of letters: it will decide also whether there is to be a special Southern variety. The South has had little chance for a great literary tradition under the successive powers of aristocracy and plutocracy. What is the power to be? A few Southern writers will hope that it may be nothing that we have had before. Let us be prepared to name the unborn child, should he care for the fond detachment of the arts, Independence.

— From the *Virginia Quarterly Review,*
April, 1935. Reprinted by permission.

SOUTHERN HUMOR

By John Donald Wade

Long ago, at the sanguine age when one hopes at length to know everything, I had it as my business once to write something about a man who was notable as a humorist. My first obligation seemed to me to find out what humor, after all, was — what its sources were, what its charms. Or, more simply, to find out what makes a thing funny, and why, indeed, we are pleased to have funny things brought to our attention, whether relevantly or not.

I read much, then, on that score, and the result was like most results, not satisfying; I was left for all my effort not much the wiser. Incongruity, contrast, from what I could make out, seemed to be the bedrock found uniformly by all pundits seeking humor's origin. What bedrock was found by those seeking its fascination remains to me to this day unknown, as it apparently did to my masters, in spite of their profound method of saying so. What I had been able to reckon for myself, I found after irksome suspense to be what other people also had reckoned. What I had not been able to reckon — why humor is delightful — I found after irksome suspense was a question that other people also had found always beyond them.

Naturally, one hazards guesses, and the guesses about the fascination of humor group themselves for the most part either about the conscientious motive of correction or the quite unconscientious one of escape. To jeer at a person or a state of affairs leads the jeerer, with more or less earnest inimicalness on his part, into satire or irony. But some of us fell short, somehow, of acquiring our just endowment of inimicalness, and we have come to cherish the idea that a mordant earnestness on our part about other people's activities is an impulse to be eschewed. People of this stripe laugh, certainly; they cannot go about sighing always. They regard the story's butt not with detestation, but with affection, and they do not cherish hope of remodeling anybody or anything very speedily — not even themselves.

These by all rules are life's ineffectuals; but their justification in humanity is that without them humanity would take on an aspect too horrible to contemplate, too indubitably governed by dullness or malice for anybody to wish its continuance. And if facts are regarded and not rules, it is these people who bring about for us, all the betterments we ever get.

As for *Southern*, which qualifies *Humor* in my title, I have put some thought on that for a long time. I learned the word early, and as a child in a Georgia village school yearned at times to emulate some of my less restrained peers and punch out with a pencil-point the eyes of the Northern generals pictured in my textbooks. Restrained, I comforted myself by inscribing encomiumistic phrases under the pictures of Southern generals. Later I learned better than to wish to occupy myself so barbarously. But I knew by then, and I know still, how to look at a book and without reading it to be aware, somehow, of every word on the pages that remotely looks like *Southern*. I conceived it as my duty, once, over many years, to inspect that word every time it occurred on a page and to ascertain the veracity or falsehood of the sentence containing it. Sometimes the sentence said merely that on the southern slope of these mountains the climate is mild — and that was indeed disappointing. But I was powerfully affected if it declared the Southern temperament sluggish, or, on the other hand, if it declared it generous.

I rehearse this autobiography in my anxiety to show that the word *Southern* has long had its importance in my consciousness. Has it a meaning, really, other than the geographic one? It has been fashionable to think so for many years, and if the legend which in the beginning ascribed it meaning was at first legend merely, it is not likely by now legend merely, any more. A dog badly named — or well named, for that matter — will justify what is said of him, and a people will doubtless do as much. So in my mind there is a body of notions that hold their hands up and answer present when one says Southern; yet to define those notions (since in definition one must be definite) is more than I can do in this essay, or more than anybody could do, I judge, except by implications and overtones and suggestions that nobody in this swift-moving time would trouble to follow, or, indeed, would trouble in the first place to set down.

And now, writing this article, I review in my mind not merely what has been the course of Southern humor historically. I wonder what it is, in essence, and whether it is in fact different from any other humor in anything except in its setting and in the types of people it concerns itself with.

The historical phase of my activity need not cost me great effort. The extent of the contribution Southern writers have made to the merriment of this nation and of other nations is a matter chiefly of research, and research students here and yonder have unearthed much information about it — with a solemnity that one must pronounce marvelous.

But the essence of Southern humor, and the possibility of distinguishing it from other humor (except, as I have said, by perfectly objective tests) — that, truly, is a horse of a different color.

As the earliest of Southern humorists, consider William Byrd, that good Briton. Young, he was a debonair blade of a fellow, as familiar in London as in Virginia; old, when sickness had him, and the inevitable knowledge that he would not come to as much as he had hoped to, he was very tragical. He noted the antics of his contemporaries and wrote about them, not as himself an antic-doer, but as one superior, remote. On one side is his sophistication and his fastidiousness; on the other, their ignorance and blundering. That contrast was accidental; it was not a device of his to make the situation more amusing. His characters seemed to him ludicrous enough, himself not ludicrous at all.

Everything of his that has been published waited, in manuscript form, till Byrd was a hundred years dead. That late, his writings were no longer capable of proving a literary influence; times had changed so greatly, toward libertarianism in politics, toward finical delicacy in social intercourse, that his writings lay neglected for almost a further hundred years. So much for what he wrote. What he said, in its influence upon people who knew him personally, was almost surely more influential — and that disparity between what was written and what said is interesting not of itself only, but as an early instance in Southern life of a disparity that marks all life, everywhere, but particularly, I think, marks life in the South.

After Byrd, there are few echoes of Southern laughter for a long time. Laughter there was, doubtless, and gayety enough, but the soberness of Revolutionary times together with the eighteenth century ideal of decorum, and the widespread influence of evangelicalism, kept most of this gayety vocal, forbade it the dignity of being written. When Revolutionary earnestness had burnt itself out in a scene of incandescent triumph, when the old aim of decorum had slumped before the new democracy, when evangelicalism, in its ardor to save everybody, had lowered its bars to admit everybody, then there was a new day. The old heaven and the old earth of Byrd or of Franklin or of Timothy Dwight had passed away, except, perhaps, in the heart of Washington Irving. And Irving, the stranded soul, put out soon for Europe and ever afterward in general stayed there.

The new country was above all else hopeful. Democracy in politics and Arminianism in religion and free land in economics gave it hardihood to set beneath all of its amusement at the grotesque the assumption that most grotesqueness would soon end. And the same assumption humanized all the jokes because they had in them always the implication that the superiority of the joker was largely accidental, largely a matter of his having shared more fully than his humorous puppets in wholesome opportunities that would soon be open to everyone. The old storytellers are at constant pains to make this clear. I record all this now, they keep saying, because it is so ludicrous, and because soon the very clowns I write about will be behaving as punctiliously as anybody, their children turning out to be — who knows? — perhaps President. From a time as early as 1825 onward till 1900 this song was never silent in American life; and it is not silent yet — though it is audible, now that the twentieth century is a third gone, principally in the success magazines and in the sophisticated weeklies published in New York.

The Revolution was well over. Old colonials and fresh immigrants were pushing westward. And then cotton as a great commercial possibility came to tempt them all southward. Georgia for a moment became the West, and it was soon, thanks to cotton, a West that was relatively rich, relatively well ordered — though retaining the violent contrasts in cultural groups (Southerner, Yankee, immigrant, Negro) that make for humorous situations. Funny, all of this, people kept saying; record it now, set it down now; it is so transient (else it would be sad); it will be gone soon; it is, indeed, already gone.

So they set it down — Longstreet with his horse swappings and his eye gougings, Thompson with his tobacco-spitters, R. M. Johnston, and Sidney Lanier and Bill Arp Smith and Joel Chandler Harris — all in Georgia. Hooper and Baldwin wrote of Alabama, Crockett and G. W. Harris of Tennessee, Prentice of Kentucky, Thorpe and Opie Reed and Mark Twain of the South bordering the Mississippi. Even Virginia — that urbane place — offered its quota of natural men to be pictured by the romanticized and romanticizing Dr. Bagby. Even South Carolina — that sedate place — offered its quota to be pictured by the robustious Simms and the much less robustious (oh, much!) Mr. Gilman.

And except for Mark Twain, who had the advantage of having been born later as well as innately superior to the rest of them, they all said very much the same thing. Their literary form: mostly Addison-like essays or fanciful letters, with an increasing deviation from Addison as it became the practice to introduce more and more dialect, more and more bad spelling. Their subject: unsophisticated country folk (mostly white at first but at last mostly Negro) in contact with a world unfamiliarly urban. Their attitude: enjoy with me, reader, you who are cultivated, as I am, the foibles of these men and women, all of whom, as you and I both know, have hearts of gold beneath their superficial crudities.

Over and over this went on, and people everywhere found it delectable. America had at last come free of Europe's shadow; and this humor was really the humor of the nation at large at the time when the frontier was the nation's dominant interest. So far was it from sectional merely that its reception was equally clamorous in Philadelphia and in Peoria and in Vicksburg; and the fact is that of the eight Southern humorists discussed in *The South in the Building of the Nation* (the eight, I mean, who died before 1900) four were bred and born in the North and one was educated there. The victories this humor won were identical in all sections; the rebuffs it met, ineffectual rebuffs such as the disgust felt for it by females and refined gentlemen, were also identical. It went marching on, and if it had more proponents North than it did South after 1860, so much the more demonstrably was it in the current, in the torrent, indeed, of national development.

For it is worth noting that the Civil War and early post-Civil War proponents of the old humor persisted not in the new America that had taken form along the North Atlantic coast nor freely in the new America that had been driven to take form along the South Atlantic coast. It persisted in the western North, and as soon as the western North lost its distinctiveness the old humor languished there also.

Now certainly as early as the 1830's forces were at work which would render the South unable and unwilling to float its raft on the broad stream of national development. In the light of that time the democratic theories of 1800, and the Arminianism so dear then, seemed less and less tenable. Negroes, it seemed, so far as this world went, at least, were outside that picture; and as the poor whites hardened in their resentment against their betters, becoming less amenable, they also were excluded. The Southern oligarchy tended to become logically both aristocratic and Calvinistic. That is what it became *logically*. What it became actually is a different story.

There was a condition to be reckoned with that inevitably rides down, at last, most schedules of what one ought to believe in deference to one's own purely selfish interests. This consideration was that in the South, because it was a sparsely settled, farming region, people in the various classes, white and black, knew one another personally, intimately. Most often, as a result — one can risk saying so — they had a sort of affection for one another; but even if they had instead a sort of hatred, no one sinned so pointedly as to mistake people for mechanisms.

In the great North, the case went by contraries. There democracy and free will had all the official endorsement they could ever need, but the unofficial, dominating conviction of individuals endorsed far different doctrines. As industrialism proceeded men became specialists, and as population grew denser it became necessary for every man to rule out from his consciousness the ups and downs of most of the people he had contact with. It became necessary, in short, for people to act as if they believed other people made out of metal rather than of flesh and blood.

What prophet could have foreseen this — fuddled as prophets must always be by the stir about them? South, all roads led *from* America, it was said; North, all roads turned back on themselves toward the ideals of the 1776 Declaration, or toward some vague place that was perhaps heaven, and that was in any case very nice indeed. But as plain as those roads were, the travelers on them arrived at last, curiously, one group in Paterson, New Jersey, let us say, the other in Macon, Georgia — cities both of which Jefferson might have understood, but only one of which he might possibly have commended.

In the South, the forces likely to break up the old humor were largely theoretical, and any of them that were more than theoretical were broken in upon by the personal intimacies that characterize a rural civilization. Further, any hard and fast program of social stratification that might have dehumanized and standardized society there crumbled before the spectacle of Reconstruction, with its pulling down of what had been high and its exaltation of what had been low. When Marie Antoinette (for all her saying "Let them eat cake, then") is forced at last to beg crusts from her jailer, the situation is so poignantly tragic that the mind cannot last it out; it must save itself by laughter. So one's very poverty in the South in the 1870's — and in more years than those — was often the theme of one's best stories, the nucleus of ten thousand situations calculated to stir merriment.

Reconstruction, then, with its harsh anarchy, made humor mandatory. Desolate and lacking cheer, one was the more bound to simulate it — to shun madness, for simple sanity's sake, *bound*. Reconstruction with its anarchy broadened, also, the *field* of humor. Cousin Lucius, in his patched breeches, rehearsing Horace; Cousin Mintora, in homespun, fanning herself with jeweled ivory — both were figures one could not be wholly solemn about. And the laughter one accorded them, with themselves leading in it, was not far different from the laughter accorded the rough-and-ready catch-as-catch-can citizenry of Longstreet's *Georgia Scenes*. Black Sambo and his lady, the poor white and his, the colonel and his — each with his valid claim upon absurdity. And, to make the gamut complete — put in mind of doing so, perhaps, by the Negro's personification of animals and his humanization of deity — one recognizes as valid (out of neighborliness if nothing else) the claims, out absurdity-way, of beasts on the one hand, of divinity on the other. Uncle Remus' Brer Rabbit and Mr. Roark Bradford's God join hands indiscriminately with mankind, and the trio will as likely as not, if a fiddle twangs, do some trick steps worth a body's trying to catch on to.

Even fine abstractions, programs for salvation, sacrosanct now in so many places, are not likely to meet in the South with much decorousness of reception. There, there is remembrance still of a fine program that came to nothing, for all that General Lee could do to make it prevalent — it was absurd, perhaps, ever to hope it would prevail; not soon will another program obtain one's whole endorsement. A lofty pronouncement, as a pronouncement, is a marvelous thing meriting one's admiration. As something more than a pronouncement, as a signal for action, it evokes less iron resolution than it does skeptical, half-sorrowful, amusement. Life is volatile — the grave running into the comic, the comic into the grave, each perhaps dependent upon the other for its being. This ponderous listing of grievances, this meticulous study of how to rectify them, this deep drumming to organization and to action — if necessary, to violent action. Are lister, study-er, drummer really quite solemn — more actually solemn than Cousin Lucius with his Horace, than Jesus in Reverend Sambo's praying? (Come, Lenin, and say so if you will — take care when you do lest your beard bob.) *And, besides, Mr. Lenin, I know Cousin Joe — as well as one man can know another — made his money curiously too, I hear said. But Lord, more than likely he hardly knew what he was up to. And he's mighty kind to all his folks, sir, and I expect that's being kind to half the county — helped me out, personally, more than once. You talk fine, sir, to a fellow down and out like me, but you can see, I judge, how Cousin Joe being in the family, and all, I'd naturally rather look to him for help than to a man outside the family — especially, if you'll excuse me for saying so, to a foreigner.*

Through the last of the eighteen hundreds much of the recorded humor of America ran in the old channels set before the Civil War. In the South, one could observe Bill Arp and Joel Harris, both of them in many ways reminiscent of old Longstreet — could observe in the West a parallel reminiscence in Mark Twain, as long as Mark Twain stayed in the West, and as long, incidentally, as there was a West, any longer, in the historic sense, to stay in Mark Twain.

A glib man gifted in grimacing and mimicry, touched with sentimentality, did not need capital to insure profits in the South till a time that only yesterday, it seems, became the past. For long years, there, people relished incalculably the yarns of semi-professional funnymen, some of whom, when they were not delivering their hilarious "lectures" (admittance, say, 25 cents), filled in their time acceptably as ministers of this or that evangelical denomination.

They were the court jesters of a homogeneous culture and they are extinct now not because the culture they represented has crumbled utterly, but because it has grown self-conscious and ashamed, wistful to be cosmopolitan. En route, as it were, to extinction, they lived for years in the smoking compartments of railway trains and gabbed there interminably, to their own joy and with cost to nobody. Cosmopolitanism, with its creed of efficiency and its experience of human depravity, warned all travelers at length with printed bulletins to beware of all other travelers, and prohibition left those who were warned ready to heed the warnings and often half ready to justify them.

But even in 1932, in the effectible privacy and brevity of a newspaper perusal, one can catch (and many are intent to catch) the echoes of that old buffoonery in the comic-strip depiction of one Hambones, true son of frontier America. Except for Hambones, then, and suchlike, the old humor is gone — that is, in its professional aspect. In its non-professional aspect it has waned little to this day.

For consider, now, such a group of people as comes together at countless places in the South to celebrate Christmas by heavy eating. There is grandfather first. The mossy marble has these many years been all anybody has seen of grandmother — but not all that anybody has heard of her. That lady's sayings, her eccentricities (always whispered about), her preferences in dress and food and flowers, are well understood by her descendants regardless of whether or not they ever had the happiness of seeing her. And there is grandfather's friend, invited in for dinner, a retired small merchant he; grandfather, a retired farmer. Between the two, so far as one can discern, there is one point of congeniality: they are both upwards of eighty. How they enjoy each other!

Besides these two are mother and father (he, a lawyer) and uncles and aunts, wed and unwed, farmers, doctors, merchants, a mail carrier, a teacher, a knitter of knit bedspreads. And there are countless cousins, male and female, conventional for the most part, some unconventional — but none so unconventional as not to know better than to offend this agglomeration of good nature. One cousin conducts a gallery of modern art in Chicago; one, Sorbonne trained, teaches French at Vassar. One, absent, is represented by a note from him saying how sorry he is; he for his part is in Russia, finding out for some great foundation or other about the doings of the Soviets.

Here are all these people, gorged at last, and called upon by six or eight stray diners, as diverse as they, from another family. These people are constrained to talk about something, for along with the fundamental prohibitions (don't walk pigeon-toed; don't pick your teeth, child, in public) they were all given a fundamental admonition — keep, oh, whatever you do, keep the occasion *moving*. Moving, my dear, lest we think perchance of how weakness comes at last, and pain, to all of us; lest we think too wrackingly of those whom weakness and pain already shove with brutal deliberation to their end; moving, lest a recognition of our own inadequacy — as persons, as a people — sere us here into sighers only.

Would it do, here, for Cousin Julius to talk of Proust's analyses, for Cousin Mary to tell of Epstein, for Uncle Tom to make Bergson clear, for someone else to echo Swift's mordancy, Wilde's glitter? I ask this question unabashedly as rhetorical. It would never, never do.

This is the challenge — tell a story now, you, that mail-carrying Uncle Jack and Proust-teaching Cousin Julius will both think pointed, that knit-bedspread knitter Aunt Susan can endure without fainting, that Rabelaisian Uncle Rob can endure without nodding. Scour your memory, sir; let's hear from you; it is your time now, everybody else has said something — what were you born for, anyway? Slash in where you can, echoing that word of Aunt Susie's, giving it an emphasis that she did not mean to give it, making her disclose more than she meant to, covering her with confusion, while the table roars.

"How was it, Dick, that your mother used the field glasses at the beach. . . . Yes, we have most of us heard but Julius hasn't, and besides we want to hear it again." "Now father," protests Dick's mother, Emma, "now, *father!*" And Dick tells it again, and they all shout again.

"Now that," says John, "reminds me of what old Mr. Pixley said." . . . "And Lord, Lord," says grandfather, "when have I thought of old Mr. Pixley? Why John, that man died before ever your mother and father got married." "None the less," says John, "I shall tell you about old Mr. Pixley. . . ." "Wait," says Henry. "Have you all heard about Res biting Tom Johnson's leg?" (There, naturally, everybody knows both characters. Res is short for Resaca de la Palma, a dog name in the household since the Mexican War; Tom Johnson is an esteemed but emaciated neighbor.)

"Actually bite him?" asks Howard.

"No, just snapped at him."

"I'm glad of that," says Walter, "but what odd taste of Res in the first place!"

"Now, boys," says Aunt Mattie, "I have the real truth of it. When Res's tooth struck Tom's breeches, it naturally slid off. . . ."

"How was it, Carrie," asks father, "that old black Bella set you straight about the Family when you first married into it and came here from Boston?"

"What was it, Red, the Yankee said when you bumped into him after coming back from your schooling in England? *I'm sorry*, you said — what was it he replied?"

"Uncle John," says Red, "the Yankee said 'What fer.'"

"What was it, Andrew, that little rapscallion said when he encountered for the first time — and too late at that — quinine with his natural milk?" "Uncle John," says Andrew, "it was like this. The child's name was Micajah, and when he became aware of the quinine he made a wry face and said this: 'Pappy,' says he, 'give me a chaw er baccer, Mammy's been a-eatin' bitter weed.'"

And so it goes, the old Abductor, the old destroyers, torturers, weakeners, frightened for a moment to other spheres.

Now all of the people at this Christmas dinner know one another, and the fact that they know, already, most of the stories they hear told does not make those stories blunt for them. Somehow the story itself is not primarily the thing one laughs at. If that were true a story read or told by a radio entertainer or by a boresome man with a good memory would be as amusing as one heard acceptably. The important part of a story is the effect it has on the teller, and one must naturally know the teller well to perceive what that effect is. That is why a funny thing captured so that it can be drawn forth and exhibited at will by one man as well as by another loses, often, all its force.

That is why uninitiated Northern persons often find themselves impatient at the zest with which Southern persons — as sophisticated as themselves, apparently — listen to one Negro story after another, through an entire evening. They do not recognize how largely the point of such stories depends upon outside considerations. When they are aware of those considerations, when they know intimately the garrulous raconteur and his mannerisms, their impatience yields readily. For the initiated understand well enough that the teller, in the telling, is himself the main point of his story. They know that the Southerner is in many ways bi-lingual, bi-mental, bi- (if I may say so) attituded; he speaks his own language and the dialect, his own thoughts and the Negro's thoughts; he has a sentiment for the Negro that the Northerner cannot diagnose except as detestation and at the same time a sentiment for him that the Northerner cannot diagnose except as affection. It is the interplay of all these traits that makes the yarn worth listening to.

The humor of the Negro, too (I mean as displayed by Negroes), is dependent upon a sympathetic comprehension. The point is always in what the teller is really, contrasted with what he tells, and contrasted with his relation to the white man whom he placates and, with a complete understanding by each of the other, often hoodwinks.

All of this, I think, suggests with some adequacy the present-day, generally unrecorded type of humor current in the South. The South at large represents in its basic economy the persistence of a tradition long superseded elsewhere, and its humor does too. That economy, obsolete in dominant America, stimulated a social tradition that is as yet obsolescent only, and that is indeed not clearly doomed to extinction, ever. It is a tradition which insists that human beings must quite inescapably remain human if they are to remain human, and one may well believe that it will reassert itself.

Even New York, for example, as late as the nineteen hundreds, found itself as greatly amused by tar-heel O. Henry as pioneer Georgia in its time was amused by Longstreet. And most of O. Henry's merits arise from restatements of the old fundamental theme of American humor, which is in 1932 perhaps less fashionable than it has ever been. I think that it will be fashionable again after a while and that O. Henry would be fashionable again also if it were not for the tawdry newfangledness which he proudly affected and which his contemporaries vulgarly admired.

Newfangledness makes slow headway in the South, and humor there is still at base rural, and all the clanging urbanism of Atlanta or of Birmingham has not been able to make most Southerners feel quite at home in the brothel of modish slang — with how great a loss to them let him who will figure. For Atlanta and Birmingham are close, still, to the fields and woods surrounding them, and the bright young people of those cities, let them strive ever so faithfully, are rarely able to pronounce "Sez you," for instance, with a conviction deep enough to keep it from proving nauseous. Most of them luckily have a better wit about them than to try. In the main, when they undertake to be mirthful, they behave themselves as much as they can like Andrew mimicking his young Micajah, or like Dick teasing his mother Emma.

But a discernible amount of Southern humor, such as Mr. Cohen's Slappey saga, has sprung from sections (more social than geographic in boundary) that are in thoroughgoing fashion both urban and industrialized. This, it turns out, has been most frequently indistinguishable from the humor current in, say, Akron, Ohio — a humor sprigs of which have been brought South and set in soil as much like that of Akron as its admirers could possibly search out.

On occasion another type has sprung up, indigenous, I think, though sophisticated beyond a doubt, and by many tests urban. Miss Ellen Glasgow, for instance, is almost wholly dependent in her subject matter upon the sources of humor which I have suggested as being somewhat definitely Southern; and it is obvious that all of the assumptions behind her hard, bright wit are authentically local. Cabell and Frances Newman and even Mencken must be reckoned with as belonging to the South. Consider those names, and pair them, not with the names Richmond, Atlanta, Baltimore, but with Detroit, Cleveland, Omaha. The pairing most manifestly will not stand. For these people too are country people, who do not manage to be at home in whirring cities. Cabell's interests are in districts that are surely not crowded; Frances Newman's were in a social plane dominated still by the ideas of Miss Winnie Davis. Mencken's interests are keener in his yokel, apparently, than in most other things — and particularly in that brand of yokel (found seldom in greater verdancy than in the South) whose folly evinces itself most notably in religion. What is more, Mencken attacks his victim with a stampeding directness which David Crockett, could he have heard it, would have mightily exulted in, which is as distant from the knowing, metropolitan Walter Winchell as if New York and Baltimore were seven universes apart. And it must not be forgotten that Cabell and Mencken, at some inconvenience to themselves, doubtless, continue living where they do, and that

Frances Newman, a little while before her death, came very definitely to the notion that her place was South or nowhere.

It is properly terrifying to observe that, as time runs, the number of things a man may be merry over is gradually diminished. "The year is dying," the poet said — and, philosophically, "let it die." So I say here: This number is diminishing — let it diminish. But the year passes, the number falls, with results that no degree of willingness on our part to have them change can keep from being in part bad. We cannot laugh ever again with a free heart at physical deformity or at madness as people — and very good people, too — did everywhere until very recently. Those sources of laughter are not sources of laughter any longer — they are gone from that list and will not be put back there, and I should be as unwilling as anybody else to see them put back. None the less, we laugh less. Ignorance may go off next; next, the "pain" (so hypersensitive we become) Dick caused his mother about the field glasses.

We progress toward a heaven, it appears, of unrelieved earnestness and propriety. But there are happily many people who would be unhappy at this prospect, and they are probably the same people who would be most upset at the prospect of their never having the opportunity again to exhibit kindness. Doubly hard, then, is their lot, for they are, unless all signs fail, sentimentalists — and the sentimentalist, like the humorist without a mission, is an ineffectual, and his only shadow of justification in life is that without him life would be so very little preferable to death that few would prize it.

For such reactionary persons, I think the South a good place. Many contrasts are deeply rooted here, and they promise to stay rooted. Not soon will the industrialized piedmont regions *completely* overlord the lowlands, nor the forces of modern education (which may conceivably be bad education) overwhelm *completely* in the mind of either barber or bishop the notion that white people and Negroes are somehow not identical.

More progressive sections than ours may actually reach, via standardization, before the world ends, that heaven of deadly uniformity which I am apprehensive of. But I am sure that such a heaven must be very disagreeable, and that no one of cultivated sensibilities would desire it were it not for the gullibility, latent in the best of us, which teaches men to desire anything which calls itself by an agreeable name.

Many of us would find on attaining such a heaven that the mere name was insufficient. We should want still a tightening of the heart, at times, with pity, or with indignation, a loosening down of the whole structure of our being, at times, with gigantic mirth.

— From *Culture in the South,* University of North Carolina Press, 1935. Reprinted by permission.

A MIND DIVIDED

Bayard Taylor as a Critic of America

By Richmond C. Beatty

Seventy years ago in America the name Bayard Taylor was one to conjure with marvelously. To say it aloud, with a certain breathlessness, would be to awaken for a typical contemporary the thought of a lusty but romantic person who had gaily gone into darkest Africa, who had been with Perry when Japan first opened its arms to the West, who had had his nose frozen in Finland in fifty-below weather, who had reported the gold rush for Greeley's New York *Tribune,* written verses about passionate Eastern women, smoked hashish, seen harems and eunuchs, Indian temples and Chinese pagodas, bathed in the Dead Sea, and crawled into an obscure pyramid to experience the undissipated smell of a mummy. He was the great American traveler.

Other contemporaries, more intelligent, thought of him as a fairly significant novelist; still others praised his translation of *Faust.* It is probable, however, that to our own generation not even his achievement with Goethe can be termed more interesting than the contents of some half-dozen of his fourteen lectures — lectures he delivered some half a thousand times! — which were ignored by his biographers and which remain to this day, unpublished, in the town library at West Chester, Pennsylvania. (They were briefly noticed for the first time by Robert Warnock in *American Literature* for May, 1933.) These lectures establish Taylor as, without doubt, one of the most significant Lyceum speakers of the past century and, also without doubt, as one of the most sadly confused. But what is more important than his confusion is the abiding nature of the questions he discussed, the relevance of his opinions to our present industrial and social bewilderment, the pitiless commentary they involve upon the incompatibility of the ideals of Progress and Leisure. In an odd way this fragment of Taylor's story thus seems to take on the countenance of a warning, seems to present with the detached fatal quietude of history a drama in frustration not unlike many others in process of undirected enactment today. To study it may leave one with a fitter sense of reality. But I anticipate.

Possibly the earliest lecture in point of date is entitled, appropriately, "The Animal Man." There has been too much emphasis on *spirit*, he boldly asserts, and not enough on *body*. Catholics enjoin fasts. This is wrong; it leads to disease. "Who can tell how much political oppression, how much harsh and bitter theology, how much individual cynicism and mistrust, may have their origin in the scrofula of the monarch, the dyspepsia of the priest, or the disordered liver or lung of the layman?"

Moral and mental traits are almost uniformly revealed in the physical appearance of a race. The African Negro is tall, but absolutely without grace or beauty. Correspondingly, he has no significant art. The bodies of the Chinese lack *harmony*. Moreover, "their crooked eyes are typical of their crooked moral vision." Young Arabs are physically almost perfect, he said; but he did not indicate the spiritual correspondency here; and recalling his sketch of Arab character already quoted, one is not surprised that the item was ignored. The thought of physical beauty lured him away from his thesis. He remembered the young girls he had met in the mountains of European Russia. "The women of Circassia are beyond doubt the most beautiful in the world." He had seen them all, from California eastward to Japan, and the palm of superlative went to a tribe whose geographical identity he was compelled to explain, for to his average audience the Circassians were unheard of.

The human race he concluded to have been smaller in earlier times than at present. Proof: He once tried in vain to squeeze upon his little finger a signet ring of Cheops, builder of the great pyramid. Also, he had examined the hilts of the swords of certain chieftains "of the race of Odin, found in Scandinavia," and had discovered that they were " much too small for any modern hand to grasp."

Oh, but for all their diminutiveness, men were vigorous and lusty in the past! Now we are hothouse plants. " Each year two million teeth are extracted in London alone! Yet there are no signs of bad teeth in mummies or fossils." And further, there were no surgical instruments among the Egyptians. And even during the Middle Ages, men wore armor weighing 150 pounds. We are a degenerate people; it is apparent in our literature.

" No man of ordinary penetration can fail to detect, in the poems of Elizabeth Barrett Browning, or in the tales of Poe, the evidence of a diseased body. Byron, with all the shifting play of his wit, pathos, and passion, cannot wholly purify the pages of *Don Juan* from the smell of gin; and Mrs. Radcliffe, in the nightmare horrors of her *Mysteries of Udolpho*, betrays the suppers of raw beef in which she indulged. Contrast the dark and sinful fascination of *Lucretia*, written by the exhausted and dyspeptic Bulwer, with the ruddy and healthy tone of *The Caxtons*, written by the same Bulwer after his system had been restored by the water cure."

He passed on to a castigation of his age: " The characteristic of those books which now best suit the popular taste in this country is morbid emotion." " Gutter literature " has become fashionable, and " lewd French novels," which are flagrantly reprehensible. " Give me the fresh, hearty, warm-blooded creations of Fielding and Smollett, with all their coarseness, rather than the refined and insidious immorality of modern French novelists."

Give him, indeed, the glorious, healthy Elizabethans, those " splendid animals " who were not " pale and anemic," who were not " long-haired dreamy youths " but " master spirits." Give him Shakespeare, Beaumont, and Fletcher. Give him the inspired, wise Greeks — their drama and their philosophy. Give him mountain air, the summer surf, a swift horse, a tumultuous river. Give him the great winds and storms and the long rains from heaven: " What — in the name of physiology — what sort of a race shall spring from the loins of those tallow-faced, narrow-chested, knock-kneed, spindle-shanked simpering sons of rich fathers whom we see every day!" In "three generations" we shall have become simians.

His prescription, like his diagnosis, was simple — too simple indeed, when one remembers his own harassed way of living, to appear anything but ironic. His countrymen were deteriorating, racially, for one reason: "We do not know how to *rest*. The average American works fast, sleeps fast, dresses in the twinkling of an eye, runs to his meals, eats fast, and when he has run through with his stock of health, dies fast. Our public teachers cry out to us: Think! Think! or Work! Work! but never Play! Play! or Rest! Rest!" We need fresh air and exercise, we need to "open the windows and let in the sunlight, even if the carpets do fade."

In "Man and Climate" he is considerably more sober. "Climate is beyond all doubt the most powerful of these external influences which give shape to the plastic nature of man." Certain races have always inhabited particular zones of climate. Indeed, there is no such thing as a cosmopolitan race, "one, that is, which can exist in any climate." He classifies all races, explaining their idiosyncrasies in terms of temperature. The African, for example, "is careless of the future because his existence is certain, the Esquimau because it is a matter of chance. The former does not advance because he has not the stimulus of necessity, and the latter because he has too much of it. The African has nothing to do but live, while if the Esquimau is living, he is accomplishing all that can be expected of him."

Two important conclusions follow from these facts. The first one, immensely flattering, is "that every important triumph which man has achieved since his creation belongs to the Caucasian race. Our mental and moral superiority is self-evident." The second is in part a warning. "Permanent, self-supporting colonization in another climate is impossible. This knowledge should restrain our national ambition." We cannot with safety extend our territory below the eighteenth parallel, or below Cuba and Mexico. The English have tried this, in India, but find it expedient to import fresh blood there almost constantly. Republican government, he is convinced, simply cannot succeed in the tropics. Thus it follows that the seat of government of the United States should always be where it is now, in spite of "gassy politicians who prate of pent-up utopias and claim the whole unbounded continent."

"The American People" was perhaps the most vigorous of all his speeches. It was written in November, 1861, and is burdened with his loyalty to the Union cause.

But not at first. At first he talks wisely about social differences between America and Europe. He is qualified to make comparisons: "I have had the opportunity of becoming familiarly acquainted with all the civilized races of the earth; and I know no people so paradoxical, so difficult to be fully understood, as the Americans."

We differ from the inhabitants of Europe in particular on one point. "There one finds a strongly ribbed social system" independent of the distinctions of rank and wealth. "That is, there are certain understood usages and habits of society, which are so many silent laws for its government. They exist as part of that domestic order which the American traveler finds in the families of Germany and England. It enters into the education of children, and it shapes, in one way or another, every man's plan for the future. In society it gives the charm of ease and grace, by making each person master of his position; in public intercourse it promotes a courtesy — let me rather say a *humility* — in the manner of the people at large."

Sadly, he must report that this principle is not operative in the United States. "A man's cultivation, refinement of manners, and moral fitness for society is not, with us, the only test to which he must submit. His degree of wealth is a very important consideration in some quarters, his family in others, his religious views in others, the stand which he takes on some moral or political question in others again; while in certain cities the street on which he lives, and in certain communities the very fact of his superior cultivation, would be a disadvantage to him." "In Europe," to rephrase the idea, one finds "political despotism and social freedom; here, usually, it is political freedom and social despotism." In England, no amount of recovered fortune could restore in a social way a man known to have been dishonorably bankrupt. "With us, if a man has wealth, and the power which wealth gives, his dishonesty is gracefully veiled under the term of 'sharp practice' and does not disqualify him for social consideration." This was a vicious circumstance to Taylor, as it had been a decade before to Dickens; for "one of the noblest uses of society is to step in and punish those slippery forms of injustice, and peculation, and immorality which avoid the grasp of the law. Society thus deals with character, while the law deals with actions.

"I am emphatic upon this point because I perceive, among us, a social demoralization, which is the result of giving an overdue importance to wealth. We are tormented by a feverish emulation to keep pace with one another and, as our wealthy class represents neither the intellect nor the refinement of our people, success in the race exhibits itself in display, in extravagant habits, in an ambition to keep up appearances as the main business of life."

How does he account for this blatant false pride? Largely through the realization that a comfortable living is in America so easy to obtain that poverty is regarded as a reproach, as something indicative of a want of industry or energy.

Let us place character before wealth, he goes on, and believe again that the grand old name of gentleman is a richer possession than an illustrious coat of arms. "The treason of the degenerate Washingtons of our day is not gilded by the immortal patriotism of our country's father: it becomes a blot of blacker damnation. When you hear a man boasting that he belongs to an old family, remember that you, too, are descended from Adam and Eve. I have heard so constantly from citizens of a certain state that they were connected with the best families, that I longed — for the sake of change — to make the acquaintance of a few of the worse families."

Yes, the Virginians are intolerable people, with their assumption of grandeur, and leisure, and conviviality, and their contempt for progress. They have talked of the South as though it were better and more civilized than the North — these preposterous and arrogant slaveholders who have no large cities and who gamble outrageously on horses and who are often drunk. Let us look at this section of rebels, fairly.

"The white trash of the South [according to J. T. Adams these 'poor whites' comprised only five per cent of the white population before the Civil War] represents the most depraved class of whites

I have ever seen. Idle, shiftless, filthy in their habits, aggressive, with no regard for the rights of others, these barbarians seem to have united all the vices of the Negro with those of their own race, and they almost shake our faith in the progressive instinct of the Anglo-Saxon blood."

He continued his indictment: "Society there has been slowly drifting back toward the conditions of the feudal ages. The planters have gradually absorbed the wealth and political power, and the poorer classes, utterly neglected, unschooled, unencouraged, despised even by the chattels of the former — have become, not indeed serfs, but savages. In the North, the superior dignity of *labor that is free, the beneficent system of education,* and the absence of any recognized caste, have subdued the inequalities of society to a greater extent than the human race has yet known. The surest guarantee for the permanence of our system of government is afforded by this result."

The South must be broken, by force. "It has been reserved for us to hear the most monstrous treason of history encouraged, under the plea that the suppression of it would be 'coercing' a people! In a crisis, when our national existence is at stake . . . we still hear the lament that the simplest measure of self-preservation on the part of the government is a dangerous assumption of power.

"I have never believed in submission to outrage since I was attacked by highwaymen. I have never believed in 'moral suasion' since I read that the Savior scourged the money changers out of the temple." The doctrine of states' rights is merely a device whereby to escape obedience to the will of the majority.

"The idea of loyalty to a state is so childish that a man of ordinary intelligence should be ashamed to entertain it. I was conversing, last winter, with a Virginia secessionist — one of the first families, of course — who actually had the hardihood to say: 'I am a Virginian first and an American afterwards. Allegiance to my state is superior to my allegiance to the federal government.' 'Very well,' said I, 'step outside the United States and see what good your Virginia loyalty will do you. Go to Europe with your governor's passport and see how far you will travel. Say you are a Virginian and people will ask, "What's that?" Hang out your state shield with its *sic semper tyrannis* — the meaning of which we shall make you understand some day — and you may hear the question: " Is that one of the new Polynesian kingdoms? " But say you are an *American* — point to the star of Virginia on the national flag — and no other explanation is necessary.'

" I must do the man the justice to say that he answered: ' Well, I never thought of it that way.' "

This was a hectic lecture. Taylor digressed for a time to pay his courtesies to corrupt politicians. Again, because of the overwhelming prosperity of the country, he declared, we have grown careless of the means people employ to get money. The further fact that federal and state salaries are inadequate encourages administrative dishonesty. Why not have an intelligent civil service, within which the holders of government positions are promoted according to merit? His plea for this improvement is convincing so long as he extols the increased efficiency that would result from its adoption. But the South, monstrous ogre, blinked at him again, and again he paused to hurl his rhetorical thunderbolt: Political corruption is widespread for a good reason, " when throughout the South the standard [of political probity] has fallen so low that an oath has lost its sanctity, we must not suppose that even the sublime loyalty of the North has yet purified us from a share of the reproach."

But let us take heart and " sink all narrow interests, all state arrogance, all sectional jealousies, in the nobler sentiment of loyalty to the American union. . . . We shall not exchange the security of the past for the constant presence of a rival and hostile power. For God has united North and South in a common destiny, and the devil, with rebellion as his agent, shall not put them asunder! "

In the address " Ourselves and Our Relations " he repeats a good deal of what was more comprehensively stated in the above discussion. Pleading for a stronger central government, he cites instances abroad of price-fixing, condemns our identifying culture with religious orthodoxy or financial success, and deplores the tendency in rural sections to " resent the least departure from accepted ways and habits of life." In this regard the average small community exercises so narrow and tyrannical an influence " that whoever desires a little social freedom is driven to seek it — or rather the nearest approach to it — in our large cities."

He condemns the electoral college. It thwarts majority rule and, hence, is not democratic in spirit. He pleads again for a civil service. He is frightened by the spectacle of immigration. After five years' residence here an immigrant can vote, and in so doing neutralize the will " of our wisest and most experienced native." The immigrant is a temptation to our politicians; he is easily drilled. Consider our criminals: seventy-five per cent of them are foreign-born! We should remember that " in a republic every unintelligent ballot is dangerous." It is the positive duty of every citizen to vote. Severe punishment should be meted out to those who persistently fail to do so. Education is our only hope.

The great danger this republic faces is that of decentralization — not its opposite. " Local pride — state pride, if you choose — is a natural but contracted sentiment. Yet our politicians, our authors, probably in their regional fiction have all been guilty of exalting it above the grander, *national* pride which should bind and blend all narrower affection. . . . I have been a citizen of three states, and have found that my allegiance is as easily transferred as my residence. So far from the national government encroaching on the rights of the states, I think it has allowed them the exercise of functions which properly belong to itself. As only the nation can levy war, so the militia system, which is designed to furnish it with resources, should be entirely in the nation's hands. . . . A state should be obliged to guarantee not only a republican government to its citizens, but the education without which that form of government has no certain permanence."

The South declared that the right to secede was not denied by the Constitution. Taylor answered that no government granting that right can survive. Secession was *assumed* to be a crime. The right of suicide, for that matter, is not denied in the Bible. He who helps to build a nation upon the basis of the secession principle " is either a dishonest man or a hopeless fool." The history of all confederacies — from the Greek to the German confederacies of our own day — has been " one of inevitable failure." And, of course, if the mere fact of survival is to be the only criterion of greatness, he is right, though not a few tightly-knit empires have failed, unaccountably, as well. "Do those who advocate confederacies know what they mean? Better than such a miserable abortion — which has no national name or sentiment, enjoys no respect abroad and inspires no faith at home, cheats the present of half its harvest and sows no seeds for the future — better than this would be the absolutism of Russia!"

"Life in Europe and America" contains much of Taylor's criticism of the Gilded Age. To the reformers who were beginning to agitate against the use of alcohol he mentioned the European custom of taxing the stimulant and of saying, in effect, "the citizen may do as he pleases; but if he does drink he shall be furnished the genuine article." He commends again the practice, in Germany, of fixing the price of necessities like "bread, meat, and beer." And he talked, with considerable foresight, against the Whig philosophy of governmental protection of business, a philosophy which his friend Greeley had long advocated in the *Tribune*.

The interests of business, the Whigs had reasoned, through their eloquent spokesman, Henry Clay, are the interests of society: It is therefore the duty of the state to help its citizens to make money. "Whiggery is the expression in politics of the acquisitive instinct, and it assumes as the greatest good the shaping of public policy to promote private interests." Now the fly in this sweet ointment did not escape Taylor's notice. He saw that the ideal of paternalism in the common interest had a way of degenerating, in practice, into legalized favoritism. "Lesser interests are sacrificed to greater interests, Whiggery comes finally to serve the lords of the earth without whose good will the wheels of business will not turn. To him that hath shall be given."

Protecting a business, Taylor declared, "makes that business able to cheat and oppress and corrupt the public." Was the true aim of our government apparent "when an individual three years ago chose to stop traffic between New York and the West at Albany, or when three or four individuals recently gambled with the value of gold and disturbed the business interests of forty millions of people? It is perhaps owing to this regard for the individual that, with us, corporations are far more irresponsible and tyrannical than in any other civilized country. Our politicians, of whatever party, cry out against corporations, and yet we see them controlling entire states, electing their own legislatures and members of Congress, demoralizing voters, and exercising other dangerous privileges in defiance of public interest. We are silent under impositions which would raise a popular tempest in many countries of Europe."

Materialistic personal ambitions he also deplored. "One of our prevailing national characteristics might be called *Discontent*. The more splendid and far-reaching our aims, the more haste we make to realize them, seeking short cuts and accepting all kinds of risks and hazards. The present requirements of society — a fine house, handsome furniture, and a pew in a fashionable church — are not very difficult to fulfill. Those who distance their competitors and reach what is called *the top* encourage the others to struggle after them. These in turn stimulate others farther behind until, from top to bottom, we find the whole people engaged in a struggle to keep up appearances." In Europe, this condition is anomalous. Ambition there "is sober, and aims at realizations which are not quite so far and splendid." The result is a greater stability, a peace unknown to more aspiring societies.

Finally, he deplored the rise of the cities. Throughout the republic one was able to trace "a natural ambition for further advantages, more flattering successes than small communities can offer. In a great many cases, the true remedy would be, not in deserting those communities, but in improving them. Too many of our farmers' sons become dyspeptic clerks or indifferent lawyers, or shiftless adventurers, through a mistaken estimate of their own powers. They do not see that it is more prudent to stand at the head of a simple universal profession than at the tail of any other." A city, moreover, is an expensive place in which to live. For that reason "it imposes a tax upon matrimony and thus encourages vice. There is not in the world — and probably never has been — a city where one must pay so much and get so little in return as in New York. We already behold there, and in our other cities, those extremes of reckless luxury and still more reckless poverty which we once supposed were peculiar to Europe." The home as an institution cannot long stand against the disintegrating fury of such an environment.

2

Certain other of Taylor's opinions will be indicated later. But we have seen already perhaps his most important social and political convictions. In the way of positive improvements, he endorsed the civil service, an educated citizenry capable of intelligent voting, and, most emphatically, a strong central government possessed of approximately dictatorial powers over corporations and commonwealths alike. Negatively, he decried wealth as a measure of one's social prominence, the exploitation of the public by Big Business, the philosophy of acquisitiveness, the rise of the city, the waning influence of the home, and the Southern way of life.

During the six years preceding the war, Taylor was one of the most popular lecturers in the country, and the reason for this popularity is not far to seek. Much that he said was profoundly sensible, even prophetic. It was also important and needed saying. His delivery, moreover, was direct and forceful; he had a fine sense of humor, and his courage in expressing his views was above question. The fact cannot be emphasized too strongly that Taylor was entirely sincere in his political convictions; had they differed from those then current among Northern audiences he would probably not have modified them in the least degree. It happened, however, that these convictions coincided with the vast majority of those to whom he spoke, which means simply that he was a true child of his age.

Yet it is only reasonable to add that one may be a child of his age without being, at the same time, either balanced or entirely trustworthy. And in the interest of preserving a degree of balance regarding some of the topics Taylor discussed, it would therefore perhaps be only fair to mention briefly the Southern side of that picture which he painted with so much eloquence and force. To begin with, it should be set down at once that, in spite of his sweeping declaration that "the white trash of the South represents the most depraved class of whites I have ever seen," Taylor had actually visited only as far south as St. Louis and Washington, that the Mississippians he knew were those (in no sense typical of the state) whom he met on the boat which took him to California, and that he had never seen the states of Alabama, Georgia, Florida, the Carolinas, and Tennessee, except to pass through a few of them on the train, and partly at night, en route to New York from Mobile. Taylor didn't know the South.

It should be mentioned, again, that in his defense of "free labor and a beneficent system of education" he appears to have been blind to a good deal that, appreciated, would have considerably sobered his enthusiasm. There is little point in dwelling here upon statistics, but it is well known that in 1860 higher education in the South was in a much more flourishing state than in the North. It is also well known that the reason elementary education was not as universal as elsewhere in the country is traceable to a belief — by no means refuted yet — that it is unwise to educate members of the lower classes beyond the station they will probably occupy as adults. In his tragic inability to identify himself with his race, the emancipated intellectual Negro of today presents a case which seems to indicate, at any rate, that the point of view of the one section possessed as much validity as that of the other.

On the question of "free labor" also, it appears that to determine how sound Taylor's argument was involves, first of all, a definition of terms. "The slave," as James Truslow Adams has noted, "was indeed a chattel, but in exchange for liberty he obtained security. From birth to death, in sickness and in health, he was guaranteed subsistence — including food, clothing, and shelter — medical attention, and the other necessities of life. He or she need not fear the loss of a job, the arrival of another child, or a bad crop. Whatever happened, the slave had a first lien, so to say, on the industry, indeed almost on the whole social system, of which he formed a part. It was of the very nature of that system that the profits of industry had to be such, and distributed in such a way, as to ensure security during life and at least a minimum of life's needs to every laborer contributing to the total result."

When one is faced with the further consideration that in a state of "freedom" pregnant women were harnessed to coal carts, that six-year-old children were worked fifteen hours a day in ill-ventilated factories and mines, that one mill owner in Holyoke, Massachusetts, found his laborers able to "produce 3000 yards more of cloth a week if he worked them without breakfast," that another manager in Fall River frankly admitted regarding his employees "just as I regard my machinery," and added that "so long as they can do my work for what I choose to pay them, I keep them, getting out of them all I can. What they do or how they fare outside my walls I don't know, nor do I consider it my business to know. . . . When my machines get old and useless I reject them and get new, and these people are part of my machinery. . . ." When, in short, one finds such attitudes and practices to have been *typical* in a society of "free labor," one is led to suspect the phrase of a deceptive emptiness all but criminal in its implications.

That the phrase deceived Taylor is plain. Indeed, by identifying himself with the passions of the fifties and sixties, he seems in his thinking to have been led into a basic intellectual contradiction. For that South which he despised was naturally, as a result of its way of life, more studious of manners and leisure than the North, was less acquisitive, was less prone to endorse futile hurry and speed and to mistake these things for progress, represented an established order such as he had come to admire in Europe, opposed by the very nature of its institutions the rampant rise of the cities, centered its interests in home life — exemplified, in short, practically all the virtues of civilization and decency which he was given to commending.

But there were two other characteristics of the South which blinded Taylor to these virtues. He held, as we have seen, to the sentimental conviction that there can be but one kind of slavery — the slavery of physical ownership. And the South openly practiced that kind, deaf to the hysterical protest of Garrison and other Abolitionists. He held also to the Hamiltonian conception of government, that of a government controlled by the rich and powerful. And the South was unregenerate here. There were, of course, corollary grievances against the section: The war — brought on, he believed, by Southern stubbornness — had hurt the publishing business and the Lyceum business, and he looked to these activities for his income. Besides, the rebels had killed his brother Fred at Gettysburg. The South, in brief, could not possibly be virtuous. He hated the South.

And this was unfortunate. For it happened, as a result of his hatred, that the one region in America which practiced the virtues he extolled, the one region which despised the vices he despised, he was able neither to tolerate nor understand. There was nothing real, nothing tangible, with which his point of view might be identified. He was driven, because of his dilemma, to commend the forces of unification, which were the forces of industrialism and predatory wealth; and in so doing he became in an unconscious way an advocate of all the brutality and corruption and spiritual depravity which he deplored. Universal education, he thought, would prevent this villainy. But a later and more chastened wisdom is beginning to imply that his ideal of universal education cannot arrest in mankind the impulse of selfishness, cannot commend nobility in any sweeter way to his contemplation, is indeed usually wasted upon that wretched creature — predestined, it appears to some, to perversity and evil.

— From *Bayard Taylor*, University of Oklahoma Press, 1936. Reprinted by permission.

THE PILLARS OF AGRARIANISM

By Frank L. Owsley

SINCE THE APPEARANCE of *I'll Take My Stand* in 1930, the Agrarians have been subjected to a fusillade of criticism. I suspect that our philosophy as set forth in that book and in later essays, published in certain periodicals, especially in the Distributist-Agrarian *American Review*, has irked the devotees of our technological civilization. Venturing an even stronger word, it begins to appear that the doctrines announced in *I'll Take My Stand* have actually infuriated these people. Just recently, on an important examination for a certain scholarship, it seems that the Committee inquired of each candidate what he thought of agrarianism. It was noteworthy that the successful candidate summed up his opinion by saying that the advocates of such a system were " cockeyed." One of the candidates, who was not only rejected but was urged not to apply again on the grounds of age (he has just celebrated his twenty-second birthday, and the age limit of the scholarship is several years above this age), answered that as far as he understood it he heartily approved of agrarianism. The most recent and, perhaps, the most violent attack upon the advocates of an agrarian state is that of H. L. Mencken. While Mencken's attack is so violent and lacking in restraint that it does not fall far short of libel, I have no desire to single him out as a critic worthy of an answer. However, I must confess that Mencken's attack because it is typical — outside of the billingsgate — of those coming from the pillars of industrialism, has prompted, to a certain extent, this essay. Such essays as his, appearing with amazing regularity, have without doubt troubled the mind of the neophyte, and, in many cases, have utterly confused him and made him lose sight of the principles and specific objectives of agrarianism.

Few if any of the Agrarians have expended any effort in answering the criticism of those who attack our principles. From the beginning we have pursued the attack rather than the defense; nor have we — if I may continue the military figure of speech — seen fit to consolidate our positions. However, it seems to me very proper, at the present time, for the sake of those who have been confused, or those whom we hope to draw into our way of thinking, to restate and elaborate the fundamental economic and political principles on which an agrarian society will probably have to rest in the United States, and most particularly in the South.

I shall not attempt to restate and discuss all the principles and programs of our hoped-for agrarian society, for this, as John Crowe Ransom has said in another connection, would indeed institute an infinite series. My purpose is to confine my discussion to the five great pillars upon which this society will have to rest. Before going into an exposition of the foundation of a restored agrarianism in the South (or other regions), it will be well to restate our definition of an agrarian state as set forth in the introduction of *I'll Take My Stand:*

> Opposed to the industrial society is the agrarian, which does not stand in particular need of definition. An agrarian society is hardly one that has no use at all for industries, professional vocations, for scholars and artists and for the life of the cities. Technically, perhaps, an agrarian society is one in which agriculture is the leading vocation, whether for wealth, for pleasure, or prestige — a form of labor that is pursued with intelligence and leisure, and that becomes the model to which the other forms approach as well as they may.

I shall edit this definition. We had in mind a society in which, indeed, agriculture was the leading vocation; but the implication was more than this. We meant that the agrarian population and the people of the agricultural market towns must dominate the social, cultural, economic, and political life of the state and give tone to it. Today, the Scandinavian countries are fair examples of such a state. France before the World War was a most beautiful example, where

30,000,000 people lived on the land and 10,000,000 lived in the towns and cities engaging in commerce and industry. Even today, after the disastrous war and its effects upon mechanization of industry, France presents the best-balanced economic system of any first-class nation in the world. The ownership of property is more widely distributed there than in any other nation comparable in wealth and population. Governments may rise and fall, but the French peasant and farmer seem eternal when compared to those of the United States. Today [1935] there are about 350,000 persons unemployed in France as against hardly less than 12,000,000 in the United States. Yet the United States has less than three times as large a population as France.

Before entering into the details of our fundamental program, let me say that we are not exotics, not a peculiar sect living in a vacuum, untouched by public affairs, merely irked by the noise of factory wheels and machinery. We fully realize that our program cannot be put into operation until matters affecting the nation as a whole are set aright. Everything which affects the agrarian interest also touches industry, finance, and commerce. Our program, therefore, intimately involves national problems. We are on the side of those who know that the common enemy of the people, of their government, their liberty, and their property, must be abated. This enemy is a system which allows a relatively few men to control most of the nation's wealth and to regiment virtually the whole population under their anonymous holding companies and corporations, and to control government by bribery or intimidation. Just how these giant organizations should be brought under the control of law and ethics we are not agreed. We are, however, agreed with the English Distributists that the most desirable objective is to break them down into small units owned and controlled by real people. We want to see property restored and the proletariat thus abolished and communism made impossible. The more widespread is the ownership of property, the more happy and secure will be the people and the nation. But is such a decentralization in physical property as well as in ownership possible? We are confident that it is, however much we may differ among ourselves as to the degree of decentralization that will prove desirable in any given industry.

We are all convinced, though we hold no doctrinaire principles as to method, that these robber barons of the twentieth century will have to be reduced and civilized in some form or other before any program can be realized by our state and federal governments.

While we are deeply interested in the whole nation, yet, as Agrarians and Southerners, we are not desirous of launching a crusade to convert or coerce the other sections of the country into our way of thinking. We therefore, while inviting all who wish to go with us, have a fundamental program for the South to which I have referred as the five pillars of agrarianism.

II

The first item in our agrarian program is to rehabilitate the population actually living on the soil. This farming population falls into several categories: large and small planters; large and small farmers, both black and white; black and white tenants who own their stock and tools, and rent land; black and white tenants who own no stock or tools, but are furnished everything and get a share of the crop for their labor. Finally, there is the wage hand, either colored or white, who is furnished a house, and perhaps food and a certain cash wage.

Today the farm population in the South, whether wage hand or large planter, is in a precarious and often miserable state. The exploitations by the industrial interests through high tariffs and other special favors from the federal government, which force the farmer to buy in a protected market and sell in a world market, and the periodic industrial depressions following in close order since the Civil War, have greatly oppressed the Southern agricultural population. The majority of the planters do not really own their lands; the real owners are the life insurance companies or the banks. The payment of the interest on his mortgage leaves the almost mythical landowner little on which to subsist. Repayment of the principal is out of the question. Actually, most of the planters are without credit, and are no better off than the tenant or sharecropper. In fact the renter and sharecropper frequently come out of debt with some cash, their corn, sorghum, potatoes, pigs, cows, and other livestock above the board. The fate of the small or large farmer is much better. As a rule he is thrifty, owes less than the other classes, and lives to a great extent off his farm. Sometimes he sends his children to college, especially the agricultural college. His house is usually comfortable and sometimes painted. For the farmer as a class, there is less need of state intervention in his affairs than in the affairs of the tenant and planter classes. Yet a new political economy is necessary for him as well as the planters and tenants, or he will eventually lose his land and status. This new political economy will be discussed later. As for the planter class, there are many whom even the new political economy cannot save. Their equity in the once broad acres which they held in fee simple is too small. It will be best for them to liquidate and begin over as small farmers under the plan which I shall presently offer in connection with the tenant farmers.

The most serious problem, however, is not the bankrupt planters but the tenant farmers, black or white, because of their great number. I do not know the exact ratio between the tenant farmer class and the landholding class; but I have heard it said that seventy-five per cent of the population living on the land in the South are tenants. If this estimate is too high, it will not long remain so unless strong measures are taken, for the tenant class has been increasing so rapidly in recent years that it threatens to engulf the entire agricultural population of the South. Most of the white tenants were once landowners, but have been thrust near to the bottom of the economic and social order by the loss of their lands through industrial exploitation, depression, and, frequently, through high pressure salesmanship of radio, automobile, and farm machinery agents. Industrialism has persuaded, or created a public opinion which has virtually driven, the farmer to accept industrial tastes and standards of living and forced him to mortgage and then to lose his farm. Battered old cars, dangling radio aerials, rust-eaten tractors, and abandoned threshing machines and hay balers scattered forlornly about are mute witnesses to the tragedy of industrialism's attempt to industrialize the farmer and planter.

A portion of the lower class of white tenants, especially the adults, are beyond redemption. Through diseased tonsils, adenoids, unbalanced rations, tuberculosis, hookworm, malaria, and the social diseases, many have been made into irresponsible, sometimes — but not often — vicious people who are lacking in mental alertness and the constancy of will to enable them to till the soil without close supervision. Such people would not be able to make a living on land which might be granted or sold to them on easy terms by the government. However, the county and state public health departments should be enabled to take the steps necessary to salvage the children of such families in order that they may become owners of small farms and good citizens when of proper age. It is this class of whites in particular, who own no stock, plant no gardens, raise no chickens, who are frequently and perhaps accurately described as the "po' white trash."

The higher-class white tenants, those who own their stock and cattle and have their gardens and truck patches, are ready to become the proprietors of farms. Frequently they are good farmers and send their children through the high schools. They are probably in the majority in most of the Southern states and, as I have suggested, their families have been landowners; they were, in short, once a part of the Southern yeomanry; and for a nation or section to allow these people to sink lower and lower in the social and economic scale is to destroy itself.

As for the Negro tenant class, the majority of the Agrarians agree that the really responsible farmers among them, who know how to take care of the soil and who own their own stock and cattle, should be made proprietors of small farms.

The planters and large farmers who are left after liquidating their debts will still have an abundance of tenants who work well under supervision, but who are irresponsible and incapable of taking care of themselves without supervision. In the South the wage hand is usually the son of a tenant. He is frequently young and more intelligent than the lower tenant class. He should, where his intelligence and sense of responsibility permit, be homesteaded like the better-class tenant. Otherwise he should be kept where he is, under the supervision of one who has good judgment and a sense of responsibility.

Now, instead of the federal or state government spending $2500 in building a house for the homesteaders with whom they are very gingerly experimenting, and several hundred dollars on small tracts of land, let the national and state governments buy up all the lands owned by insurance companies and absentee landlords — which are being destroyed rapidly by erosion — and part of the land owned by the large planters who are struggling to save a portion of their lands, and give every landless tenant who can qualify eighty acres of land, build him a substantial hewn-log house and barn, fence him off twenty acres for a pasture, give him two mules and two milk cows, and advance him $300 for his living expenses for one year. By this means 500,000 persons can be rehabilitated in one year at $1500 a family or $300 per person. An outright gift of the land is advocated to the homesteader with one condition attached: the land must never be sold or mortgaged, and when abandoned it should automatically escheat to the state, which should be under immediate obligation to rehabilitate another worthy family.

The next step would be to bring the technologically unemployed, intelligent city people back to the country. First, those who have had experience as farmers should be rehabilitated; next, but relatively few at a time, those without experience should be permitted to become tenants on plantations, whereupon, if such tenants and their families should feel that they would like to go on, the government should grant them a homestead with sufficient stock and cattle and enough cash to subsist them one year. It seems quite clear to the Agrarians that technological unemployment is destined to increase with rapid acceleration until the majority of the population once employed in industry will be thrown out of the system. The government will be faced with perhaps three alternatives: it could put these permanently unemployed on a dole — until the government becomes bankrupt or an orderly slave state is established; it could refuse the dole and have a revolution; or it could rehabilitate the unemployed by giving them small farms. We, as interested citizens of the United States, urge this last policy upon the government as the only permanent relief from permanent technological unemployment. As Agrarians we urge it as an opportunity to restore the healthy balance of population between city and country, which will aid in the restoration of agrarianism and in the restoration and preservation of civilization.

Next in order of importance but simultaneous with the first step should be the rehabilitation of the soil. We, in common with the agricultural colleges of the country, urge that small and large farmers, small and large planters, regard the enrichment and preservation of the soil as a first duty. Those who own the soil must be held accountable in some way for their stewardship. Undrained, unterraced, single-cropped land, and lack of reforestation, should be *prima facie* evidence that the homesteader is not a responsible person and his land should, after fair warning and action in chancery court, escheat to the state. As for those farmers and planters who acquire their land by purchase or inheritance, a heavy suspended fine should be imposed upon them; and unless the planter or farmer remedies the abuses within a reasonable time or gives good reason why he has not been able to do so, the fine should be collected. The county agent and three men appointed by the state department of agriculture should serve in each county as a kind of court to pass on such matters, and appeal from their decision should be allowed to go to chancery court. In short, land must be conserved for future generations and not exploited, as has too often been the practice, by the present owners. Another drastic proposal which would aid in conserving the land as well as preventing its being alienated or becoming encumbered with debt is that, by state constitutional amendment, no land could be mortgaged except by consent of a court of equity; nor should any kind of speculative sale be permitted. It must become impossible for land to be sold to real estate and insurance companies or banks. In thus making alienation of the soil difficult and its proper management necessary, I am suggesting a modified form of feudal tenure where, in theory, the king or state has a paramount interest in the land.

When the rehabilitation and conservation of the soil and stability of tenure have been provided for, the next consideration must be the products of the soil.

Subsistence farming must be the first objective of every man who controls a farm or plantation. The land must first support the people who till it; then it must support their stock. In the olden days when there were no money taxes or mortgages to meet, nor automobiles and fine carriages to buy, nor life and fire insurance to keep up, and when the priest and the teacher were paid in kind, this type of farming, if carried on with the scientific knowledge available today, would have supported the grandest of establishments. But today a minimum outlay of cash is necessary even for those fortunate souls who are without debts: taxes, insurance, clothing, certain articles of luxury, and medical attention require cash.

After subsistence crops are peanuts, rice, sugar cane, tobacco, and cotton. Cotton and tobacco, the two leading staples, can be raised in the South in almost limitless quantities and must always depend, to a large extent, upon the foreign or world market. Considerable talk has been going its rounds concerning the danger of losing the foreign market because of crop limitation. Crop limitation, however, has no bearing at the present time, at least, upon the problem of cotton and tobacco. There are between nine and twelve million surplus bales of cotton, and large quantities of tobacco above current crops, stored in the United States; and there can hardly be any question about loss of world markets because of crop limitation when we are unable to dispose of this terrific surplus. Further, considerable alarm has been expressed concerning the inability of American cotton growers to compete with Russia, Egypt, Brazil, Turkey, China, and India. This is a groundless fear; for even in the days when the South produced the scrub variety of cotton, the world depended largely upon American cotton, because, with the exception of limited areas in Egypt, the Sudan, and South Africa, no part of the world could raise as much cotton per acre or as good a fiber as the American South. Now that Coker of South Carolina and other plant breeders have produced an upland staple with a fiber about two inches in length, which will grow on any soil in the South, and which is being rapidly introduced everywhere, there can hardly be any serious competition with the South as far as cheapness of production, quality, and quantity are concerned.

Everything being equal in the world markets, the South could soon drive its competitors out, as it did until past the turn of the century when other factors entered. These factors will have to be dealt with intelligently by the government of the United States or by the regional governments to be discussed later, else the South will be wiped out economically. One factor is that within the last twenty years America has ceased to be a debtor nation and become a creditor. As a debtor we shipped cotton to England, France, or Germany which created foreign exchange with which to pay the principal and interest on our debts and purchase foreign goods. The South could raise large cotton and tobacco crops and be sure that the world markets would take all. As soon as we became a creditor we could no longer ship our cotton and tobacco with the assurances of a sale. England and Germany and France and even Japan, wherever possible, have bought cotton from those countries which owed them money. This loss of a foreign market was seemingly made permanent by the rising tariff scale in America, which effectually cut off foreign goods from our markets and thereby destroyed the chief sources of foreign exchange in this country with which Southern staples could be bought. The tariff, which was a guarantee of the home markets for the industrial interests of the country, principally located in the East and a belt following the Great Lakes, has been the greatest permanent factor in destroying the foreign market on which the South chiefly depended.

It must be said, at this point, that such a situation was envisaged in 1833 when South Carolina nullified the tariff law of 1832, and again when the Southern states seceded from the Union in 1861. The belief that industrialism, as soon as it got control of the federal government, would not only exploit agriculture but would destroy the South was behind the whole secession movement. Today we Agrarians witness the fulfillment of the jeremiads of Robert Barnwell Rhett and John C. Calhoun. We, however, are not hoping for or advocating another break-up of the Union; but we are demanding a fair hearing for the fundamental cause of the South — now that slavery can no longer befog the real issue. If the industrial interests continue the monopoly of the home market and thereby cause the agricultural South (and West) to pay a much higher price for goods than the world price level, we must have a *quid pro quo:* a subsidy on every bale of cotton and pound of tobacco or other important agricultural products shipped abroad, based on the difference between world and domestic prices. In order that foreign countries shall have sufficient American exchange with which to purchase our staple farm exports we further insist that all farm products and raw material shipped into the United States be used in creating foreign exchange with which cotton and tobacco may be purchased and exported. (James Waller in *A New Deal for the South* suggests this technique of establishing parity between agriculture and industry.) In short, the South — and, if I may be so bold as to speak for the agrarian interests of another section, the West — must have agriculture put upon the same basis as industry.

III

With such political economy the South would soon become one of the most important parts of the world, and it would add much to the prosperity of the other sections of the country. It is doubtful, however, whether such intelligent legislation is possible under a government dominated by particular sectional interests.

For that reason — which is founded upon the history of the last one hundred and forty-six years — we are striving for a new constitutional deal which will help put the several sections on equal footing and prevent the exploitation of one by the other. We are in the front ranks of those who insist that the United States is less a nation than an empire made up of a congeries of regions marked off by geographic, climatic, and racial characteristics. It has been suggested that New England would form a distinct region, the Middle states another, the Middle West another, the Rocky Mountain and Pacific states another, perhaps, and the South another. Of course the region to which a state wished to affiliate would be determined by a plebiscite. W. Y. Elliott of Harvard suggests that the regional governments be granted the present powers of the states, and that the states themselves be deprived of anything save administrative functions. He further suggests that one set of courts should serve both as federal and state courts, thus eliminating the maze of courts by which justice is delayed and defeated and encouragement thereby given to lynch law.

Mr. Elliott suggests that in the new setup the federal government retain its present powers much more clearly defined. He further urges that all concurrent powers be eliminated. As far as I know, Mr. Elliott is not an Agrarian; but his plan is essentially what the Agrarians have urged constantly, except in the matter of division of power between federal and regional governments. His plan seems very reasonable and conservative. Something like it will have to be adopted if the United States is to endure. The Agrarians, I believe, advocate that, in the redivision of powers in a new constitutional convention, the regional governments should have much more autonomy than the states have ever had. The federal government should have supreme control over war and peace, the army and navy, interregional or even interstate commerce, banking, currency, and foreign affairs. On the other hand, the sections should have equal representation in the federal legislative body and in the election of the President and in the cabinet. The legislative body should be composed of a senate only and should be elected by the regional congresses. Finally, the regions should have control of the tariff: that is, the several regions should have an equal share in making the tariff, which would be in the form of a treaty or agreement between all the sections, somewhat in the fashion of the late Austro-Hungarian tariff treaties. In case one region, say the South, failed to agree to the tariff treaty, then the South should be exempted from the operation of the law until an agreement could be reached. Such an arrangement does not mean that there would be interregional tariffs; it does mean that, if the South should have a lower tariff than the other regions, goods imported through the South from abroad would have to pay an extra duty on entering the other regions operating under the treaty. There would be some smuggling across the Potomac and Ohio, but not any more than through Mexico and Canada.

The Supreme Court, like the proposed Senate, should have equal representation from all the sections, regardless of political parties, and the members of the Supreme Court should not be the creatures of the Senate or the President, but, like the Senate, should be appointed by the regional governors subject to the ratification of the regional legislature, which also should be only a senate. The courts — that is, courts of appeal and circuit courts — should be constituted regionally, but should be considered both federal and regional, sitting one time as federal and one time as regional.

In our Agrarian program, it seems necessary to grant more local autonomy not only because of differences of economic interest, but because of differences of social and racial interests as well. Under such a government, the Civil War would not have been possible, nor would Reconstruction and the ensuing difficulties and hatreds have arisen. And what is more to the point at the present time, communist interference in the Southern courts, and even conservative interference from other sections, would hardly take place. In other words, the Agrarians — who come nearer representing the opinion of Southern people than do newspapers largely subsidized by Northern-owned power companies and Wall-Street-owned banks, or the Southern liberals fawning for the favor of these corporations or of other powerful Northern groups — believe that under regional government each section will find it less difficult to attend to its own social and economic problems, and thereby will be encouraged to restore the old friendships which were crippled or destroyed under our present system.

Let me sum up. The five pillars on which it would appear that an agrarian society must rest are: (1) The restoration of the people to the land and the land to the people by the government purchasing lands held by loan companies, insurance companies, banks, absentee landlords, and planters whose estates are hopelessly incumbered with debt, and granting to the landless tenants, who are sufficiently able and responsible to own and conserve the land, a homestead of eighty acres with sufficient stock to cultivate the farm, and cash enough to feed and clothe the family one year. (2) The preservation and restoration of the soil by the use of fines and escheat, and by making land practically inalienable and non-mortgageable — that is by restoring a modified feudal tenure where the state had a paramount interest in the land and could exact certain services and duties from those who possessed the land. (3) The establishment of a balanced agriculture where subsistence crops are the first consideration and the money crops are of secondary importance. (4) The establishment of just political economy, where agriculture is placed upon an equal basis with industry, finance, and commerce. (5) The creation of regional governments possessed of more autonomy than the states, which will sustain the political economy fitted for each region, and which will prevent much sectional friction and sectional exploitation.

Once this foundation is securely built, the agrarian society will grow upon it spontaneously and with no further state intervention beyond that to which an agricultural population is accustomed. The old communities, the old churches, the old songs would arise from their moribund slumbers. Art, music, and literature could emerge into the sunlight from the dark cramped holes where industrial insecurity and industrial insensitiveness have often driven them. There would be a sound basis for statesmanship to take the place of demagoguery and corrupt politics. Leisure, good manners, and the good way of life might again become ours.

— From the *American Review*, March, 1935. Reprinted by permission.

HAPPY FARMERS

By John Crowe Ransom

THE TRUTH is sometimes brutal; and probably no statement about the American farmer's condition has yet had so much of this quality as that made by Mr. Louis M. Hacker in *The Farmer Is Doomed*, a John Day Pamphlet.

So sweeping is the argument, even after it allows for mitigations under Mr. Roosevelt's farm program, that the piece must be regarded as one of the bitterer jeremiads of our economic despair; unless it is regarded as a masterpiece of irony, hoping after all to provoke opposition and amelioration for a set of affairs painted in horrid colors. But on the basis of the internal or literary evidence I do not think the latter construction likely. Mr. Hacker sees the American farmer as fallen into the very state in which his course has always destined that he should rest at last: " a peasant bound to the soil because he can go nowhere else "; barely possessed of his chattels, not at all of his land; without hope of ever obtaining fair prices for products, or the old values for his land; underprivileged forever. The author does not sentimentalize over him; the author's feelings it is difficult to assess; he is not a farmer.

The Tennessee Agrarians by a less formal train of argument came to a similar conclusion and anticipated Mr. Hacker by several years. But with a remarkable difference. They did not hold and do not hold that the American farmer is doomed, but that the American commercial farmer is doomed. It is possible that Mr. Hacker would not care to distinguish between a commercial farmer and any other farmer, but the Agrarians do, and it is this if anything which gives meaning to their agitation. Throughout Mr. Hacker's article appears the refrain, " American commercial agriculture is doomed." If in his title he drops the qualifying adjective, it must be pointed out that the thesis carried in the title is not the thesis carried in the text.

American commercial agriculture is doomed because its great day is past beyond recall. It served its function once for all, though it did not understand the function it was serving, and reveled in the rôle without much apprehension of inevitable disaster. That is Mr. Hacker's reading of history.

Farming had a special importance in the American economic system so long as we were a debtor nation: the farm exports, and almost nothing else, were paying the interest, paying the debt. As the tide of our agriculture moved always westward into virgin fields, it could manage more and more of foreign debt. And why should we incur a foreign debt? Capital was wanted to finance our tender industries; agriculture was serving industry. It took railroads, banks, mines, machinery, management, to raise the infant; it was the farmers who found the money.

Industry must have looked kindly on agriculture in that period, fancying that healthy exportable surplus. But industry was scarcely in the game for the ultimate benefit of agriculture. Our Civil War seemed to be fought on a certain issue, but perhaps what it settled chiefly was quite another issue, and probably a war was required to settle that issue: between farmers who wanted free trade in which to sell and buy, and industrialists who wanted them to sell, for the time being, but were already beginning to use protective tariffs for the industries emerging from embryo, and forcing the farmers to buy in an artificially high market with the proceeds of their free exports. It is useless to tickle the glands of indignation at this distance. The Civil War was won, and then the industrialists put through the last item of their program. They developed American industries completely. Assisted by the innocent farmers at the critical stages, and presented by a kind Providence with the windfall of a European war that invited the exportation both of farmstuffs and of industrial products on an incredible scale, they have finally seen our national credit position reversed, and America no longer a debtor nation but the largest creditor nation. They have successfully invaded the foreign markets with their own wares, but against accumulating difficulties. They see their fellow countrymen, the farmers, still prepared — more than ever prepared — to produce for those markets, but mourning for a trade which today is nearly lost.

It is lost for several reasons. There are other young debtor countries now with exportable farm surpluses, farms not eaten up by debts and taxes, farmers therefore able to undersell our farmers. Continental Europe, and even Britain a little way behind, our old customers, have decided to restrict the importation of farm goods and to profit their own farmers. And there is another reason much more fundamental: such is now our own industrial sufficiency, symbolized by prohibitive tariffs, that Europe has little or nothing that we will allow to enter this country, and could not pay for American farmstuffs on a big scale even if she wanted to do it.

The farmers were not crucified on a cross of gold, then, exactly, as it seemed to William Jennings Bryan and other agriculturists, as it seems to many farmers today. (If gold were the cross, tampering with gold and raising the domestic price level would be taking the victims down; but an inflation would not help the farmers more than other debtors; it would not affect the *comparative* level of farm prices.) Their cross, according to Mr. Hacker's plausible thesis, was the foreign trade. They built up a scale of production far beyond domestic needs, and their present pains are somewhat proportionate to the collapse of the foreign markets.

Nearly anything may happen eventually in the economic world, which has a high rate of contingency and is apt to make fools of its prophets. But certainly there is no visible prospect of recovering the foreign markets for American farmers. Mr. Hacker makes out the case as even worse than that. The industrialists now want cheap foodstuffs here at home, in order to be able to pay low wages and undersell their foreign competitors, and therefore intend the free importation of foods from the new agricultural countries. That would be depriving the American farmer of his domestic market as well as foreign. But to attempt legislation in this direction would require gall, and be difficult for our handsome industrialists. It is politically next to impossible, even in industrial America, which grew up by forcing its agriculture and then leaving this vast business stranded, that a Congress should come to power soon with the hardihood to deny to the farmer the equal benefits of our famous protection. He need scarcely fear that last ignominy; he may have his home market.

If the foreign market is closed or closing to our wheat, meat products, fruits, and canned foods, it is still open to cotton and tobacco, large items on the export list. Both crops have to reach the market over a certain amount of recent competition, and are too large in the first place, owing to overproduction here at home. But they will continue to be sold abroad, provided their producers do not demand so high a price that foreign buyers will make arrangements for them elsewhere, and subject to the reservation that they cannot be offered in excessive volume and sold at satisfactory prices at the same time.

Even here there is an obstacle, as stubborn as it is subtle. Farmers, like any other exporters, are subject to a principle coming more and more to light in the present practice of foreign trade. The United States in proportion to the volume of its commerce is less than other countries in a position to claim a large export trade: it wants and will accept very few imports. In the half-dozen great years that culminated in 1929 we used to have a favorable trade balance reaching annually towards a billion dollars. During the World War it had been several billions annually. The sales were properly made, but the collections have not been made and for the most part cannot be made. What is the use of sending goods abroad to this fate? International trade in the future is likely to occur only among nations whose exports and imports are balanced; that is, nations able to pay each other; default will be the natural recourse of nations whose temporary excess of imports over exports cannot be made up with reasonable ease by a subsequent excess of exports. That is the lesson of the cycle of international trade which began in 1914 and is just now completing itself. If the United States continues to try, and try successfully, for the favorable trade balance, placing its farmstuffs and other goods on the foreign market regardless, it will be from lack of intelligence, or else because we want to demonstrate to a weary world that there is a Santa Claus.

Economists ought to warn us steadily, farmers and all, about the perils of an ambitious export trade. It is dangerous to develop the exportable surplus which cannot continue to be exported; our agricultural exports of last century are one example; our exports of all sorts since 1914 are another. The first of these efforts came to a stop when we ceased, as it might be said that we intended all the time to cease, to be a debtor nation; the second comes to a stop because it has evidently served only to make us a creditor nation with uncollectible credits. But stops of exports are stops of production, and they are too painful; disastrous when a great productive establishment is involved.

Our exports are consistently too large, since they are larger than our imports, and they will be reduced. What sort of exports shall have the right of way? Equity suggests that farmstuffs should have it, even if it were necessary to levy export tariffs upon the industrial products which crowd them for place; farmstuffs were here first. But it would be difficult to resort to legislation, and it is probably unnecessary, since the grind of economic forces will accomplish the same result. The foreigners will buy less of us, and what they buy will be what they most urgently require of us. That means, among a few other things, cotton and tobacco.

The South, then, where these staples are grown, is likely to remain in the export business. But it cannot be said with extreme emphasis that the South is therefore luckier than the West, whose foodstuffs will miss the foreign market. The combination of an export trade with a protective tariff is bad business for the exporter. The South, so far as her interests are defined by cotton and tobacco, is in an underprivileged position within the Union; and as long as the South remains within the Union, and the protective tariff is a fixity in American policy, as it must be henceforth, there is nothing to be done about it.

II

Generally speaking, the American farmer, if he continues to produce, or lies in wait to produce, for a foreign trade that has evaporated or is unprofitable, is doomed.

But perhaps the American commercial farmer has a sufficient market at home to take all his produce. Is there some nationalist program, independent of the foreign trade, which can give him occupation and prosperity? It is a rhetorical question, to which everybody knows the answer.

Two of the present ills of farming, and sore ones, we may dismiss for the sake of argument as being not quite essential to the business, and possibly momentary. Not long ago the land received an exorbitant valuation, first from the bankers who lent money on it, and second from the public assessors who levied taxes. The mortgages and taxes are too high; the overhead from these items comes to nearly twenty per cent of gross farm income. As for the mortgages: many farmers will find it impossible in this life to pay out. Even if there is to be a general price inflation which will improve the dollar value of the crops, it will not improve their exchange value against other commodities. The two billion dollars thrown out for the purpose of refinancing will be lent, not given; the bulk of the farm paper, aggregating around ten billions, will not be touched, and in no cases will its face values be reduced. The farmers made a bad gamble when they borrowed so heavily in an unprofitable business, and they lost, and many of them are marked for economic extinction. But they will be replaced, and agriculture will continue. Eventually the debt burden on the land may disappear. As for the tax burden, that may be lifted much more quickly, through political action. The local governments will probably take the necessary steps to relieve the farmer of his excessive taxes.

But even if all the commercial farmers owned their land unincumbered, and were taxed like other people somewhere in accordance with their earnings, they could not expect to make money within the limits of a domestic market, and they would be doomed. The reason is simple. The land we have is greatly in excess of what we require for our needs in this country. A glance at the maps will show the enormous disproportion between our holding of land and that of other great nations. The advocates of commercial farming do not dare to draw the implication of this comparison boldly. The single state of Texas is much bigger than Germany, which manages if necessary to sustain upon its land a population half as great as that of the United States. We have never worked our land on the intensive European plan, nor have we worked it with anything like a uniform effectiveness, and still it is superabundant, as if it contained so much waste land. And the farmers on it are too numerous. In economic language, commercial farming is a business with too much fixed capital and too large an apportionment of labor; overcapitalized and overproductive. It is true that the fixed capital is only the land, which is the gift of nature; yet it is owned, and it yearns to produce, precisely like the capital fixed in railroad and factory properties.

There is some analogy between the railroads and the farms. Suppose the railroads have twice the fixed capital they need, in tracks, rolling stock, stations. They would become a standard paying proposition only if half the fixed capital were abandoned; which in the course of economic events might well eventually happen. The owners of the bonds and the employees would have to pocket the loss, but the world would go on. The rights-of-way would be sold if possible, the excess of rolling stock and rails would bring something as scrap, and the stations could at least be disposed of to the wrecking companies. The excess of capital would then have disappeared, the extra employees would be somewhere else, and there would no longer be a railroad problem.

But the farm business has its points of difference. Its excess of fixed capital cannot be destroyed. Its colony of workers cannot be evicted. (There is a way to remain on the land after it has ceased to bring in a money income; not known to the " labor " of industry, which must shift with the source of its wage.) The first show of returning prosperity in the business would bring back these marginal farms and these marginal farmers, and farm prices would quickly drop again below the profit level. As long as the farms are all there and the farmers are all there, agriculture as a business is doomed. A government which undertook to rent the whole excess of land, and to pay the farmers to do no work upon it, would be inviting an indefinite number of millions of men to accept a dole in lieu of an earned income. I do not of course mean to say that farm prices may not be raised by a reduction of acreage secured in this way, and something resembling a former prosperity recovered to the producers of a given season. But the effort can hardly be sustained. When it is established that a certain crop commands a good price this year, the marginal farmers decide to grow that crop next year and participate in the scheme, while the farmers already in the scheme decide to farm their permitted acres more intensively and raise more of that crop. High prices, artificial or otherwise, do not discourage but stimulate production. The saving feature of the present price-raising program is that it is regarded as temporary.

The only permanent rescue for commercial agriculture in this country would be by a desperate measure, the act of a Soviet or other tyranny: to create a public domain out of all the marginal land, evacuate all the marginal owners, and hold it rigorously out of production or the threat of production. How much land would that be? If the government applied to its determination the usual standards of maximum productivity through applied science, there is no doubt that much the greater part of the arable land would have to go out of use, though the whole American population would not cease to be lavishly furnished. The latest calculation upon this point that I have seen runs something like this: Let the present supernumerary farms be disregarded (though they comprise the fraction I have referred to above); then divide the area which is left by 7; this is the American farm area of the future, when all the farmers have become masters of the new science of cultivation called "agrobiology"; it may come to five or ten per cent of the present farm land.

It has been supposed that the reduction of the farm area and population will occur naturally, without official compulsion; that with the increasing prosperity of industry the land will surrender its miserable inhabitants and diminish its production until it is producing in just the right amount, and rewarding its owners and workers according to the regular American standard. In the boom twenties of blessed memory, when industry prospered if agriculture did not, the farm population actually, and for the first time in our history, decreased a little, and some abandoned farms were to be seen. The exhibit was not conclusive. With the industrial collapse the movement stopped suddenly, but it might have dwindled out anyway. It may, very possibly, never resume. Even where the farms were abandoned the titles were not thrown away, and it was always predictable that a recovery in farm prices, even before it reached the point of yielding a "fair" return, would call the absent owners back into production and, incidentally, wreck the recovery. Some sort of bias which is not at all a piece of strict business principle seems to move Americans to cling to the land. The farm population since 1910, when it might be said to have spread at last pretty well over the whole surface of the United States, up to a comfortable American degree of density, has been very nearly a constant. It is impossible to believe, when we observe the American habit of mind, that the farm population, abused as it thinks it is, is now going to recede to some figure that abstract economists may prescribe. It is altogether likely, on the contrary, that there will always be so many marginal farmers dribbling their unwanted quotas into the general glut, or hiding in the bushes and threatening to do it, that commercial agriculture will be exceptional, unprofitable, and messy among the income-producing businesses that make up our total economy.

In Europe it is quite different. A European country has an underproduction of farmstuffs to attend to, and gives a bounty to its wheat growers, for instance, to encourage production. We, with our overproduction, give a bounty too, but for the purpose of buying off and stopping production; naturally we do it only once in a while, and suddenly, and for a short time only, before the terrific potentialities of the marginal land can be brought into play. The European nations can hardly support their populations on their land, while we cannot support our land with our population. We are indeed an unbalanced economy: our agriculture is permanently capitalized beyond its proportion and our largest business is doomed. We are pioneering with a new economic problem when we attempt to help the farmers, and the example of Europe cannot be of much instruction to us. But it will be an old problem by the time the big young countries like Argentina and Canada grow up; they will be able to learn from our example what to do with it; or, perhaps, what not to do.

A Soviet tyranny in this country would not have allowed agriculture to run the course it has. Imagine one possessed of invincible authority and perfect foresight, committed to the modern economy of specialized income-producing functions. It would have been slow to cede to private owners the land of its successive acquisitions. Intending doubtless an industrial development and needing capital, it would have got it in the easiest way, by developing an exportable farm surplus; but it would have understood that this must eventually disappear, that then its producers must be assigned elsewhere, and that the land it came out of must revert to the public domain. In 1933 it would be tolerating neither a farm acreage nor a farm population in excess of economic need. But the country it ruled would be a strange one: populous, yet comparatively unpeopled, with three fourths of the people living in cities, and vast uninhabited tracts outlying. Its chief administrative care would be to keep down the natural desire of its citizens to go and occupy the vacant land, though it might give them instead incomparable facilities for picnics, hunts, and Boy Scout camps.

That is not our way of managing the land. Like other capital it is at the disposal of its private owners, but it is unlike other capital in being excessive in the nature of the case; and the owners are unlike other owners in being too numerous for their own business good and yet determined not to part with their property.

And now appears a great anomaly. One part of the doctrine which has made its way from Washington recently is that there is too much farming done in this country. Mr. Roosevelt discovers an "imbalance" of population as other economists do; but it is just the reverse of theirs, the excess being in the cities and deficiency being on the farms. He applauds the present movement from city to country, and will not see in it only one of those temporary distress migrations that occur in depressions when wretched laborers go anywhere to find work, but a movement that is good in itself and must not be reversed when prosperity returns to the city. With one hand he measures acreage to be ordered out of production, and with the other hand waves city men to the farm. How is it possible for Mr. Roosevelt to increase the occupation of the land without damning commercial agriculture to a yet lower hell? So far as I am aware, he has not yet explained himself.

III

Nevertheless, to some subtle organ of judgment in us, the President of the United States seems right in wanting to see more of the citizens upon the land. He proceeds, I shall suppose, from an intuition which is political and profoundly American. He knows that it is according to the national temperament, with which he is made acquainted by his own hearty habit of mind, that so many of us propose to own land and work it. He also probably reflects, I imagine, with other political philosophers, that a superior kind of citizen may be raised on the farm.

Farmers do not operate the farms of America merely to carry on a commercial agriculture; it pains me that I have had to assume up to this point that they do. (Of course they may, but only if they are content to be a doomed economic remnant.) New farmers cannot intelligently go to the land for that purpose, nor old farmers stay there. For the purpose of fitting into our money-making economy, the abundance of our land is a national liability, and those who make a business of it are only infatuated. But for the purpose of homemaking, for the breeding of citizens, for the attainment of personal happiness, it is the finest physical asset that we have, and enough to make us blessed among the nations.

What sort of economy is it that will support happiness on the farm? The proper economy for the American farmer is the one called, for the lack of a better title, the agrarian economy. (It was so called in *I'll Take My Stand*, which came out of the Tennessee group in 1930.) Agrarianism means old-fashioned farming; or the combination of a subsistence farming of the first place with a money farming of the second place. The farmer is lucky in that it is in his power easily to withdraw very largely from his dependence on money income, which is never forthcoming on a sufficient scale; and in going to this extent " out of production " he has a quite definite program to which he may devote the land and labor thus released. Agrarianism is a kind of amphibianism: the farmer, wonderful creature, is capable of sustaining his life in either or both of two different economic elements. It should be both, but in a certain order; his private or subsistence economy first, and his social or money economy second.

It is the word *agrarian*, or its equivalent, which we have been waiting to hear pronounced by this Democratic and pro-farmer administration. Our society apparently has lost sight of the simple concept it denotes, by reason of its rather hurried and nearly unanimous adoption of the pure money economy; and before this present economy the concept never had a name, nor needed one. All farmers till recently were agrarians. That is, they practiced self-maintenance before they made money by providing maintenance for others. The farmer who did otherwise did not rate as a good farmer. The farmer's economic dualism was a commonplace, though little was thought or said about it. But modern society has called upon its members to become always more professional, more abstract, in their functions; and they have persuaded the farmers too. There is probably nothing inherently destructive in a thorough money economy; that is, at least, if all the capital and the labor are properly assigned. The chief trouble with ours is that this condition cannot obtain. If we take as a fixture the present farm land and the present farm population, they are so out of proportion that the whole nation is sick, and agriculture on a business basis is impossible. What then have the farmers to lose in going agrarian? The pure professional or income-earning status to which they have been aspiring in recent years is not really open to them.

The technique of subsistence on good land, with inexpensive tools, is an ancient one, much older than our present absolute money economy, and productive of a high standard of living (provided we do not have to measure it in money) on millions of American farms two or three generations ago. The tradition has fallen into disuse now, but has not been so long out of mind that it cannot be recovered; if it has, it can be built up from the ground again. In order to be specific, I shall merely mention some of its constituent canons: to raise the great bulk of the foods for the family, including vegetables, fruits, poultry, dairy products, meats; to can, preserve, and cure for the winter (this involves the smoke-house); to do plain carpentering to the extent at least of repairs, to paint and whitewash, to do amateur landscape gardening, in order that the home may be pleasant and decent; to work mainly with literal horse power, mule power, man power; to feed all the animals, as well as the persons, from the land; to fertilize the land by the periodic use of grass crops. All these measures tend to cancel out heavily the farmer's need of money. They round into a single economy, in which one thing involves another, and this economy is complex, not simple on the order of ordinary money farming. But that is to its credit rather than otherwise, and it is practicable enough.

The apostasy of American farmers from primary subsistence farming is the greatest disaster our country has yet suffered; it is fortunate that it can still be undone. In the latter half of the nineteenth century it looked as if our country existed in order to feed Europe. It could easily do so; it was doing so. We were mostly farmers, and with fertile land we were producing heavily. But in that period our farmers were still spending of their strength on their own subsistence, and therefore not realizing their maximum productivity as we can now understand it; nor had the modern application of power machinery, and the modern art of soil-doctoring, had a real arrival; we were capable of bigger and better crops than those. In exchange we took finished goods from Europe and, increasingly, from our own industries. Aside from the steady rise of the latter, the exchange suited Europe very well, and Europe almost ceased to farm. But the situation could not last. Several things happened all at about the same time. While we were becoming industrially sufficient for ourselves, and other big countries were entering into agriculture, and for both reasons the European market was being taken away from our farmers; and while they were rapidly learning new tricks that increased production — in that very period these same farmers as a class went over to the pure money economy and began to produce exclusively for sale.

The consequence, to an *ex post facto* judgment, is as clear as it is frightful. The farmers are economically ruined and spiritually desperate; and a great stabilizing and sanifying influence has gone out of American political life.

It is reversible. The destiny of our broad acres is not to be the simple feed-bowl of the western world, filled and steaming; nor even the simple feed-bowl of the United States, absurdly big for the job, and half-filled. It is to be hoped that its destiny is to support an excellent order of citizens, who will be economic dualists, men of unusual integrity and freedom even while they perform a professional function; farmers with more room and more heart than most of the farmers of the world; happy farmers.

I do not use the penultimate word above without deliberation. Proper farming promotes happiness if occupation has anything to do with happiness. Even commercial farming is one of the better occupations — or would be if the farmer had security and could pursue it without being brought to despair by debts and imminent ruin. But agrarian farming possesses much more fully the peculiar occupational benefits. They seem to be fundamentally two.

The first quality of a good occupation is that its labor is capable of being enjoyed. But enjoyment is mainly the consequence of the satisfaction of the senses; or of the expression of that general and diffuse interest which thoughtful moderns have at last learned to value (now that it is nearly lost) and which they call sensibility. The labor of bookkeeping, of banking, of shop-clerking, of tending monotonous machinery, of "screwing on bolt No. 47," is too abstract and specialized to be enjoyed. The characteristic labors of an industrial society are mean. Farming is by comparison a free labor and not a routine; such is the variety of even its simpler operations. Its background is the infinitude of an open landscape, where the distraction of the senses never ceases. Its tempo is not fierce, but almost of necessity leisurely. I am acquainted with some white farmers, too well instructed in the duty of maximum production and its supposed regards, who wear themselves out by laboring in the blind insensitive manner of the sweatshop; but no good white farmers; and no black farmers at all.

The second quality of the good occupation is that it is responsible. The laborer should control the whole job; it is even better if he is the independent owner and therefore can devote his whole intelligence to it. Some recent publicists have mourned the decline of the individual in our business life. Big business has disposed of little business, and the hirelings have replaced the masters. The English Distributists, in particular, have called for the general restoration of ownership as necessary to the happiness of our society in these bad days. In America that suggests the thought that the farmers comprise the biggest of our economic groups, and the only group which still has any considerable measure of ownership. But if they practice pure money farming their ownership becomes mostly nominal, and their freedom of operation disappears under their pressing obligations. The agrarian farmer, if he is an owner, is free beyond most men to design and to execute, being perhaps in that respect exceeded by the creative artist alone. If he is a tenant, he is permitted to express his own character better than any hired man left in our society.

IV

The farmer will have to work out his salvation mainly for himself. But while he makes his own living in the first place, he must make some money in the second place; and in this latter capacity he will be exposed to the competition of those farmers who will want to make money in the first place, and nothing in the second place. He may need some official protection. Furthermore, the farmer has sinned, and he will be tempted to sin again. Therefore he may need some official encouragement.

I conclude by specifying a few of the possible forms of legislation that may need to be enacted for his benefit.

(1) We are familiar with the sort of taxation meant to affect the natural economic system according to some bias of political or social faith, and not merely to raise revenue. Such taxation might be employed to encourage the agrarian farmer and to penalize the pure money farmer. Taxes might be levied, after a few further years of grace, upon all fresh farm loans, provided they do not figure as payment on the purchase of land or in retirement of existing loans. The American farmer has formed the habit of borrowing, and it is against his own interests and the public welfare; he ought to pay for future indulgence by meeting a tax; and without borrowed money, if he does not want to pay the tax, he will probably be obliged to be an agrarian farmer.

Taxes, high but not quite prohibitive, might be levied against the sale of farm tractors and other specified heavy farm machinery. Economists may object in the name of maximum productivity. But I assume that agriculture is not normal among American businesses, but special, and that maximum productivity is anything but its proper objective. I assume also that there is no relation between a farmer's employment of machinery and his happiness; unless perhaps there is a relation of discordance.

The same reasoning suggests that the sale of commercial fertilizers also should be hit by taxation.

(2) Taxation for revenue touches the farmer heavily in the shape of the local land taxes. These should be reduced or, preferably, be replaced by straight income taxes or taxes on land as the land might be appraised according to its production of income. So far as state constitutions permitted, the farmers' income tax might be graduated, at the expense of the larger money farmers, who will probably be the purer money farmers.

(3) We are now engaged in raising the prices of farm produce through a bounty which is levied on the processors and ultimately on the public. But the benefit applies evenly, not on a graduated scale. If it were graduated, with a maximum going to the small producer and an inconsiderable minimum or nothing going to the large producer, it would not relieve the pure money farmers as it now does and it would relieve the agrarian farmers more; it would cost us much less, and it could be maintained for some time before the money farmers retired from the field and the business of supplying the market fell more largely into the hands of a multitude of agrarian farmers; but its purpose would have been to that extent achieved.

(4) The program of our agricultural schools and experiment stations, both federal and local, which offer instruction at the public expense, should be reformed. At present they teach the farmer almost exclusively the separate money-making units of agriculture. They should teach him a proper farm *economy* — that is, a whole of many parts and functions, which would consist in the management of a farm chiefly from the standpoint of a secure and comfortable subsistence. They should teach him the art of making a family decently and pleasantly at home on the farm; and the way a country community may organize its many common interests. The beginning of this revolution might be made by the schools which the Tennessee Valley Authority is going to operate.

(5) Probably the best unemployment relief that has come to

light yet, or at least what would be the best if it were administered just a little more handsomely, is that which puts the destitute citizen back on the land to make his own living and stay off the public charity. Such relief has been given by local governments and private philanthropies; it might well be considered by federal government, which has had an ample experience with homesteading, and now for some time will have ample opportunities to acquire land. But there should never again be a free distribution of land to private owners without one radical provision in the conditions of gift: that the homesteader shall be subject to instruction in agrarian farming, and subject to a long period of inspection which will determine whether he is making a direct living or only making an income, and therefore whether he is on the way to clear his title or to be evicted.

— From the *American Review*, October, 1933. Reprinted by permission.

LOOKING DOWN THE COTTON ROW

By George Marion O'Donnell

NOT LONG AGO cotton-growing in the South was a Big Business venture that paid well, because cotton was a good export product, demanded on the markets of the world, and the South was the part of the world best suited to cotton production. Banks and holding companies found it worth their while to capitalize the production of cotton; and resident Southern landowners took to planting more and more of their land in cotton. It was an era of mass production.

These Big Business planters found land cheap and labor plentiful. And they found, all ready for their purpose, the system of farm tenancy which grew up after the Civil War as a substitute for slavery. The system works about like this:

The planter contracts with tenants to work on his land, providing each of them with a house. And through the production months he "furnishes" the tenants: he allows them a certain amount of money each month, he allots them groceries and clothes from his own commissary, or he gives them orders for supplies to be charged against the plantation account at a store in the nearest town. These payments, with interest, he charges against the tenants on the plantation books.

If the tenant is a sharecropper, or "half-hand," he supplies only labor; at the end of the year, tenant and planter each receive half of the crops. If he is a "third-and-fourth hand," the tenant furnishes everything necessary to the making of a crop except land; at the end of the year the landowner is entitled to one fourth of the cotton as rent. There is a third type of tenant-planter contract, in which the tenant pays a fixed sum of money per acre as rent and usually supervises his own farming operations.

Opportunities for abuses under this system should be apparent at once: the planter keeps the books; the planter alone knows the true prices of supplies; the planter is his own boss in fixing interest rates on plantation accounts — rates which sometimes run as high as forty per cent.

Of course any Southern cotton planter is himself victimized by a financial system practically forced upon the South after the Civil War. And it is often this system, exploiting the planter, which forces him to take to exploitation; thus the system is the real villain. Yet there are planters who have willfully connived with the system, deserting the agrarian economy deliberately in order to share in the great profits of a money economy dominated by finance capitalism. It is these planters whom we label Big Business planters.

More important than financial abuses, perhaps, are the unfortunate living conditions among tenants on great Southern cotton plantations. Let us look at a large establishment — say in the Mississippi Delta, which shares with Texas the questionable distinction of having more large plantations than any other section of the South.

At the heart of the place stands a group of buildings, connected with the highway by a gravel road. There is a manager's house (for this place is owned by an absentee landlord) with hardwood floors and steam heat; a plantation store, neatly painted and filled with canned goods; an electric gin with a private siding for freight cars; a large modern barn for the mules (or a garage for the tractors). Around this group of buildings, which constitutes the main office of the establishment, lie the fields, neatly divided by well-kept roads. Tenant houses dot the fields, perhaps trim and efficient-looking, but more often rundown, unpainted, lacking shingles, with chimneys leaning at an angle to the house wall. Almost invariably they are without adequate yards or shade trees or outhouses. A garden — so wisdom runs here — would remove from use land that might be planted in cotton. Trees, if allowed at tenant houses, will occasionally shade the ends of cotton rows nearby, stunting the growth of as many as two dozen plants! Barns are not needed, for the landlord owns all the mules — if he is still old-fashioned enough to use them instead of tractors; and he keeps them all at the big modern barn near the manager's house. Front yards are generally small and unfenced: small because the landlord does not want to sacrifice any of his land, unfenced because there are no woodlands on the place from which to get fence palings. Here is the tenant farmer's house; to call it a home would be impious.

In such conditions many of the Southern tenant farmers live on the great plantations. These people are on the soil, to be sure, but they are essentially industrial workers — and badly treated industrial workers at that. The instruments of production are all controlled by the capitalists (the landlord), the labor is hard and regular, though not so unvarying as the work in a factory; farmers are not attached to the soil by emotional ties; the whole system is " efficient " and impersonal.

Improperly fed and clothed, living in a house improperly heated in winter and open to the terrible Southern heat in summer, cheated by landlords, uneducated, perhaps diseased, the tenant continues to work in the hope that the next year he may get out of debt, the next year the price of cotton may rise, some day he may own a home.

Moreover, in recent years the troubles of the tenants have been aggravated. Tractors are replacing man-and-mule power in Big Business cotton farming; and the planters need fewer tenants. In Mississippi, on one plantation owned by absentee landlords, twenty families were evicted: their services were no longer needed, since the work of cultivation could be done by two or three men with tractors, and day labor could be hired for the chopping and picking seasons.

The evicted tenants asked for permission to stay on in the plantation houses, which would be unoccupied. But no, the company didn't want them on the place; they would have to look for homes elsewhere. Still more evictions have resulted from the complete shutting down of plantations for one or two years under depression conditions.

Yet it is unwise to assume that tenant farming is invariably vicious, or that tenants always live in unbearable conditions. On other plantations, operating alongside of the plantations devoted to mass production of cotton, and in enforced competition with them, tenant and planter share together in an agrarian economy, the economy of men who love the land and who derive their whole sustenance from it. Here labor is varied, crops are diversified, and the aim of the work is not to make enormous profits but to induce the land to give up its riches that men may live and be happy.

On these places there is a larger percentage of renting tenants than elsewhere. Big Business planters prefer sharecroppers to " third-and-fourth hands " or money renters, sometimes refusing even to enter into a renting contract; but the agrarian planter is glad to see his tenants provide their own mules, their own implements, their own seed. That the renting tenant enjoys a status higher than that of the sharecropper is clear; the renter needs nothing but land to enable him to leave the tenant class entirely.

But agrarian planters still have to depend upon cotton for tax money and for cash to purchase supplies which may not be produced conveniently at home. And, selling cotton on a market glutted because of the overproduction of Big Business growers, they find it difficult to retain their own way of farming — there is upon them a constant pressure to desert agrarianism for specialized cotton production.

II

One does not need to be a prophet to see that the whole system of mass production in cotton may eventually disappear. The system depended upon Southern domination of the world cotton supply, and that domination is a thing of the past. Annually, the world supply of cotton fiber becomes more broadly distributed. In 1929, the world consumption of Indian cotton was ten million bales, and in this year the world used only fourteen million bales of Southern cotton. The Egyptian Sudan, Uganda, Asiatic Turkey, Asiatic Russia, and lately Brazil are other competitors with the Southern crop on the world market. Labor in all of these places is cheaper than labor in the South. Foreign planters can afford to accept on the world market a lower price for cotton than the Southerner (buying on a protected domestic market) can take profitably. This morning the average Liverpool price for cotton is about six pence per pound; at the most conservative estimate, this cotton would cost twelve cents per pound to produce in the Southern cotton area!

Now a great many Southerners (for whom Mr. Peter Molyneaux, of the *Texas Weekly*, is a vigorous spokesman) believe that if only the tariff were reduced, the problem of the export market would be solved. They reason like this, I suppose: Lower the tariff, giving Europe a favorable balance of trade; then Europe can buy more American raw materials, including cotton; moreover, cotton producers can import goods at world market prices.

There are difficulties with this reasoning. First, the scheme would work havoc with the standard of living in our industrial centers. Second, much of the European profit would not be invested in American raw materials, but in American stocks — witness the manner in which Europe recently disposed of the American dollars it received when the United States purchased foreign gold. And third, even granting that the lowering or the abolition of the tariff would operate to aid Southern cotton planters, one must recognize that this tariff revision cannot be accomplished without a political change of such magnitude as to appear Utopian.

But the government farm program! Well, the national government is hardly concerned with the restoration of a market for unlimited production of cotton fiber; it is hardly concerned with propping up the Big Business plantation. (Consider the widespread disapproval of government farm plans among great landowners who howl for "liberty" — to work toward their own doom!) On the contrary, the whole direction of the administration farm program has been toward the removal of more and more land from cotton production, the use of this land in the growth of food crops for home consumption.

However, not even a project along the lines of the defunct AAA can solve the problem of the oversupply of cotton on the American market. The world carry-over of American cotton last August 1st was around nine million bales — still three million bales larger than the average annual carry-over in the period 1922–1932 in spite of the acreage reduction effected by the government farm program. And it seems safe to predict that the government cannot permanently subsidize any crops by guaranteeing a certain price.

Under the conditions imposed by Big Business planters in financial straits, particularly under the constant threat of eviction, the tenant farmers of the South are growing restless, manifesting their discontent in the organization of tenant farmers' unions and in open revolt against the landlords. Whether or not this attempt at unionization is wise, it is clearly an important sign of the times, pointing to the collapse of the King Cotton plantation system.

Labor is revolting against Big Business agricultural methods; it is causing trouble. So is the land. Soil wears out when cotton is planted on it year after year; it grows white and thin; the cotton stalks are so small that workers have to crawl down the rows on hands and knees at picking time. Leaching and erosion destroy the soil. And the time is past when the planter could desert the land which he had worn out and move on to new, uncultivated acres. Today, man must stop exploiting the land, or the land itself will stop him.

Faced with the possible collapse of foreign trade and an oversupply on the domestic market, saddled with debt, threatened with the revolt of his labor and of his land, the Big Business planter — like many another Big Business executive — is in a desperate situation. And it appears that the overcapitalized cotton-growing industry, the agricultural South, must change its way of life considerably.

III

We have already noticed the agrarian plantation operating (at a disadvantage, to be sure) alongside the Big Business plantation in the cotton area. But there is another kind of farm tradition which has been almost entirely neglected in general discussion of Southern farm problems.

Yeoman is a good, healthy, Anglo-Saxon word for the sort of farmer who lives within this tradition; yeoman means a lesser freeholder who cultivates his own land. The word is strong, and it has connotations of independence, character, and bravery.

Now, the yeoman farmer in the Southeast has always existed, in larger numbers in the hill sections. In the Southwest, where Big

Business cotton production is most exaggerated, he is practically unknown. The yeoman was of the frontier tradition in the Old South, not of the great slaveholding tradition. Before the Civil War he owned his land, and he worked on his land himself. Perhaps he had a few slaves to help him, but his slaves were no burden to him, and his cotton crop was not of overbearing importance. His interest was in making for himself a home, in possessing a way of life marked by liberty, a way of life in which he could pursue his own happiness.

The yeoman did not pass with the frontier; he has not passed today. But he stands alone, completely apart from modern capital-labor terminology; neither communism nor fascism knows him. He is at once a capitalist (since he owns his own land, and since he may have a tenant or so) and a laborer (since he himself works on the land); yet he is neither, in the strict sense of the word, since his main concern is not to exploit his capital and his labor for a money income but to use them in making a living in goods.

It is chiefly to the yeoman farmer that the cotton-growing South must look for its salvation; it is for his benefit that plans must be made. Heretofore, he has worked at a disadvantage, being forced always to plant more and more cotton in order to get enough money to pay high taxes and to buy the things that he could not produce for himself, and being compelled to live under an economic system which operated solely in terms of money.

This change of emphasis — toward the yeoman farmer and away from the planter — seems to be an economic necessity. Luckily, the life of the yeoman is in itself a good life. He possesses liberty based on property — the only true liberty. He is assured of permanence, of variety in his work, of healthy conditions of labor. Moreover, he is freed from dependence upon the unpredictable fluctuations of prices in the markets of the world. He is neither poor nor rich; he is neither grooved in a semi-servile occupation with no hope of advancement, nor is he engaged in a mad struggle for economic power. And the increased division of the land among independent farmers will mean natural restriction of cotton production to American consumption needs; it will mean that the economic status of tenant farmers can be raised.

The yeoman farmer is the key to the solution of the main problems in Southern agriculture. And the solution will prove of benefit to the entire nation. A good life is possible in the South — generally possible, I mean, for in some sections of the South it is an accomplished fact — if the emphasis is shifted from the plantations working for mass production of cotton to the agrarian plantations and to the small farms operated by yeomen. And it is important to remember that this is not a new thing; it is merely the recognizing and the utilizing of a tradition too long neglected. Nor do we turn back the clock when we choose a system that was not invented day before yesterday.

IV

The prospect is pleasant. And it would be pleasant to end the discussion of the cotton problem here, as though the general utilization of subsistence-farming methods throughout the cotton area would come about easily and naturally within the next few years. But many obstacles stand in the way of the yeoman farmer, and these problems require consideration.

The question of taxation arises, a difficulty of which every would-be subsistence farmer is conscious. According to Department of Commerce statistics, the cotton states all have an excessively high state debt. And these statistics do not include the county debts which usually represent an even more important factor in determining tax rates. For instance, in the year 1934 the state ad valorem tax levied by Mississippi was five mills; in some counties, the tax rate on land would have been eighty mills had the county attempted to pay off its obligations (in principal and interest on bonds) for that year. Even choosing to default on their bond payments of principal, some of the counties still had tax rates as high as fifty mills!

This means that the owner of a hundred-acre farm, assessed at fifty dollars an acre, paid about $275 in taxes for 1934. Now, at its highest, cotton was selling for ten cents per pound in this year. On his farm, then, our farmer had to raise seven bales of cotton to pay his taxes alone.

Under this system of taxation, subsistence farming becomes impossible; the farmer is forced to rely more and more on his money crop (cotton) in order to pay his taxes, or he is forced to borrow heavily, mortgaging his land and ultimately forfeiting it.

There is one community in Mississippi, for example, where a few years ago there were ten farms operated by yeomen within three or four miles. Rising from the tenant-farmer class and buying their own farms, these men were independent, capable, sturdy. But taxes became higher and higher as the road-building fever of the twenties attacked their county. Today, every one of these yeomen is a tenant once more; his land belongs to a bank from which he borrowed money to pay taxes.

An analysis of the nature of the county debt in most of the high-tax counties of the South will show, I believe, that the greatest single cause of the high tax burden is road bonds (in Mississippi, for example, seventy-five per cent). Flood protection, for the Delta counties of Mississippi, Arkansas, and Louisiana, constitutes another substantial item. And county school bonds add to the county debt.

It is probable that this situation can be relieved only if the national government takes over a large part of this indebtedness. And in the case of the road bonds this seems only just. Most of these bonds represent paved highways for interstate traffic or for long-distance traffic within the state. Meanwhile, the farmers use gravel or dirt roads for the greater part of their hauls, since the paved highways are as straight and as central as possible. Buses, interstate trucking lines, tourists — these enjoy the highways while the farmer pays for them in land taxes.

That the national government should finance the building of levees and the digging of drainage canals in the river states seems reasonable. The floods in Mississippi, Arkansas, and Louisiana are invariably caused by the condition of the Mississippi River, the control of which should be a national project; and the expense of local flood protection (made necessary by the failure of the government properly to solve the Mississippi River flood problem) should not be assessed against the farmers who happen to be threatened with overflows.

These relief measures on the part of the federal government would do much to make the tax burden in the cotton states tolerable. The manufacturing states will be unenthusiastic; but it is fair to point out that a manufacturing economy naturally exploits an agrarian economy, and it should contribute something to the support of the agrarian economy, without which it could not exist. Besides, the agricultural economy in the South has always suffered in order that the industrial economy of the East might have special privileges in tariff protection.

The subsistence farm is desirable in Southern agriculture. Yes, says the skeptic, but land is now largely concentrated in the hands of a few big owners, planters who do not wish to practice an agrarian economy, since they look for some miraculous restoration of profits in cotton. How is this land to be transferred to the people who would like to own subsistence farms?

On the agrarian plantation — the place where an agrarian policy is the rule and where tenants are treated as co-workers by the planters — this question is easily settled. On plantations of this kind, the owner is usually ready to sell parts of his land, particularly the rich cut-over land which may be cleared and made ready for cultivation with comparative ease. He is willing to sell this land at a fair price, on terms. And if the renting tenant were rid of the tax problem (and if he had a respectable homestead exemption), he could buy his own land easily enough, live on it, cultivate it with subsistence-farming methods, and so establish a home for himself.

In the case of the large planter, other measures are needed to secure the gradual return of the land to the people. For one thing, the tax on excess production of cotton, which was a part of the Bankhead Act, might have done a great deal toward encouraging the Big Business planter to adopt an agrarian economy. In time it might have brought him to consider selling some of his land to his tenants!

Dr. Frank L. Owsley, writing in the *American Review* for March, 1935, suggests a program for restoring the land to the people and transforming worthy tenants into yeomen, which should be considered carefully:

Now, instead of the federal or state government spending $2500 in building a house for the homesteaders with whom they are very gingerly experimenting, and several hundred dollars on small tracts of land, let the national and state governments buy up all the lands owned by insurance companies and absentee landlords — which are being destroyed rapidly by erosion — and part of the land owned by the large planters who are struggling to save a portion of their lands, and give every landless tenant who can qualify eighty acres of land, build him a substantial hewn-log house and barn, fence him off twenty acres for a pasture, give him two mules and two milk cows, and advance him $300 for his living expenses for one year. By this means 500,000 persons can be rehabilitated in one year at $1500 a family or $300 per person. An outright gift of the land is advocated to the homesteader with one condition attached: the land must never be sold or mortgaged, and when abandoned it should automatically escheat to the state, which should be under immediate obligation to rehabilitate another worthy family.

In any such program, of course, one must remember that not all tenants are capable of working without careful supervision; the less able and responsible tenants will be left to work on the agrarian plantations. Thus the plan is a flexible one; it does not attempt to produce an equalitarian state, in which each man owns the same number of acres and no man can ever own more. But the plan does attempt to insure, to every worthy farmer who wants to be independent, that liberty which comes with ownership of real property.

One must consider, too, in any such program, the disposition, the "set of mind," of the Southerner, which opposes modern super-efficient methods and which resents the making of individuals into units of smoothly working systems. And one must not expect results to be immediate; the building of a strong class of yeoman farmers is not a job to be finished in a year or in five years.

Besides tax relief and new opportunities to secure land, the would-be subsistence farmer needs cheap electric power. The national government has already made a good start toward furnishing the farmer such power, in its work with the Tennessee Valley Authority. The small farmer would welcome an extension of TVA or similar activities.

Experimentation in crops and their adaptability to soils in the cotton states can also do the subsistence farmer a great deal of good. What new crops can he plant with reasonable expectation of a good yield? Are there new crops to replace cotton in the alluvial deposits of the Mississippi Delta country, or in the clays of Alabama, or in the sandy loam of North Carolina? Our scientists can determine this for the subsistence farmer. Already they have done much, and the farmer has found out much for himself. But he needs to know a great deal more about these matters.

Of the great difficulties confronting the yeoman farmer, all may be solved by political action. Taxes on land must be provided for scientific investigation of new crop possibilities; cheap electric power must be provided; the right kind of agricultural schools must be established. Here are problems for the national government; here are the matters with which our political leaders must deal if they are interested in a healthy Southern agrarianism to replace the cotton-growing industry.

V

In the rocky hill country of Arkansas there lives a man who provides us with a complete example of how the agrarian economy works in practice; his farm is in itself an answer to the question: How can it be done? This man does not stand alone in the South; in fact he is typical enough to be worth detailed consideration.

Three years ago [in 1933], George Smith wanted to make a home for himself on a farm. He and his wife moved to land which had been homesteaded by his great-grandfather. The first year they lost money because they tried to raise only cotton and corn. But the next year they began to try a live-at-home program. And this is their story, as reported in a large Southern newspaper:

> When they moved to the present farm . . . they had a two-and-a-half-room house, no lights, no fencing to amount to anything, no running water and only a barn.
>
> During the year, Mr. Smith and his wife . . . added two rooms to their home with only a little help. . . .
>
> Through a little trading, Mr. Smith bought an old store and used the lumber for his house. He traded two pigs for an electric system and bought wire from an abandoned miniature golf course and wired his house and the shops about the house. He also acquired a pressure tank for his running water.
>
> From bare necessities of the first year, he has in three years com-

pleted his model home. Take a look now. From the outside the home looks like any other farmhouse in the community. But inside there is a different story.

The living-room has been floored with narrow white pine, stained in its natural color. Two window seats that serve as chests are beneath each of the front windows. Mr. Smith made them himself. The large open fireplace is modern and inviting, with large logs ablaze. In one corner are a radio and a telephone. Several chairs, a couch, book racks, and a table make the room cozy.

The bedroom is not floored with finished flooring, but the floor is immaculate and the furnishings are modern, even to the bed-light. A smaller bedroom is west of the living-room. The kitchen is almost a show place. . . .

Outside, a few feet from the steps, is the insulated storage house for canned foods, potatoes, and onions. Mr. Smith has a well-built garage for his truck. . . . The well house is well built and modern. To the rear of the garage is Mr. Smith's workshop with everything in its place. Nothing is scattered, all the tools are in their places. He had only a hammer and a saw when he moved there.

He has a forge where he makes nearly all the tools he needs. He has a pair of pruning shears that are "better than I could buy." They were made from a couple of automobile springs. On the creek he has built a hog-scalding vat where one man can clean a hog easily. He is glad to let his neighbors use it. Mr. and Mrs. Smith look after the entire farm, the chickens, the cows, and the gardens.

And this is within the very state in which the tenant farmers' union started, growing out of unrest among workers on large cotton plantations!

It will be interesting to see what Mr. Smith planted on his farm last year. On one patch of ground he had ten acres of cotton, followed by vetch; next year this ground will be planted in corn. He had ten acres of corn, to be followed next year by cotton. There was a seven-acre peach orchard, sown to lespedeza for soil improvement, erosion prevention, and seed. There were nine more acres of lespedeza, which is useful not only for soil improvement but as a forage. There were permanent Bermuda grass and Dallas grass. There were permanent meadows. Certain areas were planted in oats, followed by soy beans. And, besides, there were crops of popcorn, peanuts, Hegari, sorghum, Laredo soy beans, and cow peas.

Food crops for the farm workers, food crops for animals, crops for soil enrichment, money crop in moderate quantity, a larder full of provisions for the winter months: here is good living.

Nor does this way of life require that those who follow it be isolated. On the contrary, Mr. and Mrs. Smith are prominent in the activities of their home county; they are respected, useful citizens.

It would be strange if there were not a great many other people in the South just as anxious as Mr. Smith to have homes and farms. But they must have land first; they must have a tax burden that does not oppress them; they must have government help of some sort in order to get their start. (Mr. Smith was considerably benefited by the AAA, which rented part of the land which he had formerly planted in cotton.) Under the Owsley plan, or under some other plan of similar nature, small farmers may be so assisted; and so to assist small farmers, so to assist tenants in becoming yeomen, is to restore liberty based on property.

— From *Who Owns America?*, Houghton Mifflin Company, 1936. Reprinted by permission.

THE WASTE OF THE PEOPLE

By Gerald W. Johnson

The Southeast has dealt with its human wealth exactly as it has with the wealth of its soil — part it has let slip away altogether, part it has failed to cultivate at all, and part it has clearly misused.

Here, again, it is far from having a monopoly. There is no country in the world that is not guilty, to some extent, of the same sort of waste. But here, again, the figures for the Southeast run so inordinately high as to raise a question as to the survival of the region at its present level of culture; and this in spite of vigorous and by no means ineffective efforts toward the conservation of human wealth.

It has been the fashion in some quarters to assume that the Southeast has remained almost completely inert in the presence of its social problems. This is far from the truth. A mere glance at the educational statistics of the region is enough to dissipate the impression that the Southeast has been indifferent or lethargic in this respect. The state of Florida, for example, spends 5.76 per cent of its total income for school purposes, and North Carolina 4.38 per cent; this is a larger percentage than is spent for similar purposes by any other states save the Dakotas. Nor is the effort confined to primary schools. The Southeast spends .3 per cent of its total income for higher education, the highest percentage in the nation. It enrolled more high school students in 1930 than the whole country did in 1900, and there are more accredited high schools in this region than there were in the United States at the end of the century. Its present army of 60,000 high school graduates annually represents an increase of 500 per cent within the last two decades.

Such an advance is not achieved without vigorous and unremitting labor. Whatever else the Southeast may lack, it is not deficient in energy, although this is precisely the deficiency that superficial observers have most frequently attributed to it. The waste of its human resources is attributable to a wide variety of causes, but inertia does not figure importantly among them.

2

The counterpart of the Southern lands eroded beyond the possibility of any use is to be found, in the inventory of human wealth, in the item of three and a half million Southerners lost to the South. This figure, worked out by T. J. Woofter, Jr., is the difference between the number of persons born in the Southeast who are living in other regions and the number born in other regions now living in the Southeast. That this enormous tide of emigration represents a huge monetary loss is obvious, but the economists exhibit a distressing tendency to dispute among themselves as to its size. There are a dozen methods of calculating the value to society of a human life, and each economist prefers his own.

Sir William Petty, the first to make an estimate based on something rather more valid than guesses, in 1690 calculated the worth of a man to England at £80, which, allowing for the alteration in the value of money, would be approximately $895 today. Two hundred years later Giffen and Farr, approaching the problem from different angles, increased that figure largely, Giffen to $6,712 and Farr to $3,356. In 1891 Nicholson, figuring in still another way, made it $13,985, while Marshall, in 1895, could see no more than $2,237 as the value of a life. Perhaps the most elaborate studies made up to that time were those of Barriol, a French actuary, who in 1910 published estimates varying for different countries. Barriol's figure for the United States, expressed in terms of the present dollar, is $10,561, which is a good deal closer to Nicholson than to Petty.

If one assumes, however, that Barriol was guilty of an error of more than 110 per cent — surely a generous estimate — one is left with a figure of $5,000 as the monetary value of a human being to society. Remember that the South has lost three and a half million of them, and it is apparent that this represents a loss in the order of magnitude of the national debt. It is probable that most living men, if called upon to cite instances of the most terrific spending within their experience, would mention the war against Germany and the New Deal expedition against the depression. The war increased the national debt by something over $25,000,000,000. The first four years of the New Deal increased it about $10,000,000,000, leaving out the soldiers' bonus as not attributable to the New Deal. But the South's monetary loss by emigration, at $5,000 a person, comes to $17,500,000,000 — two-thirds of the cost of the war, or enough to pay not for four but for seven years of the New Deal. That incomprehensible sum would pay for one thousand Department of Commerce buildings, or for 1,150 Louisiana Purchases. The most populous state in the Southeast is North Carolina, with 3,170,000 people. Emigration has drained away human resources equaling more than the entire population of the region's biggest state.

The irony of the situation is the fact that these people sought opportunity — and evidently found it, since they have stayed away — by leaving the region of the country richest in natural wealth and going into poorer regions. In the face of that fact, is it possible to doubt that there is something seriously amiss in the present economic and social organization of the Southeast?

3

Studies of the population of the Southeast have long ago made the whole country familiar with certain of its characteristics. Its biracial composition, of course, is its most conspicuous feature, and the first to meet the observer's eye. It is the most thoroughly American region in the sense that almost all its people are natives of this country. It is homogeneous in another way, too, for the racial origins of the bulk of the population are still the British Isles and Africa, despite strong infiltrations of Germans in the piedmont country and French in Louisiana, a slighter infiltration of Spanish along the Gulf coast, and scattered enclaves of other nationalities here and there. In spite of the existence of numerous exceptions, it remains true that the typical Southerner is either Negro, or English, Scotch, Welsh, or Irish. His culture is British; his religion, Protestant, predominantly Nonconformist, Calvinistic; his politics, traditionalist; his economic theory, individualist; his social code, a modification of that of Great Britain; his legal code, based on the English common law. There are important exceptions — the Code Napoléon, for example, is the basis of Louisiana law, and there are wide Catholic areas in Kentucky as well as in Louisiana — but the exceptions do not modify the general picture radically.

What has been almost entirely overlooked, however, until Odum [1] brought it to light, is the curious and extremely important fact that the people of the Southeast are young people, markedly younger than those of any other section. In 1930 more than 50 per cent of the people of South Carolina were under twenty years of age, and more than 49 per cent of those of North Carolina. Less than 8 per cent of South Carolinians and less than 9 per cent of North Carolinians were over fifty-five.

In the Southeast as a whole, 45 per cent of the population were minor in 1930 as against something under 40 per cent for the nation.

The implications of this fact are far-reaching. In the first place, it means that the Southeast has proportionately more children to feed and educate, and fewer adults in the prime of life to do it, than any other region. It follows that in this region we should expect to encounter the greatest difficulties in the elimination of child labor and in the provision of the best type of public education — which is exactly what we do find. But add to this the fact that emigration from this region is very large and the problem takes on national significance. Emigrants from the South constituted nearly 4 per cent of the population of other regions in 1930; the Southeastern birth rate continues high, and if emigration also continues, it is reasonable to assume that the proportion of Southern-born and Southern-trained people in the total population of other regions will continue to increase. Handicaps laid upon Southern children therefore may have far-reaching effects.

The typical Southerner, these figures show, is a poor man with many children. This must be borne in mind in estimating the

[1] Johnson states in the Foreword to *The Wasted Land*, of which this essay is a part: "This book is essentially a commentary on *Southern Regions of the United States*, written by Howard W. Odum."

value of any social program that may be proposed for the region. For example, it has an important effect on the public attitude toward such schemes as old-age pensions. In Kentucky 12.1 per cent of the people are over fifty-five years old — the highest percentage in the Southeast. Compare this with the 18.6 per cent of New Hampshire, the 17.8 per cent of Maine and Vermont, the 15.6 per cent of Oregon, and it is at once apparent that the problem of caring for the aged is much more serious in other regions than it is in the Southeast. This undoubtedly has something to do with the fact that in 1936 the Townsend Plan aroused less interest in this than in any other region.

The statement that the population of the Southeast is young might lead to the inference that it is therefore an enterprising, not to say reckless population, for enterprise and daring are commonly associated with youth. It is necessary, therefore, to emphasize the fact that the people of the Southeast are not merely young, but very young. When the population of South Carolina consists of 50.6 per cent less than twenty years old, and only 41.5 per cent between twenty and fifty-five, the people of voting age in that state are likely to think, act, and vote, not so much as young people as, rather, the parents of large families; and enterprise and recklessness are not commonly associated with the parents of many children.

It follows, therefore, that anyone who would formulate a social program that will appeal to the Southeast must frame it to appeal to a population distinctly different from that of any other region not in more or less vague and debatable ethnic traits but in the sharp, definite factors of economic level and family responsibility. If two men obviously think differently the difference may or may not be due to the fact that one is a Celt and the other a Teuton; psychologists and ethnologists can debate endlessly over the point. But nothing is more certain than that two men will adopt different attitudes toward life if the first has one child and the second has seven, although both may be Celts or both Teutons. The typical Southerner's racial origin and cultural background are hardly as powerful factors in formulating his attitudes as the fact that he is a poor man with many children.

4

Next in importance in measuring the situation as it exists is the fact that the population of the Southeast is an agricultural population. Notwithstanding the immense growth of industry within the last generation it is still an agrarian region; more than that, it is still too strongly agrarian to afford the variety of opportunities to its people that it must afford if its civilization is to attain the highest possible level.

This assumption is sharply challenged by an important body of opinion within the region itself. Even the relatively minor industrialization that has already taken place has brought into the Southeast some of the characteristic evils of industrialization. Bitter and sometimes bloody struggles between employers and employees have occurred in the South with what seems to be increasing frequency. There are Southern factory towns where conditions of labor and of living have developed a dreary sterility of life comparable to the conditions in Lancashire which moved British humanitarians to blistering denunciation a hundred years ago.

These ominous developments have persuaded some very alert Southern thinkers that further development of Southern industrialism must tend toward duplication in this region, if not of the slums of Glasgow, at least of the most undesirable conditions that prevail in heavily industrialized regions of the United States. They insist, therefore, that the emphasis henceforth should be laid on the perfection of an agrarian culture, rather than on further industrialization.

The question, of course, is one of relative, not of absolute, values. The Southern Agrarians, needless to say, realize that a purely agrarian economy is an impossibility, and that if it were possible it would be as far removed from the ideal as the opposite impossibility, a purely industrial economy. The question is not, Should the South abandon its machines and factories? but, Is it now at or close to the degree of industrialization that will afford its population maximum opportunity for the development of their capacities?

Part of the answer is to be found in the figures for interregional population movement. That movement still runs heavily against the South. People, in general, do not leave their homes and birthplaces without a compelling reason. The born wanderer is a rarity; it is beyond belief that the South has produced three and a half millions of them in this generation. Even rarer is the man with a highly specialized talent which can be exercised only in a special environment. An opera singer, an actor, a great baseball player will naturally find restricted opportunities everywhere except in the largest cities; the Southeast has produced a considerable number of such specialists, but not millions.

The enormous exodus of its people from the Southeast is explicable only on the assumption that opportunities for people of ordinary capacity are limited in the South; and part of the explanation of that condition is found in the fact that the region is still overwhelmingly agrarian. In so far as natural conditions are concerned — soil, climate, rainfall, the existence of undeveloped land — the opportunity for farmers in the South is virtually unlimited. Unfortunately, this is not true when artificial conditions are taken into account — the economic system. Moreover, there remains the fact, basic but frequently ignored, that not all men are born farmers. Whatever may have been the condition of the race when Adam delved and Eve span, its subsequent history has conditioned a considerable proportion of it to occupations not directly connected with the tilling of the soil.

To force such people into agriculture is plainly a waste of humanity; yet there is reason to believe that the Southeast is so predominantly agrarian that it affords no adequate outlet for the energies of its people who are artisans, not husbandmen, by temperament. Therefore they leave in hordes. More than that — one is tempted to say, worse than that — there are many who do not leave, but who remain to become bad farmers — unhappy, inefficient, a drag upon the economy of the entire region and a point of weakness in its social structure.

It is arguable that such people would be still worse off in the slums of a factory district, although the proof is not immediately visible; but to assume that factories inevitably and necessarily connote slums is not merely to adopt a defeatist attitude, but to ignore demonstrated fact. Slums are the product, not of industrialism itself, but of its undesirable concentration — a concentration no longer necessary in view of the wide distribution of electric power.

As a matter of fact, such undesirable conditions as have attended the growth of the existing industry of the Southeast have usually developed in spite of, rather than because of, topographical conditions. Very few Southern factories, especially those belonging to the textile industry, are cramped by lack of available building land. The industrial tenement is almost unknown in this region. For every one in existence there are probably a dozen communities inhabited by industrial workers which, as far as fresh air, sunlight, grass and trees are concerned, are almost ideal.

Without doubt, it would be detrimental in the extreme for the Southeast to develop tremendous industrial concentrations, crowding thousands of people into a few acres. But the present trend is plainly toward a system of widely scattered factories and against congestion of population. The Tennessee Valley project, whatever may be said of governmental participation in its direction and financing, is physically in line with the more recent development of Southern industrialism in general, in that it tends to develop industrial plants scattered over a wide area. This sort of development has certainly not reached the maximum desirable for the orderly and symmetrical development of the region's cultural and economic potentialities.

Certain sinister features of industrialism in the South can neither be denied nor defended; which does not alter the fact that a further industrial development, on socially more efficient lines, might be expected to reduce the human waste that now characterizes the region.

5

The most conspicuous characteristic of the Southern population, however, is its biracial character. A group of eight million people of a different color from the other seventeen million is a feature so startling that it may be expected to attract more attention than perhaps it deserves.

It may be argued plausibly that one of the difficulties of the South is the fact that the Negro has been given more attention, as a Negro, than he deserves, and a good deal less attention, as a Southerner, than he deserves. Odum proceeds on " the assumption that the Negro is an integral, normal, and continuing factor in the culture of the Southeast." The novelty in this is the word " normal." The very term, " Negro problem," introduces to most minds a suggestion of abnormality. Much of the thinking and writing on the subject, whether done by Southerners, by Northerners, or by foreigners, has, consciously or unconsciously, adopted the same point of view — the point of view, that is to say, that the Negro is something in the nature of an extraneous substance, in, but not of, the South, producing a condition abnormal, not to say pathological.

Hence, it has come about that the average man tends to regard anything touching on the biracial situation as in the field of therapeutics, rather than in that of prophylaxis; something to be cured, rather than something to be developed. There is an adequate historical explanation for this sudden, violent alteration of the Negro's political status at the time of the Civil War. Considering the terrific emotional stresses of the post-war years, it is hard to imagine how it could have been otherwise. Nevertheless, it certainly imposes no strain on credulity to suggest that this is not the ideal approach to the problem.

The range of medicaments offered to cure the Negro problem is immense. It runs from murder to enthronement. Immediately after the war it was seriously proposed by certain bitter Northerners that the Negro race be made sovereign in the South, and the white reduced to subjection; and ever since the war certain violent and lawless elements in the South have been attempting to cure what they regard as a malady by process of extermination. Between these extremes men of innumerable grades of wisdom and sincerity have offered innumerable panaceas. But relatively few — and this includes Negro thinkers as well as white — have been able to disabuse their minds entirely of the theory of medication.

The inevitable result has been enormous waste of the Negro's potential value to the social structure. Not all of this is the fault of the white South, by any means. The hasty and ill-advised effort made in the sixties to project the newly emancipated slaves into a political and social position they were not prepared to occupy has made any realistic treatment of their position extremely difficult. Not only did it create appalling prejudices, but it erected very substantial legal barriers against any direct and forthright approach, and forced Southern political and social polity into a sinuousness that has been productive of a thousand evils.

This is, however, water over the dam. What confronts the Southeast today is the problem of making the best possible use of eight million blacks. But this is no special problem. The same deficiencies that have wasted the energies of the white population are precisely the deficiencies that have handicapped the black, and any technique that will supply the one will supply the other. The Southern Negroes, like the Southern whites, lack capital, technical skill, and institutional services. From this standpoint there is no Negro problem, only a Southern problem.

There is, of course, a very ugly and very refractory psychological difficulty born of that fecund mother of psychoses, Fear. Originally it was the whites' fear of political domination by the Negro, supported by Northern bayonets. Later it was transformed into fear of the Negro's economic competition. These fears have produced hideous outbreaks of violence which, in turn, have filled the Negroes with a paralyzing fear of the ferocity of the white race. Together they are responsible for appalling waste of the energies of both races. This, not any marked economic differentiation, is the real Negro problem.

Yet there is much in the existing situation to indicate that even the intangible emotional complex that is the Negro problem will yield to a rational treatment. The basis of fear is being steadily reduced. In the first place, the Negro birth rate, while fairly high, as measured by the national average, is not keeping pace with the white birth rate in the Southeast. In the second place, within the last twenty years there has been a remarkable dispersal of the Negro population through other regions. New York, Chicago, and Philadelphia all have larger Negro populations than any Southern city. In 1930 Cook County, Illinois, with 246,992, had the largest concentration of Negro population in the world, while New York with 224,670 and Philadelphia with 219,599 were not far behind.

Seven other cities outside of the South have more than 50,000 Negroes, and there are 149 Northern and Western counties with more than 2,500.

This has had the effect of transferring race conflict to other regions, but it has also had the effect of relieving the population pressure in the Southeast; and the lessening of this tension permits the belief that a more unemotional examination of race relations is not only possible, but is actually taking place in the region.

One may argue with something more than a mere color of reason that many of the difficulties that have arisen from the South's biracial composition are due to the fact that the situation has been studied too intensively in detail, and not enough in general. That is to say, countless projects for the alleviation of specific troubles have been advanced by whites, by Negroes, by Southerners, by non-Southerners, by wise men and by fools. Many of them, including some of the very worst, have been adopted and enacted into law by Southern legislatures, while others have been incorporated into the manners and customs of the people; which is to say, they have been made into law more rigid and binding than any statute.

But only comparatively recently has any considerable effort been made to treat the disease, rather than to alleviate its symptoms — or, rather, only recently has the idea begun to spread that perhaps there isn't any organic disease, but only a series of functional disturbances. Since the turn of the century the Southeast has been making real, if not always adequate, efforts in the field of Negro education. With the rise of the Negro in the cultural and economic scale, there has come also an appreciable reduction of the rigor of civil and social disabilities. And with both there is a strengthening belief that perhaps the traditional approach to this situation has been faulty.

This approach has been based largely on the assumption that there is something separate and apart about the Negro question that differentiates it from other questions. It has been too frequently assumed that here is a problem with only one aspect. From the standpoint of the whites, this one aspect is the threat that the Negro affords to Southern social organization and cultural development. From the standpoint of the Negroes it has been the threat that white dominance offers to the very existence of the Negro, as well as to his economic and cultural development. A tremendous proportion of the energies of both races has been wasted — on one side in exerting pressure to "keep the Negro in his place," on the other side in resisting this pressure.

This habit of mind still dominates much of the thinking of the region and the waste continues. But there is another body of opinion, already important, and increasing steadily. This opinion rallies around the theory that eight million people ought to be an asset of enormous value, and that the real Negro problem is not how to render him innocuous, but how to get the largest possible value out of him.

Once this attitude is adopted, a good many Southern theories as to race become untenable immediately. A society that proposes to develop all the potentialities of any population group obviously must open to that group every opportunity that it is capable of improving. This does not necessarily mean any sudden, violent reversal of the white Southern attitude towards the Negro. Right after the Civil War the disastrous results of any such attempt were demonstrated with a clarity so frightful that it should be a guarantee against any repetition of that mistake. But it does mean that the Negro's demonstrated capacity in the professions, in business, and in finance is to be recognized, not as a threat to white dominance, but as an addition to the total strength of the region. It involves a realization that every cultural, economic, or social advance made by the Negro involves, not something lost to the whites, but something gained for the entire region, white and black alike.

Idealists have relied too much on the altruism of the white South in arguing for this or that alteration in race relations. No doubt the white South ought to treat the Negro justly because it is right to do so; but no doubt the white South is as fallibly human as the rest of the race and as feeble in its response to the categorical imperative. No man, however, needs constantly reiterated adjuration to do that which is patently to his own interest. The plain fact is that the Negro is, in Odum's words, "an integral, normal, continuing factor" in the social structure; the equally plain inference is that the stronger the Negro, the stronger the social structure. Let this once come home not merely to a few leaders but to the great body of the people and no argument will be necessary to persuade the South to open the gates of opportunity to the Negro.

Incidentally, this shift in attitude is not, and ought not to be, confined to the whites. The more clear-headed Negroes realize that the American Negro has, to set off against his undeniable disabilities, certain tremendous advantages. He enjoys, for example, a high degree of political security; he is not exposed to the risk of invasion by imperialistic adventurers. Nor is he a colonial; the fruit of his labor is added to the wealth of his own country, and is not carried off as tribute to increase the splendor of some European capital. His standard of living may be lower and his death rate higher than either ought to be, but both compare very favorably indeed with those of most parts of Africa. He has fallen heir to a rich cultural tradition, and in adapting it to his own emotional and artistic requirements he may at once enrich his own existence and make a contribution to the tradition. He has no small part to play in eliminating the human waste that is involved in racial conflict.

6

Reference has already been made to the relatively great weight that rests upon the Southeast in the matter of educating its countless children. To measure the full weight, however, one must take into consideration other factors than merely the number of children in the region in proportion to total population. For one thing, the maintenance of a separate school system for Negroes leads to some duplication of effort and increase of expenditure, especially in supervisory and administrative services and in higher education.

It is not, however, in the elementary schools that the educational system of the Southeast is most markedly wasteful and inefficient. It is true that salaries paid teachers in the elementary schools are frequently so low that the tendency is to drive the abler teachers out of the profession. It is also true that the onset of the depression caused many states and municipalities to make cuts in the school budget so drastic that they constituted, not economy, but gross waste. Such things, however, are not faults inherent in the system itself, representing nothing more than its ill-advised administration.

When one turns to the system of higher education, on the other hand, it is evident at once that there are elements in its very organization that make for waste. First and most conspicuous of these is the fact that here are twenty-five million people without a single university of the first rank. Neither is there an engineering school of the first rank, nor a school of agriculture of the first rank. This means that the whole educational system lacks, first, the institutional services that cannot be performed by any other than an institution of the highest grade and, second, the influence making for increasingly high standards that such an institution exerts.

Odum describes the condition of the Southern education system as one of "immaturity." Certainly the essential economy of maintaining in so large a population at least one university of the very highest standard and technical schools of corresponding quality is not obvious to the immature. The tendency in the Southeast has been to regard institutions of higher learning, if not exactly as luxuries, certainly as dispensable. Southerners have been slow to concede the possibility that the excellence of the public schools of New England is attributable largely to the excellence of the universities there. The effort has been to build up a system of primary schools without first making sure of a continuous supply of highly trained directors of the system; and this procedure has been slow and wasteful.

It is not to be inferred, of course, that this policy was adopted of deliberate choice. When the Southeast first began to stir from the lethargy following a great and disastrous war, it confronted a condition and not a theory. There was an appalling illiteracy rate to be reduced at all speed and by such means as were at hand. In the Southeast, as in the Northeast, the business of higher education in the beginning had been taken in hand largely by the churches. The College of William and Mary, for instance, was at first dominated by the clergy almost as completely as was Harvard University. In later years it became the practice of each of the larger denominations to build in each state at least one college for men and one for women. In some states these institutions actually outranked the state university both in age and importance. The program of public education that began about 1900 therefore encountered formidable opposition in the realm of higher education from these institutions, which naturally objected to being displaced. Many leaders who devoted their time and energy without stint to support of the public schools not only failed to support but actively opposed the establishment of adequately equipped public universities.

Unfortunately, none of the church colleges had the resources that were supplied to a Harvard, a Yale, a Princeton, to erect it into a university of the highest standing. The only organization strong enough to build a university was the state; but with most of the educated men in the population graduates of denominational colleges, it was difficult to organize support for a program frankly designed to lift the state university above all other schools. There was a moment, just before the depression, when it seemed that North Carolina was about to do it. Educational leaders cleverly took advantage of the enthusiasm of boom times to drive the University of North Carolina far up toward the rank of a first-rate institution; but terror engendered by the collapse of the boom defeated that hope. Financial support was withdrawn to an extent that made the university's assumption of the first rank impossible, and it has had much ado to maintain its standing even among the universities of the Southeast.

The lack of such a university, and of comparable schools of agriculture and engineering, has made the development of an adequate system of public education in the Southeast doubly hard. It is, therefore, a conspicuous example of waste.

Another is to be found in the multiplicity of church schools. Each denomination has felt the necessity not only of maintaining one college, and usually two, but of maintaining one in each state. The Baptists, for example, the most numerous of the sects, have colleges all the way from Virginia to Arkansas, but no institution in any sense comparable to the University of Chicago, which also began as a Baptist college. The Methodists have as many colleges or more, and at various times they have threatened to concentrate on one great regional institution, as at Vanderbilt, at Emory, and at Duke; but no university of the first rank has been built as yet.

Hitherto state lines have presented an insurmountable barrier to the development of a great privately endowed university out of any of the Southern denominational colleges.

More important, perhaps, in its effect on the cultural development of the region has been the separation of the sexes. As in the Northeast, so in the Southeast higher education has been duplicated by the building of women's colleges; but the Southeast has been slower than the Northeast to convert them into liberal arts colleges rather than finishing schools.

An argument can be made for women's colleges. Education is asexual, or ought to be. It is perhaps particularly important for the Southern girl, considering her environment and traditional inheritance, to learn somewhere in the course of her education that intellectual rivalry between women is possible. In coeducational schools it too often happens that the girl who is popular with the male students is regarded as a success, rather than the one who exhibits intelligence and industry. In a women's college this extraneous success is not so easily achieved, and the only road to recognition lies through intellectual effort.

But while the theory can be defended, it has no application if the women's " college " is really not a college but an institution for training in " domestic economy " or for dabbling in the arts, or a normal school for teachers. This has been the state of many so-called women's colleges in the South. The waste here involves not only the individuals of the present generation. It tends also to strengthen skepticism as to the value of higher education for women among women themselves, and therefore tends to perpetuate the waste in the future.

In any event, the maintenance of separate institutions for the sexes involves the duplication of many costs, especially in the administrative and disbursing departments. Without going into consideration of the desirability of separate education for women, it is a question whether the South, in view of the narrowness of its resources, on the one hand, and the greatness of its needs, on the other, is in position to afford the luxury of separate colleges for women. Nor is it necessary to debate the value of sectarian education to reach the conclusion that the South can ill afford to maintain as large a number of independent church colleges as it has now. Grant the desirability of having Baptist colleges, Methodist colleges, Presbyterian colleges, and so on — does it follow that it is necessary to have one of each in every state? Yet in many instances the larger denominations are maintaining, not one, but four or five institutions giving college work in the same state.

In the Southeast the problem of higher education, so far from being handled as a unit, is subdivided, first by the division between church and state, then by races, then by sexes, then by denominations, and then by state lines. It is beyond belief that such fine subdivision does not involve some inefficiency, duplication of effort, lost motion — in brief, some waste. In view of the gigantic size of its education problem, due to the great numbers of its children, the loss occasioned by unnecessary division undoubtedly is one explanation of the relatively slow progress the region has made despite tremendous effort during the past thirty years.

7

Some critics have explained the obvious deficiencies of the Southeast by the markedly religious character of the population — religious, that is to say, in the sense of church membership. This assumption, however, does not stand up well under the test of Odum's analysis. The truth seems to be rather that the characteristic religion of the region is more affected by its general culture than the general culture is affected by the religion.

In the Southeast 61.4 per cent of the total adult population are church members as against 54.3 per cent for the whole nation. Only the Northeast, with 60.2 per cent, comes close to this region. Except in Louisiana and Kentucky, where Roman Catholics lead, the Baptists are the largest denomination in all of the Southeastern states, white Baptists in four states, Negro Baptists in five, with Methodists, white and Negro, coming next. With only 19.7 per cent of the adult population of the country, the Southeast has 33.4 per cent of the adult Protestant church membership and 22.3 per cent of the total church membership.

The mere recitation of its numerical strength is proof that the church plays an important part in the life of the region. But its influence is rather toward the fixation of attitudes than toward the determination of programs. For one thing, the membership is divided into a large number of relatively small units, the average membership of the individual church in the Southeast being 137 as against an average of 235 for the nation as a whole. Moreover, the congregational organization of the sect strongest numerically, the Baptists, makes virtually impossible any concerted effort toward a specific social objective. The Southern Baptist Convention, being without ecclesiastical authority, cannot pledge any Baptist church to any specific program. The Baptists, moreover, having been for centuries a persecuted minority, are traditionally suspicious of any organic connection of church and state, a suspicion which they carry over from politics to secular affairs in general. In 1936 a proposal that the convention put itself on record formally as opposing certain notorious abuses, including the brutality of the chain-gang system and agricultural peonage, was emphatically rejected, not that any delegate had any defense of the abuses in question, but because reform of the social system was regarded as lying outside the proper field of work of the denomination.

Without doubt this attitude of the Baptists has had some influence upon the smaller denominations in the region. It does not prevent their clergy, including the Baptist clergy, from intervening informally in all sorts of political contests. The participation of the Methodist Episcopal Bishop Cannon in the presidential campaign of 1928, for example, was an epos of American politics which politicians of all parties not only remember but still discuss with awe and terror. Still, such excursions beyond the bounds of the realm of theology are usually individualist enterprises without acknowledged institutional backing. The churches did, for the most part, give their formal approval to prohibition, but their policy as a rule is to leave the formulation of social programs to other agencies.

This is frequently used as the basis of an indictment of the church in the Southeast, but it is by no means certain that it is an unwise policy. Considering the intense emotionalism that characterizes large sections of Calvinistic Protestants, the participation of the churches, as such, in the formulation of specific programs might contribute more confusion than enlightenment. The participation of the faithful in the control of church colleges in the Southeast, for example, does not encourage the belief that the church membership is a competent authority to pass upon technical methods and details of administration. The more successful colleges without exception are those over which the denomination does not attempt to exercise direct control, but delegates its authority to some representative body; and one of the weaknesses of the church schools is the reluctance of the denominations to delegate broad enough authority.

It is extremely difficult, therefore, to trace any connection between the deficiencies of the region and its unusually high rate of church membership. The attitude of the churches on social questions is determined by the general culture of the region, not the attitude of the people by that of the churches.

8

The rise of industrialism has brought to the Southeast a new familiarity with the various types of conflict known of old to regions industrialized earlier. If there is anything distinctly individual in the relations of labor and capital in the Southeast; it is the evidence that here is an obvious lag. The battles now being fought in the South are to a noticeable extent precisely the battles that were fought years ago in the Northeast and decades ago in England. The organization of labor in trade-unions, for example, is as far behind the Northeast as the Northeast is behind England.

Here is a form of waste that was, perhaps, inevitable, but that is none the less serious and none the less regrettable. Its existence is demonstrated by the very fact that in some cases it is being avoided. Here and there in the industrial regions one encounters an employer and a labor leader with a sense of historical analogy and a knowledge of the history of industrialism. In such cases some of the old errors have been avoided and some of the old conflicts escaped. Such men are exceptional, but their experience shows how heavily the region has lost by the lack of leaders conversant with the history of industrial conflict in other regions.

Southern industry is wasting time, energy, and money learning by its own experience a great deal about labor relations that might have been learned from the experience of others. This is, however, a human rather than a Southern failing; we are all inclined to say, or at least to think, "It can't happen here," until it actually does happen. What is peculiarly Southern about the situation is the striking time lag between this and other regions of the country. This is not confined to Southern industrialism. It is markedly characteristic of the entire picture. The educational situation, for example, in many of its aspects is remarkably similar in the Southeast today to what was characteristic of the country as a whole in 1900. So are certain aspects of the region's agriculture, commerce, fiscal organization, and social customs.

The point most worthy of emphasis in this connection, however, is that it is a decreasing gap. If most of the indices employed by Odum to measure Southern civilization show a distinct lag, most of those used to measure advancement within the last thirty years show an astonishing leadership. The backward region is still backward, but it has been catching up at an amazing rate. If it could contrive to reduce its wastes, human and material, there is hardly any aspect of its culture that could not soon be brought abreast of the rest of the country.

This is emphatically true of its industrialism. The men who founded it and built it largely on the basis of a paternalistic relation to labor are now old and are rapidly relinquishing control to younger hands. With them the era of individual proprietorship is yielding to that of corporate control, which has long ruled in the older industrial regions. The question before Southern industrialism is whether or not employers and employees in the Southeast will be able to profit by the experience of other regions.

This is by no means certain. Chambers of Commerce in some Southern towns are still advertising cheap labor and absence of union organization as advantages. In some localities there have been outbreaks of violence in industrial disputes in which labor resorted to sabotage and capital to the use of hired gunmen. The road is wide open to a repetition of the old error of ordeal by battle, with all its frightful waste of money and men.

On the other hand, there are the exceptional men referred to earlier. There is also a possibility that the governmental experiment in the Tennessee Valley may develop into a demonstration of a saner industrial order which will have an influence upon all Southern industrialism in other ways than by the distribution of electric power. The Southeast can avoid the greater part of the waste of industrial warfare. There is no assurance that it will do so; but it can.

9

A form of human waste which is probably destined to receive much more consideration in the future than it has been given in the past is waste of the people's leisure. It is already evident that technological development has presented the whole country with new problems of leisure, and every indication points to the belief that these problems are more likely to increase than to diminish in the near future. It is, therefore, of great and increasing importance for society to equip itself to meet this condition.

The Southeast is markedly ill-equipped to deal with leisure. From time immemorial the development of the fine arts, and especially music, drama, and literature, has depended upon the judicious employment of someone's leisure — sometimes that of the artist, as in the case of the most celebrated officer of engineers in military history, Leonardo da Vinci, but more frequently that of the patron of the arts, whether that patron be a Pericles, a Lorenzo de' Medici, a Pope Julius, or merely an appreciative and discriminating public. By contrast, it is hardly to be denied that the more corrosive and socially destructive vices are advanced most rapidly by the unwise employment of leisure. That sagacious and penetrating if unconventional critic, H. L. Mencken, many years ago suggested the organization of a brass band in every Southern village as the most effective deterrent of lynching. His belief — pretty strongly supported by the evidence — is that an important contributory factor in many lynchings is sheer boredom, which makes any sort of excitement a welcome interruption of an eventless existence.

In any case, it is clear that there are wide areas in the Southeast where facilities for the profitable employment of leisure are entirely lacking, as far as institutional services are concerned. The individual is thrown back upon his own resources; and if these are inadequate, waste is inevitable. Certain forms of recreational organization, of course, are obviously not adapted to the region. To note, for example, that there is not a single great orchestra in the Southeast is beside the point. There is not a city in the region large enough to support one. As much may be said of the lack of theaters, which, since the rise of the movies, have been more and more confined to the largest cities in the country.

But dozens of Northeastern and Middle states villages have proved that no great population is needed to support admirable singing societies and even well-trained choruses. Symphony orchestras may be beyond the means of the South — although at least one, partially supported by federal government funds, has done respectable work in North Carolina recently — but small ensembles do not require the backing of millionaires. Their scarcity in the region is evidence of its failure adequately to prepare for the use of leisure.

The monumental proof of this failure, however, is the situation with regard to books and libraries. Take any sort of index you please, and the deficiency of the Southeast is marked. There are more than six hundred counties in the Southeast without a public library. Compare this with nineteen in the Far West, forty-six in the Northeast, and eighty-five in the Middle states. The American Library Association has fixed as the standard of income for libraries — that is to say, the amount necessary to furnish really adequate service — one dollar per capita. The Far West spends $1.08; the Southeast, 16 cents. The same authority estimates that a public library really well used will circulate five books a year for each person in the area it serves. Again the Far West does a little better than this, while the libraries of the Southeast circulate seventy-seven hundredths of one book per capita. Again, it is estimated that in a community where reading habits are well established about 30 per cent of the total population will be registered as users of the library. The Far West has 29.9 per cent, the Southeast 5 per cent.

The situation regarding periodicals is similar. In the whole country there are 3.20 people for each copy of a daily newspaper issued. In Mississippi there are 18.11, in South Carolina, 12.44, in Arkansas, 12.29. In the whole country, for each copy of forty-seven leading magazines issued there are 3.97 people. In Mississippi there are

12.49, in South Carolina, 10.81, in Alabama, 10.76. It brings to mind the melancholy dictum of J. Gordon Coogler, the Alabama poetaster:

> Alas for the South! Her books have grown fewer,
> She never was much given to literature.

The curious fact is, however, that Mr. Coogler was wrong. It remains true that the South's books are few, much below her needs. But to say that they are growing fewer is altogether false. On the contrary, here is another instance of a lag that has been reduced notably within the last generation. In the Southeast are four of the thirteen states that have State Library Commissions. The Southeastern and Southwestern Library Associations, in conjunction with the American Library Association and four great non-Southern foundations, have been doing notably successful work in establishing library service where it never existed before, and in extending the effective range of existing libraries.

Remarkable as this work has been, however, it is proceeding too slowly to keep pace with the increasing need. Granting that the seven years following 1929 were abnormal times, presenting an unemployment problem out of all proportion to what may be expected in the future, the fact remains that both technological innovation and social organization tend toward giving the population an increasing amount of leisure. Facilities for its proper utilization therefore assume an increasing importance. This increased leisure may be equally effective in contributing to a raising or lowering of the level of civilization. The direction that the Southeast will take unquestionably depends to no small degree upon her success or failure in supplying her people with the things necessary to assist them in avoiding waste of this leisure.

10

The foregoing is not an exhaustive list, but it includes the principal forms of human waste that Odum's inventory reveals in the Southeast. There are dozens, perhaps hundreds, of minor wastes easily traceable by the statistician; but these are the greatest.

Like the waste of the land, the waste of the people in the Southeast is, in practically every form it takes, avoidable and remediable. This is not to be effected by any panacea, to be sure. The problem is complex and not to be solved by the application of any neat and simple formula. But while it is complex, it is not obscure. Every phase of it has been encountered before somewhere in the world, and somewhere a remedy has been found and applied. The Southeast is under no compulsion to sail uncharted seas in search of remedies for the evils that beset her. Her business is to apply the known, the tried, the tested; although it does include the application of some things hitherto unknown in her experience, they are all sufficiently well known in other times and other climes. Much of it, indeed, is so obvious that even mention of it is justified only by the fact that so far it hasn't been done. And yet, all experience goes to show that one of the most difficult aspects of the conduct of human life is precisely the application of common sense to every situation. It would be fatuous to assert that the task lying before the Southeast is an easy one. But it can be done.

— From *The Wasted Land*, University of North Carolina Press, 1937. Reprinted by permission.

SOUTHERN TOWNS AND CITIES

By Edd Winfield Parks

ALMOST FIFTY years ago Lord Bryce wrote that, with a few notable exceptions, American cities differed from each other chiefly in that some were built more with brick than with wood, and others more with wood than with brick. He missed entirely the local traditions and idiosyncrasies and the development of purely local products and specialties that gave character and individuality to European cities. Yet even Bryce's sarcastic distinction would hardly hold good today, when the processes of standardization have tended to make each town more like every other town, until differences in population remain the chief mark of distinction. But in 1880 there were few Southern cities, and New Orleans was, significantly, among his exceptions. Even judged by the urban standards of that day, Nashville, Atlanta, Charleston, Richmond, and Memphis were little more than towns; Birmingham, a high vision wallowing in mud; and New Orleans, our one great city.

The reason for this lack of cosmopolitan development in the South is obvious. Before the Civil War, it was neither an industrial nor a commercial section. And its people were not only agrarian; they had, in addition, a localism that was largely self-sufficient. The town or city was a useful clearing-house, which disposed of money crops, such as cotton and tobacco, and which supplied, in turn, the luxuries that could not be made or produced. But even then, although in most cases the balance remained constantly on the side of the city, with the farmer and plantation-owner borrowing from year to year on his anticipation of future crops, it was only the financial balance, as measured in dollars, that favored the city. The true center of power, the basis of the entire economic structure, rested on the land and on the people who owned that land. If cotton was not king in all sections, the power typified by cotton held dominion over the South. The system was almost feudal, for the ownership of land and of slaves carried with it duties and responsibilities to dependents, as well as definite claims upon them. The men living under such a system tried to avoid buying any article that could be made at home, and every plantation was in effect an independent manufacturing unit.

Whatever the defects of this system, the men produced under it had little need for great cities. But Southern defeat in 1865 ended abruptly a worn-out yet human way of life, and it may be that both victor and vanquished have failed to replace it with a better one. Then, all was confusion. Peace came, but without order. The fields were laid waste; guerrilla bands harried many sections; irresponsible Negroes, encouraged by Federal soldiers and accustomed only to obedience, found the heady wine of freedom too much to control. The isolated farm was no longer safe.

The farmer had no choice. In times of stress, men must band closely together, and Southern men in large numbers moved to the town or city for safety and security. Between 1865 and 1875, most Southern towns doubled in size, although the new residents generally continued to think of themselves as farmers. Yet the type of farming had changed. For a time after the war, when cotton was fifty cents a pound and other produce equally high in price, the planters attempted to resume large-scale production. But taxes were disproportionate, workers irresponsible, and all materials expensive — and prices soon dropped back to a normal level. Once a man could ride over broad fields in the full pride of ownership, and direct a group of workers on a communal project. Now each man wanted his own definite number of acres, to farm as he pleased. From this developed a system of tenant farming, on the share-crop or money-rent basis, with each tenant farmer and small landowner quite independent. Yet his independence was limited and circumscribed: the self-sufficient farm community was a thing of the past. Now the farmer became dependent on town or city for farm implements, for articles of clothing, and, in many instances, even for food that he could easily have raised on his own land. For the first time in the history of the South, the agrarian community was subsidiary to the urban community.

This transition can be charted with reasonable accuracy. The farmer moved to the small town to escape the dangers of Reconstruction, while he rented out his farm to poorer whites or Negroes; more often, he superintended the farm work by day and returned to town at nightfall. The sons of these men knew little of farming, and that little was unpromising. Farms, then as now, often failed to make enough money to pay running expenses, and the migration went on, from farm to town, and from town to city. By 1880, these younger men had acquired enthusiasm for other things. If money could not be made from raising cotton or tobacco, it could from the manufacture of products from those same staples. The South, men said, must be revived, " not with cotton in the fields, but cotton in the mills." Every town of consequence desired a cotton mill or a manufacturing plant of any variety.

In general, these industries came to established cities, rather than to newly founded towns. New Orleans, Louisville, Richmond, Atlanta, Memphis, and Chattanooga all gained rapidly, both in manufacturing and in population. At first, these new industries were chiefly financed by local men, and progress was heart-breakingly slow. In addition, not one of these cities welcomed industrialism with entirely open arms. A stubborn group of older men and women remembered an earlier and, it may well be, a better way of life, which had little to do with great factories or pushing businesses. But poverty will force most men into line, and — though Walter Hines Page at the turn of the century excoriated as mummies those who held out against new ways — soon the tide was all against tradition.

A few cities grew, almost overnight, out of nothingness. William K. Boyd, in *The Story of Durham*, traces briefly " certain well-defined periods in its growth. These are the days of origin, down to 1865, followed by an expansion from a hamlet into a small manufacturing town between 1865 and 1881; then comes the transformation into a small city, a well-defined period from 1881 to 1900; and, finally, there is the last quarter-century, when industry became more diversified, a government more complex, and new social institutions emerged." A less flattering chronicler has suggested that the city has ridden to renown on the shoulders of Bull Durham and Buck Duke. Beyond question, the story of Durham is the story of the tobacco industry, which, like the city, has advanced from infancy to such commanding position that its entrepreneurs can endow great universities.

Even more spectacular — the most striking, though the least representative — was the development of Birmingham. Least representative, because in that city alone was industrialism not at war with an older tradition: Birmingham was not founded until 1871, when the ordinary activities of the South were at a standstill, and it was planned from the beginning to be an industrial city. Men recognized the potential value of Alabama's immense natural resources in coal and iron, but for five years the new city floundered dismally along, until in 1876 Colonel J. W. Sloss proved beyond question that coke iron could be produced in Alabama. Yet vain efforts to interest Northern capital failed time and again (for Northern manufacturers refused to believe that iron, and later steel, of good quality could be made from this new bed of raw ore), until the city again seemed fated to remain small.

Then a new element entered into the life of Birmingham and, somewhat more slowly, into the life of the South. Northern capitalism was convinced of bright opportunities. In the 1890's, Andrew Carnegie, his associates, and his competitors bought into the Alabama companies, to give a literal, as well as figurative, truth to Birmingham's proud boast that it was "the Pittsburgh of the South." This was no isolated phenomenon: throughout the South, precisely the same development occurred in many and varied industries.

By 1900, the period of self-development had largely passed, and the era of exploitation had begun. The progress of Southern industrialism, as long as it depended upon its own limited capital and resources, was necessarily snail-like. Men demanded more immediate results. Then started the campaign for Northern capital, for new factories in every possible line of manufacturing. The Chambers of Commerce and allied organizations of businessmen lost no opportunity to paint in alluring colors the glowing advantages of the South, with its moderate climate, its cheap white labor, its abundant raw materials — the prospects were endless. This campaign among the cities culminated in bids that seem incredible — various places offered such concessions as freedom from taxation over a long period of years, free factory sites, and similar financial attractions for which no adequate recompense was ever received.

Whatever the ultimate profits and losses may have been, the tangible result was, more and more, to justify Lord Bryce's statement. The Richmond of 1870 was indubitably a part of Virginia, and Atlanta was definitely an integral part of Georgia. Each was dependent on the state for sustenance. But Richmond and Atlanta were definitely unlike in certain respects — in architecture and in industries, for example. The result of the change sketched above has been to make Atlanta more like Richmond, and also, on a lesser scale, more like New York and Cleveland, but much less like Georgia. It has become, as far as its business is concerned, the representative of New York in the South, and it has striven for, and attained, much of New York's cosmopolitanism. In greater or in less degree, precisely that same development has occurred in every Southern city.

The cities of the South have thrived almost unbelievably, but even this remarkable growth, when compared with that of certain other sections of the country, does not seem so great after all. Knoxville, in 1920, could advertise itself blatantly on automobile license tags as the 114 per cent city — the growth of a single decade; Birmingham had grown from nothing in 1871 to 175,000 in 1920, and to more than 250,000 in 1930. New Orleans, Louisville, Atlanta, and Memphis all had passed well beyond this same high mark, though only the first, at the turn of the century, had approached it. Bigness, for its own sake, had become a megalomania: at each census the various cities would annex surrounding towns, and make concerted drives for more inhabitants, in order that they might surpass rival cities. Yet Atlanta, though it may seem to us a metropolis, is smaller than Toledo or Columbus, and only a trifle larger than Akron; Birmingham and Memphis cannot equal Jersey City and Newark. Even New Orleans does not begin to compare in size with a dozen cities scattered over other sections of the United States.

There are several reasons for this lack of urban development. The

South started late, and this initial handicap has been hard to overcome. The small industries that antedated the Civil War were destroyed, and money was lacking to revive or to replace these infant industries. But there were less obvious, and possibly more important, reasons. Although after 1900 the advocates of industrial progress seemed to dominate the cities, there remained an older, more leisurely civilization that set little store by progress, that insistently held out for individual, as opposed to corporate, growth. This attitude has been labeled prejudice, and has been subjected to bitter and fairly effective attack from Chambers of Commerce and kindred organizations, but it has never been completely uprooted. Men and women prefer to trade where clerks know them by name, and at least seem interested in them as individuals. Chain stores and any other store that fails to deliver its goods to the purchaser's door have found difficulty in securing patronage, though they might sell goods a little cheaper than their old-fashioned competitors.

This attitude has carried over into other, less superficial aspects of business. For two generations it made men chary of investing money in factories or intangible stocks and bonds; accustomed to the ownership of tangible land, men could not easily reconcile themselves to paper tokens, however valuable. The sons of gentlemen were educated for the professions, and even today in the South the professional man retains a faint dignity that has been completely denied him elsewhere. Only a change in public opinion could bring about the urban development of the South, and that change was necessarily slow.

It was relatively easy for the commercial Northeast to shift from a mercantile to an industrial economy. But the South had never been capitalistic, although it had possessed a few shipping centers — New Orleans, Savannah, Charleston, and, partly Southern, Baltimore — and it had to build up an entirely new set of values. After 1900 this conversion came rapidly, in part through the propagation of new ideas by such publicists as Walter Hines Page, but primarily and most effectively through the demonstration that financial prosperity could be achieved only through an industrialized society. In 1930 the city seemed dominant and continued to grow apace. This was the tangible symbol of the new South, and bitterly, that year, our cities fought for supremacy when the census counted heads. The results of the last three years will be considered briefly at the end of the article; in discussion here, it seems better to treat the cities without exact regard to the immediate present, but in a more general time-sense, which may loosely be called "modern."

II

In what respect do Southern cities differ from those of the North and the West? That, it seems to me, is a question that might reasonably be asked; it is a question that becomes increasingly difficult to answer. Before attempting such a task, it would be necessary to describe, briefly and pointedly, certain Southern cities and to make some differentiation between them. For it is worthy of note that these cities differ radically among themselves, and it is no mean tribute that each name carries with it connotations and traditions that are peculiar to it.

At once the largest and most picturesque city in all the South is New Orleans — which, as Lyle Saxon has discerningly pointed out in *Fabulous New Orleans*, is in reality two cities. There is the old French city — the Vieux Carré — and the newer "American city." Here, more clearly than in any other town, can one observe the incessant yet rarely noticeable struggle between progress and tradition. For the two sections pay allegiance to strangely dissimilar gods, and it is with regret that one notices unmistakable signs of predominance of the god of business.

The streets in the old city are narrower; in the newer section they frequently have a center drive, which is planted with palms or evergreen trees. Canal Street, the business center, is neutral ground; in "old town," as it is frequently called, the houses are predominantly French or Spanish, closely joined together, with much graceful ironwork around small balconies, and with inner courtyards. The entire atmosphere is leisurely and cosmopolitan: in part the work of artists and Bohemians who inhabit the Vieux Carré, in part the survival of French and Spanish family life. Here, too, are memories and realities: of Antoine's, Galatoire's, La Louisianne, and older, not quite forgotten restaurants that made of eating and drinking a fine art; the St. Louis cemetery and cathedral; the old

Ursuline Convent that served also as an archbishop's palace; the great " dueling oaks " that belong in spirit, if not in location, to the old town — all these, and a score of blocks of houses, a few fine government buildings, are relics of French and Spanish days. Yet, as I write this, newspapers chronicle the doom of the old and famous French Market House — *Halle des Boucheries*. In a few months it will be torn down and replaced with a new and up-to-date building. Fire, also, has taken its toll, in the old Opera House; and, caught between these twin agents of destruction, the Vieux Carré seems fated, some day, to disappear.

Yet the subtle forces of tradition permeate even the new city, with its wide streets and miscellaneous architecture. Men work in leisurely fashion, and go out, each morning and afternoon, for coffee that, according to legend, will help to ward off malaria. And New Orleans bears the imprint of the river and ocean. It is distinctly a Mississippi River town, although commerce on the river has lost its economic importance and adds today only a touch of color and strangeness. But floods are ever threatening, and men can never forget that the city is often ten feet below the level of the Mississippi and dependent upon levees for its safety. Once, too, the great bend in the river gave to the city a rounded shape and the name of the " Crescent City " — a name without meaning today, save that its principal streets running north and south curve to follow the bend in the river. New Orleans remains a great seaport, a gateway for such Southern products as cotton, grain, and lumber, and a center for imports from South America. But there is little manufacturing: New Orleans, as much today as before the Civil War, depends upon the surrounding country for its support. It is a clearing-house for the lower South.

Men have turned the brilliant social life of an older day into a first-rate tourist attraction. Mardi Gras has become an institution, with its Rex, its Mystic Krewe of Comus, Knights of Momus, and Crewe of Proteus. There are balls and street parades, river carnivals, and both organized and impromptu revelry, but the ancient flavor has gone, to a large extent, in the modern effort to entertain visitors. True, business stops while society plays . . . but business reaps in the end, one feels, a twofold harvest. Yet in this, as in so many other instances, the old and the new are in combat.

Far removed from such conflict is Birmingham, city of the new South. It is the one industrial center between New Orleans and Atlanta, the center of the iron and coal industry south of Pennsylvania. The buildings are all of a kind: relatively new, with a preponderance of modern skyscrapers dwarfing the more ordinary store buildings and the semi-classic governmental and institutional structures. Situated on the slope of Red Mountain, it escapes a monotonous regularity chiefly through this natural ruggedness of the terrain. For Birmingham is predominantly a child of the twentieth century, and it has no old traditions that cause men to regret the passing of old landmarks.

In physical location Richmond possesses one likeness to Birmingham: the capital of Virginia was originally built on seven hills, and once it was called " modern Rome." But the hills, overhanging the James River, are small — and there, abruptly, the resemblance ceases. For Richmond, like New Orleans, is a blend of old and new; even the principal industry — the preparation of tobacco for use — far antedates the Revolutionary War. Few towns possess more definitely the intangible stamp of historical associations. The public buildings have one quality even rarer than tradition: they have architectural merit. The capitol building was designed by Thomas Jefferson after the model of the ancient Roman temple, the Maison Carrée, of Nîmes, and the later additional wings have conformed to the same general type. All the public buildings in Richmond have, in fact, conformed to this adapted classical style, and the statuary commemorating notable men of yesteryear adds to this impression of Richmond as a classical American city. Prominent landmarks and historic buildings recall memories of Washington, Jefferson, Marshall, Madison, Lee, and a veritable host of men only slightly less famous. One cannot easily forget such names, or forget that in 1730 Richmond was known as " Byrd's Warehouse," or that once it was the capital of the Confederacy. But Richmond is sorely divided, one group feeling that memories can be bought at too high a price, and striving desperately for business growth; the other prizing an older way of living that seems inevitably in conflict with modern progress.

"No city should be a museum, kept intact under glass." That statement was hurled at Richmond some years ago; with even more justice can it be applied to Charleston. Although it has an extremely fine port and is an important commercial city, this phase of its life has been rather largely neglected. All historic places and features have been carefully preserved: the Battery, with its magnificent view of the harbor and of Fort Sumter; wooded White Point Garden, with its monuments to great men of another day; the Powder Magazine, the Slave Market, and the old residential houses that recall days when Pringles and Heywards and Hugers ruled the community. Twelve miles from town are the Magnolia Gardens, perhaps the principal attraction to tourists, and certainly an integral part of the community. Like New Orleans, it possesses one of the few really important social events of the nation, but Charleston has retained for its St. Cecilia's Ball an exclusiveness that commercial prosperity has never tarnished. Here family is all-important, and relatives are counted to the "nth" generation; yet here, too, is a Gallic lightness of manner, and at times a fiery zeal bringing a recollection that Charleston is tempered with a large group of people of French Huguenot descent. That zeal once led the state into nullification and, again, led the South into a war. But today it seems dormant — primarily interested in preserving faded but imperishable glories.

Although Savannah was founded by James Oglethorpe in 1733, it seems to have less of history and somewhat more of humanity than Charleston. The tang of the marsh is in the air, and the picturesque scenes native to any port town are constantly in view. For Savannah remains undeniably a small town, though an exceedingly busy port, and its air of leisurely dignity seems far more in keeping with Georgia than do the bustling ways of Atlanta.

Perhaps it is not by accident that two of our most prosperous cities have little connection with the agrarian South. Unlike Birmingham, Atlanta did not spring up overnight. Before the Civil War the first name of the village, Marthasville, was changed to Terminus, because increasingly the railroads centered round that town. And Terminus in due time became Atlanta, the central goal of General Sherman, who described it as "the wrist of a hand whose fingers reach five principal ports of the Gulf and South Atlantic coasts." During the days of Reconstruction, Atlanta became capital of the state; since that time, its valuable central location and its easy accessibility have made it, in sober truth, the "New York of the South." For Atlanta also is new, with broad streets and a metropolitan air, and it has become a center of manufacturing as well as of distribution. Rural Georgia has little tangible connection with it, save to supply it with food, and the city quite evidently is not proud of Georgia. All emphasis is thrown on its fine buildings and educational institutions, and above all, on the fact that Atlanta is the metropolis of the South and, basically, a branch of New York. Although a leisureliness, an old-time courtesy and gentility, pervades the atmosphere, the casual visitor is rarely allowed to forget, in his business contacts, that this way of life is less important than the city's commerce.

Compared with Atlanta, Nashville seems an overgrown small town, with narrow and outmoded streets, grimy old buildings, and the settled placidity of middle age. This, however, is only a half-picture. Once it was a frontier town, but those days are completely past, and long since forgotten; today it is "the Athens of the South," boasting of fine educational institutions and of grand old days, yet reaching somewhat reluctantly for new commercial projects. It has Vanderbilt, Peabody, Ward-Belmont, and Fisk: the four extremes in modern education. For Vanderbilt represents the old-line classical college that has branched out into a large university; Peabody, the modernized institution that believes men can be transformed into teachers if they are taught the correct methods; Ward-Belmont remains an outstanding boarding school for well-to-do young ladies; and Fisk is preëminent in the field of cultural education for Negroes. Here are four radically different schools, in a city that rebuilds the Greek Parthenon and now puts on, through its Chamber of Commerce, a five-year plan to lure new industries from the North. A divided city that prizes, on the one side, Friendly Five shoes — and, on the other, the Hermitage. Like every Southern city, it lives on inconsistencies: allows baseball on Sundays, yet forbids movies; prides itself on culture, but has no decent theater and is shunned even by road shows; points with pride to historical tradition while it seeks the very things that, inevitably, must destroy the value and the validity of those traditions.

Memphis, like Atlanta, owes much of its development to the accident of location. It is the trade center for the upper Mississippi Delta and other less famous, but hardly less rich, valleys. Distinctly a river town in pre-Civil War days, Memphis retains a picturesque quality through its location on the bluffs of the Mississippi and the docks and river boats that give it something of the appearance of a port town. No longer is the river an important commercial adjunct of the city, however; but railroads have kept it a focal point for trade in the old Southwest. Unlike most cities today, Memphis is directly dependent on the surrounding country, for practically all of its commerce and industry revolves around cotton and hardwood. It is the largest inland market handling actual cotton in the country and the greatest center for the manufacture of cottonseed products. An open city, with wide streets and many handsome buildings, it has remained a type of the old plantation center — and its attempt to rival larger cities in the North and the West received one tangible check quite recently when its newest skyscraper was sold at auction under the bankruptcy law. When the surrounding country is prosperous, Memphis thrives; when, as at present, the farmer and the planter are poverty-stricken, the city suffers in equal proportion.

There are other cities that might, with equal justice, be sketched in greater detail: the industrial cities of Chattanooga and Knoxville, the pleasant port of Mobile, the resort city of Asheville, and the tobacco town of Durham. But any sketches of this nature must be inconclusive and unsatisfactory. I have omitted, deliberately, the Texas cities, for Dallas and Fort Worth belong to the Southwest; and San Antonio, though a fascinating blend of Spanish, Mexican, Southern, Western, and military life, seems outside the scope of this discussion. For a similar reason I have omitted Louisville, though it might well be labeled "Southern" — but Louisville seems clearly comparable with St. Louis, and far removed, somehow, from Memphis or New Orleans. With equal arbitrariness I have neglected the tourist cities of Florida. They represent a transplanted East. Some day this culture may bulk large in a study of Southern life; at the present moment it is quite negligible. These arbitrary distinctions were unfortunate, but necessary in any attempt to describe or to analyze the Southern city as a type that is representative and that has become, in some instances, a section within the larger section that is the South.

III

Yet, when one takes a wider view of this group of cities, these distinctions seem less important than certain other elements that lead inevitably to the conclusion that Southern cities have much in common. And the elements of kinship, not the differentiations, give to all, in varying degree, a certain character that may be called " Southern " and that separates these cities quite distinctly from cities in other sections.

Most important is the amazing homogeneity of the people. Without undue exaggeration, Konrad Bercovici could write a book that dealt with many close-knit tribes of men, and title it *Around the World in New York*. But foreign colonies of people as yet unassimilated boil down, in the South, to one race: the Negro. (It may be well here to qualify this generalization; there exist, of course, a few colonies, such as the Spanish Ybor City in Tampa, the Greek settlement at Tarpon Springs, the Portuguese settlements along the Gulf coast, and similar small but unassimilated groups. These colonies are too unimportant to influence any considerable portion of Southern life.) And the Negro, though an integral part of the community life, does live, and apparently is destined for many years to live, in sections that are exclusively his own. The Negro has churches, schools, newspapers, of his own; to some extent, he has business houses that have strict regard for the color line. Undoubtedly this is imposed upon him — quite often unfairly — by the white race; but the essential point here is that the Negro represents the one alien group of considerable size and influence in the South.

Only the Negro, however, constitutes a separate communal group within the larger community. The South remains predominantly Anglo-Saxon. This was not entirely through intention: for many years, after 1865, the various states made strenuous efforts to attract immigrants. Virginia sent recruiting agents to Great Britain and Germany; a Southern Immigration Society, organized in 1883, attempted to secure immigrants from European countries. Even Chinese coolie labor was tried, but soon abandoned. Perhaps the most outspoken advocate of this movement was Henry Grady, who desired for Georgia one hundred thousand immigrants — and seventy-five thousand of these men he would place in the factories. But immigrant wage-earners continued to prefer the North, and the movement failed completely. Today such movements work more indirectly, in the attempt to lure industries to this section; and it is not by accident that Birmingham, most industrial of our cities, has by far the largest number of foreign-born residents.

The inevitable result is that we continue to value, as no city save Boston or San Francisco does value, tradition and family. The power of wealth is rarely disregarded for long, even in Charleston, but each city has an aristocratic, though often poverty-stricken, set of old gentlemen and ladies who refuse flatly to countenance certain people. And men have been known, within the past five years, to build great sporting clubs, primarily for the purpose of showing these dowager duchesses that, whatever the South may think, the world has moved forward, and does regard great wealth with proper awe. Yet in the slow but inevitable course of time these sturdy exponents of aristocracy also seem doomed; the entire course of life is set against them. They continue to exert, in some instances, a powerful influence; they add color and distinctiveness to a social life that is rapidly aping New York in flat monotony — even to the smart society columns in newspapers — but they are a remnant that soon will pass.

Included in this remnant is the one foreign element that has given something of tone and color to New Orleans and Charleston. In a sense, it is a mistake to think of the French in Charleston, or the French and Spanish in New Orleans, as foreign. They have been a part of these communities for always, relatively; they are quite unmistakably part of the grand tradition. Possibly for that reason these cities retain an element of lightheartedness that other cities lack. Somehow (perhaps through the influence of our Biblical defense of slavery) we came to adopt the American tradition of "work while you work, and play while you play." This adage and others like it have led the Southerner to feel ashamed of leisureliness — the trait most often assigned to us by outsiders — and to feel that haste is a necessary part of life. The man of business in New Orleans must have a leisurely cup of coffee; in Nashville or Atlanta, his cousin will gulp a coca-cola. The noon meal has become lunch, and must be eaten hurriedly, often at drugstores.

This change in superficial matters has carried over into larger and graver affairs. On Sunday a man must attend church or go to some opposite extreme, such as playing golf or getting drunk. No longer can there be a middle ground that affords ease and pleasure. We must work or play; attend church or dissipate; but rarely, now, do we consider that conversation is an art, and drinking only a nectar that adds sparkle to casual talk. Yet even in this respect the South, I believe, has gone less rapidly than the nation. We have tried valiantly to be swift, but we are not swift enough. The force of family ties does much to hold back this breakdown of leisurely living. Father and mother may go to church, while son and daughter play golf — but many families continue to regard the Sunday dinner as a delightful obligation when all the members must be present. This is a momentary check, I fear, and one rapidly disappearing, but one may be grateful even for delay.

For the cities have become swift and pushing; they have long since abandoned leisure as an ideal, and would have abandoned it in practice save for the incurable habits of an outmoded generation. These men have left an indefinable stamp; they have remained unregenerate. But one gets back, sooner or later, to the reason for this attitude: that they are not by nature cosmopolitan creatures; they were part of an agrarian tradition, of a tradition that valued local sections and local affairs, and they have given to each Southern city a remarkable individuality.

It is natural and inevitable that each city in the country should have local traits and idiosyncrasies. Less natural is the fact that the city should be governed and given character by the country immediately surrounding it. This seems to me the one important factor that differentiates Southern cities. With the single exception of Birmingham, they belong to the general sectional environment, and could not be transposed without being uprooted. This statement would be equally true of any old-line city: of Boston or Philadelphia, or the semi-Southern Indianapolis. But Akron or Chicago might easily be in Michigan, and Detroit in Ohio or Illinois. The industrial city is a unit within itself. But the Southern community has not yet been industrialized, and it retains the coloring of the surrounding section.

IV

For many years, the growth of the city seemed the death-knell for the small town. Once a local craftsman made wagons for the surrounding farmers; a shoemaker made shoes; a miller ground the wheat. Gradually these and many additional industries became standardized, until the local craftsman has practically disappeared. In the same interval, the city began to supply its inhabitants with electric lights, running water, sewerage disposal, and similar conveniences that made the small town appear, in contrast, glaringly backward and unprogressive. Today the processes of standardization have, strangely, made the town as modern as the city, for even the smallest places can have moving pictures, electric lights, radios, and filling stations. Usually, in farming sections, a single blacksmith shop remains, but it is dwarfed into insignificance by garages that repair farm tractors as well as automobiles. No longer is the small-town boy or girl subject to taunts on account of " country " clothes or manners. The town is no longer isolated. But this lack of isolation has resulted in economic disadvantage: men and women find it too easy to drive to the nearest city to shop, while they neglect the local stores. Boys continue to go to larger communities, because there is little chance for work at home.

Economically, the village has suffered, because it is directly dependent on the farmer. But it has suffered less than the city, because the floating population and, to a large extent, the laborers, completely dependent on their salary checks, do not exist among them. Wealth may exist with less frequency than in the city, but poverty also is rarer.

The traveler in the South has a distinct impression that our cities are, in many respects, overgrown small towns, and this, as I have tried to show, is often a virtue rather than a defect. But the town has, in turn, aped the city, usually with disastrous results.

The ideal picture is one of wide and shady streets, with old houses in colonial style, of wood painted white, or of aged red brick with decorous white pillars and façade. Somehow the business district remains a little obscured, except in that city peculiar to the South, the county seat. In these towns the county courthouse, a rectangular two-storied red brick building, with a monument to the Confederate dead occupying a clear space in front, gives a dignity to the small stores that surround it on every side. Here, too, is a park with green trees and grass, and inviting white benches on which old men sit and chew tobacco and spin long yarns of delightful yesterdays.

Too often this picture is ideal rather than real. The courthouse yard is likely to be littered with trash, the store windows to be dirty, and the goods displayed to be shoddy and ill-arranged. Too often the buildings in the business district are flat and tasteless, with a fourth of them derelict and deserted: the toll taken by concrete roads that lead with increasing swiftness and directness to better-stocked places in some neighboring city. And the townspeople tend, like the city folk, to huddle together on fifty-foot lots, in small white bungalows or in garish little stucco and ornamental brick dwellings. By an adaptation of the classic style, architecture in the Old South evolved a large house of great dignity and beauty, but so far the small one-story or story-and-a-half dwelling has, it would seem, defied successfully all efforts to give it charm and individuality. Yet most of these houses are screened by vines, and they present, except in winter, a not unattractive front.

Perhaps the most notable physical characteristic that differentiates these Southern towns from those of any other section is the presence of the Negro. Each town has its Negro section, usually given such expressive names as " Black Bottom " or " Nigger Hill." These titles might imply that the Negro is badly treated, but this most certainly is far from true. He is segregated socially, but in all other respects he is a normal and generally a happy part of the community, with his own school and churches. For the small-town

Negro, also, is not philosophical, and he remains unworried over subtle distinctions of race equality or of right and wrong. Enough for him that he is treated as a human being, with a consideration and courtesy that is rarely bestowed, in larger centers, upon the poorer class of immigrants.

There is another type of Southern town, which has exact counterparts in many other sections of the country. Although relatively few in number, these purely industrial small towns of the South have received far more attention than any other type. Little of good can be said for our Gastonias and Scottsboros and Old Hickorys, where men exist rather than live, where row after row of drab and practically uniform houses stretch into a monstrous eyesore, where even existence depends upon the whistle of the factory, and where, until recently, men labored for ten or twelve hours a day for meager wages, and returned home each night too exhausted to value the few moments of leisure allowed them. Under a new régime such towns may soon disappear; at present they exist and cannot, unfortunately, be forgotten.

The manner of living in the small town is less attractive than in more urban communities, but the way of life is simpler and, in many ways, more pleasant. Here leisureliness and neighborliness are vital and real. No man is too busy to stop and chat, to loaf in the drugstore or courthouse yard. Such talk deals in the main with tangible facts, with weather or crops or business conditions or sport. Gossip and discussion rarely aspire to the philosophical, though men at times are wiser than they intend to be. But at least the human relationship has never become mechanical.

In a novel that attacks the village, Sinclair Lewis describes a funeral where the corpse is taken to the grave in a wagon, attended only by a solitary mourner. The first part of that description might be true of a Southern small town, and it need reflect no discredit on either family or community. But no family, however poor, would be thus neglected. Men and women would come to visit the sick, and to " sit up " with the dead body, until a decent burial had occurred. Sickness and death bring out the finest elements of small-town people, for almost invariably they are kind and considerate.

The women have even greater leisure, and even greater preoccupation with small things. They are, in general, kindly to a fault, but they are concerned always with the affairs of other people. Gossip is ever among us, at the bridge table and the missionary society, and the person who strays in any manner from the conventional path is certain to furnish a topic of conversation — often condemnatory — to every inhabitant. Yet this gossip springs more often from curiosity than from malice. Recent novelists have tended to see too large the viciousness and meanness and lack of breadth of the small town, and too little its tolerant humanity. They have been impressed with the size of events, and have forgotten that the Fourth of July celebration, with its greased pig and amateur baseball game between two neighboring towns, is as important as the world series.

Unconsciously, our townspeople have made this distinction. Rarely are they troubled with great events. Life flows on quietly, yet not, for the most part, monotonously. The cares and concerns of little things, and above all of people, occupy the time of most of them. They have time to stand and stare, or to sit and chat. In a word, the life of the Southern town is serene.

V

Three years of depression have served to emphasize the close resemblance, the essential kinship, between the city and the town. Hard times have sobered, at least temporarily, our city folk. No longer do bulletins put forth proudly the population, wealth, industry, and, above all, the desirability of each city. Closed factories and shops, breadlines, and threat of revolution have caused instead some discussion of a "back to the farm" movement that would deplete the urban community of its idle population. But this seems to be a temporary truce.

For complex forces are at work, and the cities are busily attempting to take full advantage of them. As I attempt a final revision of this article, late in the autumn of 1933, I can find relatively few certainties, either of fact or of prediction. The cities, long quiescent under the specter of depression, have begun to stir themselves and to put on new drives for outside industries of any nature. The insignias of the NRA, with its blue eagle, grace every factory and store, and men have begun to speak with optimism of the new day. But even the casual observer has noticed that in this period of depression the industrialistic cities, like Birmingham, have suffered most; they have lacked the greater reserve of the surrounding section to fall back upon.

And the NRA threatens to change the way of city life. Men who have rarely known leisure, save when penniless and jobless, have suddenly been thrown for hours each day upon their own resources. Although the city has not lagged in new effort to secure, from any source and without regard to local need, any new business, the leaders in our cities have been remarkably negligent about planning ways and means to make the cities more attractive to this unprepared leisure class. Quite conceivably, this minor social revolution may result in a more beautiful and more pleasant community, with well-kept houses and lawns, and with men who are more contented than ever urban dwellers have been previously; more probably, it seems to promise only that men will scurry aimlessly hither and thither, in search of pleasant and effortless ways to kill time. Whether the city will provide suitable means of recreation, and a type of education that will help adults to enjoy leisure, is an unknown and doubtful question. At the moment, all men seem bewildered, and they neglect this greater problem for the more immediate one that deals solely with profits and dollars.

In the background, also, is the shadowy yet dominating skeleton of the Tennessee Valley Authority. What it may do, no man can predict . . . and it has, as yet, done nothing. Conceivably, once more, it may change the entire alignment of our cities, in more drastic fashion than did the Civil War, until small Florence will overshadow Birmingham; but this seems unlikely. Once again it is probable that new industries will come chiefly to the existing large cities, that it will entrench and make more powerful such places as Knoxville, Chattanooga, Atlanta, and Birmingham. Meanwhile, newspaper editors predict, somewhat alarmingly, that we shall become " the Ruhr of America." They envision the South as a gigantic industrial factory in a time when our relatively small cities will rival and surpass the Detroits and Pittsburghs of other sections. More sober-minded folk hope to see a sane and well-regulated development, which will adapt itself primarily to local needs, which will give the vanishing small town a new means of sustenance without destroying its leisureliness or its integral dependence upon its own surroundings, and which will build toward the small local industries that supply basic and essentially local markets.

Whatever the result may be, the TVA has rendered it completely impossible to judge with any accuracy what our Southern towns and cities, in the next ten years, may become. Only one generalization remains true. In no remote yesterday these communities were an integral part of this section, but the tendency of the past thirty years has been to make of the city a new section, with interests that were often inimical to the surrounding country. And the cities have been scenes of peaceful, though at times bitter, conflict between the forces of tradition and of progress. There is no reason to suppose that harmony will come. Every possible forecast implies that the continued growth of the city, with a concomitant advance of industrialism, will tend to standardize our cities and make them more completely like all other American cities. But at present they remain a group apart, small and uncertain of their destiny, but stamped with the atmosphere of an old South that gives to each, in varying degrees, a character and individuality all its own.

— From *Culture in the South,* University of North Carolina Press, 1935. Reprinted by permission.

EVERYWHERE IN CHAINS

By Walter Prescott Webb

As I WRITE this I sit by a window that looks out on a city of perhaps seventy thousand people. Viewed from the purple hills to the west, or from any vantage point, it appears to be as clean and bright as if it had just been scoured by an industrious housewife. There is no smoke because there are no factories worth mentioning, and as a result of the absence of smoke the buildings, whether of stone or wood, remain as they originally were, white, gray, green, or brown, faded a little by the weather and the warm Southern sun.

In the center of the city rises a state capitol, similar to a score of others in other capital cities, while to the north a tower pierces the sky, rising even above the three-hundred-foot dome of the capitol, marking the location of a university that houses eight or nine thousand students from all parts of the state and the nation.

This city represents a cross section of the state, which lies half in the South and half in the West; it typifies in a manner all the towns of its size throughout these two great sections. What I see here, especially in the business district with which we shall be mainly concerned, is typical of what may be seen in every city of the South and the West with a population ranging from five thousand to a quarter, or even a half, million people. Every reader of this book who lives in any city within this population range may walk out on the streets of his town and see the things that I see in my town. His canvas may be larger than mine, or smaller, but that is of no consequence, for the design is about the same, whether in Memphis, Fayetteville, Boulder, Cheyenne, San Antonio, Emporia, or Austin.

When Sinclair Lewis looked out on such towns, he saw " Main

Street" filled with vulgar characters who hardly knew how to conduct themselves in a world that was changing under them. But as I look out on the business sections of the same towns I see people everywhere in chains. Wherever I turn in the South and the West I find people busily engaged in paying tribute to someone in the North. If I could paint a picture representing the general scene, it would be in the form of a great field stretching from Virginia and Florida westward to the Pacific and from Texas and California northward to Canada, an L-shaped region comprising nearly four fifths of the country. Here millions of people would be playing a game with pennies, nickels, dimes, and dollars, rolling them northward and eastward where they are being stacked almost to the moon.

As I sit writing I hear hundreds of automobiles swishing by on the semibusiness street that leads into the main part of the town. Similar automobiles are parked so closely on the downtown streets that I have to circle a block three times before I can find a place to park my car. I know that the garages and motor ramps and parking lots are filled with others. Every car in this town, and in every town in the South and the West, came from one of three or four manufacturers of the North. For every car that I see, for the 5,058,070 registered in the South and the 5,682,889 registered in the West — more than ten million all told — the owner has paid on an average $500 . . . and of this amount the ultimate profit, to say nothing of most of the labor cost, has flowed to the North. If the car was purchased on time, the owner paid interest (six per cent is twelve per cent in motor circles), insurance, service charges, and other incidentals that go for the most part to the same section.

When we transfer our attention from the car to the corporation that made it we find a closely articulated system which can be described only as a chain. Henry Ford's thousands of dealers all over the country constitute units in the Ford chain. It is well known that he directs these dealers with a firm hand, and that they have to conform to regulations that issue from Detroit. He gives the dealers specifications for their shops, sets their commission, and tells them how many cars they must sell. At one time he shipped the cars C.O.D. without waiting for orders, and if he wanted to throw in a few Fordson tractors, with the idea that the farmers should pension their mules and use his machines, he did so. Though Henry Ford rules his feudality with a strong hand, he is careful at all times to inform the public that his sole purpose is to give a maximum of service at a minimum cost. By such philanthropy he has built up perhaps the greatest private fortune in the world. Neither his modest benefactions nor his lofty proclamations of noble motives should obscure the fact that he is master of a chain that exercises economic control in varying degrees over millions of people.

Henry Ford has this control [1] because he was able, through the use of machinery, to make a car suitable for every family in America, to nationalize a commodity. He now takes tribute for every item of that commodity that passes from him into the hands of the user.

General Motors is not so simple, either in its origin or in its operations. That confederation of feudal-national enterprises was built up by a process of consolidation of various more or less independent enterprises, and in this respect it is typical of most of the great corporations. We know that the control of General Motors rests today in the hands of the Du Pont dynasty. General Motors is also a great chain with many units in my town and some in practically every town of over five thousand people. It is ruled by methods almost as arbitrary towards dealers as Henry Ford's and slightly less considerate either of the customer or of the laborers. General Motors has the advantage of impersonality that the Ford Company lacks. People do not know the name of the president, and they do not blame Alfred P. Sloan for the sins of General Motors as they blame Henry Ford for the faults that may be committed by his motor company. The result is that General Motors can commit more sin without hurting business than can the Ford Motor Company. The point not to be lost sight of is the same whether the Southerner or the Westerner purchases a Ford or a Buick. In one case he pays in Detroit; in the other he sends at least a few dimes to the Du Ponts in Wilmington, Delaware.

[1] This control may have country-wide and serious consequences should there be a determined attempt to organize labor throughout the Ford Motor Company.

Every automobile is propelled by gasoline supplied by other gigantic chains — Texaco, Gulf, Sinclair, Socony, and other companies. Here the relationships of these great feudal business organizations are such that one can neither untangle nor understand them. It is generally known, however, that if one buys Standard products he pays tribute to John D. Rockefeller; if he buys Gulf he aids Andy Mellon; and if he chooses Sinclair he contributes to the man who was almost able to wreck a presidential administration.

The oil stations may be divided into two classes, company-owned stations and individual stations. The company-owned stations were acquired principally during the period of 1920–1929 when profits were such that expenditures were beneficial in handling income tax reports. Since the depression the oil chains have ceased largely to purchase stations, but content themselves with operating on other people's money.

If the company operates the station, it supervises it and pays the attendants a wage or commission. There is no individualism there. The boys are told what to wear and how to wear it, what to sell and how to sell it, and are held to a strict accounting for their conduct. Recently I drove into a company station in a neighboring town and noted considerable excitement among the attendants. The manager of that station drove up, brought his car to a stop with all wheels sliding on the concrete, slipped out of the seat and addressed his helpers: "Hey, you guys, get your sleeves rolled down and your caps on and sweep this place up. The boss from New York is in town and will be here in a few minutes." The announcement that the President of the United States was coming would not have produced this startling effect. All over the South and the West, and in the North too, thousands of boys move by rules made from some mysterious place known as New York. "New York says do this" or "New York ordered us to do that" is the vernacular of the lower brackets of a nation in chains. Regimentation is nothing new in America. The chains had regimented their millions before the government knew the meaning of the word beyond army and navy circles.

The local offices of insurance companies, whether life, fire, or casualty, are but units in chains forged in the North. The Metropolitan, Aetna, Travelers, and dozens of others exercise direct control over their agents and indirect economic control over their policyholders and debtors throughout the country.

The public service corporations, whose complicated relationships are beyond comprehension, spread their net over the nation. They take their toll from those who use heat in winter, ice in summer, or light in the darkness. They fight the cities where the people want to manufacture their own light; they fight the government when it tries to set up a measuring stick to learn what it really costs to generate electricity; they get out injunctions to stop the construction of dams for the conservation of natural resources; they seek to control state legislatures through lobbies and lucrative retainerships; and they inspire investigations designed to oust university professors who have the intelligence to understand them and the courage to teach young men and women the truths that they have discovered. Such professors are usually charged with heresy or communism, and by some agent who would be hard pushed to define either or to realize that he is an agent.

The greatest chain in America is the American Telephone and Telegraph Company. Berle and Means tell us that one hundred such companies would control all the wealth in America. In addition to the employees, of which there are more than 450,000, every telephone subscriber is caught in this chain for life. The company has fastened itself in the affections of the public by paying dividends of nine per cent on par value of the stock to stockholders — dividends made possible by monthly or occasional toll on every user of the service. My town has an exceedingly low telephone rate, owing to a city charter of long standing, but others are not so fortunate. Recently a suit was ended in a neighboring town where the telephone company undertook to increase the rental. The company lost the suit, but had collected vast sums in the many months that the suit was pending. It was supposed to refund these overpayments to subscribers, but that was not possible in all cases because many people had in the meantime moved away. A few years ago the company brought out the French telephone and charges twenty-five cents a month extra for it, even though it costs no more to manufacture than did the old upright instrument. The average American will pay in the course of a lifetime from $90 to $120 for a gadget that can be made for perhaps $5.

If necessary, the list of chains could be extended to great length. There are Western Union and Postal, General Electric, Westinghouse, Goodyear, Firestone, and dozens of others, each with thousands of employees and millions of patrons. Nearly all of them have their capitals in the North, practice regimentation, and demand of every unit increasing profits. Let us consider some special aspects of the dependence of the South and the West on the North.

2

Since the development of the industrial revolution the North has been King of Things. As I survey the merchandise in my home town I discover that practically everything that is manufactured, processed, canned, or wrapped in a trade-mark comes from the North. My druggist tells me that he carries 10,000 items on his shelves; he estimates that 9,900 of these he buys from Northern firms. I learn that, of one hundred firms selling to him, eighty-five have their headquarters in the North, among them such distributors as Eli Lilly, Upjohn, Parke-Davis, etc., who manufacture hundreds of articles. Ten live in the South and five in the West. My grocer has on his shelves such familiar names as Libby, Heinz, Campbell (always demanding the first page given to advertising inside the magazines), American Sugar, Swift, Armour, and such all-inclusive names as General Foods and Standard Brands. Many of these articles are in containers made by the American Can Company, probably another subsidiary of United States Steel.

As I survey my home I find how dependent I am on the North for what is there. The entire furnishings from the brass knocker on the front door to the electric refrigerator in the kitchen are things for which I have paid the ultimate profit to some Northern firm. The man who financed my mortgage tells me that ninety per cent of the money lent here before the depression came from the North. I do not know the source of my loans, but it is safe to assume that a good part of the interest I pay goes to some Northern insurance firm.

The fact that the North is King of Things, that it makes practically all the commodities that are for sale, establishes the immediately dependent position of Southern and Western merchants. In the first stage the local merchant was like a commission man; he received his goods from the North, added his markup and sold the goods to his customers, taking his profit or loss. This was the situation of the old independent merchant. It is that of the few who are left. One told me recently that when he pays his bills at the end of the month, he sends ninety per cent of the money to the North, principally to New York. He has been a very successful merchant and a public-spirited citizen who took an active interest in all that was for the welfare of the town. He is no longer so successful. His business has gone to another type of merchant, and the only reason he does not close his doors is that forty families are dependent upon him for a livelihood.

Until about 1910 the North was content to use the independent merchant as an agent for the sale of things that it made. It was content to make things and to leave retail distribution to men who lived in the communities. About 1910 a change began to make its appearance. The North began to take over distribution as it had taken over manufacture. The North became the competitor of its customers throughout the South and the West, not in production, which it already monopolized, but in distribution. Since then the whole distribution scene has undergone a revolution and the whole business aspect of this town, and of all others like it, has been materially altered. It is no longer advisable for a citizen to establish a mercantile business in order that he may rear a family and provide an education for his children. The hazard of the chain competition is too great.

3

Let us view this town as it was before chains and as it is today, in 1910 and 1936. I recall how the town looked when I came as a student to the university. In two years I became familiar with the business section, and recall that every business house there was owned by a local citizen and operated by a local citizen. Less than a dozen of these firms remain, probably not more than five or six. There are now twenty-eight chains on one street. Almost a block is occupied by Kress, Woolworth, McClellan. On outlying streets Piggly Wiggly, Red & White, I.G.A., Riteway, and The Great Atlantic & Pacific have taken over much of the grocery business. Sears-Roebuck is at one end of the principal street and Montgomery Ward at the other. In 1910 the amusement center was the Opera House where the best plays of the legitimate stage came on tour. Just recently it was taken over by Paramount and remodeled. Paramount already controls three other theaters and is now constructing another. This chain now has a monopoly of the motion-picture business. The only houses not taken are a fourth-run place in the university neighborhood, which will be closed by the new Paramount under construction there, one featuring Wild West pictures, and a theater in the Negro section. It is generally known that a citizen can no longer go into motion pictures, except in small towns and suburban communities where the profit is small.

Department stores of the South and the West have felt the influence of the clothing chains. Specialty shops have eaten in on them with shoddy dresses made by sweatshops. Shoe chains such as Douglas and Thom McAn have come as outlets of Northern factories. Only the larger department stores have been able to survive this competition.

But something has happened among the department stores that the public is not so well aware of. Most of these were developed by local enterprise and continue to operate under the name of the founder, but many of them are now either owned outright or controlled by chains extending out from the North. This transfer of leading department stores to the chains has occurred in the last ten years. The manner in which it was accomplished may be of interest.

It happened in the hectic days preceding the depression. A promoter would appear in the town and offer the owner of a department store a million dollars for a business that was worth half the price. When the sale was made, stock would be issued against the business for, let us say, two or three millions. Local people were glad to buy stock because they believed in the name and prestige of the business. The sales force of the store were compelled to buy stock in order to hold their jobs. Most of them were glad to feel that they had a share in the business. My merchant friend told me that in many instances the life savings of old employees were taken in this manner. All who refused to buy stock were promptly let out and replaced by cheaper labor. Gradually came disillusionment. The stock paid no dividends and soon passed into the hands of the management. The citizens lost their investment, the employees lost their jobs and their savings, and the community lost control of a community enterprise. Thus was another link forged in the chain. A roll call of the leading department stores of this state, and probably of all others in the South and the West, would, if the truth could be learned, reveal that most of them have gone through the process described and are now under Northern control.

In some instances the chain does not acquire the whole store, but leases certain departments. A shoe factory will lease the shoe department, a millinery factory the hat shop, and a clothing factory the men's furnishings department. The result is that the store represents an aggregation of chains operating under one roof and under the name of the original department store.

Another example of how chains have succeeded the local distributor is found in the distribution of refrigerators and other electrical appliances. Formerly General Electric selected some local merchant and placed its refrigerators on sale with him. The town was growing, and the second step came when General Electric established its own store and marketed its products direct to the user.

The same thing has happened in the distribution of automobile tires. Firestone and Goodyear distributed their tires through garagemen and gasoline stations. As soon as the automobile passed out of the pioneer stage the tire business became of sufficient importance to justify the manufacturer in erecting, on land leased for a long period, superservice stations where cars are serviced from front bumper to back. The managers and employees were placed on salaries and the former commissions went to the Northern corporations.

The effects of this change on the independent garagemen and mechanics may be illustrated by true stories. In a suburb of New York I drove into a new Firestone station where I found a man who knew what the trouble was with my car, a man of fine personality. I commented on the excellent equipment, all of which was new.

"Yes, it's a fine place," said the mechanic, and then he added with a tinge of bitterness, "but it is bad on the little fellow."

"I suppose it is," I replied, "but it is very good on the employee who gets a job because Firestone must pay good salaries."

"That would be good," he said, "if Firestone paid good salaries." Then he told his story. He had risen by his mechanical ability, aided no doubt by his personal qualities, to the ownership of a shop in a Southern city. His investment was about eight thousand dollars. He was caught between the depression and stiff competition from the chain superservice stations and went broke. Because he was an expert, as he expressed it, "on the front end of an automobile," Firestone gave him a job — at $110 a month.

"How can you live in this city on that amount?" I inquired.

"I can't live," he said. "The only reason I can get by is that I got my son a job in another station in an adjoining town."

He, one of the little fellows, had been pushed out and now had joined the army that had destroyed him and was helping to destroy other little fellows. I returned to New York in the summer of 1936 and drove into another Firestone station that had just been completed. I was surprised and delighted to meet this "front end of an automobile" man. He had been made manager, and things were better with him. But just across the street was another little fellow, and one could see that his business was shriveling up, that he would soon be with Firestone to help in building the chain.

The experience of my friend whom I will call Cole Younger Jones is significant. He grew up in a railroad shop and knew a great deal about machinery of all sorts. With the advent of the automobile he set up a garage and tireshop and established a reputation as a competent and trustworthy man. His business prospered to such an extent that he purchased tires by the carload and sold them to dealers around him. Then the manufacturers set up their own tire stations and Cole Younger Jones confined himself to garagework and the sale of gasoline.

But the chains continued to reach out for the small business that was left. On a block below him was a filling station operated by two brothers for a New York oil company. One day I missed the boys from the station and saw that it had changed hands. A few weeks later I met one of them on the street and inquired why they were no longer at their place of business.

"We were let out," he replied.

"Why?"

"It was sold."

"Who bought it?"

"Henry Ford."

"I didn't know that Henry Ford is in the filling station business," I answered.

"He isn't, exactly, but he sent out orders to several hundred of his dealers to buy filling stations, and one order came here."

"What is the idea?" I asked.

"To help the sale of Fords and of Ford parts. Suppose you drive into that station for gasoline, and you remark to the attendant that you must buy a new car. The attendant notes your car number, or takes your name, and telephones the dealer, who goes after you as a prospect. If you drive a Ford and need a part, the attendant supplies it, making it unnecessary for you to go to a garage."

Ford has gone even further in his service by putting Ford trucks on the road to carry parts to every station and garage in the remotest communities. There is no quarrel with this service. It is good; nevertheless, it is gradually killing the independent garagemen or forcing them into the ever expanding chain. It is causing the business of Cole Younger Jones to shrivel up. He cannot now look forward to handing down a profitable business to his son.

The study of the destruction of local businessmen could be continued indefinitely, enlivened by a thousand personal tragedies, overtones heard above the symphony of the chains. The independents have died, are dying, slowly, and die they will. The total fatalities would not have been greater had they been driven across an open field raked by machine-gun fire. The result is that today one dares not establish a business in this town without being oppressed by the constant fear that he will be crushed by the system that has grown up around him. Those who remain independent confine themselves to commodities that are not well adapted to chain business. Those who would be independent have been driven to the highways to set up hamburger stands, tourist camps, novelty shops, whiskey dispensaries, and roadhouses. They live because of their insignificance.

These remarks are not made as a criticism of the method of economic and industrial progress, but only as a record of the facts.

4

Thus far we have considered the position of the independent merchants, or those who were recently independent. Let us now turn to the employees of the corporate chains and note some of the economic, social, and educational consequences of the system of Northern control on the South and the West. Here we may return to our feudal analogy, confining our attention to that part of the system which may be seen in any Southern or Western city, and to the employees.

Since the corporate overlords reside principally in the North, the South and the West see only the buck-passing agents — words which in translation mean local managers and local employees.

The first thing to note about them is the precarious tenure of their jobs, a fact growing out of the *laissez faire* fallacy that the serf and vassal are the equals of the overlord, that the single individual is equal in freedom with the corporation, that either is free to fire the other at will and to seek a substitute elsewhere.

The managers of chain stores have no certain tenure, no contact, no security. If you can gain their confidence, they will admit that they have none of these. They may hold their jobs only so long as they can pay homage in the form of profits, not the same homage each year, but a greater homage each year than they paid the year before. A manager of a large telegraph office told me that he was sent to that office because it had been losing business, and that the only way he could hope to remain there was to show an increase.

" Suppose," I inquired, " that crops fail and local conditions become such that you cannot show an increase? "

" That would be too bad for me," he replied. " If I cannot show an increase I shall be sent to a smaller place or dropped from the pay roll." Though he did not discuss his salary, he commented on the salaries of the boys and girls under him as being very low.

In the chain mercantile establishments, especially in the five-and-ten-cent stores, the situation is, if possible, worse. They employ young girls, work them the maximum number of hours, and pay a minimum wage. Who has not seen these spiritless girls taken from the home and the school, extending the right hand for the money while they hold the purchase back with the left? A standing regulation of these chains is that the girl must live at home with her parents or with someone who stands in the parental relation. On the face of it, this rule seems to have been made in the interest of morals, but in reality it is economic. Girls who live with their parents can work for *less* than a living wage; girls who do not must have at least a living. If the issue were a moral one, the girls would receive a wage that would make an economically independent and moral existence possible, as it is desirable.

Evidence can be found that the grocery chains, in their drive for profits, encourage downright dishonesty. Some charge the manager for all shortages, which he makes up by clipping a few ounces here and a few there; they do not, however, allow him credit for a surplusage. I heard a meatcutter, who had worked in a chain grocery, remark bitterly and as if from experience, " By God, these chains will teach a man to steal and then fire him for doing it! " It has been charged that they will put a bottle of catsup on the desk by the cash register, and when a customer brings a basket with several items, the cashier will add the price of the catsup. In most instances the customer will not count the items, but if he does the cashier explains that he thought the catsup was placed there by the customer. Another practice is for the chains to have well-known advertised goods made up in packages specially for them. The package may be identical in appearance with the standard article, but it will contain less thread, fewer ounces of powder, or small olives instead of large ones. The customer, thinking only of price, does not realize that he is paying a premium. Perhaps this last method of cheating the customer has nothing more than an economic effect upon the community, but wages so low as to promote immorality and the teaching of meatcutters to steal and of cashiers to sell the same bottle of catsup a dozen times must have results more serious than economic.

5

The managers of chain stores seem to be chosen partially for their ability to avoid community responsibility. The old independent merchant was a leading citizen. He supported the churches and the schools, served on park boards, helped build roads, and contributed liberally to local charities. He knew the majority of the people in his town, and they all knew him. Most of the chain stores avoid as far as possible all the community responsibilities. The managers are frequently sent in from the outside and they rarely become identified with the town. It is thought that they are discouraged, as a matter of policy, from identifying themselves with the community. They rarely purchase a home because they are subject to removal at any time. They take on the impersonality of the corporation that they represent.

I went into the business district of a large city and inquired of a half-dozen businessmen to learn if they could name the managers of Kress, Woolworth, Montgomery Ward, and Sears-Roebuck. The president and vice-president of a bank could name none; neither could two leading merchants. The third merchant could name one because he had been working with these men to induce them to join the local merchants in closing at five o'clock through the hot summer months.

" What do the chain organizations contribute to the Community Chest? " I inquired of a member of the Chest committee.

" Most of the time they contribute nothing," he replied. Then he made an exception of the J. C. Penney Company and the Telephone Company. In 1936, however, the contributions were more numerous, and so remarkable that the list was published in the papers.

" What do the managers say when they are called on for a contribution? "

" They usually say that they will have to take the matter up with the home office, and that is the last we hear from them." One merchant estimated that on the basis of dollar volume the chains give about ten per cent of the amount contributed by local merchants.

The meaning of this failure of the chain organizations to support the enterprises of the communities that support them has a social and cultural significance of deep and tragic import. It means that the burden of carrying local enterprises is becoming heavier and heavier for the independent merchants and for the local citizens. It has a reflex effect on schools, churches, and all civic enterprises.

The banking policy of the chains shows where the money goes, and how quickly. I had the following conversation with an official of a large bank:

"What size accounts do the chain stores ordinarily carry in the local banks?"

"Just as small as the banks will permit and service the account. We refuse to accept the account unless a daily average of $500 is maintained."

"How often is their money, in excess of $500, drawn?"

"In most cases once a week; in some cases three times a week. The managers send a report of deposits to headquarters each day. When the account runs up to $1,000 or $1,500 a draft is drawn by the 'home' office reducing it to the minimum."

It is needless to comment on the effect of this policy on the community banks and on the community. It may serve to explain partially why every bank in many towns closed its doors during the depression. It is impossible to learn the amount of money that the chains take out of a town yearly, but the following story related by a businessman is pertinent. This man owns a building adjoining one of the principal five-and-tens. The chain desires to rent this building for expansion and plans to install one of its de luxe establishments with air conditioning, indirect lighting, and all that. The chain official estimated that this improvement would increase the volume of business to the amount of $75,000 annually.

Many chains operate in a way to destroy the spirit and the initiative of the employees. A woman whose husband was gassed in the war found it necessary to seek employment and found it with, let us say, the Great Gold unit. As a part of her duties as a saleswoman she was required one morning to sweep the rest room and clean the toilets. She remonstrated, but was told that she would have to obey orders or be reported to the management. That service was regularly required of the women employees.

The following story was told by a boy who had worked for a shoe chain. He said that the store followed a plan of " breaking " a new employee. The purpose differs from that of breaking a wild horse. A good horseman breaks a horse in such a way as not to break his spirit, for it is the spirit of the horse that makes a good horse just as it is the spirit of the man that makes a useful man. The boy works during the day, and at closing time is told to move and dust every box on a certain shelf. When this is done, he is sent to another and so on until eleven o'clock. This driving is kept up for ten days or two weeks, apparently for the purpose of seeing whether the boy can take the punishment. If he stands up under it, the pressure abates and he receives more permanent employment. " Why," said the narrator, " I can put a boy to work in a shoe store that is perfectly clean and keep him busy for a week cleaning it."

Conditions as to hours of work have improved, but much night work is still done by chain employees and usually with no additional pay. An independent merchant commented on it thus: " I often come downtown with my wife at night and walk by my own store and others window shopping. I am naturally interested in windows and observe them closely. On every such visit I see shades drawn on some of the chain windows and lights within as late as eleven o'clock. The next morning I recognize a new window display built up after closing hours."

6

The chains are not only breaking the spirit of their employees, but they are breaking the spirit of independent merchants and of the local communities. Let us observe the manner in which they come to town, and depict the plight of the independent merchants who must meet them. These merchants today are like the allodial landholders of the medieval feudalism who were hemmed in on all sides by the growing fiefs of the feudal lords. The great lords were constantly at war with one another, each anxious to expand his fief. The allodial holder was caught between them and compelled to go over to one or the other or be destroyed. And so it is with the independent merchant except for the fact that he is not usually permitted to go over — is not taken in. He is merely destroyed.

Consider him as the chains approach, surround, swallow him. In medieval times people knew when the feudal barons were approaching, for they came in person or sent mailed knights with sounding trumpets and rattling swords to inspire awe and respect. The modern chain system comes into town like Carl Sandburg's Chicago fog, " on little cat feet." Having decided that the town will support the venture, the chain sends its advance agent but there are no heralds of his arrival. All is secret. The agent makes a contract with a real estate man, and the two covertly survey the city for desirable locations, count traffic for days to learn how many customers pass, take options to rent or buy. Eventually the construction or renovation of a building is begun.

Not until then does the local merchant across the street learn that a war is inevitable. He is worried, this little independent merchant, because he knows that he is not facing an adversary of his own class, just another local merchant; he is facing a great army that is fighting to expand the fief of a chain lord. He cannot surrender, as men could in real feudal days, because he will not be " taken in." He must fight as he can. (The courts tell us that the antagonists are equal — both are persons.)

Finally comes the day for the beginning of hostilities. It is called an " opening." There is a great trumpeting and " spread " of advertising. Price is the weapon used in the warfare that this feudal prince employs. The recruits are the customers who flock to the new standard, attracted by the bright weapons of price. They are deserters from the old allegiance for an immediate gain — an ultimate loss. The local merchant struggles heroically to maintain himself, but soon learns that his guns are of too short range; they cannot even throw a shell into the enemy's camp.

Three courses are open to the beleaguered merchant. He can die on his own shield. He can give up hoping to attach himself to the enemy as a vassal or serf, or he can (perhaps) go to another chain on the next block. In any case, he surrenders his independence, his chance for anything more than a subsistence, and becomes the *man* of — a corporation.

Let us assume that he is fortunate enough to have been "taken in" by the chain. His fortune will vary somewhat with his ability, age, and energy. If he has youth (no man over forty need apply), unbounded energy, and absolute obedience he may become a manager, a subvassal. In turn now he must go into the street and pick up the smaller fry, the sons and daughters of his neighbors and former customers, or those who have been less fortunate than he, and bring them in as the lowliest units of a nation-wide chain.[1]

The position of the modern chain vassal — the manager — is quite different from that of the old feudal vassal. The duties of the feudal vassal were clearly defined by contract and agreement. The overlord could require him to serve forty days in the army, serve twice or four times a year at court, and to give occasionally some token of allegiance, a few bushels of grain, a chicken or two, or a few days' hospitality to the lord and his entourage. So long as he gave homage, limited as it was, his tenure was secure and his protection guaranteed; but the chain employee is only a "tenant at will." When he goes to his office in the morning he knows that he may have a letter or telegram severing his connection with the system.

History tells us that the position of the serf on the feudal manor was a humble one and that he had little to show for his labor. History adds with emphasis, however, that he enjoyed an unalienable security. He was attached to the land that nourished him and

[1] The effort of the independent grocers to save themselves is worth noting. Some man had a brilliant idea; he would organize them into a chain too, buy for them in mass, and show them how to meet competition, provided they would follow rules made at headquarters. The organization was given the catchy name of the Independent Grocers' Association — I.G.A. The stores were repainted, the shelves rearranged, and standard goods were sold under I.G.A. labels. In appearance the I.G.A. is a compromise between an independent business and a chain, but in reality the significant thing for the South and the West has happened: control has passed to the North, to Chicago. I.G.A. has taken away the pride of complete ownership and control. For example, the merchant obligates himself to sell a certain percentage of I.G.A. goods. If it is not already so, I.G.A. will in time become another fief, owned and controlled from the same center that holds Atlantic & Pacific, Piggly Wiggly, and the rest.

he could not be separated from it. His children inherited his security. When we compare his lot with that of the clerks in a chain store (leaving aside what they have to show for their labor) we find that in point of security the serf had the better of it. Though the land was not his, he was the land's, and from it he could make a livelihood. The chain or corporate employee does not own the store and is not owned by it. He can be kicked out at any time. He has no contract, either by law or by custom, and he enjoys no security. With our theory of equality between a real and a corporate person, the tie between them can be broken by either at will. What the law loses sight of is that the tie is as strong as the chains of necessity for one and as weak as a distant, impersonal will for the other.

It may be charged that in discussing chains I have left out the consumer. There is no doubt that the chains have saved money for the consumer and improved the service. No quarrel has been raised with corporate efficiency. I am more concerned with the growing dependence and the destruction of local enterprise — with Northern control. In the long run the savings effected by the cash customers will be taken out of them or their children through low wages and long hours. The towns will stagnate and property deteriorate in value. The immediate gain to the consumer is small. The ultimate loss may ramify the whole social and economic structure of the community.

7

The feudal world set great store by symbols, insignia, and uniforms. In the days of chivalry the playboys developed heraldry into a glamorous art, if not a polite science. Every man's station was announced by what he wore. The jester had his cap and the fool had his bell. The knight was distinguished by his armor or the color of his one suit, the bishop by his staff, the king by his crown. A member of the high orders of chivalry was known by the fraternity pin he wore. There were escutcheons and coats of arms, and every color, rampant coyote, and couchant lion had a deep symbolical meaning.

As I look out upon the South and the West I not only see men everywhere in chains, but I see thousands wearing the insignia of their allegiance to their overlords. Boys clad in blue or brown and wearing caps with the symbols of the telegraph companies are hurrying along on bicycles. In oil stations young men in puttees and jackets exhibit the insignia of Standard Oil, Texaco, Humble, and Andy Mellon's Gulf. Tire punctures are mended by men in long dusters which have Goodyear or Firestone woven in bright red letters across the back. Most of these men are doubtless conscious that they are under unseen control; to a man, they must long for independence, for something they can call their own. Their baffled feeling grows from a sense of baffled manhood which one can sense in their conversation. Of recent years many of them are college boys who took service during the depression. Formerly they had hope of rising, but so many have gone into the service that they are now beginning to realize that the prospect is not promising. Some of them do not conceal their resentment. "These damned corporations don't give a man a chance," says one. "I'm through with these oil companies," said another. "I have seen all of them I want to see. I am doing my best to get a job with the International Business Machine Corporation." Thus they exchange masters, but rarely systems.

The corporations do not require all their employees to wear uniforms. They are for the service brigade, the flunkies who use their persons to give free advertising by means of clothing which they often purchase from the company. There are thousands who wear citizens' clothes, though many of them wear pins as evidence of good and faithful service. They are initiated into such clubs as Toppers, Uppers, and Cappers. If all who are employed by Northern corporations should be put into uniform, our towns would take on a very smart appearance. In addition to insurance agents, clerks and stenographers, press correspondents, and hundreds of others, there would be perhaps a few college professors, practically all the leading attorneys, practically all ex-governors, and perhaps an occasional incumbent. Many state legislatures would bear a close resemblance to a convention of firemen or hotel bellboys. Uniforms might be a good thing if they were carried far enough — upward.

This last class of ununiformed corporation employees deserves attention. The old feudal system had its parallel in a class of vassals whose exact position is also not easy to define. If a man had special ability, a good voice, a keen sense of humor, if he could act the wise man or the fool well enough, he could become attached to a lord without holding a land fief. Such professionals were spoken of as retainers. They certainly were not serfs; they were not landed fiefholders, and therefore were not vassals in the strictest feudal meaning. They were *retainers*. The word is preserved today: it means a lawyer or other professional person who takes service with one of high degree. Though he may receive a salary, the retainer differs from a regular employee in that he is not necessarily required to give full-time service. Corporation retainers do not wear uniforms, and ofttimes their connection with the corporation is not a matter of public knowledge. They are often great law firms that handle cases in local and state courts. Sometimes these retainers are called public relations men whose duty it is to meet the right people at the right time. It is through them that the corporations are continually extending their control over society, over the government, over the South and the West. When the legislatures meet, they are present in droves, overrunning the lobbies, occupying the best rooms, possessing the oldest whiskey, and providing other blessings to the taste of corrupt or naïve lawmakers. They constitute the " third " house and, behind locked doors in the leading hotels, frame many of the important laws.

These corporation retainers are like a two-edged sword. Because they are influential citizens, often powerful in the community from which the legislator came, they are able to pour the pressure of the constituents against the honest legislator who is sponsoring or supporting some bill adverse to the interests of their masters. In this manner they enlist the citizens to fight with them for a corporation that is bent on only one thing — taking as much money as possible out of the state. It is not an exaggeration to say that the retainers usually fight measures intended for the general welfare.

It is largely through these retainer agents that the Northern feudal lords have raped the states of the South and the West of their natural resources. They have taken the oil of Oklahoma, the copper of Montana, the silver of the Western mountains, the coal of West Virginia and Kentucky, the iron of Alabama, and the world's supply of sulphur in Texas and Louisiana. They rape the people too. I heard an agent state publicly that he managed to get from a Negro woman for a few thousand dollars a small tract of land from which his company took three million dollars' worth of oil.

8

The manner of recruiting retainers is illustrated in the case of my friend Bill, who graduated from a state university some twenty years ago. Blessed with a brilliant mind, Bill was able to make a gentleman's grades by sitting on a bench near the library and cultivating the acquaintance of coeds and campus politicians. It was his delight to run campus politics without holding an office. On taking his law degree he began practice in a distant city. His ability and personality were such as to enable him to earn about $5,000 a year. Everybody liked Bill, and he gave promise of becoming a valuable citizen of the state that had educated him.

Within the state lies the richest mineral deposit of its kind in all the world. Let us say it is creosote, and that it is owned by the Consolidated Creosote Company of Philadelphia. Because there was some talk (there is always some talk) of increasing the tax on creosote, the company needed a new man in its office, one with connections in the state and plenty of ability. One day Bill received a telegram asking him to come to Philadelphia to join the Creosote legal staff. Completely flabbergasted, Bill appealed to his best friend, a man accustomed to handling large affairs.

"What shall I ask these birds for my valuable services?" Bill inquired.

The friend advised him with much profanity, of which he was a master, to price himself at $25,000 a year. He did so, but had to compromise for $16,000 and the promise of an increase which has long since been granted. In this way Bill was lost to the state that nurtured him. He returns frequently, however, especially when the legislature is in session. His great capacity for friendship and his wide acquaintance have doubtless made him worth all that he is getting. I talked with Bill last summer, told him I was putting him in this book, and had him substantiate the story. He still loves his state and would like to protect it. He insists on maintaining his own views on national questions, sharply at variance with those of his high associates. As between his state and the Creosote corporation, Bill is in a dilemma. His love is for one side, but his money comes from the other. Let us leave him here to the department of ethics.

9

The problem of ethics has already been settled in the case of another young man of equal ability, educated by the same state and in the same institution. Let us call him Tom.

Tom went out of the university on the wave of prosperity, but came back on the breakers of the depression and for a time was derelict. Finally he found employment with a corporation in a minor position, considering his superior ability. The problem with him was to make his way up. The first thing he had to do was to convince himself that the service was noble. I may summarize his discussion as follows: The reason the corporations are so successful, he said, is that they are efficient. They are more efficient than government can hope to be because government does not have the drive, intelligence, or discipline necessary to achieve its ends.

Tom developed quite a thesis on discipline as the controlling force in the world, coming home always to the belief that the corporations represent all that is left of discipline in America. Greece, he said, failed because the Greeks refused to bury their individualism in discipline. Rome rose to power on military and legal disciplines. When these failed there had arisen within the empire the Christians, a minority group remarkable for obedience. Constantine, seeing that salvation for him lay in gaining the support of this group, turned Christian and won his battle. In the subsequent absence of the Roman emperor, the church supplied the severest discipline of the Middle Ages. Feudalism was a makeshift discipline that had to give way to the ordered control of absolute monarchy.

America, an offshoot of monarchical Europe, was a frontier country and as such made a daring experiment in democracy, the negation of discipline. But there have now arisen within this democracy the great corporations, and through them discipline has come to America at last. They, he said, are the only vital force, the only dynamic intelligence to be found in the land. Spirit has gone out of the church, as everyone knows; vigor has gone out of agriculture, as the farmer knows; hope has gone out of labor, as the laborer's dependents know. Creative intelligence has gone out of the colleges and universities, as everyone who has been through a graduate school knows. Discipline never existed to any extent in the government because democracy discourages it.

In contrast with these old institutions, the new corporations are alive, vibrant, throbbing with the zest of existence, fired by the zeal of conquest and expansion, animated by the desire for power and consciousness of the ability to achieve it. They are doing America's work, promoting science in a hundred practical fields and in a thousand laboratories. They and they alone, like the army of Rome and the church of the Middle Ages, offer unlimited opportunities to the individual who desires to live on the edge of adventure and in the midst of potential achievement, but always under the severest discipline.

Where do I come into the picture? he asked. I come in because I have developed a concept of the corporations as powerful states — the states of the future — that have arisen within America. They do not quite realize yet that they are states, but they are on the threshold, and I propose to help them to a full realization of their powers as states. Then they will be in need of a diplomatic corps; ambassadors to legislatures, to Congress, to news agencies, to the laborers within the company, and to the public, building up allegiance to the corporations. Corporations are attempting this already, but are proceeding like amateurs. Their propaganda is too apparent and clumsy; I will refine it, make it more palatable, more subtle. For that I shall be great.

When he had concluded this amazing profession of purpose, I looked at him, tall, keen-minded, intelligent, and I saw in him a symbol of what young men may be doing — and are doing — all over the land. They are subconsciously swearing a new allegiance, transferring their patriotism, enlisting under a new banner.

" Well, Tom," I said, " to make the case quite plain, suppose we say that you have sold out."

" Yes," he replied without hesitation, " I have sold out. I shall go with them if they want me, and I think I can make them want me."

The last time I saw Tom he had, as if by sheer good luck, gained the ear of a powerful official. He was writing addresses for his immediate superior to deliver at commencement exercises and insinuating into them the subtle propaganda for the " state " of his new allegiance.

The cases of Bill and Tom introduce the subject of education and illustrate a peculiar relationship between the state-supported universities and the corporations. The people of the state paid something like $2,500 to educate each of these two men, on the theory that they would repay the state in service and in good citizenship. The state interprets the word " service " liberally and never checks up to see whether the service is given. The corporation took Bill because he was the best in his class and because the people of the state had given him not only a general education but a technical one that made him especially valuable to it. It will take Tom for a similar reason. The corporation is taking its choice. This spring a notice appeared in the college paper announcing that General Electric would send a man to employ the graduating engineers who had made the best records. The oil companies enlist the best students in geology, and the International Business Machine Corporation takes its pick of business administration. The young lawyers have to wait before they are given retainers, as did Bill, until they have proved their ability to win a case or to keep one from going to trial.

What a revealing situation we have here — the people paying taxes to give technical training to men who immediately join the impersonal feudal forces that are controlling the states and abstracting their substance, and perhaps winning the allegiance of their citizens. Under the circumstances the corporations should " go hog wild " about higher education, because it saves them the trouble and expense of training their own men. They keep quiet on the subject, fearing taxes, but the work is being done for them by professional pedagogues who prattle about preparing people for citizenship, meaning perhaps jobs with corporations. More and more the state universities are becoming the technical and personnel bureaus for the corporate overlords. They are teaching people to do rather than to think, analyze, synthesize, and understand.

10

The whole subject of education is a tender one in the South and the West. The Southern states are particularly sensitive, because they are told so often by a surveyor that they stand thirty-seventh, forty-first, and forty-eighth in the scale of literacy, intelligence, and education. Rupert B. Vance, in his *Human Geography of the South*, page 442, says: " The statistical indices of wealth, education, cultural achievement, health, law and order reduced to a per capita basis combine in every instance to give the Southern states the lowest ranking in the Union." Many explanations are offered for this backwardness. For example, illiteracy is explained by the presence of the Negro in the South and of the Mexican in the West. But this is only an explanation. The fundamental reason is the lack of means. Beneath the ignorance of the South is not the will to be ignorant, nor an indifference to the advantages of education. It takes money to educate people, to pay teachers, to buy books from Northern publishers, and to build the little red schoolhouse so dear to vote-hunting politicians. Let us recall that out of every $100 on deposit in banks the South has less than $10 and the West less than $15. There is not sufficient economic foundation in either section to build a system of public schools such as the North can maintain with its $80 and more of every $100 in the banks.

One would think that the corporations, inasmuch as they gather their wealth from the provinces and recruit their personnel from the universities and colleges, would be liberal in their benefactions to higher education in the South and the West. As a matter of fact, they rarely give anything in the provinces, but pour out their gifts almost exclusively to Northern institutions. The colleges of the South and the West are supported either by the states or by churches. Such privately endowed institutions as Harvard, Yale, Princeton, Massachusetts Institute of Technology, and the University of Chicago are practically nonexistent in the South and the West.

We know that John D. Rockefeller salvaged the University of Chicago from a religious denomination by an initial gift of some thirty million dollars and that the gift has been increased from time to time until the total must amount to fifty or sixty millions. Eastman, the kodak king, gave Rochester so much that the financial secretary declined to name the amount in response to an inquiry. He said that Mr. Eastman's gifts had been so numerous that it would be impossible to state what the total is. Does this mean that Eastman collected this money in the North? Did the government not give him the protection of a patent, which means a monopoly, and did not a political party give him a tariff to protect him from the excellent cameras and films of Germany? Did not every Sunday-school class or party of young people who went picnicking in Florida, Georgia, North Dakota, or Kansas pay a small tribute to Eastman in order that he might endow the University of Rochester?

One of the latest gifts to be announced is that of Deering to Northwestern University in a suburb of Chicago. Deering made his fortune by selling plows and other farming implements. The newspapers announced that the gift was seven million dollars, but a member of the faculty stated that it was much more than that. Without doubt Deering collected most of his fortune from the farmers of the South and the West; yet he made his gifts to an institution more famous for law, business, and football than for agriculture.

The *World Almanac* publishes a list of colleges that have an endowment of $2,000,000 or more each. On this list as of 1935 the North has 83 institutions, the South 18, the West 12. Of the total the North has received $919,464,236, or 80.13 per cent; the South $150,380,876, or 13.1 per cent; the West $77,621,879, or 6.76 per cent. Among the ten most richly endowed institutions, the South has Texas in seventh place with $33,000,000 [1] and Duke in tenth place. The West has one institution, Stanford, in ninth place. The

[1] This large endowment came from oil produced on land given to the university by the state. The private benefactions are as yet insignificant.

North holds the first six places and the eighth. Out of each $100 of endowment the North has $80.13, the South $13.10, the West $6.76.

The argument may be advanced that this situation came about because the North got the start, and that in time the other sections will tend to overtake it. The facts do not bear this out, but indicate that the North is holding its own if not accelerating its rate of gain. The following table shows the distribution of benefactions to colleges, museums, libraries, and other educational institutions for the years 1934 and 1935.

CURRENT BENEFACTIONS TO COLLEGES, MUSEUMS, LIBRARIES, ETC.

	No.	1934	Percentage	No.	1935	Percentage
North	73	$19,760,900	76.05	63	$25,156,047	84.22
South	8	1,102,000	4.19	13	4,233,500	14.17
West	4	5,467,611	20.77	7	479,176	1.61

In 1934 all the Western gifts went to California, including one very large one. In 1936 the North received $6 where the South received $1; and more than $50, where the West received $1.

These figures explain the gap between the facilities for graduate work in the North and in the other two sections. They explain why teachers in the South carry one third more work for less pay than the average for the rest of the nation.

If it be argued that these bequests are for the benefit of the entire nation, and that boys from all sections profit from them, the argument must be accepted as valid. As a matter of fact, however, some of the institutions are run as closed corporations. Unless a boy approaches them through one of the select preparatory schools, and unless he comes from a well-established and a rich family, he can hope as an undergraduate to get little more than an education. In graduate schools ability counts for more and money and connections count for correspondingly less.

The endowments of the North have been built up through a process humorously described by a member of the faculty of one of the richest schools as "tapping the capitalists." "When we want to do something here," he said laughingly, " construct a building, establish fellowships, or buy a painting, we just go out and tap a capitalist. They really like it, because it appeals to their vanity."

Even the select preparatory schools understand the art of tapping capitalists. I once visited one of the most famous and marveled at the spacious grounds, the classic buildings, and the marble walls lined with original oil paintings. I was told that the head professors received salaries three or four times as great as the heads of departments in Southern and Western universities.

" Who is on the board of trustees? " I inquired.

" Oh," said my companion, " we try to keep two or three members of the New York Stock Exchange on it all the time."

Any university in the country is perfectly willing to tap a capitalist. Most of the presidents carry in the pocket of their memory a list of prospects and a pack of codicils to attach to wills; professors look forward to sitting in a chair made soft and luxurious by some persuasive club. But the game is scarce in the South and the West — so scarce that the keenest-eyed president would have to hunt all day in the South and for a week in the West to find a capitalist ripe enough to tap or rich enough to justify the exertions. Many of them draw their wealth from the silver, gold, oil, and coal; others by selling razor blades, refrigerators, toothbrushes, tractors, and kodak films in the South and the West, as well as in the North, but their personal range is in the North and there the institutions hunt them the year round.

There is one thing to be said, however, for the Southern and Western universities. They remain relatively free. Even a tapped capitalist is not entirely innocuous. He has been known to play possum, and watch through the crack of an eyelid to see that those who receive the bounty are not forgetful of the source.

In this chapter I have shown that much of the business of the South and the West is in chains, and that more each year is going into bondage to the North. I may add that business in the North is going into the hands of the " chains " too. The farmers, laborers, and small merchants are there caught in the same net as are their fellows in the South and the West, but with the difference that they reap some advantage by being near the barons of business, parts of the humming machines. Some find service of a personal nature with those who like to say, "We take care of our poor." They mean that they take care of some of the poor around them, those whose sufferings they see. Their compassion rarely reaches to the South and the West, where there are also poor.

This is not a story of rich and poor, and how each became such. It is a simpler story: that the North as a section is rich, and becoming richer; the South and the West are poor, and becoming relatively poorer.

— From *Divided We Stand: The Crisis of a Frontierless Democracy*, by Walter Prescott Webb, copyright, 1937, and reprinted by permission of Farrar and Rinehart, Inc., publishers.

THE REVIEW

The Review

The most accurate statement one might make about book reviews would be to say that there are as many ways of writing them as there are reviewers to do the writing. Reviewing is a loosely defined technique, and that looseness will be reflected, we think, in almost any cross section exhibit of actual examples. Many a public reviewer is content merely to tell the story if his subject is a novel; or to summarize the argument, or thesis, if it is a lengthy essay or commentary. Again, there are many writers in this form who devote themselves to elaborate quibblings with minor details — minor, that is, with respect to a book's basic intellectual intention. Some such reviewers, for instance, might quarrel with an author on the score that he is a bad proofreader; others might condemn his faulty punctuation; while still others might argue, with quite disproportionate elaborateness, that his title is too inclusive, or not inclusive enough, or somewhat inaccurate, or too popular, or too scholarly.

What we should like to point out principally, however — in terms of the present illustrations — is that one of at least two basic motives can be detected in practically every review. On the one hand, there is the reviewer who assumes that his major responsibility is to summarize the contents of the volume about which he is writing. This is the sort of commentary that seems to predominate in the New York Times — certainly the most complete reviewing medium in the country. Criticism of an author's argument, or of his technique, is reduced to a minimum in such articles. The primary intention is to indicate what the book is about.

There is another type much more ambitious in its aims. In it one finds the reviewer — usually an authority on the points raised by the book — attempting to judge and to correct the views which the author has advanced. Such commentaries as these frequently run into full essays. They represent, usually, serious and elaborate efforts to reconcile divergent attitudes toward a given subject.

Sometimes, indeed, the reviewer may be so engrossed with presenting his own opinions that those of the author may remain largely unstated. Lord Macaulay and, in our own age, H. L. Mencken were men who wrote in the light of this attitude. The most satisfactory review, however, is probably the kind in which the writer of it — himself well informed regarding the question at issue — explains both the author's point of view and his own criticism of it.

THE SLICKEST OF THE SLICKS

A Review of the Magazine *Fortune*

SOMEWHERE or other I once learned that there are two kinds of magazines, "pulps" and "slicks." The pulps are the cheap magazines that you read (if you read them) and then throw away. The slicks are the magazines that look too expensive to throw away. You keep them in the attic or basement, always intending to look them over again. But you never do. The Salvation Army always gets them in the end.

Fortune, of course, is the largest and most expensive of the slicks. I knew as much, before I read William Lydgate's article, "Romantic Business," in *Scribner's Magazine* for September, 1938. But I did not know until I read his article just how this slickest of all the slicks happened to get its start, how it is organized, how it gets up its articles, and what its purpose is in being so sumptuous and expensive. Now I know. Mr. Lydgate tells all of that and a good deal more. Perhaps he tells even more than he means to.

The secret of *Fortune*'s success, Mr. Lydgate points out, is partly, and yet only partly, in its lavish format, its arty type, its really magnificent pictures. Those are the trimmings of the "romantic business" theme. Yet the editors, Mr. Lydgate suggests, like to do things in this impressive way because they themselves "have just enough of the country yokel's awe of things Big and Successful to tickle the fancy of average Americans getting ahead in the world." They use "plush journalism" because they think business deserves plush journalism, and also because they know very well that business appreciates the compliment.

Behind the plush journalism, however, is something solid and commercial. Mr. Lydgate tells us that Henry R. Luce, co-founder of *Time*, wanted to found another magazine which would " reflect industrial life as faithfully in ink and paper and word as the finest skyscraper reflects it in stone and steel and architecture." The magazine began publication in February, 1930, when business was in a bad way. The editors were scared, but they went ahead. The circulation grew from 34,000 in 1930 to 143,000 in 1937. Its profits for the first eight years, Mr. Lydgate thinks, total about $1,300,000.

Why did *Fortune* succeed? Mr. Lydgate gives several reasons, among them the fact that *Fortune* discovered how to appeal to the general public as well as to business. " It humanized itself," he writes, " until readers were not surprised to find articles on such subjects as café society and birth control." *Fortune* found out, too, that it could criticize the industrial system, and so, " though the magazine officially believes in the capitalist regime, it likes . . . to throw little spitballs at the tycoons." But perhaps the main reason for its success is the expertness and skill of its writers, the careful organization of its staff, and the amount of genuine research into facts that goes into every article. The most interesting and illuminating part of Mr. Lydgate's article is his description of the workings of the staff, which uses for its top writers " literary prima donnas " like the poet Archibald MacLeish (who draws a salary of $15,000 for nine months' work), and for its research work a group of highly trained " research girls." The research girls collect material and turn it over to the top writers. If a corporation refuses to give information, *Fortune* resorts to the " squeeze play." That is, it submits a story (an incorrect one) to the corporation anyway, and when the corporation protests about inaccuracies, then *Fortune* invites the corporation to make the corrections.

Clearly, this technique works. That is, it produces a well-edited, well-written magazine, which has a large circulation and makes money for its owners. *Fortune's* story as Mr. Lydgate tells it is a " success " story, a typically American success story. And he tells it in a style that is a slightly mocking parody of the smart-aleck style of *Fortune, Time,* and *Life.* It is hard to tell whether or not he admires *Fortune,* or is jealous of it, or perhaps is cynical about the whole thing. Certainly he is sarcastic, if not cynical, about "the paradoxical situation that *Fortune*, a magazine for business, is in no small part written by left-wing liberals whose private views many a businessman would find shocking indeed."

If Mr. Lydgate's article is open to criticism, it is not for what he says as much as for what he does not say. He does not probe the mystery of how a left-wing liberal can be a left-wing liberal and yet glorify Big Business — and yet accept a salary in five figures! What is happening, anyhow? Are the left-wing liberals "boring from within" on the *Fortune* staff? Or do their right hands not know, under some circumstances, what their left hands do? I am puzzled. I should have expected left-wing liberals to be more concerned about misfortune than about *Fortune*. If they can play a Dr. Jekyll and Mr. Hyde rôle of this sort, is their writing sincere? Mr. Lydgate sheds no light on such mysteries.

Aside from that omission, Mr. Lydgate also omits to indicate what *Fortune* means, anyway, in American life. Is it raising the standards of journalism (and perhaps of business), or is it spoiling us by giving us one more eminent example of bigness and luxury for the sake of bigness and luxury? For my part, I certainly admire the careful research method of *Fortune* — a better method, surely, than the quick-fire method of newspapers. And I have always liked fine printing and fine illustrations. Yet I cannot take much comfort in *Fortune* if I must think, as Mr. Lydgate leads me to think, that Americans buy it not for its good and solid qualities, but because they think it the slickest of the slicks — as slick, maybe, as they would like to be themselves. That is an unhappy thought, which brings me to another unhappy thought: Is *Fortune* much read in the Salvation Army hotels, or in whatever place the Salvation Army lays out the back numbers of magazines?

— From Donald Davidson's *American Composition and Rhetoric*, Charles Scribner's Sons, 1939. Reprinted by permission.

PICTURES OF THE SOUTH, DRUNK ON COTTON

A Review of Erskine Caldwell's *You Have Seen Their Faces*

By Hudson Strode

You Have Seen Their Faces, a collaboration of the mature photographic art of Margaret Bourke-White and the vigorous prose of Erskine Caldwell, is a stirring and painful document, magnificently produced. It should provoke something of the effect that Swift's "A Modest Proposal" — to sell the babies of the groveling Irish poor for stews and fricassees — was calculated to make on the English absentee landlords and their wives. Miss Bourke-White's superb pictures are a remarkable testament to the tragic consequences of the pernicious system of sharecropping. The subjects are authentic and fairly selected. Some faces have become ennobled by suffering, some repulsively degenerate. I — or any other Southerner who has gone twenty miles from wherever he lives — have seen these faces.

The text is Mr. Caldwell at his best. In the past, the Georgia author has often presented to us two separate qualities, that of sadism and that of weakness, and postulated some sort of economic conflict between the two — assuring us that Southern sharecroppers are the victims of sadistic landowners. And he was wont to season his stark stories for popular consumption with knockout doses of ribaldry and lust. But in the present book he has discarded grotesque emphasis and tricks to attract attention, and has offered powerful evidence of this blot on American culture in the manner of a humane and superior diagnostician reporting on a disease. Both he and his cause gain immeasurably by the restraint and dignity of his new manner.

Though charged with his intense and justifiable indignation, his eloquent championship of the sharecropper is surprisingly equitable. He admits that " tenant farmers have lived for so long a haphazard, catch-as-catch-can existence that most attempts to help them have proved to be wasted effort," and he cites by chapter and verse ways of a downright cunning to predestined hunger.

Mr. Caldwell finds himself, perhaps unconsciously, also the advocate of the Southern landlord. To see the truth of this, one has only to regard Miss Bourke-White's photograph of a typical decayed plantation mansion now occupied by several families of sharecroppers (page 24, taken at Clinton, Louisiana) or to read Mr. Caldwell's first paragraph in the book about the South itself — " the dogtown on the other side of the railroad tracks that smells so badly every time the wind changes."

Mr. Caldwell must see that the plight of the tenant farmer and the landlord are really much the same, that they are really on the same side; that, except in the rich Mississippi Delta and a few isolated cases where the soil is opulent, the landowner has been steadily on the decline in fortune for the past two decades. Any number of plantation-owners in the supposedly rich Black Belt of Alabama have gradually been ruined by farming with sharecroppers. Mr. Caldwell cites the pitiable history of John Sanford, a sharecropper of Emanuel County, Georgia, who " works every dry day during the season from dawn to dusk," with three other adults besides children to help, and all he could make on his year's hard work was 640 pounds of lint cotton ($70.48) for himself and an equal amount for his landlord. Could this landlord who paid taxes on the land, provided his tenant with a mule, a share of the fertilizer, a house (shack though it may be), and firewood, be " rich and successful " on $70.48 profits from his farm, even multiplied by ten or twenty?

Moving and urgent and important as this eye-opening sociological document is, it ends with slapping big question marks. Without impressive conviction Mr. Caldwell suggests a sharecroppers' union. But will shorter hours and higher wages for sharecroppers improve the land or lengthen the seasons in Emanuel County, Georgia — will they do anything for the sharecropper short of taking some of his $70.48 for dues? Can the landlords of the South, most of whom are mortgaged to the hilt, afford to pay better wages for hired help? The worked-out Southern soil simply won't produce successful cotton without expensive fertilizer and good seasons like the present one. Even with bumper crops is there more than a bare living in it for anybody? Not with the price of cotton below ten cents. Yet, as one farmer who owned his own land says in the book,

> Government and God put together in a lifetime couldn't beat a pinch of sense into those fool cotton farmers. . . . When I was out there twelve years ago trying to make a living raising cotton I didn't act with any more sense than the farmers do now. It seemed like cotton went to my head just like a drink of raw whiskey. I thought I was somebody. . . . The first thing I knew I didn't have an inch of land left, and I was so puffed up being a cotton farmer I didn't have sense enough to know I was drunk on cotton.

The South has been drunk on cotton many decades and it is suffering from a prolonged hangover. Is the relief to come from industrialization? from diversification? from cattle raising? from the increasing demand for cellulose? Mr. Caldwell, long a passionate student of the subject, has no adequate answer. He only knows, like the rest of us, that ten million persons on Southern tenant farms are living in degradation and defeat. He and Miss Bourke-White make it startlingly clear that to the cost of raising cotton we forget to add the value of wasted human lives. Mr. Caldwell pleads the urgent appointment of a government commission invested with authoritative power to make a thorough study of tenant farming in the cotton country. Something must be done soon. The man from Augusta, Georgia, says on page 82: "If the government doesn't do something about the losing cotton farmers, we'd be doing them a favor to go out and shoot them out of their misery."

You Have Seen Their Faces is a book that should go into the house of every Southerner incorrigibly in allegiance to King Cotton and to outdated romantic feudalism. And all persons who still feel any interest in the variety and passion of life or appreciate the effect of dramatic catharsis will be rewarded by an evening with this eloquent collaboration.

—From "Books," New York *Herald Tribune*, November 21, 1937. Reprinted by permission.

ERSKINE CALDWELL'S PICTURE BOOK

A Review of *You Have Seen Their Faces*

By Donald Davidson

As might have been predicted, *You Have Seen Their Faces,* by Erskine Caldwell and Margaret Bourke-White, was prominently discussed in the metropolitan press; and here and there, as might also have been predicted, accusing fingers were leveled at a South "so sick from its old infections of prejudice and poverty that it is a menace to the nation." (The quoted remark is from a review in the New York *Nation*). Less predictable, perhaps, was a tone of disappointment that ran through many of the reviews and that made the usual expressions of moral indignation over Southern conditions seem more perfunctory and forced than on many previous occasions, easily remembered. *You Have Seen Their Faces* was doubtless expected to be a Caldwellian *Uncle Tom's Cabin,* which through matter-of-fact pictures and text would substantiate Mr. Caldwell's previous matter-of-fiction accounts of Southern life. A public already accustomed to the visual treats of *Life, Look,* and *Pic* could hope for something supremely juicy from Mr. Caldwell and Miss Bourke-White.

To all who may have expected such as this, *You Have Seen Their Faces* must have seemed as tame as the magazine section of the New York *Times.* There are no *erotica curiosa* in the book. There are no candid camera shots of the harelipped girl tumbling lasciviously in the weeds, or of the mill hand of *God's Little Acre* and his enamorata ceremonially unclothed, like Jurgen and Anaitis, before the staring rustics. Nor are there any *gesta turpia et diabolica* — no sharecroppers devoured by the boss's hogs, no old grandmothers bumped and flattened by ruthless automobilists; and (though there are chain gangs in authentic stripes) no Negroes are being hanged in chains or tortured in sweatboxes.

Instead, we have a group of sixty-four excellent photographic studies, on the whole far more romantic than realistic in selection of subject and treatment. To accompany the pictures we have appropriate " legends," or dramatic speeches put into the mouths of the characters depicted. These, Mr. Caldwell states (in suitably small type, inconspicuously placed!), are in no case the actual words of the subjects. Mr. Caldwell has made them up to fit. " The legends under the pictures," he writes, " are intended to express the author's own conceptions of the sentiments of the individuals portrayed; they do not pretend to reproduce the actual sentiments of these persons." And here, as in the pictures, the average Southern reader, if not the Northern one, is compelled to admit that Mr. Caldwell has behaved a little more handsomely than might have been expected from his previous record. The legends too are more romantic than realistic. Often they are quite near to the genuine country idiom, and are surprisingly non-rebellious and uncomplaining. " It never felt much like Sunday to me till I picked the guitar some," is the sentiment attributed to a merry-looking fellow who picks a guitar while the grandpap listens. A nursing mother is made to say, " The littlest one gets taken care of." A pipe-smoking shanty-dweller says: " I spent ten months catching planks drifting down the river to this house, and then the flood came along and washed the side of it off. Doggone if I don't like it better the way it is now." This easy-going philosophy is offset to some extent by a sharper pointing up of other legends, and even more specifically by certain longer dramatic interludes, in which sharecropper, overseer, and landlord are made to speak either bitterly or overbearingly, in the rôles one would expect a Marxian critic of the system to ascribe to them. But the general effect, while at times partial, is by no means offensively unfair, as documents fictional or non-fictional, when dealing with the complex problem of tenancy, sometimes have had a way of being.

Since the pictures are the most prominent objects in the book, they call for some special analysis to justify the observation I have made above, as to their romantic and realistic quality. Of the sixty-four pages of illustration, twenty-four would fall, by my classification at least, into the romantic category; twenty-three would be realistic; and seventeen are neutral, or may be put under either head according to one's personal tastes and predilections. I call romantic those pictures that give us faces smiling, happy, cheerful, vigorous, that tell or imply a sentimental or humorous story, or that suggest the fallen grandeurs and lush natural abundance traditionally associated with the " Deep South " and the " Cotton Kingdom." Of this order, for example, would be the following (since Mr. Caldwell has supplied no titles or page numbers I must make up titles): " Boy Plowing " (it is " child labor," of course, but he is a ruddy strong fellow and seems to take it well!); " Negro Loafers Watching Ol' Man River "; " Crumbling Mansion, Mother, and Child " (used for a cover piece; it makes a looker think of Tara and *Gone with the Wind*); " Negro Granny, Laughing "; " Plowed Hillside with Cloud Effects "; " Child Eating Watermelon "; " Sharecropper Picking Guitar "; " Negro Sermon "; " Old Women on Porch." Of the realistic order are those pictures that show some notable excess of rags, dirt, disease, bad housing, or depressing environment; or that are meant, possibly, to suggest some brutality. For example, " Poor Folks near Ringgold, Georgia, Pulling Wagon "; " Black Boy in the Jailhouse "; " Chain Gang with Armed White Guard "; " Paralyzed Negro Boy "; " Poor Whites Eating a Crust "; " Malnourished Whites "; " Old Woman with a Goiter "; " Shacks Covered with Bill Posters "; " Ragged Woman and Infant "; " Eroded Field "; " Snuffdipper and Infant "; " Overcrowded Negro School." Of the neutral type are those faces which have been photographed apparently because they make interesting subjects rather than because they convey any very explicit social message, and such items as the pictures of the political candidate, the white school room (which, unlike the Negro one, at least has desks), the signboards put up by evangelists, and so on — all of which, though they may be intended to carry overtones of meaning, are not particularly exciting one way or the other.

Two general features of the photographs are worth some special note. First, they probably magnify the art of photography a good deal more than they magnify the social ills of the sharecropping system. They are camera studies done with a fine eye for composition and for the possibilities of the subject; they are not candid camera shots. They show that the faces of country people in the South have individual character, flavor, life. These faces are not flabby, they have not been smoothed and rounded out into undistinguished uniformity, as a similar collection of city faces might seem to be; but they are strong, irregular, often beautiful, with a wild and touching nobility. Even when ugly and coarse, they conceal no guile, they betray not overmuch frustration.

Second, the photographs, with their legends, may be taken, within limits, as representative, anyway, of conditions in regions where tenancy is heaviest. It would be absurd for a Southerner to set up any claim of unfairness here. Though he may easily think of photographic representations that might be more flattering in the social sense, he will have to concede that the photographer might have shown worse scenes, worse-looking folks. I have seen a sharecropper's place in the Black Tobacco Patch where the cropper lived in a splendid house, owned hogs and cattle, and had upstanding sons who belonged to the Four-H Club. Also I have seen other sharecroppers' places in the deep South that were more like the dens of wild animals than human habitation. The photographs hit between these two extremes.

But of course the photographic job is punily, sickeningly incomplete, in quite another respect. Croppers and farmers are not the only tenant problem of the South. Nearly all Southerners are tenants, in effect or actuality. We have tenant bankers, tenant merchants, tenant manufacturers, tenant teachers, tenant clergy, yes, and even so-called farm owners who are little better than hired hands. And the absentee landlord over these tenants and hired hands is the North. Rarely before in human history has a population of such numbers, in a land so rich, exerted so little responsible control over its own economic fate. We are all held in a bondage that is the more subtle because the chains and indentures are not actually visible. To be complete, therefore, Mr. Caldwell's photographic journalism would have to find a way of picturing these things, placing in juxtaposition, after the manner of *Life,* the eroded land and people of the South and the certainly non-eroded land and people of the North. And there ought also to be pictures of matters that do not photograph well, but that may be charted or written about, such as economic unbalances and historic causes. Then there might be, too, some city squalors to show off against country squalors. But such completeness is not to be hoped for in photographic journalism. Mr. Caldwell's picture book, considered simply as picture book, is certainly fair-to-middling, by the strictest possible estimate. He shows fewer horrors, more variety, more poetry and strength than the same kind of photographs, made under nonpartisan auspices, that appear in the report of the President's Committee on Farm Tenancy.

But it is quite another thing when we come to Mr. Caldwell's text, which is a discussion of the tenancy problem itself. When we discover what interpretation we are supposed to make of the faces we have seen and what social action we are supposed to enter into, we are back in the dumps again. As a student of farm tenancy in the South Mr. Caldwell would make a splendid Curator of a Soviet Park of Recreation and Culture. The admirable photographs turn into fearsome cartoons and horrible effigies. The imagination of Mr. Caldwell may be a fine thing when it is behaving as an imagination should, though it does have a lamentable partiality for the grotesque. When it operates directly upon the data of Southern life and opines forthrightly on that subject, the Caldwellian imagination becomes irrepressible and sinister. It brings us to the dim lake of Auber, the dank tarn of Usher, the ghoul-haunted woodland of Weir.

There is a factual basis for Mr. Caldwell's argument about the evils of sharecropping. Beneath his highly colored account of the situation it is possible to discern some dim outline of social and economic truth. One can tell that he has done a little reading: he has learned about erosion; he has a smattering of Southern history —a little less than a Georgia high school student, a little more than the average contributor to the *New Masses.* The sharecropper biographies that he uses as exempla may be accepted as factually correct, as far as they go. Here and there he shows a half-hearted disposition to weigh in the balance the regional disadvantages of the South. It " has always been shoved around like a country cousin," he says. " It sits at second table and is fed short rations. . . . It has been taking a beating for a long time. . . . [It] will never be understood by the rest of America." And so on. But immediately such concessions are colored and changed by another kind of talk. " Mark against the South its failure to preserve its own culture and its refusal to accept the culture of the East and West. Mark against it the refusal to assimilate the blood of an alien race of another color or to tolerate its presence." Or, " The South perpetrated a feud, which was excusable in the beginning, and now it is guilty of perpetuating the quarrel, for which there is no excuse."

The South is " guilty," and, secondarily, Southern landlords of any and every sort are " guilty." That is the leading motif in Mr. Caldwell's interpretation. The factual basis, the occasional concessions, the scattered historical references — all mean nothing. Mr. Caldwell's argument puts the case of *United States vs. the South* back where it was a hundred years ago. It is the same old story of prosecution and judgment combined in one act:

Fury said to a mouse
Whom he met in the house,
" Come, let's both go to law.
I will prosecute you . . .

" I'll be judge, I'll be jury,"
Said the cunning old Fury.
" I'll try the whole case
And condemn you to DEATH! "

The only difference is that a Southerner with Marxian affiliations, who takes a Marxian line, assumes the rôle of Fury. All the rest is unchanged: we have the same errors and distortions of fact, the same innocent simplifications, the same nonchalant exclusion of testimony that might acquit the defendant, the same willingness to hand down a verdict beneficial to the prosecutor-judge. It is Olmstead, Garrison, John Brown, Thad Stevens, Charles Sumner, with modern trimmings.

The following is a summary of Mr. Caldwell's diagnostic description — that is, what we are supposed to think that the pictures and legends demonstrate about the South:

Ten million [*sic*] people now live under the "yoke" of the sharecropping system. This system is a direct outgrowth of the plantation system, which is an "antisocial" device for raising cotton. The plantation system which depended on slave labor was ruined by the War; the South then discovered it could not catch up economically with the East and West. So it retreated into isolation. It thought up sharecropping (1) as a means of keeping the Negro, and with him the poor white, in a kind of slavery, and (2) "as a means of getting even with the North." The general villain is the South, which insists on being "a worn-out agricultural empire." The particular villain is the Southern landlord. If he has a hundred tenants, each of whom makes six bales of cotton, he gets three hundred bales and each tenant gets only three. The landlord makes the profit; he is wealthy and generally cruel. He has the power of law and wealth behind him. He is the pernicious agent of an agricultural system "that acquires sharecroppers and mules for their economic usefulness and disposes of them when no more profit can be extracted from their bodies."

Such is the economic diagnosis, but we should not neglect to point out that Mr. Caldwell has added a little sociological-journalistic coloring to it. Upon this economic picture we must superimpose the picture of the South which has great currency in the North — being first disseminated in the 1920's by Mencken and Company and by Gerald Johnson and other Southern "liberals." That is, it is a South which makes women work in the fields; which knows not the blessings of the birth control movement; which releases its "pent-up emotions by lynching the black man in order to witness the mental and physical suffering of another human being"; which makes every white face the Negro sees "a reminder of his brother's mutilation, burning, and death at the stake"; which has rabble-rousers as leaders; which has, for religion, an opium of the people contrived to keep them servile — it excites "the ignorant who live primitive lives to give vent to their feelings by rolling on the floor, shouting, and dancing in the aisles"; which takes a contrary delight in race prejudice, backwardness, poverty, illiteracy, and social snobbery. Furthermore, this is the only South that exists at all! It is the only South presented in Mr. Caldwell's discussion, and he has taken pains to add some photographs that echo this long-established caricature.

Now for the remedy, which is as simple as the diagnosis. Mr. Caldwell would welcome a government investigation into the share-cropping evil. He would also welcome government control of cotton farming. But in any case, over and above all else, the remedy is collectivism. What Mr. Caldwell wants is a labor union for the sharecroppers — not farm ownership (for many of them would prefer not to have the responsibility of ownership) but "adequate pay . . . the same protection from unscrupulous employers that workers in steel mills and department stores receive." If we do not seize upon this remedy, we are warned to expect a genuine social uprising. The tenant farmer will, Mr. Caldwell assures us, take matters into his own hands; and he will find that his long experience of hardship will "stand him in good stead when the time comes for him to begin thinking *about taking over the job of raising cotton*" [*Italics mine*].

It is easy enough to check off Mr. Caldwell's grosser errors of fact. The 1935 census reports only 716,356 sharecroppers for the entire South, including the border states. There cannot be *ten million persons* living under the "yoke" of the sharecropping system. Sharecropping was not a devilish invention got up by the South to reënslave the Negro and spite the North. It was the only resource of the post-bellum South, which still had land to work, but no money. It was, and still is, one practical means of raising stable crops in a section that gets relatively little return on its produce, and that does not know how else to guarantee its annual labor supply, which is likely at any time to move to the nearest city. Or, if one wants to be broadly historical, it is no more an outgrowth of the plantation system in particular than of America's historic fondness for the old fee simple system of land tenure, which, however abused by later generations, seemed to our forefathers the very "palladium" of liberty. Furthermore, there is sharecropping everywhere in the United States, not only in the South. It sometimes works badly in the big-plantation regions, but it has not always worked badly elsewhere. It is entirely possible that the relatively serious condition of the tenant farmers in the South and the recent large increases in tenancy are not a specific indictment of the plantation system, but are symptomatic of the critical condition of agriculture, bad everywhere, but naturally worst in the cotton regions, which were economically sick long before the day of photographic journalism.

These facts are well known to all serious students of farm tenancy and sharecropping. They are available in all kinds of documents — magazine articles, pamphlets, books, and government reports. They were available to Erskine Caldwell, but I doubt whether, even if such material had been put into his hands, he would have used it. The facts indicate a highly complex situation; and Mr. Caldwell could do nothing with a complex situation. He wanted it simple and stark. He made it simple and stark. He does not want a solution. He wants a fight. His book, published first in a de luxe edition at $7.50 for the penthouses and later in a seventy-five cent edition for the newsstands, has the beautiful simplicity of all engines of propaganda. The North is supposed to read it, as it once read Abolitionist pamphlets; and next comes, I suppose, the 1938 equivalent of Beecher Bibles; and then in Arkansas and Mississippi the modern parallel to Bleeding Kansas. If we could be certain that *You Have Seen Their Faces* would have the effect apparently intended, it would be easy enough to predict the course of events and Mr. Caldwell's share in them.

One can hardly deem his intentions innocent, for he is a Southerner, and he himself knows what he has left out of his account. He has left out, for example, the entire tale told by Webb in *Divided We Stand:* the whole tragic story of the great agricultural region dominated and exploited by the careless sway of the still greater industrial region. He has left out of account the well-known fact that the average Southern landlord is almost as much a victim as the sharecropper. But for the recent intervention of the Triple-A there might not have been any Southern landlords for Mr. Caldwell to rail against; most Southern plantations would now be among the frozen assets of banks, mortgage companies, or insurance companies (chiefly Northern-owned), as many of them are, indeed, at this moment. Faulty as the Southern landlord may be in some respects (and I certainly do not propose to whitewash him) he does not deserve to be the villain of Mr. Caldwell's piece — except, perhaps, in certain limited areas where highly commercialized plantations are administered with studied irresponsibility by absentee landlords. If the cropper has a case against the landlord, the landlord also has a case against the cropper. No farmer in Vermont, New York, Ohio, or Kansas would put up with, in his farm labor, what the Southern landlord inescapably *must* put up with. But in any case the ultimate villain is the industrial system which makes machinery, fertilizer, and clothing high and cotton low in price; and the industrial system is not controlled by the South, least of all by the Southern cotton-grower.

As for investigation by a government commission, that has already been done, and little has come of it.

As for sharecroppers' unions, they are reasonable enough in theory, I suppose, if the great plantations are going to become simply units of an industrialized agriculture — which is probably what Mr. Caldwell wants. But even with an industrialized agriculture and sharecroppers' unions, the relative economic disadvantage of the Southern producer would remain untouched. If the plantation gave the sharecropper "adequate pay," according to some scale devised by Mr. Caldwell, he probably would be not only without profit but without a plantation. If that is to happen, the cotton land of the South had as well be signed over to Northern capital at once, without the agony of a further decay. But Mr. Caldwell does not really want that either. He wants an uprising. He is a Marxian, who has learned nothing from Stalinized Russia.

But it is probably useless to make such points. It is useless to subject Mr. Caldwell to critical analysis. He will never mend his ways. There is no easy way, either, of reaching, with the coolest possible critical analysis, the people whose opinions he hopes to influence. They do not read the *Southern Review*. Most of them do not know that it exists. But they will read *You Have Seen Their Faces*, and, because their minds are already "conditioned" in a certain direction, will accept Mr. Caldwell's interpretation of his pictures. There is no effective means open to the South for combating that interpretation. The best that the South can hope for is that the thousands of readers of *You Have Seen Their Faces* will, like some of the reviewers, be bored and inactive, since after all it is a very old story.

Is there any particular admonition that a Southerner could give to those readers, provided he should by some miracle be able to reach them? I can think of one admonition of special importance. Let the Northern reader, before he grows indignant over Southern conditions, be sure, be *very* sure, that in no way he himself is profiting at the expense of the Southern sharecropper and landlord. If any part of his income is derived from the sale of high-priced manufactured articles, if he clips any coupons from industrial paper, insurance stocks, et cetera, he is in all likelihood *particeps criminis* — he is sustained by the lifeblood of the victim he would pity as the victim of "an outworn agricultural empire."

And one more admonition. The South can never even make a decent beginning toward settling its economic problems if, while engaged earnestly in the process of studying them, it is constantly summoned to court and forced to answer libelous and malicious proceedings against its character. That has been said before. It cannot be said too often.

From all this it should appear that a great deal is the matter with Mr. Caldwell. Just what, I do not think I need to say in the most precise terms. What is the matter with any Southerner who turns state's evidence under circumstances like these? Are the proceeds of *You Have Seen Their Faces* and other notable works devoted to charity?

— From the *Southern Review*, Summer, 1938. Reprinted by permission.

THE BEST BOOK ON THE MODERN SOUTH

A Review of Jonathan Daniels' *A Southerner Discovers the South*

By Gerald W. Johnson

The best book on the modern South that has yet been written is Mr. Daniels'. This is said without forgetting the Caldwell-White *You Have Seen Their Faces,* the Odum *Southern Regions,* or the Davidson *Attack on Leviathan,* each of which, in its special field, excels *A Southerner Discovers the South.*

But whereas each of the others was aimed at a different group, more or less specialized in its interests, Mr. Daniels aims at anyone who can read. Yet the emotional who follow Caldwell-White, the statisticians who follow Odum, and the intellectuals who follow Davidson can all follow Daniels with pleasure and probably with profit, too.

His approach to the problem is one that any ordinary man can understand. He is editor of a Southern newspaper, the Raleigh, North Carolina, *News and Observer,* and it occurred to him one day that he was continually discussing Southern problems without having seen very much of the South. So he went out to look at it. He spent a summer and drove three thousand miles looking.

He saw the TVA, the federal resettlement project at Dyess, Arkansas, the coöperative plantation that idealists are running at Hillhouse, Mississippi, the biggest cotton plantation in the world — 38,000 acres — in the same state, the ghost of Huey Long stalking through Louisiana, Mobile, the Sewanee River, Birmingham and Atlanta, Florida, Savannah and Charleston.

Wherever he went he saw people, too, and talked with them or, more frequently, listened to their talk — governors, Negro farm hands, country storekeepers, college professors, hoboes, farmers, an organizer for the sharecroppers' union, the owner of coal mines and steel mills, bankers, panhandlers, aristocratic ladies and the keeper of a brothel, editors, communists, novelists, poets, Democrats, so-called Democrats, and even a Republican or two.

Then he wrote, but just what he wrote it is difficult to say — essays, yes, but not literary essays, nor sociological, nor political; travel notes, yes, but not the conventional travel notes; economics, yes, but very far indeed from anything that could truthfully be called "the dismal silence." There is, indeed, a word that will describe the book exactly, but unfortunately pedantry has wrested that word from its real meaning and converted it into an epithet. The word is "journalism." Mr. Daniels' work is reporting, but such fine reporting that it, like Hazlitt's account of the prizefight, outsoars much that by professors of English is accounted literature.

His book is a series of pictures arranged geographically along the route he took. With great economy of means he presents what he believes to be the significant element in each successive landscape; and he rarely, if ever, fails. Mr. Daniels has a brilliant but not a distorted mind; he sees better than you and I would see, but he sees the same thing, in the same colors and in pretty much the same relationships. His publishers describe him as a liberal, which doubtless is true, provided that he who hears the description bears in mind that a liberal is not always

> A greenery-yallery, Grosvenor Gallery,
> Foot-in-the-grave young man,

for this Daniels is a hard-headed, hearty person, high-spirited and full of raffish humors. Some of the tales he tells with gusto would knock the breath out of prim Daughters of the Confederacy.

More than that, some of the most cherished schemes of the liberals leave him cold. The Dyess resettlement project, for example, he admits is highly attractive, but he can't see it as a solution of the Southern agricultural problem because it is essentially charity. The coöperative at Hillhouse, backed by Sherwood Eddy, among others, was less attractive, but seemed sounder until he reflected that Sam Franklin, who runs it for love, would be worth $25,000 a year to any corporation; so it, too, is essentially charity. The plantation of the great English-owned Delta and Pine Land Company, strictly commercial but intelligent, humane, and successful, impressed him, but only as proof of the genius of the superintendent in charge. In short, nowhere did this observer find anything resembling a panacea; so perhaps he is not a liberal at all.

All of this, however, has been done by others, with greater wealth of statistics and factual details. Daniels' book is unique, not in its content, but in the manner of its presentation. One hesitates to say that he writes with conscious artistry, for that usually implies preciosity; but he does search diligently for the right word, and even more diligently for the right mood.

In Louisiana, for example, he bothered very little with facts and figures and very much with a ghost. The chapter is concerned largely with the mythology, strange, eerie, perhaps sinister, that is already collecting around the name of Huey Long.

> Life and politics go on in Louisiana as in Nicaragua and Haiti and Santo Domingo and after the same patterns Americanized. And pretty girls in nice flat New Orleans gardens run shouting after the feathered shuttlecock. Comus comes. The mint in the juleps at the Boston Club is crushed before the whiskey is put in, or not crushed, as the drinker wishes. But beside the green bayous and on the red hills Huey Long is a spirit, as stripped of comedy as of flesh, that moves as John Brown's spirit moved. And like John Brown's it is a spirit which may leave red tracks in the grass and the sand and across the flagstones to the big house door. . . . There is a ghost at large in Louisiana and not even laughter has laid him.

This is patently not true. There are no ghosts. But one is left with the uncomfortable suspicion that this ghost story contains more of the truth about Louisiana than one could glean from the Statistical Abstract of the United States.

Then there is the weird comparison made between Mr. DeBardeleben and Joe Poe. Mr. DeBardeleben is a millionaire and Joe Poe is a bum. Joe, old, feeble, disillusioned, hitchhiked a ride toward Birmingham, Alabama, where he wished, rather than hoped, that he could get a job, because he had found the old-age pension illusory and relief inadequate. Mr. DeBardeleben, old, disillusioned, but fiery, Daniels sought out in Birmingham and found him raving against Roosevelt, relief, organized labor, and Myron Taylor who " betrayed his associates " by coming to an agreement with John L. Lewis. But after talking with him Daniels mused:

He is a mountain and Joe Poe is a mouse, and both are equally lost in these times. Joe Poe seemed a little more complacent. Charles DeBardeleben seemed a great deal more angry. But both seemed old in a world brash as Lewis, hopeful as Roosevelt, pragmatic as Taylor. The two are brothers of each other and of the past.

To call a great Southern captain of industry " brother of the past " is certainly not to speak literal truth; yet to one who knows the type, there is a strong persuasiveness about it.

In the heart of Alabama there was another man, " as black as asphalt, as black as old scabbard leather; his hair was short and kinky and his lips were as wide as my thumbs. His arms hung long to tremendous hands. And his laughter came loud and cackling like defensive idiocy which Negroes erect against the dangerous answering of white men's questions." But he was a graduate of a great Northern university and he knows more about what the sharecroppers' union organizers and the communists are doing in Alabama than any white man in the state. Knowing, he is fearful. The glimpse of him is a glimpse of an underground world in the South that no white man, not even Daniels, has explored. This is unabashed melodrama; but in view of recent tales of wild violence in the Southern fields, dare one dismiss it as fiction?

A *Southerner Discovers the South* is full of delightful passages and breaks occasionally into uproarious mirth; but for all that, it is a somber book. Mr. Daniels loves the South, but he sees it too well to be very happy over it. He is not much interested in its psychopaths. He leaves them to the doctors, and to Messrs. William Faulkner and Erskine Caldwell. But he did deal at some length with one wanton, and the dealing is in some respects the most successful passage in the book. She was a little, old woman who ran a bawdy-house in Vicksburg. The account of her is curious. She is neither sentimentalized nor denounced, simply described and quoted, briefly and matter-of-factly. Her story was in no sense dramatic, and there was never a trace of glamour about her. Yet at the end, for no exactly definable reason, the poor old drab suddenly comes alive, becomes momentarily intensely human, becomes pitiful and appealing. This, though, is something above and beyond reporting. This is art.

— From " Books," New York *Herald Tribune*, July 17, 1938. Reprinted by permission.

MR. DANIELS DISCOVERS THE SOUTH

By Frank L. Owsley

One should approach the review and criticism of Mr. Daniels' book with a certain diffidence: the weekly journals, some of the reviews, and most of the newspapers have already spoken with unqualified approval; and their composite opinion is that the work is fascinating, profound, authoritative. For me, therefore, to subject the book to further examination and analysis may appear to be an act of supererogation; and for me to disagree with the general acclaim given the book will be accounted as an act of perversity. Yet I must be in considerable disagreement with the critics, for, while I have found the book interesting as a whole, I have also found it superficial. Perhaps it may be answered at once, by those very reviewers who have hailed the book as profound, that a travel book is under no special obligation to be profound; that its chief function is competent reporting. I shall agree in advance with this opinion as to the function of travel literature; but at the same time I would call attention to the fact that the book is a more ambitious undertaking than a book of travel; it is also a commentary, an interpretation.

I

As a book of travel, it is, as I shall try to demonstrate, based upon inadequate reporting; the word *incompetent* might be a better adjective. To begin with, Mr. Daniels appears from his own record to have spent barely three weeks on his journey of " discovery," and in this three weeks he traveled well-nigh four thousand miles, through Virginia, North Carolina, Tennessee, the tip of Arkansas,

Louisiana, the edge of Mississippi, the center of Alabama, both edges of Georgia, Florida, and coastal South Carolina. Great speed was necessary: an average of hardly less than two hundred miles each day. Actually the author drove from New Orleans to Birmingham by way of Biloxi, Mobile, and Montgomery in a day and night — a distance of about four hundred and fifty miles. Within three days after he spent the night in Birmingham he was back home at Raleigh. During these three days he " discovered " East Alabama, West Georgia, Florida, East Georgia, and East South Carolina, and traversed about fifteen hundred miles of concrete and asphalt highway — roads cut for convenience and not discovery. That is, he covered the second half of his journey — New Orleans to Raleigh — at the rate of five hundred miles a day; no mean feat in itself.

The author is not abashed by the inevitable implications of such haste in the collection of material for his book; on the contrary, he seems never to doubt that three weeks was time aplenty to spend in discovering the South. Yet to write a travel book upon the basis of such a marathon is to invite skepticism as to the validity of the writer's observations, the competency of his reporting. A serious examination of the book confirms our skepticism; Mr. Daniels' reporting is just what any thoughtful person should expect: inaccurate, frequently incorrect to the smallest detail. As an illustration of reporting that is incorrect to the smallest detail, I shall take Mr. Daniels' account of how the capital came to be moved to Montgomery, Alabama. He misunderstood the story in Montgomery. The little town of Wetumpka, thirty miles north of Montgomery, he says, was once the capital of Alabama and it was at the time known as Yankeetown or New Philadelphia. Montgomery, however, built the Exchange Hotel where the very best food was served; so lobbyists from that town gave to each member of the legislature then sitting at Wetumpka a menu from the recently built hotel, whereupon the poorly fed legislators immediately voted to move the capital to Montgomery. Any little Alabama school child could have given Mr. Daniels the essential facts: Wetumpka is about fifteen miles from Montgomery; it has always been called Wetumpka, not Yankeetown or New Philadelphia; it has never been the capital of the state; finally, and most amusing of all, New Philadelphia, spoken of as Yankeetown, was Montgomery itself, and the capitol building stands in the limits of the village once known as New Philadelphia. Not that this entirely incorrect account of the location of the capital in itself destroys the value of the book; but it is typical of the whole factual basis of the book as it relates to the journey itself, for I have checked the author on several other points, as for instance conversations with certain people, who have assured me that he failed to get either the letter or the spirit of what was said.

The factual weakness of the book has, however, undoubtedly made it more readable: the less one knows of a country and its people the more easily can he write with conviction and definiteness. Not unlike the vague light of dawn, the grayish light of the uninformed mind clothes commonplace objects with weirdness and mystery. Had Mr. Daniels spent a year on his tour it would have been impossible for him to have written such a sure and interesting book. Not that all the book is interesting or amusing: whenever the author forsakes the loose journalistic technique for that of the novelist — which is all too often — he is irritating. His amateurish dialogue, irrelevant vulgarities, and smart-aleck mannerisms are definitely dated 1920–1925, and I for one, though fourteen years older than I was at the end of this period, feel anything but nostalgia when reminded of literature of those years.

II

As an interpretation of the South and an analysis of the vital issues and problems of that section, the book has an uneven value. As a newspaper editor in Raleigh and as a person of intellectual attainment, Mr. Daniels should have a considerable reading acquaintance with the South; and so he says that he has. For years, he says, he has been reading books on the South, such scholarly books as those written by Vance and Odum of North Carolina, who have been digging patiently at the roots of Southern problems. I must confess, however, that I have the feeling that his excursions into such literature of the South have too often been not unlike his marathon of four thousand miles through the South. It is not surprising, then, that while the author is aware of many issues and problems in the South, he seems to lack a clear-cut conception of most, though not all, of them. The book, for this reason among others already suggested, lacks a consistent point of view. It is amazingly contradictory: the author says and unsays things so frequently that one begins to feel that his final word as to that thing or person or issue will depend upon whether he will end the subject on an odd or an even page number.

It is difficult to analyze a book organized loosely upon the framework of a journey. However, certain issues and problems had interested him more or less before he began his trip of discovery so that he naturally recurs to these in the interviews and conversations that he records. The decadence of the Southern people, the TVA, agrarianism, the tenant problem, absentee ownership of Southern resources and industry, sectional discrimination against the South in freight rates and tariff, and Southern poverty are questions which most frequently engaged his attention.

On Southern decadence — as on most, if not all, of the other questions which he discusses — the author seems to have made use of the formula of the children's game " She loves me, she loves me not " to reach his final conclusion. He began his journey at Washington. Pausing to view Arlington as he leaves the national capital, he beholds a symbol: the ghost of Lee keeping the door of a decadent or moribund South. Not only is Lee doorkeeper of the South; strangely he is still the South's model. Perhaps it was characteristic, observes the author, of a

people living in the hottest sun ever borne as native by a northern stock of people anywhere that we should have chosen Robert E. Lee as our idol. This conjunction of a sun-warmed people and white marble hero has not always been entirely beneficial. It did not take us long to discover that few of us could approximate the elevated ethics of General Lee. And, not being able to approximate General Lee, we scorned any intermediary standards. Proudly Southerners held to Lee or nothing. And it is no longer a secret that in the South nothing has had more completely faithful adherents than General Lee. . . .

Thus, this traveler who has not yet crossed the Potomac " discovers " at the outset that the Southerners are without moral stamina.

The weather did it. The only thing wrong with this explanation of Southern physical and moral laziness — if such laziness does prevail — is of course the weather. Three years ago the thermometer several times stood at ten and twelve below zero here at Nashville; and up at Crossville on the Cumberland plateau it was eighteen below zero. The first settlers at Nashville crossed their wagons and horses over the Cumberland River on ice. The first view I ever had of the James River at Richmond in 1924 found it frozen over. As a boy in Montgomery County, Alabama, I recall seeing my father not infrequently cut holes in the ice on the cattle ponds with a pickaxe so that the stock might get water.

This decadence of the Southern people and the climatic explanation occurs on page 13. Within a day or so Mr. Daniels is in North Carolina on "Gold Avenue," as he calls it, following the roads that lead through the vast string of textile villages which extend to the edge of Mississippi instead of to Atlanta, as the author asserts. He becomes suddenly dramatic and enthusiastic about these textile operatives, many of them ex-tenant farmers: they are no longer decadent. Far from it! These people are fighters, he says. They are not docile. They "are the grandchildren of those [Confederates] who opined that it was a rich man's war and a poor man's fight and who fought like lank and indestructible devils just the same. Dig McClellan up and ask *him* if they were docile." This is on page 29. On page 335 however, and at intervals between, the author reverts to the idea of Southern decadence. Southerners really never liked to work. Slavery made even the poorest have contempt for work before the Civil War, and "most of the whites were desperately poor." In fact "all the major faults and flaws in Southern economy were on the way to full growth before the war began." Thus, toward the end of the book, the author can look back and say again that the Southern people have always been shiftless and lacking in stamina. The war "served as an alibi — a magnificent alibi." "The South was poor; the war caused it. The South was ignorant; the war made us too poor to educate. The South was slow; well, after what the damn Yankees did it wasn't any use to stir. The war provided a satisfying, acceptable and even mildly exhilarating excuse for everything. . . ." In the end, however, the author decides that "the Southern white masses are not biologically degenerate." Far from being moribund, or even degenerate, all the Southern people need is a chance, an equal opportunity or not even that, to enable them to get ahead in the race. "The South is awakening, scratching at new desires." Thus, the author comes to the end of his journey and his book with a high opinion of the Southern people.

Mr. Daniels visited Norris and gently taps it on the wrist for being a planned town and for not having a cemetery. He goes in for towns that are not planned and that have cemeteries. Mr. Daniels grows whimsical. He discovers a cemetery with one grave in it, and his mild disapproval weakens. While in East Tennessee he called upon Lilienthal, and he reports quite an interesting conversation with the TVA director. Lilienthal is quoted as firmly convinced that the mountain poor whites are not biologically inferior, and as being opposed to imposing a way of life upon people from above. In fact, Mr. Daniels quotes Mr. Lilienthal as actually believing that all the Southern people need to put them ahead is an equal opportunity with the people of other sections. This is news even to friends of TVA, among whom I am one. I hope that Mr. Daniels did not misunderstand Lilienthal as he did the person who told him about moving the capital to Montgomery.

One of the ideas about which Mr. Daniels was obviously perturbed during his long journey was agrarianism as advocated by a group of writers once dwelling at Nashville but now almost completely dispersed. He devotes a considerable section of his book to a somewhat incoherent account of a meeting of the Southern Policy Association at Chattanooga which had taken place some time previous to his visit to that city. It seems from his account that Allen Tate and Dr. Amberson became embroiled in an argument concerning the tenant farmer problem in the South. Amberson is a socialist and Tate is an advocate of private ownership of property, particularly farm lands. At any rate, Mr. Daniels devotes as much space to the controversy as he does to any other subject in the book; and according to his own statement, he obtained his information from Amberson, the socialist, but rejected Tate's version: not an objective bit of reporting. He later made a special visit to Nashville to interview Donald Davidson and discuss the state of the nation with him, but his account of his interview with Mr. Davidson is not clear to me — except that he seems to be more worried over the philosophy and implications of agrarianism than he is over those of fascism, communism, or military despotism.

Because Daniels seemed genuinely perturbed over agrarianism — which, however, he kept insisting, was dead — I wonder why he did not tell the reader something about this dead though still dreadful thing. Frankly, I very much doubt that Mr. Daniels has acquainted himself with the philosophy of agrarianism. Having lived here many years where the movement originated, I am fairly well acquainted with the economic and political doctrines of agrarianism. The basic agrarian economic doctrine, as the name implies, is land reform: it is strongly advocated that tenant farmers and sharecroppers be homesteaded at government expense — though not at an expense that would entail the building of a four-thousand-dollar dwelling house and expensive outbuildings. Next in importance is an advocacy of the decentralization, wherever feasible, of industry both as to ownership and physical structure — always, however, making use of the best technical equipment. Wherever national defense or physical necessity makes decentralization questionable, some of the Agrarians advocate government ownership or government control; others are opposed to either. The original Agrarians — with the exception of one who is reported to be a fellow traveler with the communists at the present — have always advocated a balanced economy for the South, where agriculture would be the leading occupation, but where there would be industry enough for regional self-sufficiency wherever such self-sufficiency would be economical. They object to a high tariff, freight rate discrimination, and most passionately to absentee ownership of Southern industry and resources. Politically, they still believe that the doctrines of Thomas Jefferson and the Declaration of Independence are valid in most instances. In all matters they are regionalists and are opposed to the exploitation of one section by any other.

Just why Mr. Daniels objects so violently to agrarian philosophy never appears in his book, unless the implication is found in his excessive amiability towards Marxians. It is possible, too, that he has confused the Fugitive Poets with the agrarian movement. I once listened to an address by Mr. Couch of the University of North Carolina Press in which the same confusion existed. Actually, there is very little connection between the two groups. The Fugitive Poets organized and established their magazine in 1922. They were devoted to poetry and aesthetics, and the bulk of them never became Agrarians. In fact, only four became members of the agrarian movement when it was organized in 1929–1930. The others became industrialists. As far as I have been able to learn there was only one principle in common between these two groups — regionalism. If Mr. Daniels has confused the Fugitives and the Agrarians, part of his irritation undoubtedly arises from the difficulty with which he comprehends poetry.

The author was still perturbed over agrarianism when he visited the Arkansas bottoms and the Mississippi Delta to inspect the sharecroppers. Somehow, he seemed to believe that the tenant problem was confined to the Delta and the alluvial lands of the Mississippi River and its tributaries. He paid slight attention to the problem elsewhere. Yet the bulk of the tenants and sharecroppers live in the hilly and rolling lands that are poor and eroded, where the landlord is usually resident and bankrupt. Mr. Daniels visited the Hillhouse socialist colony and found no serious objection to collectivism as a solution of the tenant problem: his only criticism is that Hillhouse is not managed by trained agriculturists. He inspected the Dyess colony, which is a government experiment in homesteading landless and destitute farmers. He found that the government is building houses and furnishing equipment beyond the possible earning power of these rehabilitated farmers. This seems to me to be a sound observation. Yet Mr. Daniels also criticizes the experiment because it is an effort to restore land to the landless. He spent the night on the Delta and Pine Land Company, a corporate plantation which had 38,000 rich acres at the time, but which is reported now to own 50,000 acres. The Delta and Pine is an English-owned plantation, and Mr. Daniels finds it run as efficiently as a factory. The sharecroppers seem to be in a much better state of well-being here than elsewhere. Perhaps, he suggests, it is due to the able and sympathetic management of Mr. Johnson. At any rate corporate farming seems to appear to Mr. Daniels a possible solution of the sharecropper problem. Certainly he leaves the unmistakable impression that some form of collectivism, whether Marxian or corporate, is a better solution for the sharecropper problem than the restoration of these people to the status of landowners. That both landlords and tenants may eventually be sharecroppers on corporate farms or state-owned farms is possible. The trend is decidedly in that direction. But should it come about that corporate farming or collective state farming prove to be the solution of the tenant problem, then we shall have come to the end of our American political and economic system. That Mr. Daniels has seriously considered such eventuality is doubtful. Tenancy and sharecropping seem to be only farm problems, and Mr. Daniels is only dimly aware of the necessity of a healthy balance between agriculture and industry.

III

The last section of Mr. Daniels' book is, despite the inevitable equivocations and contradictions, an excellent statement of two of the most fundamental Southern problems: absentee ownership of Southern resources and industry; sectional discrimination by the federal government itself against the South and in the interest of the East in the matter of tariffs and freight rates. I should like to accept the author's conclusions at their excellent face value; but recalling how he has wavered and trimmed even unto the last page, I must be pardoned if I take a not inconsiderable pinch of salt at this point. It is to be regretted that Mr. Daniels has not made clear his social philosophy so as to give real meaning to such excellent statements of the problems of the South.

The author observes that absentee ownership, high protective tariffs, and freight rate discriminations have been the triple squeeze used by the East upon the South, which has done more injury than the Civil War and Reconstruction.

The war and Reconstruction were important as memory of them served as a screen of emotionalism behind which moved, ever praising Lee, those unemotional gentlemen from the North who knew what they wanted and how much they would have to pay for it, which was not much. This second wave of carpetbaggers was received with honors and banquets and bands. They were the agents of the new and ever greater absentee ownership of the South. They came from the North with excellent financial connections to buy up broken down Southern railroads and other properties and they picked up some pretty bargains. . . . The banks of those same gentlemen who bought up Southern railroads were also deeply interested in Northern railroads. It has even been suggested that while they were ever willing to make money they were also careful not to build up Southern traffic and industry at the expense of those older developed areas of the North and East through which their older lines ran.

It is probably

significant that the only industrial development which has taken place in the South since the industrial North overcame the country culture of the South has been in the widely dispersed manufacture of textiles and in the new big industry of the cigarette [Mr. Daniels overlooks the oil, iron, steel, and coal industries also largely owned by absentees]. . . . Otherwise the South, devoted to the culture of cotton and tobacco, the prices of which are fixed in world markets, still buys from the protected factories of the North. Its new overseers, faithful to the absentee owners, beg and plead and promise for more absentee investment and control while simultaneously they cry to hysteria in condemnation of foreign agitators among nice native labor.

The other two partners in the triple squeeze, protective tariff and freight rate discrimination, " did at least as much damage in Dixie as Sherman and Grant together in making the South poor and keeping it poor. Indeed, while Sherman and Grant have gone to whatever they had coming to them, the tariff remains," and freight rates " still sit providing inland the protection which tariffs provide on coast and frontier." Mr. Daniels is doubtful whether the North will relinquish these advantages and consent to live in the Union on terms of equity and equality. " Perhaps those advantages are so deeply fixed . . . that to change them to give the South a chance might do vast harm elsewhere, might cause much suffering in the areas which have grown rich on advantage, like that which wrings the hearts of Northerners when they see it in the

South." He asserts a strong belief, however, that the South will be able to do more than hold its own in the face of these discriminations — a great compliment to a people whom he has severely castigated even up to this point, at intervals, for lacking in moral and physical stamina and for offering just such sectional exploitation as their reason for not keeping pace with the North.

> Perhaps the South, as New England seems now fearing, may be able to escape its single slavery to cotton and advance to a diverse industrial and agricultural development despite the imperial advantages which New England took as its loot after the Civil War. . . . And New England is afraid: the terrible danger is that it is about to lose at last the slavery from which it profited long after Lincoln in a manner of speaking set the Negroes free. Of course everybody was free in the South, free to fight among themselves for the too little that was left when tribute was paid.

"Cato the Elder," concludes Mr. Daniels — the Cato always shouting that Carthage must be destroyed —

> was not more implacable than the Brahmins of Boston who came after the Abolitionists with considerably cooler heads. The South was not plowed up and planted with salt as Carthage was. If no more generous, Bostonians (citizens of a region and an attitude and not a town) were less wasteful. They recognized that the South kept in its place (a place in the nation geographically similar to that of the Negro in the South) might be useful and profitable. It was. And as Southerner at the end of discovery I ask now only that they recognize the poverty of the South as a part of the same civilization as Harvard and in a measure as the creation of the same people. Cato did not ride through Carthage on the train and blame its conditions on the Carthaginians [though Mr. Daniels has done this very thing throughout his book on the even pages except, of course, he used an automobile and not a train]. That much only I ask of the Yankees.

— From the *Southern Review*, Spring, 1939. Reprinted by permission.

THE RESEARCH PAPER

FROM TILLMAN TO LONG

Some Striking Leaders of the Rural South

By Daniel M. Robison

AT intervals since 1890 there have appeared in Southern politics certain striking personalities, whose names have come to symbolize, in the minds of many, a type of leadership that is new to and distinctly of this section.[1] Outstanding among these figures are Ben Tillman and Cole Blease of South Carolina, Tom Watson of Georgia, James K. Vardaman and Theodore G. Bilbo of Mississippi, Jeff Davis of Arkansas, and Huey P. Long of Louisiana. The usual treatment of these men has been to class them as demagogues, and to contrast them with those aristocratic statesmen who represented the South in former times. Their comparison with such men as John C. Calhoun, Wade Hampton, Jefferson Davis, L. Q. C. Lamar, John B. Gordon, and Benjamin H. Hill, to say nothing of the giants of the Old Dominion, has led to the frequent conclusion that Southern political standards and leadership have deteriorated.[2]

Observers have attributed this phenomenon to the ignorance of the people, to the one-party system, to the effects of Populism, to the direct primary, or to corrupt politics. Undoubtedly each explanation holds an element of truth. Yet before accepting at face value this condemnation of modern Southern leadership and, inferentially, of the Southern electorate, it is necessary to examine the comparison upon which the conclusion largely rests. Aristocratic statesmanship represents the old; demagoguery represents the new.

As a matter of fact, the aristocracy never dominated politics in the lower South, with the possible exception of South Carolina.

This myth seems to be the product of several factors, chief among which may be mentioned: failure to recognize sufficiently the frontier character of the lower South before 1860; the tendency of post-war Southerners to glorify the " good old days," when their representatives held a more commanding influence in national affairs; and, perhaps most important of all, the effect of antislavery propaganda, designed to alienate the democratic West from the slaveholding South, and preserved by historians of that school. The aristocratic legend is shattered, however, by a glance at the biographical sketches of those who held high office in the cotton South between 1828 and 1860, and from the end of Reconstruction to 1900. Not more than a third of the governors, United States senators, and congressmen during these periods came from the slaveholding aristocracy. An overwhelming majority rose from the middle class, quite as happened in other sections.[3] The legend is further discredited by the fact that the Whig party, to which the planter aristocrats tended to belong, never dominated politics in the lower South. Likewise unsupportable is the idea that, prior to 1860, the section was ruled by an oligarchy, aristocratic, slaveholding, or otherwise. From 1828 to 1860 the average tenure of the United States senators from these states was less than six years; that of the congressmen was slightly more than four; and that of the governors was scarcely three years.[4] These figures seem to indicate a turnover in public office that contradicts the nature of an oligarchy and that is more in keeping with a genuine democracy.

The older Southern leadership was not only aristocratic, according to the comparison under consideration, but the term *statesmanlike* is applied liberally. Reluctant though one may be to detract from the fame of that leadership, one cannot ignore the universal tendency to make dead politicians into statesmen. It takes but a cursory reading of American history and its source material to understand how far short of statesmanship were the vast majority of officeholders and office seekers in the eyes of their contemporaries. The uncomplimentary estimates of Southern political leaders, held by antislavery opinion, must be discounted, but many Southerners of the period were most realistic in their comments upon those who guided the political affairs of their section. Southern commentators, whether of the war period or of modern times, have dealt rather severely with the statesmanship of President Jefferson Davis, the members of his cabinet, and with those who made up the Confederate Congress, to say nothing of some of the governors and lesser political lights of the states of the Confederacy.[5] All of which is not to deny that politics, in the Old South, tended to attract the more alert and ambitious to a degree not equaled either in the North or in the New South. However, the assumption that aristocracy and statesmanship were the marked characteristics of Southern political leaders prior to 1890 must be accepted with reservations.

The further assumption that men of the Tillman-Long type were demagogues likewise calls for consideration. Without acquitting them completely of this charge, we may well question whether the estimates of their political opponents can be taken for the final judgment of history. It seems only necessary to give additional thought to the men themselves, to the policies and measures for which they stood, and to the conditions which produced them. General as this consideration must be, there will appear certain common factors contributing to their careers; factors that are by no means magic formulas to produce a perfect solution, but which do help to arrive at a sane interpretation of the men and of their significance in Southern politics.

The first requirement to an understanding of these new spokesmen of the rural South is a recognition of the changed status of the farmer in this section, and the consequent changed status of those who sponsored his interests. Although the industrial order had made beginnings in the Old South, agriculture had dominated the section and had commanded the support of a great majority, including planters, farmers, lawyers, editors, and clergymen. Such a state of affairs helped to produce a unity of public opinion, in the formation of which slavery and planter-aristocratic domination have been stressed too greatly. The difference in interests between the large planter and small farmer was largely one of degree. Both wanted high prices for the products of the land and low prices for the services of capital and industry. In other words, both were committed to those policies that were favorable to the agricultural economy.[6] Quite naturally this harmony of interest made the planter and his class fitting leaders for the small farmer, and contributed to the idea that the section was ruled by a planter oligarchy.

A number of writers have discussed the breakup of the plantation system, the increase of tenantry, and the growth of industry in the New South: [7] developments that were concurrent with agricultural depressions throughout the country. The census figures for the years 1880 and 1890 reveal unmistakably the rate at which industrialism was increasing, as compared to agricultural interests. While it is true that the total valuation of farm lands, as well as that of farm buildings, equipment, and livestock increased during the decade, the rate of increase was negligible as compared to that invested in industrial activities. In the seven states of the deep South, in which states the Tillman-Long group appeared, the increase in agricultural valuations for the decade mentioned was 47 per cent, as compared with an increase of 227 per cent in the capital invested in manufactures, to say nothing of that put into railroads, mining, and urban properties. More significant, perhaps, was the rate of increase in the value of the products of farm and factory. That of the farms was 22 per cent, while that of the factories was 143 per cent. Most significant of all is the fact that each dollar invested in agriculture yielded a gross total in products of $0.41, while the same dollar invested in manufacturing produced a gross total of $1.29.[8]

Rather than wage a disheartening war for the interests of agriculture under such conditions, the more alert and ambitious turned to the towns and cities, a movement that was by no means confined to the Southern states. To those who made this change, planting became secondary to merchandising, moneylending, railroad promotion, factory-building, and the development of resources.[9] Thus there evolved a real divergence between the economic interests of farm and town, that was to affect greatly the political and social scene. No longer the most profitable, farming could not remain the most honorable occupation; and the bar, press, pulpit, and political party soon reflected this altered state of affairs. The unanimity with which the spokesmen of the people had championed the cause of agriculture was no more. There began that steady conquest of the Democratic party, on the part of the new industrialists, that was to make for the conservatism of that party in the South. The extent to which the " Bourbons " of the New South had gained the ascendancy in Georgia has been adequately described by Professor Arnett.[10] Although this ascendancy may have varied in degree in other Southern states, the trend was general and unmistakable.[11]

Under such circumstances, the " dirt farmers " of the South came to understand that they had lost their former spokesmen, not only at Washington but at the state capitals and county seats as well. Their distresses during the agricultural depressions impressed upon them the need for new leaders, and made them resentful of those whom they had formerly trusted. Resentment against the state " machine " or the " court house rings," as well as against the plight of the rural inhabitants, largely animated such men as Alexander H. Stephens, Dr. William Felton, and Emory Speer in their earlier revolts in Georgia. Elsewhere, as in that state, these earlier efforts of the dissatisfied farmers were rendered futile by superior political organization and by that party regularity growing out of the race question.[12]

Such were the conditions attending the rise of the Tillman-Long type of leadership. A glance at the family background of those who have been included in the group shows that they were of the middle class, which had supplied the section with a majority of its leaders in former times. Ben Tillman's family owned considerable land, and he, in his own right, was a successful farmer before he entered politics. Nor was land the only inheritance received by Tillman from his family. An uncle, John Tillman, who is described as a man of strong intellectual qualities, left him a large library of the best English literature. Perhaps there may be a bit of the romantic in that picture of Tillman spending a good part of each day " lying on the piazza floor reading French history and *Paradise Lost*," [13] but there can be no question as to his strong interest in books as well as in farming.[14]

Tom Watson's biographer describes the Watson family as of the landowning and slaveholding gentry, and the mother of Tom as an " intellectual for her time." [15] Without trying to pass on the gentility of the Watson family, we do know that Watson had the gentleman's love of the land, and that one of his first acts after beginning the practice of law was to buy the family homestead. From that time until the end of his life, Hickory Hill was to him what Mount Vernon was to Washington, Monticello to Jefferson, or the Hermitage to Andrew Jackson. Nor would it be surprising, in view of Watson's attainments in the field of letters, if his mother possessed unusual qualities of mind. His *Life of Thomas Jefferson*, his *Story of France* or his *Napoleon* may not be indispensable to modern historical scholarship, but they were widely read and were favorably reviewed in the periodicals of the day.[16]

Jeff Davis of Arkansas probably had as little of personal attraction as any of the group under consideration. Yet Davis was the son of a Baptist minister, who " subsequently became a practicing lawyer of respectable attainments." Jeff Davis married, the first time, the daughter of a Methodist minister, and his second wife was " a member of one of the oldest and most respected families of western Arkansas." [17] In his younger days, Davis attended the University of Arkansas and the law schools of Vanderbilt and Cumberland universities.[18]

Without going into the family background of others of the Tillman-Long group, it is well to remember that Long attended the University of Oklahoma and the law school of Tulane University; Bilbo attended Peabody College, Vanderbilt University, and the University of Michigan; [19] Blease was a student at Newberry College, and later graduated from the law school of Georgetown University at Washington.[20] Enough has been said to suggest that these so-called demagogues compare favorably with the average public man in the United States in respect to family background, educational training, and intellectual attainments. Whatever may be said of their political views or of their following, these men were not ignorant, nor did they come from the lowest strata of Southern society.

Perhaps the most generally recognized characteristic common to the members of this group is the vividness of their campaign methods, a vividness that lends itself easily to the charge of demagoguery. They frequently resorted to intemperate language and to those "tricks of the trade" which are likely to appeal to the unthinking portion of the electorate. They appealed to the poor as against the rich, to the "common" man as against the aristocrat, to the farmer as against the townsman.[21] Such campaign methods were inevitable, however, for the reason that these men faced opposition from the Democratic organizations, the press, the bar, and the more prominent of the clergy.[22] They battled against those agencies which are most effective in molding public opinion, and which formerly had supported the agricultural interests. Under such circumstances, they were compelled to gain their publicity by individual effort, and by appeals that would be heard above the many powerful voices supporting the conservatives. When Dr. C. P. DeVore, a planter and close friend of Tillman, asked the latter why he raised "so much hell" in his campaigns, Tillman replied: "Well, . . . if I didn't, the damn fools wouldn't vote for me." [23] Whether such campaign methods are in truth demagogic, or whether they make up what is called showmanship, they are not uncommon in American politics. They seem to be necessary to the success of anyone who happens to oppose "the powers that be." In fact, the term *demagogue* itself is not absolute, and political opponents have applied it liberally to many who now hold respected places in the history of American public life. And what is the measure of a demagogue? One likes to speculate, for example, whether the charge of demagoguery can be applied to the "cross of gold" and not to the "full dinner pail"; whether it is applicable to "the forgotten man" and not to the "chicken in every pot." Whether one is to be classed as a demagogue or a statesman seems to depend quite often upon the respectability of his followers and upon the agencies of propaganda which support or oppose him.

These modern spokesmen of the rural South have been accepted as demagogues, largely because of their campaign methods. It is misleading, however, to judge them solely on this basis. The candidate spends a few months campaigning. If successful, he spends from two to six years in office. No satisfactory estimate of a man can be based upon the former to the neglect of the latter. It may be worth while, therefore, to look briefly at the official records of some of these Southern "demagogues."

When Ben Tillman became governor, he confronted the questions of whether the state should regulate the railroads; whether the property of the railroads and other corporations should be valued for taxation at figures more in line with other forms of property; and whether the influence of the roads with the political agencies of the state should not be lessened. The measures that South Carolina adopted, under Tillman's guidance, seem mild enough today. They were: the creation of a railroad commission, a revision of the tax laws, and a law prohibiting free passes. Tillman attacked the liquor question, and the result was the institution of his famous dispensary system. The plan did not work satisfactorily and was repealed in later years. However, in view of the failure of much subsequent liquor legislation in the United States and of the apparent success of the dispensary system in other countries, one hesitates to condemn this pioneer for his lack of success on so difficult an issue. Tillman's name is inseparably connected with Clemson and Winthrop colleges, and, in the words of Ray Stannard Baker, "he performed a notable service in extending popular education." Other laws of the Tillman era sought to modify the crop mortgage system to the benefit of the debtor class, to limit the hours of labor in cotton mills, and to insure against the sale of impure fertilizers as well as to break up what he termed the phosphate monopoly in the state, and he refunded the state debt to effect a yearly saving in interest. Such are some of the constructive accomplishments of Tillman the governor.[24] His record in the United States Senate, though not brilliant, was creditable. In 1906 President Theodore Roosevelt, in sponsoring the Hepburn bill, was opposed by Republican "stalwarts" in the Senate. It fell to Tillman's lot to lead the fight for the bill in the upper house, and this he did successfully.[25] It may have been this support of the Roosevelt measure that influenced a political correspondent of the *Independent* to say about this "demagogue" from South Carolina: "Within his intellectual limits — and they are by no means contracted — he is a clean, broad, potent statesman. There have been bigger men in the Senate, but few of Tillman's honesty of purpose and indomitable courage . . . and South Carolina does well by her sisters when she sends Ben Tillman to the front." [26] Several years before this, a leading magazine of the East had commented editorially to the effect that Tillman was a widely read and well-informed man "as honest as the day, as sincere as a man can be in politics." [27]

It is possible that one of the keys to Vardaman's rise to the governorship of Mississippi may be found in the inaugural addresses and messages of his predecessor. Governor Andrew H. Longino, in 1900, expressed the hope that "no more sentimental or prejudiced opposition to railroads or other corporate enterprises will find favor with the legislature, so that capital hunting investment will have no just cause to pass Mississippi." Two years later he congratulated that body on the fact that "There exists . . . a becoming liberality of sentiment by the masses toward corporate and other investments of money in our midst." [28] This "becoming liberality" towards corporate investments had found expression in an act of the legislature in 1882 exempting new railroads and manufactures from taxation for a period of ten years.[29] A similar act, applying to new manufactures, was passed in 1896.[30] Such liberality toward corporate enterprise had been paralleled by a series of deficits in the operating expenses of the state government,[31] particularly from the years 1892 to 1896 inclusive. To add to the unsatisfactory condition of Mississippi's finances, the state treasurer, in 1890, was tried and convicted for embezzlement of state funds. The embezzlement seems to have occurred over a period of fourteen years, and the amount lost to the state was considerably in excess of three hundred thousand dollars.[32] In 1901 another shortage of a hundred thousand dollars was found in the same office.[33] The editor of the *Cosmopolitan Magazine* may have resorted to exaggeration in his introduction to an article by George Creel called "The Carnival of Corruption in Mississippi," but he declared: "For years the great state of Mississippi has been under the vicious ban of political and legislative corruption. The 'interests'—the Lumber Trust, Oil-Mill Trust, and the rest—have had their will. They have bribed the Legislature, selected their own representatives in state and Congress, [and] debauched the government." [34] Creel concluded that Vardaman "gave Mississippi the best administration in its history." Vardaman, he declared, had eliminated graft and inefficiency; had made the state institutions models of their kind; had stopped "interest-grabbing" on state, county, and levee board funds; he had stopped the farming out of convicts and jail prisoners to favored politicians and had put them on state farms which had shown net cash earnings of a half million dollars in four years; he had stopped lynching in the state; and at the same time "he fought, tooth and nail, the trusts and combines that were striving to gobble up the state's resources."[35] Ray Stannard Baker was more moderate in his praise when he said: "In spite of the bitterness against Vardaman among some of the best people of Mississippi I heard no one accuse him of corruption in any department of his administration. On the whole, they said he had directed the business of the state with judgment."[36] Vardaman's administration saw the enactment of a number of laws looking toward the regulation of insurance companies, railroads, utilities, banks, manufactures, and trusts for the better protection of the public interest.[37] Other acts provided for: the erection of an institution for the deaf and dumb; the establishment of agricultural experiment stations; the creation of a textbook commission and the adoption of uniform textbooks; a Jim Crow law; the codification of the laws; the erection of hospital buildings at the state's institution for the insane; a survey of the state's resources; and the creation of a department of agriculture and commerce.[38]

Obviously it would be difficult to form a correct estimate of the official records of Theodore G. Bilbo and Huey P. Long at this time. Bilbo's career in the United States Senate is in its early stages, and his record as governor is associated, in the minds of many, with his treatment of university and college faculties in his state. Without defending him on this score, this episode tends to obscure the fact that the Bilbo administrations saw marked increase in the physical equipment of those institutions. During his first administration, the cause of public education was furthered by the creation of a commission to eradicate adult illiteracy, by attempts to prevent excess prices on textbooks, by a provision for transportation to rural consolidated schools, and by the enactment of a compulsory school law.[39] He sponsored a program for the building of hospitals and other institutions for the subnormal and underprivileged.[40] A series of laws was passed dealing with corporations, the sale of corporate stocks, the problem of public utilities, and the activities of insurance companies.[41] Other laws passed during the first Bilbo administration sought to deal with such subjects as the protection of game and fish, temperance, the evils of lobbying, tick eradication, the prohibition of public hangings, estate and inheritance taxes, and eradication of tuberculosis among cattle.[42] During his second term as governor, Bilbo encountered effective political opposition within the legislature, with the consequent defeat of a number of his proposals. Among the things which he advocated, however, were: a bureau of markets for agricultural products, an improved highway system, a sales tax, and a reorganization of the state government along modern lines.[43]

The constructive record of Huey Long in Louisiana cannot yet be disassociated in the public mind from his spectacular political methods. Among the things that his régime accomplished in that state, however, may be mentioned: an increase of the severance tax, along with the abolishment of the poll tax and the state levy against small homes and farms; a reduction in utility rates; the construction of an excellent highway and free-bridge system; and the modernization of the state's institutions. Long's interest in the Louisiana State University and his development of that institution are widely recognized. Less known is his responsibility for free textbooks in the public schools, school buses, night schools for adults, and for traveling libraries. With all this, the tax rate for Louisiana is not excessive, and his levies against special forms of wealth have not driven capital from the state.[44] If one may judge by the trend of affairs in Louisiana since Long's death, his policies were not displeasing to the voters of that state. His record in national affairs is overshadowed by his activities in Louisiana politics, by his "share the wealth" program, and by his bitter opposition to the Roosevelt administration. It seems too early to pass mature judgment on that record. This phenomenon, however, is most interesting: although Long's program appeared far more radical than those of any of the so-called Southern demagogues, his political "respectability" increased in the eyes of many conservative commentators in direct proportion to his prospects of wrecking the Roosevelt administration.

Jeff Davis of Arkansas seems to have acquired his reputation for demagoguery after he became attorney general of his state, and after he had begun vigorous action to enforce the antitrust law. In so doing, he instituted some 225 suits against the fire insurance companies operating in the state, as well as against the Standard Oil Company, the American Tobacco Company, the Continental Tobacco Company, the "Cotton Seed Oil Trust," and the express companies.[45] As governor he continued his efforts to bring the insurance companies, life as well as fire, under such restrictions as he believed would make for the protection of policyholders and public. As a result, the years 1901 to 1905 saw the passage of nine acts designed to accomplish this purpose.[46] It should be remembered that while Davis was thus enhancing his reputation for demagoguery, Charles Evans Hughes was about to gain fame through his exposures of insurance methods in New York. The Davis régime saw also the passage of a series of acts intended either to break the powers of the trusts and other corporations or to protect the public against excessive rates and other abuses of the period.[47] And many of these laws were passed at a time when Theodore Roosevelt was establishing his reputation as a "trust-buster." Arkansas, under Davis's leadership, sought to protect and better the lot of the laboring classes. Laws were passed attacking the "script" evil, prohibiting child labor in factories, limiting hours of adult labor in certain types of work, protecting miners against unfair weighing methods, prohibiting the blacklisting of employees, and seeking to redress other grievances of labor.[48] Other acts passed during the Davis régime sought to raise the level of public education by authorizing the establishment of libraries, prohibiting nepotism in the employment of teachers, establishing graded courses of study for the common schools, and by raising the standards of the teaching profession.[49] Still other acts sought to protect the public against false bank statements and the acceptance of money by banks known to be insolvent, and against impure food, false weights and measures, and untruthful advertising.[50]

Tom Watson held no executive position, but as a member of the lower house of the Fifty-second Congress (1891–1893) he stood for those measures believed by the Populists to be for the best interests of the farming groups. He introduced, among others, bills and resolutions calling for an income tax, a discontinuance of national banks as well as the further issuance of United States bonds, the establishment of the subtreasury system, and an increase in the currency.[51] As a member of the Georgia legislature he exerted himself, " ineffectively " it is true, in the interest of Confederate veterans, temperance, tenant farmers, and leased convicts.[52]

These brief sketches of efforts and accomplishments do not establish members of the Tillman-Long group as great statesmen. They do show, however, that contrary to the opinion expressed by William Allen White and held in many other quarters, the great mass of voters who supported them was not a " moronic underworld." [53] Among the measures which they advocated and effected are many which were in line with the liberal thought of the times, and which have been accepted for years as sound public policy. It would seem that such records in office must temper the charge of demagoguery.

One of the most apparent factors which were common to this new leadership of the rural South was a hostility to large corporate and financial power. Long denounced concentrated national wealth as well as the oil companies and utilities of Louisiana. Tillman deplored " the abject surrender of our statesmen to the power of corporate and financial power. Long denounced concentrated national wealth as well as the oil companies and utilities of Louisiana. Tillman deplored " the class interest." [54] Blease called upon South Carolina to renounce the new industrialism, " if we have to buy capital by murdering women and children." [55] Watson espoused the cause of Populism, inveighed against the trusts, and asserted that the free list was the only Big Stick that would club the " malefactors of great wealth " into submission.[56] Jeff Davis denounced the railroad lobby, speculators in farm products, the protective tariff, and he disregarded party lines to defend Theodore Roosevelt's antitrust message.[57] The immediate objects of their hostility varied with the decades, but they fought those great interests of an industrial age which, they held, threatened the well-being of their rural South. More frequently than not, they were in accord with the Western agrarians on questions of currency, railroad and utility regulation, and monopoly control.[58]

It is interesting, too, that a majority of the Tillman-Long group fought the national Democratic administrations of their day on important issues. Long's attacks upon the New Deal were occasioned by President Roosevelt's failure to go far enough to the left. Cleveland's conservatism called forth Ben Tillman's famous pitchfork threat and drove Tom Watson into the Populist party. President Wilson's war and League policies met bitter opposition at the hands of Vardaman, Blease, and Watson. Bilbo's promise to "out-Huey Huey" caused his election to the Senate to be interpreted as a protest against Roosevelt's conservatism. This hostility to the Democratic national leadership suggests the similar attitude that the Western progressives have maintained toward Republican administrations. The suggestion is all the more significant when it is remembered that these Southerners, like the Westerners, stood consistently to the left of their national party. Indeed, the similarities between the Southern "demagogues" and the Western "sons of wild jackasses" make it difficult to avoid the conclusion that they were the products of many similar factors. It is not surprising that Huey Long professed his willingness to support a Western progressive for President.

Attitudes on the race question provided one great difference between the Southern agrarians and those of the West. The last decade of the nineteenth century and the first of the present one saw a general movement throughout the South to disfranchise the Negro by constitutional and legislative enactment.[59] In this movement the earlier of the Tillman-Long group played conspicuous and leading parts.[60] Their attitudes on this subject not only differentiated them from the Western agrarians, but also drew frequent charges of demagoguery from the North and East[61] — charges which many Southerns have accepted on the assumption that the Negro had been removed from the politics of their section with the end of Reconstruction. As a matter of fact, those extralegal methods which had driven the black from power had not deprived him of his ballot to the extent that has generally been assumed. Conservative leaders, like Hampton and Lamar, had sought to control rather than disfranchise him.[62] Several facts will indicate the continued political influence of the Negro in post-Reconstruction days. The lower South, during this period, sent seventeen Republicans to Congress, four of whom were colored.[63] In Mississippi a Negro sat in the legislature in 1882,[64] and the blacks constituted more than eleven per cent of the total registration two years after the adoption of the literacy and "understanding" test.[65] South Carolina's constitutional convention of 1895 included six Negro delegates.[66]

Several factors contributed to that movement to deprive the Negro completely of his ballot, which had its beginnings around 1890, and with which the new Southern leadership was so closely identified. It seems that Professor Garner has overemphasized demagoguery as a cause of the "recrudescence" of the race issue.[67] In this connection, Professor Phillips recognized the Force Bill and the activities of Northern extremists as factors. "For every Lodge and Foraker," he declares, "there arose a Tillman and a Vardaman, with a Watson and a Blease to spare." [68] Theodore Roosevelt's entertainment of Booker T. Washington at the White House did nothing to allay the movement.[69] There had been a decided shift in Negro population from the upland counties to the towns and cities as well as to the delta and coastal plains.[70] The inevitable effect of such a shift, so long as the Negro voted, was to transfer political influence from the white counties to the towns and to the Black Belt. Tillman voiced the resentment of the upcountry whites at this loss of influence within the party by demanding that apportionment of representation in the Democratic convention be according to white population.[71] Too, the economic competition with the Negro was felt most keenly by the whites of the small-farmer, tenant groups. While this factor is intangible and hard to evaluate, there can be no doubt as to its presence.[72]

The most important factor, no doubt, in this "recrudescence" of the race issue was the part that the Negro had played in Southern politics during the period of the agrarian revolt. In the contests between conservatives and farmers, both sides saw the importance of the colored vote and sought to gain it. The degree to which the conservatives succeeded in these efforts is illustrated by results in

Alabama in 1892. The Populists carried all the counties of the state except twelve in the Black Belt. In these, where the Negro constituted more than two thirds of the population, the Democrats gained sufficient majorities to carry the election. Practically the same thing happened in the election of 1894.[73] Granting this as an extreme case, there can be little doubt as to the telling effect with which the conservatives voted the Negro against the revolting farmers.[74] Professor Arnett summed up the situation when he declared that the black " was generally granted a free ballot (often several of them) and a fair count (sometimes in excess of the possible voting population).[75] There is little wonder that Tillman, Watson, Vardaman, and others, as spokesmen of the farmers of the white counties, were determined to eliminate the Negro as a balance of power that was almost certain to be used against them. If their course in this respect be demagoguery, at least it is understandable.

It is not possible to estimate the significance of the Tillman-Long type of leadership in Southern politics by a single generalization. By that token, one must question the old idea of " the bottom rail on top." It is not reasonable to assume that a race, which for a hundred years had produced outstanding men in the field of government and politics, went suddenly " moronic." Of course it cannot be denied that the war had taken its toll of potential leaders. Too, greater recognition must be given the fact that, with the return of peace, more attractive opportunities drew to other sections many who might have contributed much to the leadership of the South. Nor may one overlook the influence of postwar economic and social conditions. The leisured class tended to disappear, while the fight for mere subsistence became more absorbing. The race question, with its social, economic, and political aspects changed, continued to be, in a large measure, " the central theme of Southern history."

With full recognition of the factors just mentioned, the solution to the Tillman-Long phenomena appears to lie in the growing influence of industrialism and the new system of merchandising and financing. Agriculture had lost its primacy at Washington, and was rapidly losing it in the South. Like the Westerners, Southern farmers were revolting against a changed order that seemed to threaten them with economic ruin, social inferiority, and political impotence. The Southerners, however, conducted their revolt under conditions peculiar to their section, chief among which was the race question. Again, the South differed from the West in the degree to which industrialism was commanding the support of its natural leadership. Too many of the Confederate brigadiers and their class had subordinated their planting interests to merchandising, money-lending, railroad and industrial promotion, and the development of resources. The divergence between the interests of this class and the " dirt farmers " became more accentuated. The former took for themselves the old tradition. The spokesmen of the latter came to be regarded as " demagogic upstarts " by the self-styled " better elements " of their section. As a matter of fact, a calm view of their accomplishments and of the conditions which produce them must raise a question as to their demagoguery. One reaches the conclusion that perhaps these despised " upstarts," as spokesmen of the agrarian interests, more nearly represented a continuation of the political and economic ideas of the ante-bellum South than did the " developers of resources," who were engaged in forming a New South.

NOTES

[1] Revised draft of a paper read before the American Historical Association, Chattanooga, December 30, 1935.

[2] A typical statement of this contrast is made by Ray Stannard Baker, " The Negro in Politics," in *American Magazine* (New York, 1876–), LXVI (1908), 169–73. See also John M. Mecklin, " Vardamanism," in *Independent* (New York, 1848–1928), LXXI (1911), 461–63; Gerald W. Johnson, " Live Demagogues or Dead Gentlemen," in *Virginia Quarterly Review* (Charlottesville, 1925–), XII (1936), 1–14. The usual statement of the idea is contained in " Why Blease Won," in *Literary Digest* (New York, 1890–), XLV (1912), 410. The political dictatorship of the planter aristocracy in the Old South is accepted by John D. Hicks, *The Populist Revolt* (Minneapolis, 1931), 36–37.

[3] See the *Biographical Directory of the American Congress, 1774–1927* (Washington, 1928), and *Dictionary of American Bi-*

ography, 20 vols. (New York, 1928–1936), for biographical sketches of some 550 governors, senators, and congressmen from the states of Alabama, Arkansas, Florida, Georgia, Louisiana, Mississippi, and South Carolina. Sketches of 27 governors were not found. It is thought, however, that these would not change the conclusion. Due recognition is given to the difficulty of drawing an exact line between aristocracy and non-aristocracy in America. Professor Kendrick has held that the cotton South had not developed an aristocracy by 1860. See Benjamin B. Kendrick, "Agrarian Discontent in the South: 1880–1890," in American Historical Association, *Report*, 1920, pp. 265–72.

[4] The tenure of senators and representatives is obtained from the *Biographical Directory of the American Congress*. For that of governors of the various states, see the *Encyclopaedia Britannica* (Cambridge, Eng., 1910–1911).

[5] Those who are inclined to idealize the "statesmen" of the Old South will do well to read J. B. Jones, *A Rebel War Clerk's Diary at the Confederate States Capital*, edited by Howard Swiggett, 2 vols. (New York, 1935).

[6] James Truslow Adams has noted the community of interest between the great planter and small farmer of the South, even in colonial times, and has contrasted this with the conflicting interests of the wealthy mercantile classes and the poorer farmers of the North. It would seem, however, that in explaining this condition in the South, Mr. Adams has overemphasized the influence of debt, and has tended to overlook the fact that the interests of the planter and farmer were largely identical except for degree. James Truslow Adams, *Provincial Society*, 1690–1763 (New York, 1927), 220–21. For a clear statement of the unanimity of Southern interests, see Alex M. Arnett, *The Populist Movement in Georgia*, in Columbia University *Studies in History, Economics, and Public* Law, CIV, No. 1 (New York, 1922), 19.

[7] Broadus Mitchell and George Sinclair Mitchell, *The Industrial Revolution in the South* (Baltimore, 1930); Broadus Mitchell, "Two Industrial Revolutions," in *South Atlantic Quarterly* (Durham, 1902–), XX (1921), 286–303, and "A Survey of Industry," in H. T. Couch (ed.), *Culture in the South* (Chapel Hill, 1934), 82–89; George Fort Milton, "Also There is Politics," in *ibid.*, 116, 120; William B. Hesseltine, "Economic Factors in the Abandonment of Reconstruction," in *Mississippi Valley Historical Review* (Cedar Rapids, 1915–), XXII (1935), 191–210, and "Tennessee's Invitation to Carpet-Baggers," in *East Tennessee Historical Society's Publications*, No. 4 (1932), 102 ff.; Holland Thompson, *The New South* (New Haven, 1921), 86–105, 193–97, and "The

New South, Economic and Social," in *Studies in Southern History and Politics* inscribed to William A. Dunning (New York, 1914), 291–315; Hicks, *Populist Revolt*, 37–38; Francis B. Simkins, "The Solution of the Post-bellum Agricultural Problems in South Carolina," in *North Carolina Historical Review* (Raleigh, 1904–), VII (1930), 192–219; Robert P. Brooks, *Agrarian Revolution in Georgia, 1865–1912* (Madison, Wis., 1914), 41; M. B. Hammond, "The Southern Farmer and the Cotton Question," in *Political Science Quarterly* (Boston, New York, 1886–), XII (1897), 457–59; and Henry W. Grady, "Cotton and Its Kingdom," in *Harper's New Monthly Magazine* (New York, 1850–), LXII (1881), 721–22. A recent and most suggestive discussion of the industrialization of the South may be found in Benjamin B. Kendrick and Alex M. Arnett, *The South Looks at Its Past* (Chapel Hill, 1935), 105–41.

[8] *Compendium of the Eleventh Census*: 1890, Pt. III (Washington, 1897), 614–17, 670–71. The states included are Alabama, Arkansas, Florida, Georgia, Louisiana, Mississippi, and South Carolina. It was impossible to obtain a satisfactory comparison for the decade 1870–1880. In the words of the Superintendent of Census, the figures on manufacturing for the census of 1870 are entirely unreliable and misleading.

[9] Hicks, *Populist Revolt*, 51–62; Paul Lewinson, "The Negro in the White Class and Party Struggle," in *Southwestern Political and Social Science Quarterly* (Austin, Norman, 1920–), VIII (1928), 358–82; John D. Allen, "Journalism in the South," in H. T. Couch (ed.), *Culture in the South*, 135–48; Hamilton Basso, "Huey Long and His Background," in *Harper's Magazine*, CLXX (1935), 663–73. The case is well put by A Public Man of Georgia, "Why Frank was Lynched," in *Forum* (New York, 1886–), LVI (1916), 677–92. See, also, Kendrick and Arnett, *The South Looks at Its Past*.

[10] Arnett, *Populist Movement in Georgia*, 23–26, 29–32, 39–40, 47, 53. Professor Arnett declares that all the governors elected in Georgia between 1872 and 1890, except Alexander H. Stephens, were allied with the new industrialism. The same thing, he says, is true of the congressmen and members of the legislature. Robert Toombs and Stephens, says Arnett, attempted to carry out the traditional ante-bellum leadership, but lost their dominant places in the party.

[11] Ben Tillman expressed this fact in respect to South Carolina in his first inaugural address, quoted by Basso, "Huey Long and His Background," *loc. cit.*, 668; South Carolina *House Journal*, 1890, pp. 130–54. See, also, *ibid.*, 1894, p. 19.

[12] Arnett, *Populist Movement in Georgia*, 34–35; Thompson, *The New South*, 35–37.

[13] Zach McGhee, "Tillman, Smasher of Traditions," in *World's Work* (New York, 1900–1932), XII (1906), 8014.

[14] Francis Butler Simkins, *The Tillman Movement in South Carolina* (Durham, 1926); editorial comment, in *Harper's Weekly* (New York, 1857–1916), XLV (1901), 590; A Washington Journalist, in *Independent*, LXI (1906), 1430.

[15] William W. Brewton, *The Life of Thomas E. Watson* (Atlanta, 1926), 6. See, also, Watson's story of his own life, in Thomas E. Watson, *Life and Speeches of Thomas E. Watson* (Thomson, Ga., 1911), 9–22.

[16] Typical reviews of Watson's historical writings may be found in *Arena* (Boston, 1889–1909), XXXI (1904), 325–29; *Athenaeum* (London, 1828–1921), May 3, 1902, p. 562; *Bookman* (New York, 1895–), XXXII (1910), 219; *Dial* (Chicago, New York, 1880–), XXVII (1900), 116–17; XXXVI (1904), 262–63. John Donald Wade, "Jefferson, New Style," in *American Mercury* (New York, 1924–), XVIII (1929), 293–301, discusses Watson's writings with more tolerance than he does Watson's career and political principles.

[17] Senator James P. Clarke of Arkansas, *Memorial Addresses*, in *Senate Documents*, 62 Cong., 3 Sess., XXIII, No. 1146.

[18] David Y. Thomas, "Jeff Davis," in *Dictionary of American Biography*, V, 122–23; *Biographical Directory of the American Congress*, 885; L. S. Dunaway, *Jeff Davis, Governor and United States Senator* (Little Rock, 1913).

[19] *Congressional Directory*, 74 Cong., 1 Sess., 56.

[20] *Biographical Directory of the American Congress*, *passim*.

[21] A characteristic indictment of such campaign methods may be found in the *Arkansas Gazette*, August 1, 1906, quoted in Dunaway, *Jeff Davis*, 208–26. See, also, sketch on Jeff Davis in the *Dictionary of American Biography*, V, 122–23. For comments on the methods of some other members of the group, see Wade, "Jefferson, New Style," *loc. cit.*, 298; Simkins, *Tillman Movement*, 124, 129; editorial comment, in *Current Literature* (New York, 1888–1925), XLI (1906), 154; Webster Smith, *The Kingfish, A Biography of Huey P. Long* (New York, 1933), 30–31; Hodding Carter and Gerald L. K. Smith, "How Come Huey Long," in *New Republic* (New York, 1914–), LXXXII (1935), 14; Basso, "Huey Long," *loc. cit.*, 670.

[22] Newspaper opposition to Long is well remembered. The cases of Long, Davis, and Blease may be taken as typical. See editorial, "Impeachment Proceedings in Louisiana," in *New Republic*,

LVIII (1929), 268–69; "South Carolina Rejects Blease," in *Literary Digest*, XLIX (1914), 448; O. L. Warr, "Mr. Blease of South Carolina," in *American Mercury*, XVI (1929), 25–32.

[23] Simkins, *Tillman Movement*, 169, n. 14.

[24] *Ibid.*, 99–100, 105, 138, 149–50, 174–75, 183; *Appleton's Annual Cyclopaedia* (New York, 1862–1903), N. S., XVI (1891), 798; (1892), 703–706; Ray Stannard Baker, "The Negro in Politics," in *American Magazine*, LXVI (1908), 173. Tillman's own summary of the accomplishments of his administrations is found in the Governor's Message, South Carolina *House Journal*, 1894, p. 20. For his criticisms of the old order as well as the outline of his own program, see "Inaugural Address," *ibid.*, 1890, pp. 130–54; "Governor's Message," *ibid.*, 1891, pp. 28–60; Simkins, *Tillman Movement*, 57 et seq.

[25] *World's Work*, XII (1906), 7486.

[26] A Washington Journalist, "Men We are Watching," in *Independent*, LXI (1906), 1429–30.

[27] *Harper's Weekly*, XLV (1901), 590.

[28] Dunbar Rowland, *History of Mississippi*, 2 vols. (Chicago, 1925), II, 280, 296.

[29] *Ibid.*, 224.

[30] *Annual Cyclopaedia*, 3rd Ser., I (1896), 492.

[31] *Ibid.*, N. S., XVIII (1893), 498; XX (1895), 495–96; *ibid.*, 3rd Ser., II (1897), 532.

[32] *Ibid.*, N. S., XV (1890), 559.

[33] *Ibid.*, 3rd Ser., VII (1902), 751–52; Rowland, *History of Mississippi*, II, 295.

[34] *Cosmopolitan Magazine* (New York, 1886–1925), LI (1911), 725.

[35] *Ibid.*, 725–35.

[36] Baker, "The Negro in Politics," *loc. cit.*, 172–73.

[37] State of Mississippi, *Laws*, 1904, chaps. LXXVI, LXXIX, LXXX, LXXXI, CIV, CXI, CXXVI, CLXXXII; 1906, chaps. CVII, CXL.

[38] *Ibid.*, 1904, chaps. XV, LXXXIV, LXXXV, LXXXVI, XCIX, C; 1906, chaps. XIII, XXXIV, CXI, CII, CIII.

[39] *Ibid.*, 1916, chaps. CX, CLXXXIX, CLXXX; 1918, chap. CCLVIII.

[40] *Ibid.*, 1916, chaps. L, LXVII, LXVIII, CVIII, CXLIII.

[41] *Ibid.*, chaps. XCII, XCV, XCVII, CXLVIII, CC, CCI, CCIII, CCIV, CCV, CCVI.

[42] *Ibid.*, chaps. XCIX, CIII, CIV, CV, CLXVII, CCXVIII; 1918, chaps. CIX, CCXV.

[43] Clip files of the Memphis *Commercial Appeal* and Memphis

Press Scimitar. The following administration instituted the sales tax, and received considerable applause for the resulting improvement in the state's financial condition. The present administration is effecting the long-needed improvement of the highway system.

[44] Carter and Smith, "How Come Huey Long," *loc. cit.*, 14–15; F. Raymond Daniell, "The Gentleman from Louisiana," in *Current History* (New York, 1914–), XLI (1934), 172, 175–76; *Business Week* (New York, 1929–), February 9, 1935, pp. 12–13. The Houston (Texas) *Post-Dispatch* is quoted in the *Literary Digest*, CXII (1932), February 6, p. 7, as declaring that Long "is deserving of credit for breaking the shell that had encrusted Louisiana in backwardness and conservatism, and in modernizing the state." Mention of some of the more important enactments of the Long régime may be found in articles on "Louisiana," in *New International Year Book* (New York, 1928–1935).

[45] *Annual Cyclopaedia*, 3rd Ser., V (1900), 35; Dunaway, *Jeff Davis*, 54.

[46] Arkansas General Assembly, *Acts*, 1901, Nos. 39, 46, 115, 181; 1903, Nos. 105, 111; 1905, Nos. 192, 324, 327.

[47] *Ibid.*, 1901, Nos. 23, 216; 1903, Nos. 68, 156, 183; 1905, Nos. 1, 88, 250, 282.

[48] *Ibid.*, 1901, Nos. 101, 114, 161; 1903, Nos. 4, 127, 144; 1905, Nos. 49, 143, 214, 219, 233, 309.

[49] *Ibid.*, 1901, Nos. 26, 205; 1903, Nos. 52, 93, 137; 1905, No. 311.

[50] *Ibid.*, 1901, Nos. 7, 77, 113; 1905, Nos. 121, 272.

[51] *Congressional Record*, 52 Cong., 1 Sess., *passim* (1891–1892); 2 Sess., *passim* (1892–1893).

[52] Wade, "Jefferson, New Style," *loc. cit.*, 293–301.

[53] Frank R. Kent, "Our Political Monstrosities," in *Atlantic Monthly*, CLI (1933), 407–11.

[54] Basso, "Huey Long," *loc. cit.*, 668.

[55] Simkins, *Tillman Movement*, 177.

[56] Thomas E. Watson, "The People's Party's Appeal," in *Independent*, LXV (1908), 882–86.

[57] *Cong. Record*, 60 Cong., 1 Sess., 272–85 (December 11, 1907), 5521–31 (May 1, 1908); 2 Sess., 1402 ff. (January 26, 1909); 61 Cong., 1 Sess., 3845 ff. (June 26, 1901).

[58] This opposition to concentrated wealth and economic power so permeates the campaign speeches, congressional addresses, and state papers of members of the Tillman-Long group that a detailed citation of them would be both tedious and superfluous.

[59] W. Roy Smith, "Negro Suffrage in the South," in *Studies in Southern History and Politics*, 241.

[60] Garrard Harris, "A Defense of Governor Vardaman," in

Harper's Weekly, XLIX (1905), 236–37; James W. Garner, in a letter to the *Outlook* (New York, 1870–), LXXV (1903), 139–40; editorial, in *Review of Reviews* (New York, 1890–), XXVIII (1903), 403; Brewton, *Life of Watson*, 305; Thomas E. Watson, "Why I am Still a Populist," in *Review of Reviews*, XXXVIII (1908), 306; Wade, "Jefferson, New Style," *loc. cit.*, 137. Ray Stannard Baker discusses the race issue in a series of articles appearing in the *American Magazine*, which includes: "The Riddle of the Negro," LXIII (1907), 518 ff., "The Negro in Politics," "The Black Man's Silent Power," and "The New Southern Statesmanship," LXVI (1908), 169–80, 288–300, 381–91.

[61] James W. Garner, "Southern Politics Since the Civil War," in *Studies in Southern History and Politics*, 378–85; Charles P. Sweeney, "Bigotry in the South," in *Nation*, CXI (1920), 585–86; Mecklin, "Vardamanism," *loc. cit.*, 461–63; editorial, in *Current Literature*, XXXVI (1904), 288; Warr, "Blease of South Carolina," *loc. cit.*, 25–32; editorial, in *Outlook*, CIX (1915), 156–57.

[62] Walter L. Fleming, *The Sequel of Appomattox* (New Haven, 1919), 50–52; William A. Dunning, *Reconstruction, Political and Economic* (New York, 1907), 267–69; Claude G. Bowers, *The Tragic Era* (Cambridge, 1929), 514–15. Lamar's conservative attitude appears repeatedly in Wirt Armstead Cate, *Lucius Q. C. Lamar* (Chapel Hill, 1935).

[63] *Biographical Directory of the American Congress, passim.*

[64] Cate, *Lamar*, 394.

[65] *Annual Cylopaedia*, N. S. XVII (1892), 472.

[66] Simkins, *Tillman Movement*, 209–12.

[67] Garner, "Southern Politics Since the Civil War," *loc. cit.*, 367–87.

[68] Ulrich B. Phillips, "The Central Theme of Southern History," in *American Historical Review* (New York, 1895–), XXXIV (1928), 30–43.

[69] Editorial, in *Review of Reviews*, XXVIII (1903), 403; Harris, "A Defense of Vardaman," *loc. cit.*, 236–37.

[70] This movement is suggested by Brooks, *Agrarian Revolution in Georgia*, 16. Vardaman mentioned the drift to the towns in his message to a special session of the legislature in 1906, *Journal of the Senate* for that session, as does Professor Garner in his letter to the *Outlook*, LXXV (1903), 139–40.

[71] Simkins, *Tillman Movement*, 57 ff.

[72] Mecklin recognizes the influence of economic competition in his discussion of "Vardamanism."

[73] Smith, "Negro Suffrage in the South," *loc. cit.*, 243.

[74] The part played by the Negro vote at this time is recognized

by William Garrett Brown, *The Lower South in American History* (New York, 1903), 256–58; Smith, "Negro Suffrage in the South," *loc. cit.*; Hicks, *Populist Revolt*, 253–54; Phillips, "Central Theme of Southern History," *loc. cit.*, 43; Simkins, *Tillman Movement*, 83, 106, 129; Lewinson, "The Negro in the White Class and Party Struggle," in *Mississippi Valley Historical Review*, V (1919), 12–13; Rowland, *History of Mississippi*, II, 302. The result of Negro voting in North Carolina is described by John D. Hicks, "The Farmers' Alliance in North Carolina," in *North Carolina Historical Review*, II (1925), 162 ff.; Garner, "Southern Politics Since the Civil War," *loc. cit.*, 377.

[75] Arnett, *Populist Movement in Georgia*, 42–43, 183–84.

— From *Journal of Southern History*, July, 1937. Reprinted by permission.

THE SHORT STORY

The Short Story

ONE SOUTHERN writer, Mr. Robert Penn Warren, when pressed to define the short story, was compelled to content himself with the rough-and-ready statement, " A short story is a story that is not too long." The primary fact a reader needs to hold in mind in studying it is one which applies to all the newer art forms: namely, that no ultimate formula embodying the correct and final method of producing one has yet been generally accepted. Edgar Allan Poe, one of the first exponents of the short story, appears to have been rather hopeful about limiting it both in method and approach. In 1842 he ventured to risk a definition. "The skillful literary artist," he said, " has constructed a tale. If wise, he has not fashioned his thoughts to accommodate his incidents; but having conceived, with deliberate care, a certain unique or single effect to be wrought out, he then invents such incidents, he then combines such events, as may best aid him in establishing this preconceived effect. If his very initial sentence tend not to the outbringing of this effect, then he has failed in his first step. In the whole composition there should be no word written, of which the tendency, direct or indirect, is not to the one pre-established design. And by such means, with such care and skill, a picture is at length painted which leaves in the mind of him who contemplates it with a kindred art a sense of the fullest satisfaction. The idea of the tale has been presented unblemished, because undisturbed."

Yet for all its authority, Poe's pronouncement seems to have been looked upon with no final veneration by the writers who came after him. The short story was a late art form to develop, and its exponents have approached it, for the most part, with the experimenter's eager impiety. In this respect it differs from the more traditional literary forms. Few artists today would risk tampering with the technical limitations of the sonnet — rejecting the convention of fourteen lines as its length, for instance, or the Italian or English convention with respect to its rhyme scheme. The short story, however, as a medium which is still in a fluid state, reflects a corresponding excitement and adventurousness on the part of those persons who practice it seriously.

Our more recent authors seem to believe that the Poe formula made for too obvious effects. The short story, by Poe's definition, should end with a catastrophic action designed to overwhelm the reader with its sheer cumulative intensity. The walls of the House of Usher must fall apart, precipitating chaos and disintegration as they crumble, or the sides of a furnace must rush back — as in "The Pit and the Pendulum" — in an equally violent climax. Our guess is that such climaxes are too melodramatic to interest the more competent of our contemporary Southern writers. They have probably been set down as unconvincing, because grossly overdone.

The authors represented in this book practice a more subtle and restrained technique than was formerly fashionable. Also their approach to their material has been, generally, more impersonal. Many of them are engaged in presenting character, without the violent renderings that go with caricature and exaggeration generally. They are interested also in doing this job objectively, without inserting some moral comment either of praise or disapproval of the figures treated in the story proper. Furthermore, they seem much more preoccupied than before with the psychological nature of their subjects. To understand the basic and often seemingly trivial motives behind a figure's overt conduct may be, to certain of them, a matter of fundamental importance; and the rendering of that conduct objectively may seem, likewise, an altogether sufficient excuse for a story.

Our selections, in the opinion of the reader, may appear to include an inordinate number of narratives about the so-called "po whites" of the South. He may think that the authors and the editors have deliberately excluded the less unfortunate representatives of Southern life. One might say first, on this point, that the consistent use of the "po white" by so many of our writers is an indication of their awareness of an important social phenomenon. Before the Civil War, according to the most trustworthy estimates, the "po whites" amounted to something like five per cent of the total population.

The economic system which has prevailed in the United States since 1865 has contributed to the growth of this class until now their numbers constitute a major social problem. Their frequent appearance in fiction may be but the inevitable result of a more realistic analysis on the writer's part of the material he sees most often in the life about him.

We have deliberately omitted examples of the "formula story" in this volume, for the reason that there appears to be nothing particularly significant about it — certainly nothing particularly Southern. Almost any skilled tradesman in words can turn out such narratives mechanically. One might write, for instance, a tale about a man and a woman in Alaska, who meet each other, are mutually attracted, and later are the victims of an accidental misunderstanding. Afterwards they think very meanly of one another until the exigencies of a short narrative's length bring them together in some clever fashion — he breaks his leg on the ice, inducing a highly emotional situation, or his plane crashes, or she is attacked by a polar bear, or wolves, and he happens along in the nick of time to save her. Such a story may be duplicated in a dozen ways. Instead of Alaska the author could use Panama as his setting; then his characters, instead of cursing the cold, would be privileged to curse the heat; instead of wearing furs they could be dressed in linens; and instead of using raw whiskey they could be pictured as devotees of gin. The successful producers of such "formula stories" are usually highly urbanized. They find their inspiration in the fictional requirements laid down by the editors of such weeklies as Liberty *and the* Saturday Evening Post *rather than in the life of their region.*

THE HOUSE OF THE FAR AND LOST

A Story of England

By Thomas Wolfe

IN THE fall of that year I lived out about a mile from town in a house set back from the Ventnor Road. The house was called a "farm" — Hill-top Farm, or Far-end Farm, or some such name as that — but it was really no farm at all. It was a magnificent house of the weathered gray stone they have in that country, as if in the very quality of the wet heavy air there is the soft thick gray of time itself, sternly yet beautifully soaking down forever on you and enriching everything it touches — grass, foliage, brick, ivy, the fresh moist color of the people's faces, and old gray stone — with the incomparable weathering of time.

The house was set back off the road at a distance of several hundred yards, possibly a quarter of a mile, and one reached it by means of a road bordered by rows of tall trees which arched above the road and which made me think of home at night when the stormy wind howled in their tossed branches. On each side of the road were the rugby fields of two of the colleges, and in the afternoon I could look out and down and see the fresh moist green of the playing fields, and watch young college fellows, dressed in their shorts and jerseys and with their bare knees scurfed with grass and turf, as they twisted, struggled, swayed, and scrambled for a moment in the scrimmage circle and then broke free, running, dodging, passing the ball as they were tackled, filling the moist air with their sharp cries of sport. They did not have the desperate, the grimly determined, the almost professional earnestness that the college teams at home have; their scurfed and muddy knees, their swaying scrambling scrimmages, the swift breaking away and running, their panting breath and crisp clear voices gave them the appearance of grown-up boys.

Once when I had come up the road in afternoon while they were playing, the ball got away from them and came bounding out into the road before me, and I ran after it to retrieve it as we used to do when passing a field where boys were playing baseball. One of the players came over to the edge of the field and stood there waiting with his hands upon his hips while I got the ball: he was panting hard, his face was flushed and his blond hair tousled, but when I threw the ball to him, he said "Thanks very much!" crisply and courteously — getting the same sound into the word *very* that they got in *American*, a sound that always repelled me a little because it seemed to have some scornful aloofness and patronage in it.

For a moment I watched him as he trotted briskly away on to the field again: the players stood there waiting, panting, casual, their hands upon their hips; he passed the ball into the scrimmage, the pattern swayed, rocked, scrambled, and broke sharply out in open play again, and everything looked incredibly strange, near, and familiar.

I felt that I had always known it, that it had always been mine, and that it was familiar to me as everything I had seen or known in my childhood. Even the texture of the earth looked familiar, and felt moist and firm and springy when I stepped on it, and the stormy howling of the wind in that avenue of great trees at night was wild and desolate and demented as it had been when I was eight years old and could lie in my bed at night and hear the great oaks howling on the hill above my father's house.

The name of the people in the house was Coulson. I made arrangements with the woman at once to come and live there. She was a tall, weathered-looking woman of middle age. We talked together in the hall. The hall was made of marble flags and went directly out on to a graveled walk.

The woman was crisp, cheerful, and worldly-looking. She was still quite handsome. She wore a well-cut skirt of woolen plaid, and a silk blouse; when she talked she kept her arms folded because the air in the hall was chilly, and she held a cigarette in the fingers of one hand. A shaggy brown dog came out and nosed upward toward her hand as she was talking, and she put her hand upon its head and scratched it gently. When I told her I wanted to move in the next day, she said briskly and cheerfully:

"Right you are! You'll find everything ready when you get here!" Then she asked if I was at the university. I said no, and added, with a feeling of difficulty and naked desolation, that I was a "writer," and was coming there to work. I was twenty-four years old.

"Then I am sure that what you do will be *very, very* good!" she said cheerfully and decisively. "We have had several Americans in the house before and all of them were very clever! All the Americans we have had here were very clever people," said the woman. "I'm sure that you will like it." Then she walked to the door with me to say good-by. As we stood there, there was the sound of a small motorcar coming to a halt and in a moment a girl came swiftly across the gravel space outside and entered the hall. She was tall, slender, very lovely, but she had the same bright hard look in her eye the woman had, the same faint, hard smile around the edges of her mouth.

"Edith," the woman said in her crisp, curiously incisive tone, "this young man is an American — he is coming here tomorrow." The girl looked at me for a moment with her hard bright glance, thrust out a small gloved hand, and shook hands briefly, a swift firm greeting.

"Oh! How d'ye do!" she said. "I hope you will like it here." Then she went on down the hall, entered a room on the left, and closed the door behind her.

Her voice had been crisp and certain like her mother's, but it was also cool, young, and sweet, with music in it, and later as I went down the road, I could still hear it.

❦ ❦ ❦

That was a wonderful house, and the people there were wonderful people. Later, I could not forget them. I seemed to have known them all my life, and to know all about their lives. They seemed as familiar to me as my own blood and I knew them with a knowledge that went deep below the roots of thought or memory. We did not talk together often, or tell any of our lives to one another. It will be very hard to tell about it — the way we felt and lived together in that house — because it was of those simple and profound experiences of life which people seem always to have known when it happens to them, but for which there is no language.

And yet, like a child's half-captured vision of some magic country he has known, and which haunts his days with strangeness and the sense of immanent, glorious rediscovery, the word that would unlock it all seems constantly to be almost on our lips, waiting just outside the gateway of our memory, just a shape, a phrase, a sound away the moment that we choose to utter it — but when we try to say the thing, something fades within our mind like fading light, and something melts within our grasp like painted smoke, and something goes forever when we try to touch it.

The nearest I could come to it was this: In that house I sometimes felt the greatest peace and solitude that I had ever known. But I always knew the other people in the house were there. I could sit in my sitting-room at night and hear nothing but the stormy moaning of the wind outside in the great trees, the small gaseous flare and jet from time to time of the coal fire burning in the grate — and silence, strong living lonely silence that moved and waited in the house at night — and I would always know that they were there.

I did not have to hear them enter or go past my door, nor did I have to hear doors close or open in the house, or listen to their voices: if I had never seen them, heard them, spoken to them, it would have been the same — I should have known they were there.

It was something I had always known, and had known it would happen to me, and now it was there with all the strangeness and dark mystery of an awaited thing. I knew them, felt them, lived among them with a familiarity that had no need of sight or word or speech. And the memory of that house and of my silent fellowship with all the people there was somehow mixed with an image of dark time. It was one of those sorrowful and unchanging images which, among all the blazing stream of images that passed constantly their stream of fire across my mind, was somehow fixed, detached, and everlasting, full of a sorrow, certitude, and mystery that I could not fathom, but that wore forever on it the old sad light of waning day — a light from which all the heat, the violence, and the substance of furious dusty day had vanished, and was itself like time, unearthly-of-the-earth, remote, detached, and everlasting.

And that fixed and changeless image of dark time was this: In an old house of time I lived alone, and yet had other people all around me, and they never spoke to me, or I to them. They came and went like silence in the house, but I always knew that they were there. I would be sitting by a window in a room, and I would know then they were moving in the house, and darkness, sorrow, and strong silence dwelt within us, and our eyes were quiet, full of sorrow, peace, and knowledge, and our faces dark, our tongues silent, and we never spoke. I could not remember how their faces looked, but they were all familiar to me as my father's face, and we had known one another forever, and we lived together in the ancient house of time, dark time, and silence, sorrow, certitude, and peace were in us. Such was the image of dark time that was to haunt my life thereafter, and into which, somehow, my life among the people in that house had passed.

In the house that year there lived, besides myself and Morison, the Coulsons, the father and mother and their daughter, and three men who had taken rooms together and who were employed in a factory where motorcars were made, two miles from town.

I think the reason that I could never forget these people later and seemed to know them all so well was that there was in all of them something ruined, lost, or broken — some precious and irretrievable quality which had gone out of them and which they could never get back again. Perhaps that was the reason that I liked them all so much, because with ruined people it is either love or hate: there is no middle way. The ruined people that we like are those who desperately have died, and lost their lives because they love life dearly, and had that grandeur that makes such people spend prodigally the thing they love the best, and risk and lose their lives because life is so precious to them, and die at length because the seeds of life were in them. It is only the people who love life in this way who die — and these are the ruined people that we like.

The people in the house were people who had lost their lives because they loved the earth too well, and somehow had been slain by their hunger. And for this reason I liked them all, and could not forget them later: there seemed to have been some magic which had drawn them all together to the house, as if the house itself was a magnetic center for lost people.

Certainly, the three men who worked at the motorcar factory had been drawn together for this reason. Two were still young men in their early twenties. The third man was much older. He was past forty, his name was Nicholl, he had served in the army during the war and had attained the rank of captain.

He had the spare, alert, and jaunty figure that one often finds in army men, an almost professional military quality that somehow seemed to set his figure upon a horse as if he had grown there or had spent a lifetime in the cavalry. His face also had the same lean, bitten, professional military quality; his speech, although good-natured and very friendly, was clipped, incisive, jerky, and sporadic, his lean weatherbeaten face was deeply, sharply scarred and sunken in the flanks, and he wore a small cropped mustache, and displayed long frontal teeth when he smiled — a spare, gaunt, toothy, yet attractive smile.

His left arm was withered, shrunken, almost useless; part of his hand and two fingers had been torn away by the blast or explosion which had destroyed his arm; but it was not this mutilation of the flesh that gave one the sense of a life that had been ruined, lost, and broken irretrievably. In fact, one quickly forgot his physical injury: his figure looked so spare, lean, jaunty, well-conditioned in its energetic fitness that one never thought of him as a cripple, nor pitied him for any disability. No: the ruin that one felt in him was never of the flesh, but of the spirit. Something seemed to have been exploded from his life — it was not the nerve-centers of his arm, but of his soul, that had been destroyed. There was in the man somewhere a terrible dead vacancy and emptiness, and that spare, lean figure that he carried so well seemed only to surround this vacancy like a kind of shell.

He was always smartly dressed in well-cut clothes that set well on his trim spruce figure. He was always in good spirits, immensely friendly in his clipped spare way, and he laughed frequently — a rather metallic cackle which came suddenly and ended as swiftly as it had begun. He seemed, somehow, to have locked the door upon dark care and worry, and to have flung the key away — to have lost, at the same time that he lost more precious things, all the fretful doubts and perturbations of the conscience most men know.

Now, in fact, he seemed to have only one serious project in his life. This was to keep himself amused, to keep himself constantly amused, to get from his life somehow the last atom of entertainment it could possibly yield, and in this project the two young men who lived with him joined in with an energy and earnestness which suggested that their employment in the motorcar factory was just a necessary evil which must be borne patiently because it yielded them the means with which to carry on a more important business, the only one in which their lives were interested — the pursuit of pleasure.

And in the way in which they conducted this pursuit there was an element of deliberate calculation, concentrated earnestness, and focal intensity of purpose that was astounding, grotesque, and unbelievable, and that left in the mind of one who saw it a formidable and disquieting memory because there was in it almost the madness of desperation, the deliberate intent of men to cover up or seek oblivion at any cost of effort from some hideous emptiness of the soul.

Captain Nicholl and his two young companions had a little motorcar so small that it scuttled up the road, shot around and stopped in the gravel by the door with the abruptness of a wound-up toy. It was astonishing that three men could wedge themselves into this midget of a car, but wedge themselves they did, and used it to the end of its capacity, scuttling away to work in it in the morning, and scuttling back again when work was done, and scuttling away to London every Saturday, as if they were determined to wrest from this small motor, too, the last ounce of pleasure to be got from it.

Finally, Captain Nicholl and his two companions had made up an orchestra among them, and this they played in every night when they got home. One of the young men, who was a tall fellow with blond hair which went back in even corrugated waves across his head as if it had been marcelled, played the piano; the other, who was slight and dark, and had black hair, performed upon a saxophone; and Captain Nicholl himself took turns at thrumming furiously on a banjo, or rattling a tattoo upon the complex arrangement of trap drums, bass drums, and clashing cymbals that surrounded him.

They played nothing but American jazz music or sobbing crooner's rhapsodies or nigger blues. Their performance was astonishing. Although it was contrived solely for their own amusement, they hurled themselves into it with all the industrious earnestness of professional musicians employed by a night club or a dance hall to furnish dance music for patrons. The little dark fellow who played the saxophone would bend and weave prayerfully with his grotesque instrument, as the fat gloating notes came from its unctuous throat, and from time to time he would sway in a half circle, or get up and prance forward and back in rhythm to the music as the saxophone players in dance orchestras sometimes do.

Meanwhile the tall blond fellow at the piano would sway and bend above the keys, glancing around from time to time with little nods and smiles as if he were encouraging an orchestra of forty pieces or beaming happily and in an encouraging fashion at a dance floor crowded with paying customers.

While this was going on, Captain Nicholl would be thrumming madly on the strings of a banjo. He kept the instrument gripped somehow below his withered arm, fingering the end strings with his two good fingers, knocking the tune out with his good right hand, and keeping time with a beating foot. Then with a sudden violent movement he would put the banjo down, snatch up the sticks of the trap drum, and begin to rattle out a furious accompaniment, beating the bass drum with his foot meanwhile, and reaching over to smash cymbals, chimes, and metal rings from time to time. He played with a kind of desperate fury, his mouth fixed in a strange set grin, his bright eyes burning with a sharp wild glint of madness.

They sang as they played, bursting suddenly into the refrain of some popular song with the same calculated spontaneity and spurious enthusiasm of the professional orchestra, mouthing the words of Negro blues and jazz with an obvious satisfaction, with an accent which was remarkably good, and yet which had something foreign and inept in it, which made the familiar phrases of American music sound almost as strange in their mouths as if an orchestra of skillful patient Japanese were singing them.

They sang:

> " Yes, sir! That's my baby!
> No, sir! Don't mean maybe!
> Yes, sir! That's my baby now! "

or:

> " Oh, it ain't gonna rain no more, no more
> It ain't gonna rain no more "

or:

> " I got dose blu-u-ues " —

the young fellow at the piano rolling his eyes around in a ridiculous fashion and mouthing out the word " blues " extravagantly as he sang it, the little dark fellow bending forward in an unctuous sweep as the note came gloating fatly from the horn, and Captain Nicholl swaying sideways in his chair as he strummed upon the banjo strings, and improvising a mournful accompaniment of his own, somewhat as follows: " I got dose blu-u-ues! Yes, suh! I got dose blues! Yes, suh! I sure have got 'em — dose blu-u-ues — blu-u-ues — blu-u-ues! " — his mouth never relaxing from its strange fixed grin, nor his eyes from their bright set stare of madness as he swayed and strummed and sang the words that came so strangely from his lips.

It was a weird scene, an incredible performance, and somehow it pierced the heart with a wild nameless pity, an infinite sorrow and regret.

Something precious, irrecoverable had gone out of them, and they knew it. They fought the emptiness in them with this deliberate, formidable, and mad intensity of a calculated gaiety, a terrifying mimicry of mirth, and the storm wind howled around us in dark trees, and I felt that I had known them forever, and had no words to say to them — and no door.

There were four in the Coulson family: the father, a man of fifty years, the mother, somewhere in the middle forties, a son, and a daughter, Edith, a girl of twenty-two who lived in the house with her parents. I never met the son: he had completed his course at Oxford a year or two before, and had gone down to London where he was now employed. During the time I lived there the son did not come home.

They were a ruined family. How that ruin had fallen on them, what it was, I never knew, for no one ever spoke to me about them. But the sense of their disgrace, of a shameful inexpiable dishonor, for which there was no pardon, from which there could never be redemption, was overwhelming. In the most astonishing way I found out about it right away, and yet I did not know what they had done, and no one ever spoke a word against them.

Rather, the mention of their name brought silence, and in that silence there was something merciless and final, something that belonged to the temper of the country, and that was far more terrible than any open word of scorn, contempt, or bitter judgment could have been, more savage than a million strident, whispering, or abusive tongues could be, because the silence was unarguable, irrevocable, complete, as if a great door had been shut against their lives forever.

Everywhere I went in town, the people knew about them, and said nothing — saying everything — when I spoke their names. I found this final, closed, relentless silence everywhere — in tobacco, wine, and tailor shops, in book stores, food stores, haberdashery stores — wherever I bought anything and gave the clerk the address to which it was to be delivered, they responded instantly with this shut finality of silence, writing the name down gravely, sometimes saying briefly "Oh! Coulson's!" when I gave them the address, but more often saying nothing.

But whether they spoke or simply wrote the name down without a word, there was always this quality of instant recognition, this obdurate, contemptuous finality of silence, as if a door had been shut — a door that could never again be opened. Somehow I disliked them more for this silence than if they had spoken evilly: there was in it something ugly, sly, knowing, and triumphant that was far more evil than any slyly whispering confidence of slander, or any open vituperation of abuse, could be. It seemed somehow to come from all the evil and uncountable small maggotry of the earth, the cautious little hatreds of a million nameless ciphers, each puny, pallid, trivial in himself, but formidable because he added his tiny beetle's ball of dung to the mountainous accumulation of ten million others of his breed.

It was uncanny how these clerk-like faces grave and quiet, that never spoke a word, or gave a sign, or altered their expression by a jot, when I gave them the address, could suddenly be alive with something secret, foul, and sly, could be more closed and secret than a door, and yet instantly reveal the naked, shameful, and iniquitous filth that welled up from some depthless source. I could not phrase it, give a name to it, or even see a certain sign that it was there, no more than I could put my hand upon a wisp of fading smoke, but I always knew when it was there, and somehow when I saw it my heart went hard and cold against the people who revealed it, and turned with warmth and strong affection toward the Coulson family.

There was, finally, among these grave clerk-like faces one face that I could never forget thereafter, a face that seemed to resume into its sly suave surfaces all of the nameless abomination of evil in the world for which I had no name, for which there was no handle I could grasp, no familiar places or edges I could get my hands upon, which slid phantasmally, oilily, and smokily away whenever I tried to get my hands upon it. But it was to haunt my life for years in dreams of hatred, madness, and despair that found no frontal wall for their attack, no word for their vituperation, no door for the shoulder of my hate — an evil world of phantoms, shapes, and whispers that was yet as real as death, as ever-present as man's treachery, but that slid away from me like smoke whenever I tried to meet, or curse, or strangle it.

This face was the face of a man in a tailor shop, a fitter there, and I could have battered that foul face into a bloody pulp, distilled the filthy refuse of his ugly life out of his fat swelling neck and through the murderous grip of my fingers if I could only have found a cause, a logic, and an act for doing it. And yet I never saw the man but twice, and briefly, and there had been nothing in his suave, sly careful speech to give offense.

Edith Coulson had sent me to the tailor's shop: I needed a suit and when I asked her where to go to have it made she had sent me to this place because her brother had his suits made there and liked it. The fitter was a heavy shambling man in his late thirties: he had receding hair, which he brushed back flat in a thick pompadour, yellowish, somewhat bulging eyes, a coarse heavy face, loose-featured, red, and sensual, a sloping meaty jaw, and large discolored buck-teeth which showed unpleasantly in a mouth that was always half open. It was, in fact, the mouth that gave his face its sensual, sly, and ugly look, for a loose and vulgar smile seemed constantly to hover about its thick coarse edges, to be deliberately, slyly restrained, but about to burst at any moment in an open, evil, foully sensual laugh. There was always this ugly suggestion of a loose, corrupt, and evilly jubilant mirth about his mouth, and yet he never laughed or smiled.

The man's speech had this same quality. It was suave and courteous, but even in its most urbane assurances there was something noncommittal, sly, and jeering, something that slid away from you and was never to be grasped, a quality that was faithless, tricky, and unwholesome. When I came for the final fitting it was obvious that he had done as cheap and shoddy a job as he could do; the suit was vilely botched and skimped, sufficient cloth had not been put into it, and now it was too late to remedy the defect.

Yet the fitter gravely pulled the vest down till it met the trousers, tugged at the coat, and pulled the thing together where it stayed until I took a breath or moved a muscle, when it would all come apart again, the collar bulging outward from the shoulder, the skimpy coat and vest crawling backward from the trousers, leaving a hiatus of shirt and belly that could not be remedied now by any means.

Then, gravely he would pull the thing together again, and in his suave yet oily, sly, and noncommittal phrases say:

"Um! Seems to fit you very well."

I was choking with exasperation, and knew that I had been done, because I had foolishly paid them half the bill already, and now knew no way out of it except to lose what I had paid, and get nothing for it, or take the thing, and pay the balance. I was caught in a trap, but even as I jerked at the coat and vest speechlessly, seized my shirt, and thrust the gaping collar in his face, the man said smoothly:

" Um! Yes! The collar. Should think all that will be all right. Still needs a little alteration." He made some chalk marks on me. " Should think you'll find it fits you very well when the tailor makes the alterations."

" When will the suit be ready? "

" Um. Should think you ought to have it by next Tuesday. Yes. I think you'll find it ready by Tuesday."

The sly words slid away from me like oil: there was nothing to pin him to or grasp him by, the yellowed eyes looked casually away and would not look at me, the sensual face was suavely grave, the discolored buck-teeth shone obscenely through the coarse loose mouth, and the suggestion of the foul loose smile was so pronounced now that it seemed that at any moment he would have to turn away with heavy trembling shoulders and stifle the evil jeering laugh that was welling up in him. But he remained suavely grave and noncommittal to the end, and when I asked him if I should come again to try it on, he said, in the same oily tone, never looking at me:

" Um. Shouldn't think that would be necessary. Could have it delivered to you when it's ready. What is your address? "

" The Far-end Farm — it's on the Ventnor Road."

" Oh! Coulson's! " He never altered his expression, but the suggestion of the obscene smile was so pronounced that now it seemed he had to out with it. Instead, he only said:

" Um. Yes. Should think it could be delivered to you there on Tuesday. If you'll just wait a moment I'll ask the tailor."

Gravely, suavely, he took the coat from me and walked back toward the tailor's room with the coat across his arm. In a moment, I heard sly voices whispering, laughing slyly, then the tailor saying:

" Where does he live? "

" Coulson's! " said the fitter chokingly, and now the foul awaited laugh did come — high, wet, slimy, it came out of that loose mouth, and choked and whispered wordlessly, and choked again, and mingled then with the tailor's voice in sly, choking, whispering intimacy, and then gasped faintly, and was silent. When he came out again his coarse face was red and swollen with foul secret merriment, his heavy shoulders trembled slightly, he took out his handkerchief and wiped it once across his loose half-opened mouth, and with that gesture wiped the slime of laughter from his lips. Then he came toward me suave, grave, and courteous, evilly composed, as he said smoothly:

"Should think we'll have that for you by next Tuesday, sir."

"Can the tailor fix it so it's going to fit?"

"Um. Should think you'll find that everything's all right. You ought to have it Tuesday afternoon."

He was not looking at me: the yellowish bulging eyes were staring casually, indefinitely, away, and his words again had slid away from me like oil. He could not be touched, approached, or handled: there was nothing to hold him by, he had the impregnability of smoke or a ball of mercury.

As I went out the door, he began to speak to another man in the shop. I heard low words and whispered voices, then, gasping, the word "Coulson's!" and the slimy, choking, smothered laughter as the street door closed behind me. I never saw him again. I never forgot his face.

❦ ❦ ❦

That was a fine house: the people in it were exiled, lost, and ruined people, and I like them all. Later I never knew why I felt so close to them, or remembered them with such warmth and strong affection.

I did not see the Coulsons often and rarely talked to them. Yet I felt as familiar and friendly with them all as if I had known them all my life. The house was wonderful as no other house I had ever known because we all seemed to be living in it together with this strange speechless knowledge, warmth, and familiarity, and yet each was as private, secret, and secure in his own room as if he occupied the house alone.

Coulson himself I saw least of all: we sometimes passed each other going in or out the door, or in the hall: he would grunt

"Morning," or "Good day," in a curt blunt manner, and go on, and yet he always left me with a curious sense of warmth and friendliness. He was a stocky well-set man with iron-gray hair, bushy eyebrows, and a red weathered face which wore the open color of the country on it, but also had the hard dull flush of the steady heavy drinker.

I never saw him drunk, and yet I think that he was never sober: he was one of those men who have drunk themselves past any hope of drunkenness, who are soaked through to the bone with alcohol, saturated, tanned, weathered in it so completely that it could never be distilled out of their blood again. Yet, even in this terrible excess one felt a kind of grim control — the control of a man who is enslaved by the very thing that he controls, the control of the opium eater who cannot leave his drug but measures out his dose with a cold calculation, and finds the limit of his capacity, and stops there, day by day.

But somehow this very sense of control, this blunt ruddy style of the country gentleman which distinguished his speech, his manner, and his dress, made the ruin of his life, the desperate intemperance of drink that smoldered in him like a slow fire, steadily, nakedly apparent. It was as if, having lost everything, he still held grimly to the outer forms of a lost standard, a ruined state, when the inner substance was destroyed.

And it was this way with all of them — with Mrs. Coulson and the girl, as well: their crisp, clipped friendly speech never deviated into intimacy, and never hinted at any melting into confidence and admission. Upon the woman's weathered face there hovered, when she talked, the same faint set grin that Captain Nicholl had, and her eyes were bright and hard, a little mad, impenetrable, as were his. And the girl, although young and very lovely, sometimes had this same look when she greeted anyone or paused to talk. In that look there was nothing truculent, bitter, or defiant: it was just the look of three people who had gone down together, and who felt for one another neither bitterness nor hate, but that strange companionship of a common disgrace, from which love has vanished, but which is more secret, silent, and impassively resigned to its fatal unity than love itself could be.

And that hard bright look also said this plainly to the world:

"We ask for nothing from you now, we want nothing that you offer us. What is ours is ours, what we are we are, you'll not intrude nor come closer than we let you see!"

Coulson might have been a man who had been dishonored and destroyed by his women, and who took it stolidly, saying nothing, and drank steadily from morning until night, and had nothing for it now but drink and silence and acceptance. Yet I never knew for certain that this was so; it just seemed inescapable, and seemed somehow legible not only in the slow smoldering fire that burned out through his rugged weathered face, but also in the hard bright armor of the women's eyes, the fixed set grin around their lips when they were talking — a grin that was like armor, too. And Morison, who had referred to Coulson, chuckling, as a real "bottle-a-day man," had added quietly, casually, in his brief, indefinite, but blurted-out suggestiveness of speech:

"I think the old girl's been a bit of a bitch in her day. . . . Don't know, of course, but has the look, hasn't she?" In a moment he said quietly, "Have you talked to the daughter yet?"

"Once or twice. Not for long."

"Ran into a chap at Magdalen other day who knows her," he said casually. "He used to come out here to see her." He glanced swiftly, slyly at me, his face reddening a little with laughter. "Pretty hot, I gather," he said quietly, smiling, and looked away. It was night: the fire burned cheerfully in the grate, the hot coals spurting in small gaseous flares from time to time. The house was very quiet all around us. Outside we could hear the stormy wind in the trees along the road. Morison flicked his cigarette into the fire, poured out a drink of whiskey into a glass, saying as he did so: "I say, old chap, you don't mind if I take a spot of this before I go to bed, do you?" Then he shot some seltzer in the glass, and drank. And I sat there, without a word, staring sullenly into the fire, dumbly conscious of the flood of sick pain and horror which the casual foulness of the man's suggestion had aroused, stubbornly trying to deny now that I was thinking of the girl all the time.

One night as I was coming home along the dark road that went up past the playing field to the house and that was bordered on each side by great trees whose branches seemed to hold at night all the mysterious and demented cadences of storm, I came upon her suddenly standing in the shadow of a tree. It was one of the grand wild nights that seemed to come so often in the autumn of that year: the air was full of a fine stinging moisture, not quite rain, and above the stormy branches of the trees I could see the sky, wild, broken, full of scudding clouds through which at times the moon drove in and out with a kind of haggard loneliness. By that faint, wild, and broken light, I could see the small white oval of the girl's face — somehow even more lovely now just because I could not see it plainly. And I could see as well the rough gleaming bark of the tree against which she leaned.

As I approached, I saw her thrust her hand into the pocket of her overcoat, a match flared, and for a moment I saw Edith plainly, the small flower of her face framed in the wavering light as she lowered her head to light her cigarette.

The light went out. I saw the small respiring glow of her cigarette before the white blur of her face. I passed her swiftly, head bent, without speaking, my heart filled with the sense of strangeness and wonder which the family had aroused in me.

Then I walked on up the road, muttering to myself. The house was dark when I got there, but when I entered my sitting-room the place was still warmly and softly luminous with the glow of hot coals in the grate. I turned the lights on, shut the door behind me, and hurled several lumps of coal upon the bedded coals. In a moment the fire was blazing and crackling cheerfully, and getting a kind of comfort and satisfaction from this activity, I flung off my coat, went over to the sideboard, poured out a stiff drink of Scotch from a bottle there, and coming back to the fire, flung myself into a chair, and began to stare sullenly into the dancing flames.

How long I sat there in this stupor of sullen and nameless fury, I did not know, but I was sharply roused at length by footsteps light and rapid on the gravel, shocked into a start of surprise by a figure that appeared suddenly at one of the French windows that opened directly from my sitting-room to the level sward of velvet lawn before the house.

I peered through the glass for a moment with an astonished stare before I recognized the face of Edith Coulson. I opened the doors at once; she came in quickly, smiling at my surprise, and at the glass which I was holding foolishly, half-raised in my hand.

I continued to look at her with an expression of gape-mouthed astonishment and in a moment became conscious of her smiling glance, the cool sweet assurance of her young voice.

"I say!" she was saying cheerfully. "What a lucky thing to find you up! I came away without any key — I should have had to wake the whole house up — so when I saw your light —" she concluded briskly "— what luck! I hope you don't mind."

"Why no-o, no," I stammered foolishly, still staring dumbly at her. "No — no-o — not at all," I blundered on. Then suddenly coming to myself with a burst of galvanic energy, I shut the windows, pushed another chair before the fire, and said:

"Won't you sit down and have a drink before you go?"

"Thanks," she said crisply. "I will — yes. What a jolly fire you have." As she talked she took off her coat and hat swiftly and put them on a chair. Her face was flushed and rosy, beaded with small particles of rain, and for a moment she stood before the mirror arranging her hair, which had been tousled by the wind.

The girl was slender, tall, and very lovely with the kind of beauty they have when they are beautiful — a beauty so fresh, fair, and delicate that it seems to be given to just a few of them to compensate for all the grimly weathered ugliness of the rest. Her voice was also lovely, sweet, and musical, and when she talked all the notes of tenderness and love were in it. But she had the same hard bright look in her eye that her mother had, the faint set smile around her mouth. As we stood there talking she was standing very close to me, and I could smell the fragrance of her hair, and felt an intolerable desire to put my hand upon hers and was almost certain she would not draw away. But the hard bright look was in her eye, the faint set smile around her mouth, and I did nothing.

"What'll you have?" I said. "Whiskey?"

"Yes, thank you," she said with the same sweet crisp assurance with which she always spoke, "and a splash of soda." I struck a match and held it for her while she lit a cigarette she was holding in her hand, and in a moment returned to her with the drink. Then she sat down, crossed her legs, and for a moment puffed thoughtfully at her cigarette, as she stared into the fire. The storm wind moaned in the great trees along the road, and near the house, and suddenly a swirl of rain struck the windows with a rattling blast. The girl stirred a little in her chair, restlessly, shivered:

" Listen! " she said. " What a night! Horrible weather we have here, isn't it? "

" I don't know. I don't like the fog and rain so well. But this — the way it is tonight — " I nodded toward the window — " I like it."

She looked at me for a moment.

" Oh," she said noncommittally. " You do." Then, as she sipped her drink, she looked curiously about the room, her reflective glance finally resting on my table where there was a great stack of the ledgers in which I wrote.

" I say," she cried again. " What are you doing with all those big books there? "

" I write in them."

" Really? " she said, in a surprised tone. " I should think it'd be an awful bother carrying them around when you travel? "

" It is. But it's the best way I've found of keeping what I do together."

" Oh," she said, as before, and continued to stare curiously at me with her fair, lovely young face, the curiously hard, bright, and unrevealing glance of her eye. " I see. . . . But why do you come to such a place as this to write? " she said presently. " Do you like it here? "

" I do. As well as any place I've ever known."

" Oh — I don't know — Paris — London — some place like that where there is lots of life — people — fun — I should think you'd work better in a place like that."

" I work better here."

" But don't you get awfully fed up sitting in here all day long and writing in those enormous books? "

" I do, yes."

" I should think you would . . . I should think you'd want to get away from it sometime."

" Yes. I do want to — every day — almost all the time."

" Then why don't you? " she said crisply. " Why don't you go off some week-end for a little spree. I should think it'd buck you up no end."

"It would — yes. Where should I go?"

"Oh, Paris, I suppose. . . . Or London! London!" she cried. "London is quite jolly if you know it."

"I'm afraid I don't know it."

"But you've *been* to London," she said in a surprised tone.

"Oh, yes. I lived there for several months."

"Then you know London," she said impatiently. "Of course you do."

"I'm afraid I don't know it very well. I don't know many people there — and after all, that's the thing that counts, isn't it?"

She looked at me curiously for a moment with the faint hard smile around the edges of her lovely mouth. "— should think that might be arranged," she said with a quiet, an enigmatic humor. Then, more directly, she added: "That shouldn't be difficult at all. Perhaps I could introduce you to some people."

"That would be fine. Do you know many people there?"

"Not many," she said. "I go there — whenever I can." She got up with a swift decisive movement, put her glass down on the mantel and cast her cigarette into the fire. Then she faced me, looking at me with a curiously bold, an almost defiant directness of her hard bright eyes, and she fixed me with this glance for a full moment before she spoke.

"Good night," she said. "Thanks awfully for letting me in — and for the drink."

"Good night," I said, and she was gone before I could say more, and I had closed the door behind her, and I could hear her light swift footsteps going down the hall and up the steps. And then there was nothing in the house but sleep and silence, and storm and darkness in the world around me.

Mrs. Coulson came into my room just once or twice while I was there. One morning she came in, spoke crisply and cheerfully, and walked over to the window, looking out upon the velvet lawn and at the dreary, impenetrable gray of foggy air. Although the room was warm and there was a good fire burning in the grate, she clasped her arms together as she looked and shivered a little:

"Wretched weather, isn't it?" she said in her crisp tones, her gaunt weathered face and toothy mouth touched by the faint fixed grin as she looked out with her bright hard stare. "Don't you find it frightfully depressing? Most Americans do," she said, getting the sharp disquieting sound into the word.

"Yes. I do, a little. We don't have this kind of weather very often. But this is the time of year you get it here, isn't it? I suppose you're used to it by now?"

"Used to it?" she said crisply, turning her hard bright gaze upon me. "Not at all. I've known it all my life but I'll never get used to it. It is a wretched climate."

"Still, you wouldn't feel at home anywhere else, would you? You wouldn't want to live outside of England."

"No?" she said, staring at me with the faint set grin around her toothy mouth. "Why do you think so?"

"Because your home is here."

"My home? My home is where they have fine days, and where the sun is always shining."

"I wouldn't like that. I'd get tired of sunlight all the time. I'd want some gray days and some fog and snow."

"Yes, I suppose you would. But then, you've been used to having fine days all your life, haven't you? With us, it's different. I'm so fed up with fog and rain that I could do without it nicely, thank you, if I never saw it again. . . . I don't think you could ever understand how much the sunlight means to us," she said slowly. She turned, and for a moment looked out the window with her hard bright stare, the faint set grin about her mouth. "Sunlight — warmth — fine days forever! Warmth everywhere — in the earth, the sky, in the lives of the people all around you nothing but warmth and sunlight and fine days!"

"And where would you go to find all that? Does it exist?"

"Oh, of course!" she said crisply and good-naturedly, turning to me again. "There's only one place to live — only one country where I want to live."

"Where is that?"

"Italy," she said. "That's my real home. . . . I'd live the rest of my life there if I could." For a moment longer she looked out the window, then turned briskly, saying: "Why don't you run over to Paris some week-end? After all, it's only seven hours from London: if you left here in the morning you'd be there in time for dinner. It would be a good change for you. I should think a little trip like that would buck you up tremendously."

Her words gave me a wonderful feeling of confidence and hope: I think she had traveled a great deal, and she had the casual, assured way of speaking of a voyage that made it seem very easy, and filled one with a sense of joy and adventure when she spoke about it. When I tried to think of Paris by myself it had seemed very far away and hard to reach: London stood between it and me, and when I thought of the huge smoky web of London, the soft gray skies above me, and the enormous weight of lives that were hidden somewhere in that impenetrable fog, gray desolation and weariness of the spirit filled me. It seemed to me that I must draw each breath of that soft gray air with heavy weary effort, and that every mile of my journey would be a ghastly struggle through some viscous and material substance of soft heavy gray, which weighted down my steps and filled my heart with desolation.

But when Mrs. Coulson spoke to me about it, suddenly it all seemed wonderfully easy and good. England was magically small, the Channel to be taken in a stride, and all the thrill, the joy, the mystery of Paris mine again — the moment that I chose to make it mine.

I looked at her gaunt weathered face, her toothy mouth with the faint fixed grin, the hard bright armor of her eyes, and wondered how anything so clear, so sharp, so crisp, and so incisive could have been shaped and grown underneath these soft and humid skies that numbed me, mind and heart and body, with their thick numb substance of gray weariness and desolation.

A day or two before I left, Edith came into my room one afternoon bearing a tray with tea and jam and buttered bread. I was sitting in my chair before the fire, and had my coat off: when she came in I scrambled to my feet, reached for my coat and started to put it on. In her young crisp voice she told me not to, and put the tray down on the table, saying that the maid was having her afternoon away.

Then for a moment she stood looking at me with her faint and enigmatic smile.

"So you're leaving us?" she said presently.

"Yes. Tomorrow."

"And where will you go from here?" she said.

"To Germany, I think. Just for a short time — two or three weeks."

"And after that?"

"I'm going home."

"Home?"

"Back to America."

"Oh," she said slowly. "I see." In a moment, she added, "We shall miss you."

I wanted to talk to her more than I had ever wanted to talk to anyone in my life, but when I spoke all that I could say, lamely, muttering, was:

"I'll miss you, too."

"Will you?" She spoke so quietly that I could scarcely hear her. "I wonder for how long?" she said.

"Forever," I said, flushing miserably at the sound of the word, and yet not knowing any other word to say.

The faint hard smile about her mouth was a little deeper when she spoke again.

"Forever? That's a long time, when one is young as you," she said.

"I mean it. I'll never forget you as long as I live."

"We shall remember you," she said quietly. "And I hope you think of us sometime — back here buried, lost, in all the fog and rain and ruin of England. How good it must be to know that you are young in a young country — where nothing that you did yesterday matters very much. How wonderful it must be to know that none of the failure of the past can pull you down — that there will always be another day for you — a new beginning. I wonder if you Americans will ever know how fortunate you are," the girl said.

"And yet you could not leave all this?" I said with a kind of desperate hope. "This old country you've lived in, known all your life. A girl like you could never leave a place like this to live the kind of life we have in America."

"*Couldn't* I?" she said with a quiet but unmistakable passion of conviction. "There's nothing I'd like better."

I stared at her blindly, dumbly for a moment; suddenly all that I wanted to say, and had not been able to say, found release in a movement of my hands. I gripped her by the shoulders and pulled her to me, and began to plead with her:

"Then why don't you? I'll take you there! — Look here —" my words were crazy and I knew it, but as I spoke them, I believed all I said — "Look here! I haven't got much money — but in America you can make it if you want to! I'm going back there. You come, too — I'll take you when I go!"

She had not tried to free herself; she just stood there passive, unresisting, as I poured that frenzied proposal in her ears. Now, with the same passive and unyielding movement, the bright armor of her young eyes, she stepped away, and stood looking at me silently for a moment, the faint, hard smile at the edges of her mouth. Then slowly, with an almost imperceptible movement, she shook her head. "Oh, you'll forget about us all," she said quietly. "You'll forget about our lives here — buried in fog — and rain — and failure — and defeat."

"Failure and defeat won't last forever."

"Sometimes they do," she said with a quiet finality that froze my heart.

"Not for you — they won't!" I said, and took her by the hand again with desperate entreaty. "Listen to me —" I blundered on incoherently, with the old feeling of nameless shame and horror. "You don't need to tell me what it is — I don't want to know — but whatever it is for you — it doesn't matter — you can get the best of it."

She said nothing, but just looked at me through that hard bright armor of her eyes, the obdurate finality of her smile.

"Good-by," she said, "I'll not forget you either." She looked at me for a moment curiously before she spoke again. "I wonder," she said slowly, "if you'll ever understand just what it was you did for me by coming here."

" What was it? "

" You opened a door that I thought had been closed forever," she said, " a door that let me look in on a world I thought I should never see again — a new bright world, a new life and a new beginning — for us all. And I thought that was something which would never happen to anyone in this house again."

" It will to you," I said, and took her hand again with desperate eagerness. " It can happen to you whenever you want it to. It's yours, I'll swear it to you, if you'll only speak."

She looked at me with her direct hard glance, an almost imperceptible movement of her head.

" I tell you I know what I'm talking about."

Again she shook her head.

" You don't know," she said. " You're young. You're an American. There are some things you'll never be old enough to know. — For some of us there's no return. — Go back," she said, " go back to the life you know — the life you understand — where there can always be a new beginning — a new life."

" And you — " I said dumbly, miserably.

" Good-by, my dear," she said so low and gently I could scarcely hear her. " Think of me sometime, won't you — I'll not forget you." And before I could speak she kissed me once and was gone, so light and swift that I did not know it, until the door had closed behind her. And for some time, like a man in a stupor, I stood there looking out the window at the gray wet light of England.

The next day I went away, and never saw any of them again, but I could not forget them. Although I had never passed beyond the armor of their hard bright eyes, or breached the wall of their crisp, friendly, and impersonal speech, or found out anything about them, I always thought of them with warmth, with a deep and tender affection, as if I had always known them — as if, somehow, I could have lived with them or made their lives my own if only I had said a word, or turned the handle of a door — a word I never knew, a door I never found.

— From *Scribner's Magazine*, August, 1934. Reprinted by permission of Maxwell Perkins, executor.

HOW BEAUTIFUL WITH SHOES

By Wilbur Daniel Steele

By the time the milking was finished, the sow, which had farrowed the past week, was making such a row that the girl spilled a pint of the warm milk down the trough-lead to quiet the animal before taking the pail to the well-house. Then in the quiet she heard a sound of hoofs on the bridge, where the road crossed the creek a hundred yards below the house, and she set the pail down on the ground beside her bare, barn-soiled feet. She picked it up again. She set it down. It was as if she calculated its weight.

That was what she was doing, as a matter of fact, setting off against its pull toward the well-house the pull of that wagon team in the road, with little more of personal will or wish in the matter than has a wooden weathervane between two currents in the wind. And as with the vane, so with the wooden girl — the added behest of a whip-lash cracking in the distance was enough; leaving the pail at the barn door, she set off in a deliberate, docile beeline through the cow-yard, over the fence, and down in a diagonal across the farm's one tilled field toward the willow brake that walled the road at the dip. And once under way, though her mother came to the kitchen door and called in her high flat voice, "Amarantha, where you goin', Amarantha?" the girl went on apparently unmoved, as though she had been as deaf as the woman in the doorway; indeed, if there was emotion in her it was the purely sensuous one of feeling the clods of the furrows breaking softly between her toes. It was springtime in the mountains.

"Amarantha, why don't you answer me, Amarantha?"

For moments after the girl had disappeared beyond the willows the widow continued to call, unaware through long habit of how absurd it sounded, the name which that strange man her husband had put upon their daughter in one of his moods. Mrs. Doggett had been deaf so long she did not realize that nobody else ever thought of it for the broad-fleshed, slow-minded girl, but called her Mary or, even more simply, Mare.

Ruby Herter had stopped his team this side of the bridge, the mules' heads turned into the land to his father's farm beyond the road. A big-barreled, heavy-limbed fellow with a square, sallow, not unhandsome face, he took out youth in ponderous gestures of masterfulness; it was like him to have cracked his whip above his animals' ears the moment before he pulled them to a halt. When he saw the girl getting over the fence under the willows he tongued the wad of tobacco out of his mouth into his palm, threw it away beyond the road, and drew a sleeve of his jumper across his lips.

"Don't run yourself out o' breath, Mare; I got all night."

"I was comin'." It sounded sullen only because it was matter of fact.

"Well, keep a-comin' and give us a smack." Hunched on the wagon seat, he remained motionless for some time after she had arrived at the hub, and when he stirred it was but to cut a fresh bit of tobacco, as if already he had forgotten why he threw the old one away. Having satisfied his humor, he unbent, climbed down, kissed her passive mouth, and hugged her up to him, roughly and loosely, his hands careless of contours. It was not out of the way; they were used to handling animals both of them; and it was spring. A slow warmth pervaded the girl, formless, nameless, almost impersonal.

Her betrothed pulled her head back by the braid of her yellow hair. He studied her face, his brows gathered and his chin out.

"Listen, Mare, you wouldn't leave nobody else hug and kiss you, dang you!"

She shook her head, without vehemence or anxiety.

"Who's that?" She hearkened up the road. "Pull your team out," she added, as a Ford came in sight around the bend above the house, driven at speed. "Geddap!" she said to the mules herself.

But the car came to a halt near them, and one of the five men crowded in it called, " Come on, Ruby, climb in. They's a loony loose out o' Dayville Asylum, and they got him trailed over somewheres on Split Ridge, and Judge North phoned up to Slosson's store for ever'body come help circle him — come on, hop the runnin'-board! "

Ruby hesitated, an eye on his team.

" Scared, Ruby? " The driver raced his engine. " They say this boy's a killer."

" Mare, take the team in and tell pa." The car was already moving when Ruby jumped it. A moment after it had sounded on the bridge it was out of sight.

" Amarantha, Amarantha, why don't you come, Amarantha? "

Returning from her errand, fifteen minutes later, Mare heard the plaint lifted in the twilight. The sun had dipped behind the back ridge, and though the sky was still bright with day, the dusk began to smoke up out of the plowed field like a ground-fog. The girl had returned through it, got the milk, and started toward the well-house before the widow saw her.

" Daughter, seems to me you might! " she expostulated without change of key. " Here's some young man friend o' yourn stopped to say howdy, and I been rackin' my lungs out after you. . . . Put that milk in the cool and come! "

Some young man friend? But there was no good to be got from puzzling. Mare poured the milk in the pan in the dark of the low house over the well, and as she came out, stooping, she saw a figure waiting for her, black in silhouette against the yellowing sky.

" Who are you? " she asked, a native timidity making her sound sulky.

" ' Amarantha! ' " the fellow mused. " That's poetry." And she knew then that she did not know him.

She walked past, her arms straight down and her eyes front. Strangers always affected her with a kind of muscular terror simply by being strangers. So she gained the kitchen steps, aware by his tread that he followed. There, taking courage at sight of her mother in the doorway, she turned on him, her eyes down at the level of his knees.

" Who are you and what d' y' want? "

He still mused. "Amarantha! Amarantha in Carolina! That makes me happy!"

Mare hazarded one upward look. She saw that he had red hair, brown eyes, and hollows under his cheekbones, and though the green sweater he wore on top of a gray overall was plainly not meant for him, sizes too large as far as girth went, yet he was built so long of limb that his wrists came inches out of the sleeves and made his big hands look even bigger.

Mrs. Doggett complained. "Why don't you introduce us, daughter?"

The girl opened her mouth and closed it again. Her mother, unaware that no sound had come out of it, smiled and nodded, evidently taking to the tall, homely fellow and tickled by the way he could not seem to get his eyes off her daughter. But the daughter saw none of it, all her attention centered upon the stranger's hands.

Restless, hard-fleshed, and chap-bitten, they were like a countryman's hands; but the fingers were longer than the ordinary, and slightly spatulate at their ends, and these ends were slowly and continuously at play among themselves.

The girl could not have explained how it came to her to be frightened and at the same time to be calm, for she was inept with words. It was simply that in an animal way she knew animals, knew them in health and ailing, and when they were ailing she knew by instinct, as her father had known, how to move so as not to fret them.

Her mother had gone in to light up; from beside the lamp-shelf she called back, "If he's aimin' to stay to supper you should've told me, Amarantha, though I guess there's plenty of the side-meat to go 'round, if you'll bring me in a few more turnips and potatoes, though it is late."

At the words the man's cheeks moved in and out. "I'm very hungry," he said.

Mare nodded deliberately. Deliberately, as if her mother could hear her, she said over her shoulder, "I'll go get the potatoes and turnips, ma." While she spoke she was moving, slowly, softly, at first, toward the right of the yard, where the fence gave over into the field. Unluckily her mother spied her through the window.

" Amarantha, where *are* you goin'? "

" I'm goin' to get the potatoes and turnips." She neither raised her voice nor glanced back, but lengthened her stride. " He won't hurt her," she said to herself. " He won't hurt her; it's me, not her," she kept repeating, while she got over the fence and down into the shadow that lay more than ever like a fog on the field.

The desire to believe that it actually did hide her, the temptation to break from her rapid but orderly walk grew till she could no longer fight it. She saw the road willows only a dash ahead of her. She ran, her feet floundering among the furrows.

She neither heard nor saw him, but when she realized he was with her she knew he had been with her all the while. She stopped, and he stopped, and so they stood, with the dark open of the field all around. Glancing sidewise presently, she saw he was no longer looking at her with those strangely importunate brown eyes of his, but had raised them to the crest of the wooded ridge behind her.

By and by, " What does it make you think of? " he asked. And when she made no move to see, " Turn around and look! " he said, and though it was low and almost tender in its tone, she knew enough to turn.

A ray of the sunset hidden in the west struck through the tops of the topmost trees, far and small up there, a thin, bright hem.

" What does it make you think of, Amarantha? . . . Answer! "

" Fire," she made herself say.

" Or blood."

" Or blood, yeh. That's right, or blood." She had heard a Ford going up the road beyond the willows, and her attention was not on what she said.

The man soliloquized. " Fire and blood, both; spare one or the other, and where is beauty, the way the world is? It's an awful thing to have to carry, but Christ had it. Christ came with a sword. I love beauty, Amarantha . . . I say, I love beauty! "

" Yeh, that's right, I hear." What she heard was the car stopping at her house.

" Not prettiness. Prettiness'll have to go with ugliness, because it's only ugliness trigged up. But beauty! " Now again he was looking at her. " Do you know how beautiful you are, Amarantha,

Amarantha sweet and fair?" Of a sudden, reaching behind her, he began to unravel the meshes of her hair-braid, the long, flat-tipped fingers at once impatient and infinitely gentle. "*Braid no more that shining hair!*"

Flat-faced Mare Doggett tried to see around those glowing eyes so near to hers but, wise in her instinct, did not try too hard. "Yeh," she temporized. "I mean, no, I mean."

"Amarantha, I've come a long, long way for you. Will you come away with me now?"

"Yeh — that is — in a minute I will, mister — yeh . . ."

"Because you want to, Amarantha? Because you love me as I love you? Answer!"

"Yeh — sure — uh . . . *Ruby!*"

The man tried to run, but there were six against him, coming up out of the dark that lay in the plowed ground. Mare stood where she was while they knocked him down and got a rope around him; after that she walked back toward the house with Ruby and Older Haskins, her father's cousin.

Ruby wiped his brow and felt of his muscles. "Gees, you're lucky we come, Mare. We're no more'n past the town, when they come hollerin' he'd broke over this way."

When they came to the fence the girl sat on the rail for a moment and rebraided her hair before she went into the house, where they were making her mother smell ammonia.

Lots of cars were coming. Judge North was coming, somebody said. When Mare heard this she went into her bedroom off the kitchen and got her shoes and put them on. They were brand-new two-dollar shoes with cloth tops, and she had only begun to break them in last Sunday; she wished afterwards she had put her stockings on too, for they would have eased the seams. Or else that she had put on the old button pair, even though the soles were worn through.

Judge North arrived. He thought first of taking the loony straight through to Dayville that night, but then decided to keep him in the lock-up at the courthouse till morning and make the drive by day. Older Haskins stayed in, gentling Mrs. Doggett, while Ruby went out to help get the man into the Judge's sedan. Now that she had them on, Mare didn't like to take the shoes off till Older went; it might make him feel small, she thought.

Older Haskins had a lot of facts about the loony.

" His name's Humble Jewett," he told them. " They belong back in Breed County, all them Jewetts, and I don't reckon there's none on 'em that's not a mite unbalanced. He went to college though, worked his way, and he taught somethin' 'rother in some academy-school a spell, till he went off his head all of a sudden and took after folks with an axe. I remember it in the paper at the time. They give out one while how the Principal wasn't goin' to live, and there was others — there was a girl he tried to strangle. That was four-five year back."

Ruby came in guffawing. " Know the only thing they can get 'im to say, Mare? Only God thing he'll say is, ' Amarantha, she's goin' with me.' . . . Mare! "

" Yeh, I know."

The cover of the kettle the girl was handling slid off the stove with a clatter. A sudden sick wave passed over her. She went out to the back, out into the air. It was not till now she knew how frightened she had been.

Ruby went home, but Older Haskins stayed to supper with them and helped Mare do the dishes afterward; it was nearly nine when he left. The mother was already in bed, and Mare was about to sit down to get those shoes off her wretched feet at last, when she heard the cow carrying on up at the barn, lowing and kicking, and next minute the sow was in it with a horning note. It might be a fox passing by to get at the henhouse, or a weasel. Mare forgot her feet, took a broom-handle they used in boiling clothes, opened the back door, and stepped out. Blinking the lamplight from her eyes, she peered up toward the outbuildings, and saw the gable end of the barn standing like a red arrow in the dark, and the top of a butternut tree beyond it drawn in skeleton traceries; and just then a cock crowed.

She went to the right corner of the house and saw where the light came from, ruddy above the woods down the valley. Returning into the house, she bent close to her mother's ear and shouted,

"Somethin's afire down to the town, looks like," then went out again and up to the barn. "Soh! Soh!" she called in to the animals. She climbed up and stood on the top rail of the cowpen fence, only to find she could not locate the flame even there.

Ten rods behind the buildings a mass of rock mounted higher than their ridgepoles, a chopped-off buttress of the back ridge, covered with oak scrub and wild grapes and blackberries, whose thorny ropes the girl beat away from her skirt with the broom-handle as she scrambled up in the wine-colored dark. Once at the top, and the brush held aside, she could see the tongue-tip of the conflagration half a mile away at the town. And she knew by the bearing of the two church steeples that it was the building where the lock-up was that was burning.

There is a horror in knowing animals trapped in a fire, no matter what the animals.

"Oh, my God!" Mare said.

A car went down the road. Then there was a horse galloping. That would be Older Haskins probably. People were out at Ruby's father's farm; she could hear their voices raised. There must have been another car up from the other way, for lights wheeled and shouts were exchanged in the neighborhood of the bridge. Next thing she knew, Ruby was at the house below, looking for her probably.

He was telling her mother. Mrs. Doggett was not used to him, so he had to shout even louder than Mare had to.

"What y' reckon he done, the hellion! He broke the door and killed Lew Fyke and set the courthouse afire! . . . Where's Mare?"

Her mother would not know. Mare called. "Here, up the rock here."

She had better go down. Ruby would likely break his bones if he tried to climb the rock in the dark, not knowing the way. But the sight of the fire fascinated her simple spirit, the fearful element, more fearful than ever now, with the news. "Yes, I'm comin'," she called sulkily, hearing feet in the brush. "You wait; I'm comin'."

When she turned and saw it was Humble Jewett, right behind

her among the branches, she opened her mouth to screech. She was not quick enough. Before a sound came out he got one hand over her face and the other arm around her body.

Mare had always thought she was strong, and the loony looked gangling; yet she was so easy for him that he need not hurt her. He made no haste and little noise as he carried her deeper into the undergrowth. Where the hill began to mount it was harder though. Presently he set her on her feet. He let the hand that had been over her mouth slip down to her throat, where the broad-tipped fingers wound, tender as yearning, weightless as caress.

" I was afraid you'd scream before you knew who 'twas, Amarantha. But I didn't want to hurt your lips, dear heart, your lovely, quiet lips."

It was so dark under the trees she could hardly see him, but she felt his breath on her mouth, near to. But then, instead of kissing her, he said, " No! No! " took from her throat for an instant the hand that had held her mouth, kissed its palm, and put it back softly against her skin.

" Now, my love, let's go before they come."

She stood stock-still. Her mother's voice was to be heard in the distance, strident and meaningless. More cars were on the road. Nearer, around the rock, there were sounds of tramping and thrashing. Ruby fussed and cursed. He shouted, " Mare, dang you, where are you, Mare? " his voice harsh with uneasy anger. Now, if she aimed to do anything, was the time to do it. But there was neither breath nor power in her windpipe. It was as if those yearning fingers had paralyzed the muscles.

" Come! " the arm he put around her shivered against her shoulder blades. It was anger. " I hate killing. It's a dirty, ugly thing. It makes me sick." He gagged, judging by the sound. But then he ground his teeth. " Come away, my love! "

She found herself moving. Once when she broke a branch underfoot with an instinctive awkwardness he chided her. " Quiet, my heart, else they'll hear! " She made herself heavy. He thought she grew tired and bore more of her weight till he was breathing hard.

Men came up the hill. There must have been a dozen spread out, by the angle of their voices as they kept touch. Always Humble Jewett kept caressing Mare's throat with one hand; all she could do was hang back.

"You're tired and you're frightened," he said at last. "Get down here."

There were twigs in the dark, the overhanging of a thicket of some sort. He thrust her in under this, and lay beside her on the bed of groundpine. The hand that was not in love with her throat reached across her: she felt the weight of its forearm on her shoulder and its fingers among the strands of her hair, eagerly, but tenderly, busy. Not once did he stop speaking, no louder than breathing, his lips to her ear.

"*Amarantha sweet and fair — Ah, braid no more that shining hair . . .*"

Mare had never heard of Lovelace, the poet; she thought the loony was just going on, hardly listened, got little sense. But the cadence of it added to the lethargy of all her flesh.

"*Like a clew of golden thread — Most excellently ravelléd . . .*"

Voices loudened; feet came tramping; a pair went past not two rods away.

"*. . . Do not then wind up the light — In ribbands, and o'er-cloud in night . . .*"

The search went on up the woods, men shouting to one another and beating the brush.

"*. . . But shake your head and scatter day!* I've never loved, Amarantha. They've tried me with prettiness, but prettiness is too cheap, yes, it's too cheap."

Mare was cold, and the coldness made her lazy. All she knew was that he talked on.

"But dogwood blowing in the spring isn't cheap. The earth of a field isn't cheap. Lots of times I've lain down and kissed the earth of a field, Amarantha. That's beauty, and a kiss for beauty." His breath moved up her cheek. He trembled violently. "No, no, not yet!" He got to his knees and pulled her by an arm. "We can go now."

They went back down the slope, but at an angle, so that when they came to the level they passed two hundred yards to the north of the house, and crossed the road there. More and more her walking was like sleepwalking, the feet numb in their shoes. Even where he had to let go of her, crossing the creek on stones, she stepped where he stepped with an obtuse docility. The voices of the searchers on the back ridge were small in distance when they began to climb the face of Coward Hill, on the opposite side of the valley.

There is an old farm on top of Coward Hill, big hayfields as flat as tables. It had been half past nine when Mare stood on the rock above the barn; it was toward midnight when Humble Jewett put aside the last branches of the woods and let her out on the height, and half a moon had risen. And a wind blew there, tossing the withered tops of last year's grasses, and mists ran with the wind, and ragged shadows with the mists, and mares'-tails of clear moonlight among the shadows, so that now the boles of birches on the forest's edge beyond the fences were but opal blurs and now cut alabaster. It struck so cold against the girl's cold flesh, this wind, that another wind of shivers blew through her, and she put her hands over her face and eyes. But the madman stood with his eyes wide open and his mouth open, drinking the moonlight and the wet wind.

His voice, when he spoke at last, was thick in his throat.

" Get down on your knees." He got down on his and pulled her after. " And pray."

Once in England a poet sang four lines. Four hundred years have forgotten his name, but they have remembered his lines. The daft man knelt upright, his face raised to the wild scud, his long wrists hanging to the dead grass. He began simply:

> " *O western wind, when wilt thou blow*
> *That the small rain down can rain?* "

The Adam's-apple was big in his bent throat. As simply he finished.

> " *Christ, that my love were in my arms*
> *And I in my bed again!* "

Mare got up and ran. She ran without aim or feeling in the power of the wind. She told herself again that the mists would hide her from him, as she had done at dusk. And again, seeing that he ran at her shoulder, she knew he had been there all the while, making a race of it, flailing the air with his long arms for joy of play in the clouds of spring, throwing his knees high, leaping the moon-blue waves of the brown grass, shaking his bright hair; and her own hair was a weight behind her, lying level on the wind. Once a shape went bounding ahead of them for instants; she did not realize it was a fox till it was gone.

She never thought of stopping; she never thought anything except once, " Oh, my God, I wish I had my shoes off! " And what would have been the good in stopping or in turning another way, when it was only play? The man's ecstasy magnified his strength. When a snake-fence came at them he took the top rail in flight, like a college hurdler, and, seeing the girl hesitate and half turn as if to flee, he would have releaped it without touching a hand. But then she got a loom of buildings, climbed over quickly, before he should jump, and ran along the lane that ran with the fence.

Mare had never been up there, but she knew that the farm and the house belonged to a man named Wyker, a kind of cousin of Ruby Herter's, a violent, bearded old fellow who lived by himself. She could not believe her luck. When she had run half the distance and Jewett had not grabbed her, doubt grabbed her instead. " Oh, my God, go careful! " she told herself. " Go slow! " she implored herself, and stopped running, to walk.

Here was a misgiving the deeper in that it touched her special knowledge. She had never known an animal so far gone that its instincts failed it; a starving rat will scent the trap sooner than a fed one. Yet, after one glance at the house they approached, Jewett paid it no further attention, but walked with his eyes to the right, where the cloud had blown away, and wooded ridges, like black waves rimed with silver, ran down away toward the Valley of Virginia.

" I've never lived! " In his single cry there were two things, beatitude and pain.

Between the bigness of the falling world and his eyes the flag of her hair blew. He reached out and let it whip between his fingers. Mare was afraid it would break the spell then, and he would stop looking away and look at the house again. So she did something almost incredible; she spoke.

" It's a pretty — I mean — a beautiful view down that-a-way."

" God Almighty beautiful, to take your breath away. I knew I'd never loved, Belovéd — " He caught a foot under the long end of one of the boards that covered the well and went down heavily on his hands and knees. It seemed to make no difference. " But I' never knew I'd never lived," he finished in the same tone of strong rapture, quadruped in the grass, while Mare ran for the door and grabbed the latch.

When the latch would not give, she lost what little sense she had. She pounded with her fists. She cried with all her might: " Oh — hey — in there — hey — in there! " Then Jewett came and took her gently between his hands and drew her away, and then, though she was free, she stood in something like an awful embarrassment while he tried shouting.

" Hey! Friend! whoever you are, wake up and let my love and me come in! "

" No! " wailed the girl.

He grew peremptory. " Hey, wake up! " He tried the latch. He passed to full fury in a wink's time; he cursed, he kicked, he beat the door till Mare thought he would break his hands. Withdrawing, he ran at it with his shoulder; it burst at the latch, went slamming in, and left a black emptiness. His anger dissolved in a big laugh. Turning in time to catch her by a wrist, he cried joyously, " Come, my Sweet One! "

" No! No! Please — aw — listen. There ain't nobody there. He ain't to home. It wouldn't be right to go in anybody's house if they wasn't to home, you know that."

His laugh was blither than ever. He caught her high in his arms.

" I'd do the same by his love and him if 'twas my house, I would." At the threshold he paused and thought, " That is, if she was the true love of his heart forever."

The room was the parlor. Moonlight slanted in at the door, and another shaft came through a window and fell across a sofa, its covering dilapidated, showing its wadding in places. The air was sour, but both of them were farm-bred.

"Don't, Amarantha!" His words were pleading in her ear. "Don't be so frightened."

He set her down on the sofa. As his hands let go of her they were shaking.

"But look, I'm frightened too." He knelt on the floor before her, reached out his hands, withdrew them. "See, I'm afraid to touch you." He mused, his eyes rounded. "Of all the ugly things there are, fear is the ugliest. And yet, see, it can be the very beautifulest. That's a strange queer thing."

The wind blew in and out of the room, bringing the thin, little bitter sweetness of new April at night. The moonlight that came across Mare's shoulders fell full upon his face, but hers it left dark, ringed by the aureole of her disordered hair.

"Why do you wear a halo, Love?" He thought about it. "Because you're an angel, is that why?" The swift, untempered logic of the mad led him to dismay. His hands came flying to hers, to make sure they were of earth; and he touched her breast, her shoulders, and her hair. Peace returned to his eyes as his fingers twined among the strands.

"*Thy hair is as a flock of goats that appear from Gilead* . . ." He spoke like a man dreaming. "*Thy temples are like a piece of pomegranate within thy locks.*"

Mare never knew that he could not see her for the moonlight.

"Do you remember, Love?"

She dared not shake her head under his hand. "Yeh, I reckon," she temporized.

"You remember how I sat at your feet, long ago, like this, and made up a song? And all the poets in all the world have never made one to touch it, have they, Love?"

"Ugh-ugh — never."

"*How beautiful are thy feet with shoes* . . . . Remember?"

"Oh, my God, what's he sayin' now?" she wailed to herself.

"*How beautiful are thy feet with shoes, O prince's daughter! the joints of thy thighs are like jewels, the work of the hands of a cunning workman.*
Thy navel is like a round goblet, which wanteth not liquor; thy belly is like an heap of wheat set about with lilies.
Thy two breasts are like two young roes that are twins."

Mare had not been to church since she was a little girl, when her mother's black dress wore out. " No, no! " she wailed under her breath. " You're awful to say such awful things." She might have shouted it; nothing could have shaken the man now, rapt in the immortal, passionate periods of Solomon's Song.

" . . . *now also thy breasts shall be as clusters of the vine, and the smell of thy nose like apples.*"

Hotness touched Mare's face for the first time. " Aw, no, don't talk so! "

" *And the roof of thy mouth like the best wine for my belovéd . . . causing the lips of them that are asleep to speak.*"

He had ended. His expression changed. Ecstasy gave place to anger, love to hate. And Mare felt the change in the weight of the fingers in her hair.

" What do you mean, I mustn't say it like that? " But it was not to her his fury spoke, for he answered himself straightway. " Like poetry, Mr. Jewett; I won't have blasphemy around my school."

" Poetry! My God! if that isn't poetry — if that isn't music — " . . . " It's Bible, Jewett. What you're paid to teach here is *literature*."

" Doctor Ryeworth, you're a blasphemer and you're an ignorant man." . . . " And your Principal. And I won't have you going around reading sacred allegory like earthly love."

" Ryeworth, you're an old man, a dull man, a dirty man, and you'd be better dead."

Jewett's hands had slid down from Mare's head. " Then I went to put my fingers around his throat, so. But my stomach turned, and I didn't do it. I went to my room. I laughed all the way to my room. I sat in my room at my table and I laughed. And then, about ten, somebody came and stood beside me in my room."

" ' Wherefore dost thou laugh, son? '

" Then I knew who He was, He was Christ.

" ' I was laughing about that dirty, ignorant, crazy old fool, Lord.'

" ' Wherefore dost thou laugh? '

"I didn't laugh any more. He didn't say any more. I kneeled down, bowed my head.

"'Thy will be done! Where is he, Lord?'

"'Over at the girls' dormitory, waiting for Blossom Sinckley."

"Brassy Blossom, dirty Blossom . . ."

It had come so suddenly it was nearly too late. Mare tore at his hands with hers, tried with all her strength to pull her neck away.

"Filthy Blossom! and him an old filthy man, Blossom! and you'll find him in hell when you reach there, Blossom . . ."

It was more the nearness of his face than the hurt of his hands that gave her power of fright to choke out three words.

"*I — ain't — Blossom!*"

Light ran in crooked veins. Through the veins she saw his face bewildered. His hands loosened. One fell down and hung; the other he lifted and put over his eyes, took it away again and looked at her.

"Amarantha!" His remorse was fearful to see. "What have I done!" His hands returned to hover over the hurts, ravening with pity, grief, and tenderness. Tears fell down his cheeks. And with that, dammed desire broke its dam.

"Amarantha, my love, my dove, my beautiful love —"

"*And I ain't Amarantha neither, I'm Mary! Mary, that's my name!*"

She had no notion what she had done. He was like a crystal crucible that a chemist watches, changing hue in a wink with one adeptly added drop; but hers was not the chemist's eye. All she knew was that she felt light and free of him; all she could see of his face as he stood away above the moonlight was the whites of his eyes.

"Mary!" he muttered. A slight paroxysm shook his frame. So in the transparent crucible desire changed its hue. He retreated farther, stood in the dark by some tall piece of furniture. And still she could see the whites of his eyes.

"Mary! Mary Adorable!" A wonder was in him. "Mother of God."

Mare held her breath. She eyed the door, but it was too far. And already he came back to go on his knees before her, his shoulders so bowed and his face so lifted that it must have cracked his neck, she thought; all she could see on the face was pain.

"Mary Mother, I'm sick to my death. I'm so tired."

She had seen a dog like that, one she had loosed from a trap after it had been there three days, its caught leg half gnawed free. Something about the eyes.

"Mary Mother, take me in your arms . . ."

Once again her muscles tightened. But he made no move.

". . . and give me sleep."

No, they were worse than the dog's eyes.

"Sleep, sleep! why won't they let me sleep? Haven't I done it all yet, Mother? Haven't I washed them yet of all their sins? I've drunk the cup that was given me; is there another? They've mocked me and reviled me, broken my brow with thorns and my hands with nails, and I've forgiven them, for they knew not what they did. Can't I go to sleep now, Mother?"

Mare could not have said why, but now she was more frightened than she had ever been. Her hands lay heavy on her knees, side by side, and she could not take them away when he bowed his head and rested his face upon them.

After a moment he said one thing more. "Take me down gently when you take me from the Tree."

Gradually the weight of his body came against her shins, and he slept.

The moon streak that entered by the eastern window crept north across the floor, thinner and thinner; the one that fell through the southern doorway traveled east and grew fat. For a while Mare's feet pained her terribly and her legs too. She dared not move them, though, and by and by they did not hurt so much.

A dozen times, moving her head slowly on her neck, she canvassed the shadows of the room for a weapon. Each time her eyes came back to a heavy earthenware pitcher on a stand some feet to the left of the sofa. It would have had flowers in it when Wyker's wife was alive; probably it had not been moved from its dust-ring since she died. It would be a long grab, perhaps too long; still, it might be done if she had her hands.

To get her hands from under the sleeper's head was the task she set herself. She pulled first one, then the other, infinitesimally. She waited. Again she tugged a very, very little. The order of his breathing was not disturbed. But at the third trial he stirred.

"Gently! gently!" His own mutterings waked him more. With some drowsy instinct of possession he threw one hand across her wrists, pinning them together between thumb and fingers. She kept dead quiet, shut her eyes, lengthened her breathing, as if she too slept.

There came a time when what was pretense grew a peril; strange as it was, she had to fight to keep her eyes open. She never knew whether or not she really napped. But something changed in the air, and she was wide awake again. The moonlight was fading on the doorsill, and the light that runs before dawn waxed in the window behind her head.

And then she heard a voice in the distance, lifted in maundering song. It was old man Wyker coming home after a night, and it was plain he had had some whiskey.

Now a new terror laid hold of Mare.

"Shut up, you fool you!" she wanted to shout. "Come quiet, quiet!" She might have chanced it now to throw the sleeper away from her and scramble and run, had his powers of strength and quickness not taken her simple imagination utterly in thrall.

Happily the singing stopped. What had occurred was that the farmer had espied the open door and, even befuddled as he was, wanted to know more about it quietly. He was so quiet that Mare began to fear he had gone away. He had the squirrel-hunter's foot, and the first she knew of him was when she looked and saw his head in the doorway, his hard, soiled, whiskery face half up-side-down with craning.

He had been to the town. Between drinks he had wandered in and out of the night's excitement; had even gone a short distance with one search party himself. Now he took in the situation in the room. He used his forefinger. First he held it to his lips. Next he pointed it with a jabbing motion at the sleeper. Then he tapped his own forehead and described wheels. Lastly, with his whole hand, he made pushing gestures, for Mare to wait. Then he vanished as silently as he had appeared.

The minutes dragged. The light in the east strengthened and turned rosy. Once she thought she heard a board creaking in another part of the house, and looked down sharply to see if the loony stirred. All she could see of his face was a temple with freckles on it and the sharp ridge of a cheekbone, but even from so little she knew how deeply and peacefully he slept. The door darkened. Wyker was there again. In one hand he carried something heavy; with the other he beckoned.

"Come jumpin'!" he said out loud.

Mare went jumping, but her cramped legs threw her down halfway to the sill; the rest of the distance she rolled and crawled. Just as she tumbled through the door it seemed as if the world had come to an end above her; two barrels of a shotgun discharged into a room make a noise. Afterwards all she could hear in there was something twisting and bumping on the floorboards. She got up and ran.

❦ ❦ ❦

Mare's mother had gone to pieces; neighbor women put her to bed when Mare came home. They wanted to put Mare to bed, but she would not let them. She sat on the edge of her bed in her lean-to bedroom off the kitchen, just as she was, her hair down all over her shoulders and her shoes on, and stared away from them, at a place in the wallpaper.

"Yeh, I'll go myself. Lea' me be!"

The women exchanged quick glances, thinned their lips, and left her be. "God knows," was all they would answer to the questionings of those that had not gone in, "but she's gettin' herself to bed."

When the doctor came though, he found her sitting just as she had been, still dressed, her hair down on her shoulders and her shoes on.

"What d' y' want?" she muttered and stared at the place in the wallpaper.

How could Doc Paradise say, when he did not know himself?

"I didn't know if you might be — might be feeling very smart, Mary."

"I'm all right. Lea' me be."

It was a heavy responsibility. Doc shouldered it. "No, it's all right," he said to the men in the road. Ruby Herter stood a little apart, chewing sullenly and looking another way. Doc raised his voice to make certain it carried. "Nope, nothing."

Ruby's ears got red, and he clamped his jaws. He knew he ought to go in and see Mare, but he was not going to do it while everybody hung around waiting to see if he would. A mule tied near him reached out and mouthed his sleeve in idle innocence; he wheeled and banged a fist against the side of the animal's head.

"Well, what d' y' aim to do 'bout it?" he challenged its owner.

He looked at the sun then. It was ten in the morning. "Hell, I got work!" he flared, and set off down the road for home. Doc looked at Judge North, and the Judge stared after Ruby. But Ruby shook his head angrily. "Lea' me be!" He went on, and the Judge came back.

It got to be eleven and then noon. People began to say, "Like enough she'd be as thankful if the whole neighborhood wasn't camped here." But none went away.

As a matter of fact they were no bother to the girl. She never saw them. The only move she made was to bend her ankles over and rest her feet on edge; her shoes hurt terribly and her feet knew it, though she did not. She sat all the while staring at that one figure in the wallpaper, and she never saw the figure.

Strange as the night had been, this day was stranger. Fright and physical pain are perishable things once they are gone. But while pain merely dulls and telescopes in memory and remains diluted pain, terror looked back upon has nothing of terror left. A gambling chance taken, at no matter what odds, and won was a sure thing since the world's beginning; perils come through safely were never perilous. But what fright does do in retrospect is this — it heightens each sensuous recollection, like a hard, clear lacquer laid on wood, bringing out the color and grain of it vividly.

Last night Mare had lain stupid with fear on groundpine beneath a bush, loud footfalls and light whispers confused in her ear. Only now, in her room, did she smell the groundpine.

Only now did the conscious part of her brain begin to make words of the whispering.

"*Amarantha*," she remembered, "*Amarantha sweet and fair.*"

That was as far as she could go for the moment, except that the rhyme with " fair " was " hair." But then a puzzle, held in abeyance, brought other words. She wondered what " ravel Ed " could mean. " *Most excellently ravelléd.*" It was left to her mother to bring the end.

They gave up trying to keep her mother out at last. The poor woman's prostration took the form of fussiness.

" Good gracious, daughter, you look a sight. Them new shoes, half ruined; ain't your feet *dead?* And look at your hair, all tangled like a wild one! "

She got a comb.

" Be quiet, daughter; what's ailin' you. Don't shake your head! "

" *But shake your head and scatter day.*"

" What you say, Amarantha? " Mrs. Doggett held an ear down.

" Go 'way! Lea' me be! "

Her mother was hurt and left. And Mare ran, as she stared at the wallpaper.

" *Christ, that my love were in my arms . . .*"

Mare ran. She ran through a wind white with moonlight and wet with " the small rain." And the wind she ran through, it ran through her, and made her shiver as she ran. And the man beside her leaped high over the waves of the dead grasses and gathered the wind in his arms, and her hair was heavy and his was tossing, and a little fox ran before them across the top of the world. And the world spread down around in waves of black and silver, more immense than she had ever known the world could be, and more beautiful.

" *God Almighty beautiful, to take your breath away!* "

Mare wondered, and she was not used to wondering. " Is it only crazy folks ever run like that and talk that way? "

She no longer ran; she walked; for her breath was gone. And there was some other reason, some other reason. Oh, yes, it was because her feet were hurting her. So, at last, and roundabout, her shoes had made contact with her brain.

Bending over the side of the bed, she loosened one of them mechanically. She pulled it half off. But then she looked down at it sharply, and she pulled it on again.

"*How beautiful . . .*"

Color overspread her face in a slow wave.

"*How beautiful are thy feet with shoes . . .*"

"Is it only crazy folks ever say such things?"

"*O prince's daughter!*"

"Or call you that?"

By and by there was a knock at the door. It opened and Ruby Herter came in.

"Hello, Mare old girl!" His face was red. He scowled and kicked at the floor. "I'd 'a' been over sooner, except we got a mule down sick." He looked at his dumb betrothed. "Come on, cheer up, forget it! He won't scare you no more, not that boy, not what's left o' him. What you lookin' at, sourface? Ain't you glad to see me?"

Mare quit looking at the wallpaper and looked at the floor.

"Yeh," she said.

"That's more like it, babe." He came and sat beside her; reached down behind her and gave her a spank. "Come on, give us a kiss, babe!" He wiped his mouth on his jumper sleeve, a good farmer's sleeve, spotted with milking. He put his hands on her; he was used to handling animals. "Hey, you, warm up a little; reckon I'm goin' to do all the lovin'?"

"Ruby, lea' me be!"

"What!"

She was up, twisting. He was up, purple.

"What's ailin' of you, Mare? What you bawlin' about?"

"Nothin' — only go 'way!"

She pushed him to the door and through it with all her strength, and closed it in his face, and stood with her weight against it, crying, "Go 'way! Go 'way! Lea' me be!"

— From *Harper's Magazine*, August, 1932. Reprinted by permission.

THE MUSTYDINES WAS RIPE

By Howell Vines

One Thursday fifty years ago this September I was walkin' a little sandy road through the woods. It was in '77; and I always remember that the mustydines was ripe when I found Patsy. The sun was goin' down fast and I had a crockersack on my shoulder with all my belongin's in it, and I was a little blue and dead tired of strollopin' around. I remember just as well how the sun looked. It was like a ball of fire. I was dressed in homespun and home-made from top to bottom, had a few dollars in my pocket, and had strolloped on foot all the way from Savannah River in Georgia. I'd been gaddin' about workin' as a hireling since I was sixteen, and I was twenty-one then. I had started to Toadvine, and some men in Birmingham had directed me. Birmingham was a wide place in the road then — just six years old.

I was thinkin' about a place to stay all night and draggin' the sand beds when I seed some young squirrels cuttin' hickernuts up a little bitty hickory tree. I took a red flint rock about the size of a Dommer hen egg from my pocket and throwed it at the bunch of squibs. I killed one of 'em — but I hadn't expected to — and I picked it up thinkin' as how I'd give it to the madam of the house where I stayed all night that night. I thought to myself that they was plenty of game and lots of timber and some good land in this country, and I said to myself that I'd like to settle here and live.

I set down by a bank spring on the side of the road and took out my knife and gutted my squirrel. It was a little boar just big enough to kill. You know and I know what good eatin' that is. It was a good spring of water. It tasted good. And it was cold. That spring made me think more about livin' in this country. It minded me of a spring back home in Georgia. A good spring of water in one country the good Lord made makes that country kin to any other country He made with good springs of water in it. A spring'll do that more'n most anything else. I've studied that out. You just notice it and you'll see that that's the way it is.

The sun was gone and it was gettin' dusty and I got up and started on. Old Darkus would catch me in the timber if I didn't move on, I thought to myself. But I just had to stop at a big mustydine vine up some pines before I'd made many steps. I shook the vine and they peppered to the ground. They was dead ripe and black as bess bugs. They's nothin' better in this world, I figgered to myself, as I eat a dog's bait of 'em. This made me think more good thoughts about the country I had strolloped to. When you eat a bait of good mustydines in a place, you never do get over it. You always do love that place after that. So I walked on thinkin' as how if I could find me a good nice young woman I wouldn't mind endin' up here bein' buried in the same hole with her. I wasn't feelin' much blue if any, and I had forgot that I was so tired.

II

I got to a house just ahead of Old Darkus and stopped to see if I could get to stay all night. It was a comfortable-lookin' place. The livin' house was a big log house most hid in a cluster of big white oaks, and all the outbuildin's showed that this was a good farm. A big yaller cur dog run out at me and barked and took on. He like to a bit me. Somebody said, "Hush your mouth, Caeser," and the madam of the house come to the door. I muched the dog and he smelt of me good all over and then sidled off. I axed the madam if a body could get to stay all night there. She said, "My old man's out at the lot feedin' his oxen. Go see him about it." I walked out to the lot and the man of the house was seein' to his beasts and talkin' to 'em. He called 'em Buck and Ball. They's big black-and-white spotted steers. I axed him could a body get to stay all night at his house. He sized me up and said I could stay. I told him my name and where I's from, and where I'd started to.

A grown girl was milkin' a red cow in a big gourd. Her pap spoke to her and called her Patsy. She was barefooted and just makin' the milk talk in the gourd with both hands. By the time I took her in, the milk had 'come witched and was singin' a tune in the gourd. I didn't know the difference. I didn't know what it was all about any more'n I knowed what the katydid song all around us and over us was all about. It would a took a Solomon to have 'splained all them mysteries. But everything was laughin' with me. I knowed that much. I told the girl that I could milk good and to let me help her. She was shy, but she smiled at me and said I could if I wanted to. She said Pied wouldn't care for me milkin' her. She gave me a rope to rope Pied's calf; and I roped the bull calf and he tried to butt me and the girl laughed. But I let him suck to get Pied to give down her milk, and then I milked with one hand while I held the gourd she gave me with the other hand. I didn't mean for the cow to turn the gourd over, so I milked as hard as I could with one hand to make the girl see that I was a good milker. The girl finished her cow and roped Heifer's calf and started to milk, and by then I'd finished. She said Heifer wouldn't let me milk her, and while she was milkin' Heifer I skinned my squirrel and told her I killed it for her to eat, but didn't know it at the time. She smiled at me and thanked me when she took it and put it in her apron, and then I walked to the house with her pappy.

A strong wild varment of a somethin' got hold of me and made me want Patsy. It got in me and jumped and urged me to stay at the lot with the girl. I never in all the days of my life had wanted anything half as bad. And no wonder. The way she was built up and the way she moved minded me of a well-pastured filly. I knowed she was the she-un I would like to be buried in the same hole with. I was sick all over for Patsy. She could a took a little bran in her apron and a tolled me to the jumpin'-off place. All the things that made Patsy a woman had got to me and was makin' me groan and take on to myself.

At the supper table we begin to get acquainted and everything they was hummed to the tune of Patsy. I'd catch her castin' sheep's eyes at me. Her pappy told me that he needed a hand and that he wanted to hire me. Then if we suited each other I wouldn't need to go on to Toadvine at all. We'd make a trade in a day or two. I knowed we could satisfy each other, I told him. He said yes, he thought we'd suit.

The supper was a good one and hit the spot. They had plenty to eat at this house. I seed that. They had flour bread and corn bread raised on the farm and plenty of garden stuff at a time when garden stuff was sca'ce, and good meat from the smokehouse. They had milk and butter from the spring and fried peach pies. The squirrel had been salted and put in a pan in the spring for breakfast.

I told 'em about the dog's bait of mustydines I had had, and the girl said she eat a bait of 'em somewhere every day. She said she had her lots of vines nobody else knowed where was. I believe that's all she said at the supper table that night. Well, in spite of the mustydines I had put down, I eat a hearty supper that night. It was fun to eat a bite when Patsy did and look across the table at her and catch her lookin' at me. I seed by the fatlighten'd torch that Patsy was purty in the face and that she had long dark purty hair. I seed this better than I could out at the lot. I thought she had blue eyes and I was right. She had that purty hurt look that all girls has that makes a decent boy want to be kind to 'em and take good care of 'em. Even girls that ain't purty has that look. And it makes them purty. But when a purty girl that's well built up has that look it's a sight for sore eyes. When I got older and knowed more about women I understood that that purty hurt look all girls has is callin' for a mate. Patsy, she was seventeen then, and that look of hern seemed to be askin' me to be her mate.

Patsy's pappy and mammy told me things about theirselves that night at supper and I told 'em things about myself. Since I was goin' to stay with 'em I axed 'em not to call me Mr. Freeland, but to call me Benny. And they did. They had two other girls, they said, who had married their cousins and was homesteadin' now — one of 'em over on Lick Creek and the other one down on Mud Creek. They said Patsy's pap was jerked up by the hair of the head down in Canebrake near the river and strolloped off up to the Piney Woods and hired out to her pap and married her. They married five years before the war and homesteaded their place on Rock Creek adjoinin' her pap's place. They'd just got the title to it when Patsy's pappy went off to the war. Patsy's pappy told me how her mammy kept the place goin' and looked after her three babies while he was away. She was just a girl herself, he said; and he was just a boy three years older, his wife put in. She had a hard time in more ways than one, he said, but he come back from the war and found everything all right. When I got older I heard men talk about how Wed Tucker come back and found his true-blue Minnie waitin' with open arms and no secrets and somethin' to eat at the house and in the ground. It made 'em sympathize with me when I told 'em how the war 'stroyed my pappy's and mammy's worldly goods and broke us up, and how Pappy never did come back. And when I told 'em of how Mammy had died and how all of us children had strolloped over Georgia and Alabama ever since, Patsy's mammy looked tender-like toward me. She said I's just the age of her oldest girl. But best of all I could see that Patsy had tender feelin's toward me.

Soon after supper I went to bed in a good bed in a side room and lay awake thinkin' that Patsy would be worth her weight in gold to me there in the bed with me. There was just a wall between us, but I went to sleep thinkin' that that wall was mighty big. I meant to sleep with Patsy by Sunday night if I could work that fast. I didn't think I could stand it any longer than that.

III

The next mornin' after we eat a hearty breakfast of eggs and cured meat and coffee and flour bread Patsy's mammy cooked over the big fireplace in the kitchen, and I watched Patsy gnaw the squib's bones and wouldn't touch it myself, I went to the field to pick cotton, and glory be if Patsy didn't go with me. Her pappy yoked Buck and Ball up to the plow and went to plowin' in his wheat patch by the cotton patch. He was fixin' to sow his wheat.

Patsy was shy, but she'd talk when I talked to her. I axed her if she had a sweetheart and she said she didn't have — that they was no boy around she wanted for a sweetheart. Her sisters growed up with their cousins and went to lettin' 'em kiss 'em for pleasure, and the first thing she knowed they upped and married and went off to homestead some land of their own. But there was no boy for her. I said I's glad of that and she axed me why. I told her cause I wanted to be her sweetheart. She axed me if I left a sweetheart in Georgia and I told her that I didn't, but that I had my mind set on her. She smiled at me, but didn't say nothin' to that. We picked more cotton and carried our rows on a little fudder, and I axed her if she'd ever been kissed. She said she didn't know nothin' about that kissin' business, but that her sisters said it was the very thing. She said good girls wasn't supposed to go to kissin' before they found 'em a husband. I axed her if she wanted a husband and she laughed, but didn't answer me. She axed me if I wanted a wife and I told her yes, that I did, and that I wanted her to be it. She laughed, but didn't say nothin', and I couldn't get her to give her 'sponse to that. She'd just laugh when I'd try to get her to say somethin'. Well, that laughin' of hern made things like a tune to me, and I picked cotton to that tune. And she picked on, keepin' her row about up with mine, and played that tune. She seed she had me eatin' out of her hand, and pickin' the cotton wasn't hard for her. She just smiled and looked at me, and her hands went from stalk to stalk like little songbirds.

Every time we'd see a little old bird we'd speak to each other about it. I found out that she liked birds and knowed as much about 'em as I did. We had a lot of fun tryin' to catch a mole, and she told me all she ever had heard about a mole. We seed some field mice and she knowed all about them, too. I said to myself that here was a purty female that was as stout as I was and liked the ground and everything on top of the ground as good as I did. We'd even as much as talk about a lizard or a scorpion when we seed one. When a body's interested the way we was, even a little old butterfly is enough to get up excitement. When I'd try to get her to talk about love she wouldn't do nothin' but smile or laugh; but when we seed anything alive or looked out over the timber toward Rock Creek she was all tongue. She said she sometimes waded in Rock Creek when she's by herself, and I don't guess she knowed how such a purty sight in my mind made me nearly jump out of my skin. I just picked cotton and thought about that sight. I wanted to see that sight.

She said she sometimes seed little fawns down in the creek field when she'd be lookin' for the sheep, and she told about how her pappy loved to deer-hunt. I told her all I knowed about deer and little deers. She told me she liked to go fishin' down on the creek. She said she knowed how to catch 'em and I told her I knowed all about fish. Then she said she's goin' down on the creek the next week and gather mustydines to make wine. I axed her if she'd let me climb the trees for her and she said she could climb 'em herself and that her pappy and mammy wouldn't let her go off down there with me by herself. That wasn't the way good girls acted. I said they wouldn't care for it if we got married Sunday, would they? She laughed and said no, they wouldn't care for her goin' off in the timber with me if that was to happen, but that to get married Sunday was somethin' else.

By the time we'd filled our sacks we got us some guinea watermelons in the cotton patch and I busted their hearts out on a stump. Some was red-hearted and some was yaller-hearted and they all tasted sorter like the fall of the year and was as cold as the dew and shade could make 'em. Well, from then on till dinner time we picked cotton and talked about things the good Lord made and what we liked to do, and eat watermelons and emptied our cotton in the pen. Her pappy was right close so we could hear all his words to Buck and Ball every time he spoke, and we never did get out of his sight 'cept when we'd go in the cotton pen. I talked love mighty hard and she listened good, and I soon got to touchin' her with my hands when we'd go in the cotton pen. Then I got her to puttin' her hand on me when she'd smile.

Before dinner I made a believer out of her by fast work on how I didn't have nobody but myself, and how I wanted her to take what I did have and let me take her and us make the best out of it. And the last time or two when we's emptyin' our cotton I got to huggin' and kissin' of her, and we worked up a weddin' for Sunday if her pappy and mammy would give in. She said she loved me and liked to look at me and for me to hold her and kiss her. Enough said. I'd won a wife. Back in them days when a girl got to lettin' a boy hug and kiss her and handle her it meant a weddin' would soon take place. On the way back to the house for dinner I watched her climb over the rail fence and I seed her leg above her knee.

It was somethin' to see a good nice young girl's leg back then. And it was more good luck than hardly ever come to a young buck to get to see a purty girl's leg 'bove her knee. Then it'd be a accident like this was. Well, that sight made me crazy. She axed me if I seed her knee. I 'fessed up that I did and she cried. Nice girls was like that way back then. She said I oughtn't to a done it. I told her I knowed I oughtn't to, but I just couldn't help it. But as we walked on to the house ahead of her pap I made her believe it wasn't a sin and didn't matter much, and had her smilin' as we entered the yard gate.

IV

Well, she smiled all through dinner that day and laughed with me all that evenin' in the cotton patch. She said she's as happy as a little old bluebird in April and let me kiss her every time we could catch her pappy not lookin'. All that evenin' I'd pick cotton and help her fill her apron when we'd get the sacks full, and she'd just stand there between the rows and let me hold her hand and feel of her arms. Sometimes some tears would come in her eyes and she'd tell me she's just so happy she couldn't keep from cryin'. That hurt look that stays in every girl's eyes kept me busy bein' good to her and sayin' kind words to comfort her. Girls is funny that way. They're not at all like boys. I felt duty-bound to that girl. I didn't mean for a thing to harm a hair of her head as long as I could help it. And that feelin' for Patsy never did leave me.

I broke the news at the supper table and Patsy stuck it out with me. The old folks axed us if we was certain sure we knowed our minds. We both made 'em believe we did. Her mammy said that it minded her of her own sparkin' days 'cept that I had worked faster. Her pappy said they both liked my 'pearance and that they seed at first that me and Patsy liked each other's looks, but that he's afraid we didn't know one another well enough. But me and Patsy kept to our side, and by the time we'd finished supper they both 'greed with us that this way of waitin' about gettin' married after a weddin' had been worked up was not to their way of thinkin'. They'd been through the same mill together that me and Patsy was goin' through together then, and that helped us win 'em to our side. It didn't matter much if I worked faster than Patsy's pap did. The cases was similar. You know a good catch didn't come to girls often in them times. The boy mostly had to grow up with the girl and be kin to her. And Patsy had been left out that way. Not many girls got to marry strange boys back then. And strange boys fascinate girls. The old folks said my pappy's Irish blood and my mammy's Dutch blood ought to mix well with Patsy's English and Scotch-Irish blood and that if nothin' else would do us we could go on and get married Sunday. But they would have to make one request of me. They'd have to axe me not to never take Patsy away from 'em, but to let her live on with 'em or always in hollerin' distance of 'em, and me be one of 'em. Their other girls didn't live by 'em and they'd lost their two youngest children, and they wanted to keep Patsy with 'em. We closed our bargain that way.

That night after supper I sparked Patsy on the porch and made no secret of it. But we didn't leave the porch. Girls was modest way back in them times and didn't go away from the house with boys much to do their sparkin'. The old folks went to bed inside and lay on their bed with the wall between us and the door standin' open. We could hear 'em talkin' about us and about the ways of a man with a maid. They could hear some of our words and some of 'em they couldn't, for lots of our words didn't need a audience. When a hog or somethin' would come up, Caeser he'd run out and bark at it. One time he barked terrible at Patsy's sheep when they come up behind the smokehouse.

That night we didn't feel much need for King David or somebody to be there with us and 'splain the hollerin' of the katydids and everything like that. It just drawed us closer together and made us kiss and hug and handle one another more, and the world didn't need 'splainin' then. A old whoo owl down about the spring made her want me to hold her tighter. All that was needed was for Patsy to say somethin' like, "Listen at that little old cricket," and I'd think that was Bible wisdom. Everything 'splained itself that night. But people knowed all about the mysteries and feelin's of the timber back in them times anyhow. Everybody knowed a lot about everything like that. The good Lord was on the fur side of it and people was on the near side and that 'rangement kept the good Lord and the people purty close together after all. Everything Patsy'd say that night I'd think she's the smartest girl that ever was and the cutest little trick that ever lived. Like when she said, "I try to catch every purty thing I see that's alive and I know won't hurt me." She said them very words. I mind 'em just as well. And she said somethin' else I mind well. She said, "I love the wild flowers lots better'n I do the tame ones, but Mammy she don't." Finally me and Patsy went to bed in different beds that night, but it was mighty hard on both of us. Patsy had found her a mate that would stay with her, and she couldn't foller out the good Lord's best design for a grown girl that night, but had to go to bed by herself.

V

The next mornin' we had company from Toadvine for breakfast. Uncle Jake Smith was riding his horse to Birmingham and had made it there in time to set down at the breakfast table with us. Patsy's pappy introduced us and 'splained that me and Patsy was goin' to get married the next day. Uncle Jake said that I looked like I'd be all right and that he knowed Patsy was above an average, and that they was no use in puttin' it off even if it was fast work. He was goin' to town so he could see some friends there that Saturday night and stay with a friend and be on the jury Monday mornin'. He said I could ride his horse part of the time and walk 'longside him and up about Hueytown or Rutledge Springs I might catch a ride on a wagon. "You help him fix everything up with Judge Mudd, Jake," Patsy's pappy said. Uncle Jake give his word and said he'd be as good as his word, and we got up from the table and left the house together with me walkin' 'longside the horse.

Me and Uncle Jake had a big time talkin' and gettin' acquainted that mornin'. His pappy and mammy had come to the Warrior River from the Savannah River in Georgia and I had to tell him lots of things about Georgia. But he told me a lot more about Alabama. I caught a ride with a man drivin' a team of mules at Rutledge Springs and rode on into town and Uncle Jake rode his horse 'longside the wagon. The first thing when we got in town we went around to the courthouse and he helped me get the license. Then we went to a restaurant and ordered two big beef stews and coffee. After that we went to a saloon and had two good drinks and separated.

I walked all the way back to Piney Woods. I walked mostly in the night and got to the roof over Patsy's head at the first blue crack of day. Patsy was still in the bed asleep, but her pappy hit the floor about the time I walked up on the porch and her mammy went to the kitchen by the time I got in the house good. I went to Patsy's bed and as I looked at her lyin' there asleep I thought she was too purty and too sweet for any man like me. A man'll think that. You just notice and you'll see that he'll think that about the girl he's sparkin' and goin' to marry. When I woke her up and showed her the license she looked at it and at me in such a way with that hurt female look in her eyes that I thought to myself that grown girls was not supposed to sleep by theirselves. It was not natural and was not intended to be that way. The good Lord made it the most natural thing in the world for them to bed up with a mate. I went on to the big kitchen and set down by the fireplace till her mammy got breakfast on the table. Then Patsy come in with the license and we all set down to breakfast and looked at the license.

I got up from the breakfast table and went to bed and went to sleep, and slept till nearly the middle of the day. Patsy spent that mornin' lookin' through quilts she had quilted and the blankets she had wove 'ginst the day she got married. And she worked with her best dress and looked at it and handled it and got out her shoes and stockin's and talked to her mammy about the weddin' that was about to take place. After that she told me how she'd walk to my bed and gaze down at me and think of how we was about to give ourselves to one another for keeps. I'd brought her stick candy of all flavors and she sucked on that while I was sleepin'.

VI

While I was asleep Patsy's pap walked up to Uncle Tillman Salter's, who didn't live far away, to gas off with Uncle Till and Squire Joe Lisper. Squire Joe was the justice of the peace and we all called him the country lawyer. Him and Uncle Tillman spent most of their Sundays together talkin' law and politics. They was goin' to start to town together sometime in the night hours of Monday and be on the jury with Uncle Jake Smith the next week. And all the people in the country said that Squire Joe and Uncle Till had to be in town on such occasions to help Judge Mudd run his court. Patsy's pap went on up to the house early to tell Squire Joe to wait till we got there right after dinner to get married. He would eat dinner there and wait for us.

Right after dinner me and Patsy walked up to Uncle Till's. I don't believe any man ever got to feelin' close to a new country as quick as I did this country. It seems like I was already feelin' my roots in the place while me and Patsy walked along armed up goin' to get married. But Patsy — she was the cause of this. It takes love for a woman to make a man feel at home in a place. Without that a man never can be nothin' much more'n a stranger on top of the ground in any country. I don't care how much a man loves to be on top of the ground. He needs to have a woman on top of the ground by his side. Saint Paul didn't love no woman and no woman loved him, else he couldn't a talked so about bein' a stranger on earth. It'll do that to any man. You just notice it and see if I ain't right. No man's ever been won to a place 'cept by some woman. No man's goin' to be won to life at all 'cept by some woman.

Well, we got married and that's enough to say. I had a jovial time with the older men in the time of it and always did feel close to them and Uncle Jake after that. Patsy, she had a bashful time amongst 'em. She blushed a lot and talked to Uncle Till's girls while we was there gettin' the knot tied. We walked back towards home by ourselves. It was gettin' dusty when we got to the big mustydine vine up the pines, and I led Patsy through the timber to it and shook the vine till the ground was covered. And Old Darkus caught us in the timber together not far from the mustydine vine. From then on to now it's been me and Patsy.

— From the *Atlantic Monthly*, July, 1935. Reprinted by permission.

JERICHO, JERICHO, JERICHO

By Andrew Nelson Lytle

SHE OPENED her eyes. She must have been asleep for hours or months. She could not reckon; she could only feel the steady silence of time. She had been Joshua and made it swing suspended in her room. Forever she had floated above the counterpane; between the tester and the counterpane she had floated until her hand, long and bony, its speckled-dried skin drawing away from the bulging blue veins, had reached and drawn her body under the covers. And now she was resting, clear-headed and quiet, her thoughts clicking like a new-greased mower. All creation could not make her lift her thumb or cross it over her finger. She looked at the bed, the bed her mother had died in, the bed her children had been born in, her marriage bed, the bed the General had drenched with his blood. Here it stood where it had stood for seventy years, square and firm on the floor, wide enough for three people to lie comfortable in, if they didn't sleep restless; but not wide enough for her nor long enough when her conscience scorched the cool wrinkles in the sheets. The two foot posts, octagonal-shaped and mounted by carved pieces that looked like absurd flowers, stood up to comfort her when the world began to crumble. Her eyes followed down the posts and along the basket-quilt. She had made it before her marriage to the General, only he wasn't a general then. He was a slight, tall young man with a rolling mustache and perfume in his hair. A many a time she had seen her young love's locks dripping with scented oil, down upon his collar. . . . She had cut the squares for the baskets in January, and for stuffing had used the letters of old lovers, fragments of passion cut to warm her of a winter's night. The General would have his fun. *Miss Kate, I didn't sleep well last night. I heard Sam Buchanan make love to you out of that farthest basket. If I hear him again, I mean to toss this piece of quilt in the fire.* Then he would chuckle in his round, soft voice; reach under the covers and pull her over to his side of the bed. On a cold and frosting night he would sleep with his nose against her neck. His nose was so quick to turn cold, he said, and her neck was so warm. Sometimes her hair, the loose, unruly strands at the nape, would tickle his nostrils and he would wake up with a sneeze. This had been so long ago, and there had been so many years of trouble and worry. Her eyes, as apart from her as the mirror on the bureau, rested upon the half-tester, upon the enormous button that caught the rose-colored canopy and shot its folds out like the rays of the morning sun. She could not see but she could feel the heavy cluster of mahogany grapes that tumbled from the center of the headboard — out of its vines curling down the sides it tumbled. How much longer would these never-picked grapes hang above her head? How much longer would she, rather, hang to the vine of this world, she who lay beneath as dry as any raisin. Then she remembered. She looked at the blinds. They were closed.

"You, Ants, where's my stick? I'm a great mind to break it over your trifling back."

"Awake? What a nice long nap you've had," said Doctor Ed.

"The boy? Where's my grandson? Has he come?"

"I'll say he's come. What do you mean taking to your bed like this? Do you realize, beautiful lady, that this is the first time I ever saw you in bed in my whole life? I believe you've taken to bed on purpose. I don't believe you want to see me."

"Go long, boy, with your foolishness."

That's all she could say, and she blushed as she said it — she blushing at the words of a snip of a boy, whom she had diapered a hundred times and had washed as he stood before the fire in the round tin tub, his little back swayed and his little belly sticking out in front, rosy from the scrubbing he had gotten. *Mammy, what for I've got a hole in my stummick; what for, Mammy?* Now he was sitting on the edge of the bed calling her beautiful lady, an old hag like her, beautiful lady. A good-looker the girls would call him, with his bold, careless face and his hands with their fine, long fingers. Soft, how soft they were, running over her rough, skinny bones. He looked a little like his grandpa, but somehow there was something missing . . .

"Well, boy, it took you a time to come home to see me die."

"Nonsense. Cousin Edwin, I wouldn't wait on a woman who had so little faith in my healing powers."

"There an't nothing strange about dying. But I an't in such an all-fired hurry. I've got a heap to tell you about before I go."

The boy leaned over and touched her gently. "Not even death would dispute you here, on Long Gourd, Mammy."

He was trying to put her at her ease in his carefree way. It was so obvious a pretending, but she loved him for it. There was something nice in its awkwardness, the charm of the young's blundering and of their efforts to get along in the world. Their pretty arrogance, their patronizing airs, their colossal unknowing of what was to come. It was a quenching drink to a sin-thirsty old woman. Somehow his vitality had got crossed in her blood and made a dry heart leap, her blood that was almost water. Soon now she would be all water, water and dust, lying in the burying ground between the cedar — and fire. She could smell her soul burning and see it. What a fire it would make below, dripping with sin, like a rag soaked in kerosene. But she had known what she was doing. And here was Long Gourd, all its fields intact, ready to be handed on, in better shape than when she took it over. Yes, she had known what she was doing. How long, she wondered, would his spirit hold up under the trials of planting, of cultivating, and of the gathering time, year in and year out — how would he hold up before so many springs and so many autumns. The thought of him giving orders, riding over the place, or rocking on the piazza, and a great pain would pin her heart to her backbone. She wanted him by her to train — there was so much for him to know: how the south field was cold and must be planted late, and where the orchards would best hold their fruit, and where the frosts crept soonest — that now could never be. She turned her head — who was that woman, that strange woman standing by the bed as if she owned it, as if . . .

"This is Eva, Mammy."

"Eva?"

"We are going to be married."

"I wanted to come and see — to meet Dick's grandmother . . ."

I wanted to come see her die. That's what she meant. Why didn't she finish and say it out. She had come to lick her chops and see what she would enjoy. That's what she had come for, the lying little slut. The richest acres in Long Gourd valley, so rich hit'd make yer feet greasy to walk over'm, Saul Oberly at the first tollgate had told the peddler once, and the peddler had told it to her, knowing it would please and make her trade. *Before you die.* Well, why didn't you finish it out? You might as well. You've given yourself away.

Her fierce thoughts dried up the water in her eyes, tired and resting far back in their sockets. They burned like a smothered fire stirred up by the wind as they traveled over the woman who would lie in her bed, eat with her silver, and caress her flesh and blood. The woman's body was soft enough to melt and pour about him. She could see that; and her firm, round breasts, too firm and round for any good to come from them. And her lips, full and red, her eyes bright and cunning. The heavy hair crawled about her head to tangle the poor, foolish boy in its ropes. She might have known he would do something foolish like this. He had a foolish mother. There warn't any way to avoid it. But look at her belly, small and no-count. There wasn't a muscle the size of a worm as she could see. And those hips —

And then she heard her voice: "What did you say her name was, son? Eva? Eva Callahan, I'm glad to meet you, Eva. Where'd your folks come from, Eva? I knew some Callahans who lived in the Goosepad settlement. They couldn't be any of your kin, could they?"

"Oh, no, indeed. My people . . ."

"Right clever people they were. And good farmers, too. Worked hard. Honest — that is, most of 'em. As honest as that run of people go. We always gave them a good name."

"My father and mother live in Birmingham. Have always lived there."

"Birmingham," she heard herself say with contempt. They could have lived there all their lives and still come from somewhere. I've got a mule older 'n Birmingham. "What's your pa's name?"

"Her father is Mister E. L. Callahan, Mammy."

"First name not Elijah by any chance? Lige they called him."

"No. Elmore, Mammy."

"Old Mason Callahan had a son they called Lige. Somebody told me he moved to Elyton. So you think you're going to live with the boy here."

"We're to be married . . . that is, if Eva doesn't change her mind."

And she saw his arm slip possessively about the woman's waist. "Well, take care of him, young woman, or I'll come back and han't you. I'll come back and claw your eyes out."

"I'll take very good care of him, Mrs. McCowan."

"I can see that." She could hear the threat in her voice, and Eva heard it.

"Young man," spoke up Doctor Edwin, "you should feel powerful set up, two such women pestering each other about you."

The boy kept an embarrassed silence.

"All of you get out now. I want to talk to him by himself. I've got a lot to say and precious little time to say it in. And he's mighty young and helpless and ignorant."

"Why, Mammy, you forget I'm a man now. Twenty-six. All teeth cut. Long trousers."

"It takes a heap more than pants to make a man. Throw open them blinds, Ants."

"Yes'm."

"You don't have to close the door so all-fired soft. Close it naturally. And you can tip about all you want to — later. I won't be hurried to the burying ground. And keep your head away from that door. What I've got to say to your new master is private."

"Listen at you, Mistiss."

"You listen to me. That's all. No, wait. I had something else on my mind — what is it? Yes. How many hens has Melissy set? You don't know. Find out. A few of the old hens ought to be setting. Tell her to be careful to turn the turkey eggs every day. No, you bring them and set them under my bed. I'll make sure. We got a mighty pore hatch last year. You may go now. I'm plumb worn out, boy, worn out thinking for these people. It's that that worries a body down. But you'll know all about it in good time. Stand out there and let me look at you good. You don't let me see enough of you, and I almost forget how you look. Not really, you understand. Just a little. It's your own fault. I've got so much to trouble me that you, when you're not here, naturally slip back in my mind. But that's all over now. You are here to stay, and I'm here to go. There will always be Long Gourd, and there must always be a McCowan on it. I had hoped to have you by me for several years, but you would have your fling in town. I thought it best to clear your blood of it, but as God is hard, I can't see what you find to do in town. And now you've gone and gotten you a woman. Well, they all have to do it. But do you reckon you've picked the right one — you must forgive the frankness of an old lady who can see the bottom of her grave — I had in mind one of the Carlisle girls. The Carlisle place lies so handy to Long Gourd and would give me a landing on the river. Have you seen Anna Belle since she's grown to be a woman? I'm told there's not a better housekeeper in the valley."

"I'm sure Anna Belle is a fine girl. But Mammy, I love Eva."

"She'll wrinkle up on you, Son; and the only wrinkles land gets can be smoothed out by the harrow. And she looks sort of puny to me, Son. She's powerful small in the waist and walks about like she had worms."

"Gee, Mammy you're not jealous are you? That waist is in style."

"You want to look for the right kind of style in a woman. Old Mrs. Penter Matchem had two daughters with just such waists, but 'twarnt natural. She would tie their corset strings to the bed posts and whip'm out with a buggy whip. The poor girls never drew a hearty breath. Just to please that old woman's vanity. She got paid in kind. It did something to Eliza's bowels and she died before she was twenty. The other one never had any children. She used to whip'm out until they cried. I never liked that woman. She thought a whip could do anything."

"Well, anyway, Eva's small waist wasn't made by any corset strings. She doesn't wear any."

"How do you know, sir?"

"Well . . . I . . . What a question for a respectable woman to ask."

"I'm not a respectable woman. No woman can be respectable and run four thousand acres of land. Well, you'll have it your own way. I suppose the safest place for a man to take his folly is to bed."

"Mammy!"

"You must be lenient with your Cousin George. He wanders about night times talking about the War. I put him off in the west wing where he won't keep people awake, but sometimes he gets in the yard and gives orders to his troops. 'I will sweep that hill, General' — and many's the time he's done it when the battle was doubtful — 'I'll sweep it with my iron brooms'; then he shouts out his orders, and pretty soon the dogs commence to barking. But he's been a heap of company for me. You must see that your wife humors him. It won't be for long. He's mighty feeble."

"Eva's not my wife yet, Mammy."

"You won't be free much longer — the way she looks at you, like a hungry hound."

"I was just wondering," he said hurriedly. "I hate to talk about anything like this . . ."

"Everybody has a time to die, and I'll have no maudlin nonsense about mine."

"I was wondering about Cousin George . . . if I could get somebody to keep him. You see, it will be difficult in the winters. Eva will want to spend the winters in town. . . ."

He paused, startled, before the great bulk of his grandmother rising from her pillows, and in the silence that frightened the air, his unfinished words hung suspended about them.

After a moment he asked if he should call the doctor.

It was some time before she could find words to speak.

"Get out of the room."

"Forgive me, Mammy. You must be tired."

"I'll send for you," sounded the dead voice in the still room, "when I want to see you again. I'll send for you and — the woman."

She watched the door close quietly on his neat square back. Her head whirled and turned like a flying jennet. She lowered and steadied it on the pillows. Four thousand acres of the richest land in the valley he would sell and squander on that slut, and he didn't even know it and there was no way to warn him. This terrifying thought rushed through her mind, and she felt the bed shake with her pain, while before the footboard the spectre of an old sin rose up to mock her. How she had struggled to get this land and keep it together — through the War, the Reconstruction, and the pleasanter after days. For eighty-seven years she had suffered and slept and planned and rested and had pleasure in this valley, seventy of it, almost a turning century, on this place; and now that she must leave it . . .

The things she had done to keep it together. No. The one thing. . . . From the dusty stacks the musty odor drifted through the room, met the tobacco smoke over the long table piled high with records, reports. Iva Louise stood at one end, her hat clinging perilously to the heavy auburn hair, the hard blue eyes and the voice:

"You promised Pa to look after me" — she had waited for the voice to break and scream — "and you have stolen my land!"

"Now, Miss Iva Louise," the lawyer dropped his empty eyes along the floor, "you don't mean . . ."

"Yes, I do mean it."

Her own voice had restored calm to the room: "I promised your pa his land would not be squandered."

"My husband won't squander my property. You just want it for yourself."

She cut through the scream with the sharp edge of her scorn: "What about that weakling's farm in Madison? Who pays the taxes now?"

The girl had no answer to that. Desperate, she faced the lawyer: "Is there no way, sir, I can get my land from the clutches of this unnatural woman?"

The man coughed; the red rim of his eyes watered with embarrassment: "I'm afraid," he cleared his throat, "you say you can't raise the money. . . . I'm afraid —"

That trapped look as the girl turned away. It had come back to her, now trapped in her bed. As a swoon spreads, she felt the desperate terror of weakness, more desperate where there has been strength. Did the girl see right? Had she stolen the land because she wanted it?

Suddenly, like the popping of a thread in a loom, the struggles of the flesh stopped, and the years backed up and covered her thoughts like the spring freshet she had seen so many times creep over the dark soil. Not in order, but as if they were stragglers trying to catch up, the events of her life passed before her sight that had never been so clear. Sweeping over the mounds of her body rising beneath the quilts came the old familiar odors — the damp, strong, penetrating smell of new-turned ground; the rank, clinging, resistless odor of green-picked feathers stuffed in a pillow by Guinea Nell, thirty-odd years ago; tobacco on the mantel, clean and sharp like smelling salts; her father's sweat, sweet like stale oil; the powerful ammonia of manure turned over in a stall; curing hay in the wind; the polecat's stink on the night air, almost pleasant, a sort of commingled scent of all the animals, man and beast; the dry smell of dust under a rug; the overstrong scent of too-sweet fruit trees blooming; the inhospitable wet ashes of a dead fire in a poor white's cabin; black Rebeccah in the kitchen; a wet hound steaming before a fire. There were other odors she could not identify, overwhelming her, making her weak, taking her body and drawing out of it a choking longing to hover over all that she must leave, the animals, the fences, the crops growing in the fields, the houses, the people in them. . . .

It was early summer, and she was standing in the garden after dark — she had heard something after the small chickens. Mericy and Yellow Jane passed beyond the paling fence. Dark shadows — gay, full voices. *Where you gwine, gal? I dunno. Jest a-gwine. Where you? To the frolic, do I live. Well, stay off'n yoe back tonight.* Then out of the rich, gushing laughter: *All right, you stay off'n yourn. I done caught de stumbles.* More laughter.

The face of Uncle Ike, head man in slavery days, rose up. A tall Senagalese, he was standing in the crib of the barn unmoved before the bush-whackers. *Nigger, whar is that gold hid? You better tell us, nigger. Down in the well; in the far-place. By God, you black son of a bitch, we'll roast ye alive if you air too contrary to tell. Now, listen ole nigger, Miss McCowan ain't nothen to you no more. You been set free. We'll give ye some of it, a whole sack. Come on, now* — out of the dribbling, leering mouth — *whar air it?* Ike's tall form loomed towards the shadows. In the lamp flame his forehead shone like the point, the core of night. He stood there with no word for answer. As she saw the few white beads of sweat on his forehead, she spoke.

She heard her voice reach through the dark — *I know your kind. In better days you'd slip around and set people's barns afire. You shirked the War to live off the old and weak. You don't spare me because I'm a woman. You'd shoot a woman quicker because she has the name of being frail. Well, I'm not frail, and my Navy Six an't frail. Ike, take their guns.* Ike moved and one of them raised his pistol arm. He dropped it, and the acrid smoke stung her nostrils. *Now, Ike, get the rest of their weapons. Their knives, too. One of us might turn our backs.*

On top of the shot she heard the soft pat of her servants' feet. White eyeballs shining through the cracks in the barn. Then: *Caesar, Al, Zebedee, step in here and lend a hand to Ike.* By sun the people had gathered in the yard. Uneasy, silent, they watched her on the porch. She gave the word, and the whips cracked. The mules strained, trotted off, skittish and afraid, dragging the white naked bodies bouncing and cursing over the sod: *Turn us loose. We'll not bother ye no more, lady. You ain't no woman, you're a devil.* She turned and went into the house. It is strange how a woman gets hard when trouble comes a-gobbling after her people.

Worn from memory, she closed her eyes to stop the whirl, but closing her eyes did no good. She released the lids and did not resist. Brother Jack stood before her, handsome and shy, but ruined from his cradle by a cleft palate, until he came to live only in the fire of spirits. And she understood, so clear was life, down to the smallest things. She had often heard tell of this clarity that took a body whose time was spending on the earth. Poor Brother Jack, the gentlest of men, but because of his mark, made the butt and wit of the valley. She saw him leave for school, where he was sent to separate him from his drinking companions, to a church school where the boys buried their liquor in the ground and sipped it up through straws. His letters: *Dear Ma, quit offering so much advice and send me more money. You send barely enough to keep me from stealing.* His buggy wheels scraping the gravel, driving up as the first roosters crowed. *Katharine, Malcolm, I thought you might want to have a little conversation.* Conversation two hours before sun! And down she would come and let him in, and the General would get up, stir up the fire, and they would sit down and smoke. Jack would drink and sing, *If the Little Brown Jug was mine, I'd be drunk all the time and I'd never be sob-er a-gin* — or, *Hog drovers, hog drovers, hog drovers we air, a-courting your darter so sweet and so fair.* They would sit and smoke and drink until she got up to ring the bell.

He stayed as long as the whiskey held out, growing more violent towards the end. She watered his bottles; begged whiskey to make camphor — *Gre't God, Sis Kate, do you sell camphor? I gave you a pint this morning.* Poor Brother Jack, killed in Breckinridge's charge at Murfreesboro, cut in two by a chain shot from an enemy gun. All night long she had sat up after the message came. His body scattered about a splintered black gum tree. She had seen that night, as if she had been on the field, the parties moving over the dark field hunting the wounded and dead. Clyde Bascom had fallen near Jack with a bad hurt. They were messmates. He had to tell somebody; and somehow she was the one he must talk to. The spectral lanterns, swinging towards the dirge of pain and the monotonous cries of *Water,* caught by the river dew on the before-morning air and held suspended over the field in its acrid quilt. There death dripped to mildew the noisy throats . . . and all the while relief parties, moving, blots of night, sullenly moving in the viscous blackness.

Her eyes widened, and she looked across the foot posts into the room. There was some mistake, some cruel blunder; for there now, tipping about the carpet, hunting in her wardrobe, under the bed, blowing down the fire to its ashes until they glowed in their dryness, stalked the burial parties. They stepped out of the ashes in twos and threes, hunting, hunting and shaking their heads. Whom were they searching for? Jack had long been buried. They moved more rapidly; looked angry. They crowded the room until she gasped for breath. One, gaunt and haggard, jumped on the foot of her bed; rose to the ceiling; gesticulated; argued in animated silence. He leaned forward; pressed his hand upon her leg. She tried to tell him to take it off. Cold and crushing heavy, it pressed her down to the bowels of the earth. Her lips trembled, but no sound came forth. Now the hand moved up to her stomach; and the haggard eyes looked gravely at her, alert, as if they were waiting for something. Her head turned giddy. She called to Dick, to Ants, to Doctor Ed; but the words struck her teeth and fell back in her throat. She concentrated on lifting the words, and the burial parties sadly shook their heads. Always the cries struck her teeth and fell back down. She strained to hear the silence they made. At last from a great distance she thought she heard . . . *too late . . . too late*. How exquisite the sound, like a bell swinging without ringing. Suddenly it came to her. She was dying.

How slyly death slipped up on a body, like sleep moving over the vague boundary. How many times she had laid awake to trick the unconscious there. At last she would know . . . But she wasn't ready. She must first do something about Long Gourd. That slut must not eat it up. She would give it to the hands first. He must be brought to understand this. But the spectres shook their heads. Well let them shake. She'd be damned if she would go until she was ready to go. She'd be damned all right, and she smiled at the meaning the word took on now. She gathered together all the particles of her will; the spectres faded; and there about her were the anxious faces of kin and servants. Edwin had his hands under the cover feeling her legs. She made to raise her own hand to the boy. It did not go up. Her eyes wanted to roll upward and look behind her forehead, but she pinched them down and looked at her grandson.

"You want to say something, Mammy?" — she saw his lips move.

She had a plenty to say, but her tongue had somehow got glued to her lips. Truly it was now too late. Her will left her. Life withdrawing gathered like a frosty dew on her skin. The last breath blew gently past her nose. The dusty nostrils tingled. She felt a great sneeze coming. There was a roaring; the wind blew through her head once, and a great cotton field bent before it, growing and spreading, the bolls swelling as big as cotton sacks and bursting white as thunderheads. From a distance, out of the far end of the field, under a sky so blue that it was painful-bright, voices came singing, *Joshua fit the battle of Jericho, Jericho, Jericho — Joshua fit the battle of Jericho, and the walls come a-tumbling down.*

— From the *Southern Review*, Spring, 1936. Reprinted by permission.

EVE AND THAT SNAKE

By Roark Bradford

WELL, A LONG TIME AGO things was diffrunt. Hit wa'n't nothin' on de yearth 'cause hit wa'n't no yearth. And hit wa'n't nothin' no-wheres and ev'y day was Sunday. Wid de Lawd r'ared back preachin' all day long ev'y day. 'Ceptin' on Sadday, and den ev'ybody went to de fish fry.

So one day ev'ybody was out to de fish fry, eatin' fish and b'iled custard and carryin' on, to all at once de Lawd swallowed some b'iled custard which didn't suit his tas'e.

"Dis custard," say de Lawd, "ain't seasoned right. Hit's too thick."

"Hit's got a heap of sugar and aigs and milk and things in hit, Lawd," say Gabriel.

"I know," say de Lawd, "but hit tas'es like hit needs jest a little bit more firmament in hit."

"Us ain't got no more firmament, Lawd," say Gabriel. "Us ain't got a drap in de jug."

"You been usin' a heap of firmament," say de Lawd. "Seem like ev'y time I come to a fish fry I got to create some more firma-ment. I bet I'm gonter make enough dis time to last a month of Sundays. I'm sick and tired of passin' a miracle ev'y time I wants some firmament."

So de Lawd r'ared back and passed a miracle and say, "Let hit be some firmament. And when I say let hit be some firmament, I mean let hit be a whole heap of firmament. I'm sick and tired of lettin' hit be jest a little bitty dab of firmament when I pass a miracle."

And you jest ought to see de firmament! Hit jest sloshed all over ev'ything so de angels and cherubs couldn't hardly fly, and ev'ybody was standin' round, knee deep, shiverin' and chatterin' and squirmin' round.

"Well," say de mammy angel, "I guess I better git my cherubs and git on home and dry 'em out. They's shiverin' like they got a buck aguer, right now."

"Don't go bustin' up de fish fry jest 'cause de cherubs is wet," say de Lawd. "I'll dry 'em out."

So de Lawd passed another miracle and say, "Let hit be de sun to dry out deseyar cherubs." And dar was de sun. And de cherubs got dried, but quick as they got dried they got wet again, 'cause hit was so much firmament.

"Dis ain't gittin' us nowheres," say de Lawd. "Gabriel, maybe us menfolks better git out and ditch around some and dreen some of disyar firmament off."

"Good idea," say Gabriel, "only hit ain't no 'count, 'cause hit ain't no place to dreen hit off to."

"Well," say de Lawd, "I guess I got to pass another miracle and make a place to dreen hit off to. Hit look like when I git started passin' miracles hit's always somethin' else." So he r'ared back and passed a miracle and said, "Let hit be de yearth to hold dis firmament." And dar was de yearth.

Well, de firmament runned on de yearth, and hit runned in de rivers and creeks and ditches — 'cause firmament wa'n't nothin' but a fancy name for water — and dar was de yearth wid de firmament dreened off and a heap of dry land left.

"Now looky what you done done, Lawd," say Gabriel. "Cou'se hit ain't none of my business, 'cause I got to practice on my hawn all time. But somebody got to go work dat land, 'cause you know good as me dat de land ain't gonter work hitself."

Well, de Lawd looked round to see who he gonter send to work his land, and all de angels was mighty busy. "Well," he said, "I guess I got pass one more miracle to git somebody to work dat land. And I bet de next time I pass a miracle for some firmament I bet I won't git so brash about hit."

So de Lawd got a handful of dirt and made hit in a ball and passed a miracle over hit and say, "Let dis dirt be mankind." And de dirt turn to a man.

De Lawd looked at de man and say, "What's yo' name, man?"

"Adam," say de man.

"Adam — which?" say de Lawd.

"Jest plain Adam," say de man.

"What's yo' family name?" say de Lawd.

"Ain't got no family," say Adam.

"Well," say de Lawd, "I got to change dat. I ain't gonter have none of deseyar single mens workin' on my farm. They runs around wid de women all night and come de next day they's too sleepy to work."

"I don't run around wid no women," say Adam. "I ain't studdin' de women."

"Yeah?" say de Lawd. "But I ain't gonter take no chances. Yo' heart might be all right now, but de first good-lookin' woman come along she gonter change yo' mind. So I'm jest gonter put you to sleep again."

So de Lawd put Adam to sleep and tuck out a rib and turned de rib into a woman name Eve. So when Adam woke up again, dar was Eve, stretched out by his side, wid her haid on his pillow.

"Where'd you come from, gal?" say Adam.

"No mind whar I come from," say Eve, "I's yar, ain't I?"

So Adam and Eve got married and settled down to raise a crop for de Lawd.

So ev'ything went along all right to summertime. Eve was out pickin' blackberries, and de Lawd come wawkin' down de road.

"Good mawnin', Sister Eve," say de Lawd. "Pickin' a few blackberries?"

"A few, Lawd," say Eve. "Adam 'lowed he'd like to has some for preserves next winter."

"Help yo'self," say de Lawd. "Put up all de blackberries you want. And peaches too. And plums, efn you and Adam likes 'em. Hit ain't but one thing which I don't want you to tech, and dat's de apple orchard. 'Cause from de news I yars, apples is kind of scarce and they ought to bring a good price next fall. So help yo'self to de berries and de peaches and things, but jest stay out of de apples."

Well, hit jest goes to show you. Eve didn't like apples and Adam didn't too. But no quicker do de Lawd wawk on down de road to Eve see a great big highland moccasin crawlin' long twarg her.

" Look at dat scound'el," say Eve, and she pick up a rock. " I'm gonter mash his old haid quick as I gits a shot at him." So de snake crawls through de apple orchard fence, and Eve climbs over hit.

Well, Eve and dat snake went round and round. Eve was chunkin' at him and de snake was dodgin' to finally Eve got a clear shot at him and she r'ared back and let de big rock go.

Eve was all right, but she was a woman. And hit ain't never yit been a woman which could throw straight. So Eve missed de snake and hit de apple tree. And down come a big red apple, right in front of her.

" Well, I be doggone! " she say. " Look at dat apple! " So she stood and looked at hit a long time. " I didn't aim to knock hit down," she say, " but hit's down, now, and I can't put hit back. And does I let hit lay, de hawgs is gonter eat hit and hit's too purty for de hawgs to eat." So she tuck a bite.

" Don't taste like much," she say. " I wonder do Adam want to eat hit? " So she tuck de apple out to whar Adam was plowin' de cawn, and give hit to him.

" I don't like apples, gal," say Adam. " Whyn't you give me somethin' I like? "

" Cou'se you don't like apples," say Eve. " You don't never like nothin' I gives you. You got to think of hit yo'self before you likes hit," and Eve blubbers up and commences to cry.

" Aw, don't cry, sugar," say Adam. " I was jest funnin' wid you. I likes apples. Give me a bite."

" Nawp," say Eve. " You's jest mean, dat's what you is. You treats me mean 'cause I ain't nothin' but a poor little weak woman and you's a big, stout man. I ain't gonter give you nothin'."

" Aw, honey, don't tawk like dat," say Adam. " Dat ain't de way hit is, a-tall. I was jest playin' wid you. Give me a bite of apple and I buys you a new dress."

Well, when a man go to tawkin' new dresses to a woman he gonter git some action. So Eve dry up her cryin' and Adam et de apple and got her de dress. But dat wa'n't all.

De Lawd seed Eve's new dress and he found out all about hit. And he got mad, 'cause he didn't aim to have nobody on his place which stole his apples. So he bailed old Adam's trover and leveled on his crop and mule, and put Adam and Eve off'n de place. And de next news anybody yared of old Adam, he was down on de levee tryin' to git a job at six bits a day.

Populating the Earth

Well, Adam and Eve had two chilluns name Cain and Abel. So when Adam got to gittin' along in de years so's he couldn't do no heavy work, he called his boys and say: "Well, you boys better settle down and git to work. I and de old lady been s'portin' y'all up to now and hit's about time y'all was s'portin' me and yo' maw."

"Well," says Abel, "I b'lieve I'll herd de sheep."

"You smells like a sheep, anyhow," says Cain.

"Boys!" say Eve. "Don't start argyin' and fightin' again."

"Abel started hit," say Cain.

"I bet I'm gonter start you," say Abel.

"And git yo' nappy haid busted wid a rock," say Cain.

So Adam reached for de poker and de boys went on out and went to work. Abel went out and lay back on de hillside, herdin' de sheep and sleepin', and Cain got de mule and plow and started dirtin' de cawn down in de creek bottom.

Well, Cain was plowin' 'long, 'tendin' to his own business, and Abel was layin' back in de shade watchin' him work. To all at once Abel decided he'd have some fone out'n Cain, so he say: "Well, Cain, how is you gittin' along wid yo' work?"

"Mindin' my own business; dat's how," say Cain. "And you better mind yo's."

"Me, I'd be skeered to git out in dat hot sun," say Abel. "Hit might cook my brains. Cou'se hit ain't gonter cook yo' brains 'cause you ain't got no brains to git cooked."

"You better go on, now," say Cain. "I ain't botherin' you. But naw, you ain't got sense enough to know when you's happy. So you jest gonter keep on messin' round me to I gits mad and scatter you all over de hillside."

Abel laughed and r'ared back and started to sing:

"What you gonter do when de devil git you?
Hoe cawn and dig I'sh taters, Lawd, Lawd!"

Well, dat was mo'n Cain could stand, so he up wid a rock and ker-blip! He tuck Abel behind de year, and Abel sort of grinned and rolled over, lookin' jest as natchal as efn he had a lily in his hand.

Well, dem was de days when de Lawd wawked de yearth like a natchal man. So de Lawd wawked up to Cain and say, "Cain, looky what you done did to Abel."

"I ain't studdin' Abel," say Cain. "I was mindin' my own business and he come monkeyin' round wid me. So I up and flang a rock at him and efn hit missed him, all right, and efn hit hit him, all right. One way or de yuther, I ain't studdin' Abel and nobody which looks like him."

"All right," say de Lawd, "but I'm yar to tell you de sheriff is liable to git you. And when de new jedge gits done tawkin' to you about hit, you'll be draggin' a ball and chain de rest of yo' life."

"Well, what did he want to come monkeyin' round me for, den?" say Cain. "I was jest plowin' and mindin' my own business and not payin' him no mind. And yar he come puttin' me in de dozens. Cou'se I busted him wid a rock. I'd bust anybody which put me in de dozens. Black or white."

"Well, I ain't sayin' you's wrong," say de Lawd, "and I ain't sayin' you's right. Onderstand? But what I is sayin' is dis: Was I you, and scusin' how hard de new jedge is, I'd jest git my hat and git myself on down de road. And I wouldn't stop to I got plum out'n de county, too. And den when I got out'n de county, I'd take and git married and settle down and raise me a family and forgit all about Abel. 'Cause hit ain't nothin' which kin settle a man down and make him forgit his yuther troubles like gittin' married and havin' a lot of chilluns and things runnin' round de house."

So Cain tuck de harness off'n de mule and rid off. He rid for fawty days and fawty nights and de first think he know he was over in a place name Nod.

"Well," say Cain, "yar's whar I settles down and raises me some chilluns." So he got off'n his mule and tied him to a stump and set down in de shade to wait. And about dat time de Lawd wawked up.

"What you waitin' for, Cain?" say de Lawd.

"I's waitin' for a woman to come down de road," say Cain, "so's I kin git married, like you said, Lawd."

Well, de Lawd laughed and wawked on and left old Cain settin' on de stump tryin' to figger out what de Lawd was laughin' at. To all at once hit come to him.

"Well, I be doggone!" say Cain. "Yar is me waitin' for a woman to git married wid, and hit ain' no woman on de yearth ceptin' Eve, and she done married! Dat ain't gittin' nowheres!" So he sot and figgered and figgered. So about dat time he yared somebody up in de tree singin':

> "I done done all I kin do,
> And I can't git along wid you.
> I'm gonter git me another papa,
> Sho's you bawn!"

So Cain looked up and seed a big gorilla gal prancin' up and down de limb like a natchal-born woman.

"Hey-ho, Good-lookin'!" say Cain. "Which way is hit to town?"

"What you tryin' to do, Country Boy?" say de gorilla gal. "You tryin' to mash me? I be doggone efn hit ain't gittin' so a gal can't hardly git out'n de house to some of dese yar fast mens ain't passin' remarks at her."

"I ain't passin' remarks," say Cain.

"Efn I thought you was one of deseyar mashin' men tryin' to mash me," say de gal, "I'd call de po-lice and they'd show you which away hit is to de First Precinct."

"Looky yar, gal," say Cain. "I ain't got no time to play wid you. I ax you a question and you better answer me right now. 'Cause efn you don't I'm gonter bend you cross my knee and burn you up."

So de gorilla gal look like she's mighty skeered. And den she sort of grins and slides down de tree and sets down by Cain.

"I bet you kin handle a gal mean wid dem big old arms of yo'n," she say. "I bet you's a mean scound'el when you gits mad. I sho would hate to git you mad at me, Big Boy."

"I'm purty stout in my arms," say Cain, "but I ain't so mean."

" You got a bad-lookin' eye," say de gorilla gal. " I bet you's mean to de womenfolks."

" Naw, you got me wrong," say Cain. " I don't b'lieve in whuppin' a gal onless she makes me mad."

" Well, I sho don't want to make you mad, Big Boy," say de gorilla gal. So they sot and tawked awhile and purty soon they up and got married and settled down and raised a family, jest like de Lawd said. And they peopled de yearth.

— From *Ol' Man Adam an' His Chillun*, Harper and Brothers, 1928. Reprinted by permission.

THAT EVENING SUN GO DOWN

By William Faulkner

MONDAY IS no different from any other weekday in Jefferson now. The streets are paved now, and the telephone and electric companies are cutting down more and more of the shade trees — the water oaks, the maples and locusts and elms — to make room for iron poles bearing clusters of bloated and ghostly and bloodless grapes, and we have a city laundry which makes the rounds on Monday morning, gathering the bundles of clothes into bright-colored, specially made motorcars: the soiled wearing of a whole week now flees apparition-like behind alert and irritable electric horns, with a long diminishing noise of rubber and asphalt like tearing silk, and even the Negro women who still take in white people's washing, after the old custom, fetch and deliver it in automobiles.

But fifteen years ago, on Monday morning the quiet, dusty, shady streets would be full of Negro women with, balanced on their steady, turbaned heads, bundles of clothes tied up in sheets, almost as large as cotton bales, carried so without touch of hand between the kitchen door of the white house and the blackened washpot beside a cabin door in Negro Hollow.

Nancy would set her bundle on the top of her head, then upon the bundle in turn she would set the black straw sailor hat which she wore winter and summer. She was tall, with a high sad face sunken a little where her teeth were missing. Sometimes we would go a part of the way down the lane and across the pasture with her, to watch the balanced bundle and the hat that never bobbed or wavered, even when she walked down into the ditch and up the other side and stooped through the fence. She would go down on her hands and knees and crawl through the gap, her head rigid, uptilted, the bundle steady as a rock or a balloon, and rise to her feet again and go on.

Sometimes the husbands of the washing women would fetch and deliver the clothes, but Jesus never did that for Nancy, even before Father told him to stay away from our house, even when Dilsey was sick and Nancy would come to cook for us.

And then about half the time we'd have to go down the lane to Nancy's cabin and tell her to come on and cook breakfast. We would stop at the ditch, because Father told us to not have anything to do with Jesus — he was a short black man, with a razor scar down his face — and we would throw rocks at Nancy's house until she came to the door, leaning her head around it without any clothes on.

" What yawl mean, chunking my house? " Nancy said. " What you little devils mean? "

" Father says for you to come on and get breakfast," Caddy said. " Father says it's over a half an hour now, and you've got to come this minute."

" I ain't studying no breakfast," Nancy said. " I going to get my sleep out."

" I bet you're drunk," Jason said. " Father says you're drunk. Are you drunk, Nancy? "

" Who says I is? " Nancy said. " I got to get my sleep out. I ain't studying no breakfast."

So after a while we quit chunking the cabin and went back home. When she finally came, it was too late for me to go to school. So we thought it was whiskey until that day they arrested her again and they were taking her to jail and they passed Mr. Stovall. He was the cashier in the bank and a deacon in the Baptist church, and Nancy began to say:

" When you going to pay me, white man? When you going to pay me, white man? It's been three times now since you paid me a cent — " Mr. Stovall knocked her down, but she kept on saying, " When you going to pay me, white man? It's been three times now since — " until Mr. Stovall kicked her in the mouth with his heel and the marshal caught Mr. Stovall back, and Nancy lying in the street, laughing. She turned her head and spat out some blood and teeth and said, " It's been three times now since he paid me a cent."

That was how she lost her teeth, and all that day they told about Nancy and Mr. Stovall, and all that night the ones that passed the jail could hear Nancy singing and yelling. They could see her hands holding the window bars, and a lot of them stopped along the fence, listening to her and to the jailer trying to make her stop. She didn't shut up until almost daylight, when the jailer began to hear a bumping and scraping upstairs and he went up there and found Nancy hanging from the window bar. He said that it was cocaine and not whiskey, because no nigger would try to commit suicide unless he was full of cocaine, because a nigger full of cocaine wasn't a nigger any longer.

The jailer cut her down and revived her; then he beat her, whipped her. She had hung herself with her dress. She had fixed it all right, but when they arrested her she didn't have on anything except a dress and so she couldn't make her hands let go of the window ledge. So the jailer heard the noise and ran up there and found Nancy hanging from the window, stark naked, her belly already swelling out a little, like a little balloon.

When Dilsey was sick in her cabin and Nancy was cooking for us, we could see her apron swelling out; that was before Father told Jesus to stay away from the house. Jesus was in the kitchen, sitting behind the stove, with his razor scar on his black face like a piece of dirty string. He said it was a watermelon that Nancy had under her dress.

" It never come off of your vine, though," Nancy said.

" Off of what vine? " Caddy said.

" I can cut down the vine it did come off of," Jesus said.

" What makes you want to talk like that before these chillen? " Nancy said. " Whyn't you go on to work? You done et. You want Mr. Jason to catch you hanging around his kitchen, talking that way before these chillen? "

" Talking what way? " Caddy said. " What vine? "

" I can't hang around white man's kitchen," Jesus said. " But white man can hang around mine. White man can come in my house, but I can't stop him. When white man want to come in my house, I ain't got no house. I can't stop him, but he can't kick me outen it. He can't do that."

Dilsey was still sick in her cabin. Father told Jesus to stay off our place. Dilsey was still sick. It was a long time. We were in the library after supper.

"Isn't Nancy through in the kitchen yet?" Mother said. "It seems to me that she has had plenty of time to finish the dishes."

"Let Quentin go and see," Father said. "Go and see if Nancy is through, Quentin. Tell her she can go on home."

I went to the kitchen. Nancy was through. The dishes were put away and the fire was out. Nancy was sitting in a chair, close to the cold stove. She looked at me.

"Mother wants to know if you are through," I said.

"Yes," Nancy said. She looked at me. "I' done finished." She looked at me.

"What is it?" I said. "What is it?"

"I ain't nothing but a nigger," Nancy said. "It ain't none of my fault."

She looked at me, sitting in the chair before the cold stove, the sailor hat on her head. I went back to the library. It was the cold stove and all, when you think of a kitchen being warm and busy and cheerful. And with a cold stove and the dishes all put away, and nobody wanting to eat at that hour.

"Is she through?" Mother said.

"Yessum," I said.

"What is she doing?" Mother said.

"She's not doing anything. She's through."

"I'll go and see," Father said.

"Maybe she's waiting for Jesus to come and take her home," Caddy said.

"Jesus is gone," I said. "Nancy told us how one morning she woke up and Jesus had gone."

"He quit me," Nancy said. "Done gone to Memphis, I reckon. Dodging them city *po*-lice for a while, I reckon."

"And a good riddance," Father said. "I hope he stays there."

"Nancy's scaired of the dark," Jason said.

"So are you," Caddy said.

"I'm not," Jason said.

"You, Candace!" Mother said. Father came back.

"I am going to walk down the lane with Nancy," he said. "She says that Jesus is back."

"Has she seen him?" Mother said.

"No. Some Negro sent her word that he was back in town. I won't be long."

"You'll leave me alone, to take Nancy home?" Mother said. "Is her safety more precious to you than mine?"

"I won't be long," Father said.

"You'll leave these children unprotected, with that Negro about?"

"I'm going too," Caddy said. "Let me go, Father."

"What would he do with them, if he were unfortunate enough to have them?" Father said.

"I want to go, too," Jason said.

"Jason!" Mother said. She was speaking to Father. You could tell by the way she said the name. Like she believed that all day Father had been trying to think of doing the thing she wouldn't like the most, and that she knew all the time that after a while he would think of it. I stayed quiet, because Father and I both knew that Mother would want him to make me stay with her if she just thought of it in time. So Father didn't look at me. I was the oldest. I was nine and Caddy was seven and Jason was five.

"Nonsense," Father said. "We won't be long."

Nancy had her hat on. We came to the lane. "Jesus always been good to me," Nancy said. "Whenever he had two dollars, one of them was mine." We walked in the lane. "If I can just get through the lane," Nancy said, "I be all right then."

The lane was always dark. "This is where Jason got scaired on Hallowe'en," Caddy said.

"I didn't," Jason said.

"Can't Aunt Rachel do anything with him?" Father said. Aunt Rachel was old. She lived in a cabin beyond Nancy's, by herself. She had white hair and she smoked a pipe in the door, all day long; she didn't work any more. They said she was Jesus' mother. Sometimes she said she was and sometimes she said she wasn't any kin to Jesus.

"Yes, you did," Caddy said. "You were scairder than Frony. You were scairder than T. P. even. Scairder than niggers."

"Can't nobody do nothing with him," Nancy said. "He say I done woke up the devil in him and ain't but one thing going to lay it down again."

"Well, he's gone now," Father said. "There's nothing for you to be afraid of now. And if you'd just let white men alone."

"Let what white men alone?" Caddy said. "How let them alone?"

"He ain't gone nowhere," Nancy said. "I can feel him. I can feel him now, in this lane. He hearing us talk, every word, hid somewhere, waiting. I ain't seen him, and I ain't going to see him again but once more, with that razor in his mouth. That razor on that string down his back, inside his shirt. And then I ain't going to be even surprised."

"I wasn't scaired," Jason said.

"If you'd behave yourself, you'd have kept out of this," Father said. "But it's all right now. He's probably in St. Louis now. Probably got another wife by now and forgot all about you."

"If he has, I better not find out about it," Nancy said. "I'd stand there right over them, and every time he wropped her, I'd cut that arm off. I'd cut his head off and I'd slit her belly and I'd shove —"

"Hush," Father said.

"Slit whose belly, Nancy?" Caddy said.

"I wasn't scaired," Jason said. "I'd walk right down this lane by myself."

"Yah," Caddy said. "You wouldn't dare to put your foot down in it if we were not here too."

II

Dilsey was still sick; so we took Nancy home every night until Mother said, "How much longer is this going on? I to be left alone in this big house while you take home a frightened Negro?"

We fixed a pallet in the kitchen for Nancy. One night we waked up, hearing the sound. It was not singing and it was not crying, coming up the back stairs. There was a light in Mother's room and we heard Father going down the hall, down the back stairs, and Caddy and I went into the hall. The floor was cold. Our toes curled away from it while we listened to the sound. It was like singing and it wasn't like singing, like the sounds that Negroes make.

Then it stopped and we heard Father going down the back stairs, and we went to the head of the stairs. Then the sound began again, in the stairway, not loud, and we could see Nancy's eyes halfway up the stairs, against the wall. They looked like cat's eyes do, like a big cat against the wall, watching us. When we came down the steps to where she was, she quit making the sound again, and we stood there until Father came back up from the kitchen, with his pistol in his hand. He went back down with Nancy and they came back with Nancy's pallet.

We spread the pallet in our room. After the light in Mother's room went off, we could see Nancy's eyes again. "Nancy," Caddy whispered. "Are you asleep, Nancy?"

Nancy whispered something. It was oh or no, I don't know which. Like nobody had made it, like it came from nowhere and went nowhere, until it was like Nancy was not there at all; that I had looked so hard at her eyes on the stairs that they had got printed on my eyeballs, like the sun does when you have closed your eyes and there is no sun. "Jesus," Nancy whispered. "Jesus."

"Was it Jesus?" Caddy said. "Did he try to come into the kitchen?"

"Jesus," Nancy said. Like this: Jeeeeeeeeeeeeeesus, until the sound went out, like a match or a candle does.

"It's the other Jesus she means," I said.

"Can you see us, Nancy?" Caddy whispered. "Can you see our eyes too?"

"I ain't nothing but a nigger," Nancy said. "God knows. God knows."

"What did you see down there in the kitchen?" Caddy whispered. "What tried to get in?"

"God knows," Nancy said. We could see her eyes. "God knows."

Dilsey got well. She cooked dinner. "You'd better stay in bed a day or two longer," Father said.

"What for?" Dilsey said. "If I had been a day later, this place would be to rack and ruin. Get on out of here now, and let me get my kitchen straight again."

Dilsey cooked supper too. And that night, just before dark, Nancy came into the kitchen.

"How do you know he's back?" Dilsey said. "You ain't seen him."

"Jesus is a nigger," Jason said.

"I can feel him," Nancy said. "I can feel him laying yonder in the ditch."

"Tonight?" Dilsey said. "Is he there tonight?"

"Dilsey's a nigger too," Jason said.

"You try to eat something," Dilsey said.

"I don't want nothing," Nancy said.

"I ain't a nigger," Jason said.

"Drink some coffee," Dilsey said. She poured a cup of coffee for Nancy. "Do you know he's out there tonight? How come you know it's tonight?"

"I know," Nancy said. "He's there, waiting. I know. I done lived with him too long. I know what he is fixing to do 'fore he know it himself."

"Drink some coffee," Dilsey said. Nancy held the cup to her mouth and blew into the cup. Her mouth pursed out like a spreading adder's, like a rubber mouth, like she had blown all the color out of her lips with blowing the coffee.

"I ain't a nigger," Jason said. "Are you a nigger, Nancy?"

"I hellborn, child," Nancy said. "I won't be nothing soon. I going back where I come from soon."

III

She began to drink the coffee. While she was drinking, holding the cup in both hands, she began to make the sound again. She made the sound into the cup and the coffee splashed out onto her hands and her dress. Her eyes looked at us and she sat there, her elbows on her knees, holding the cup in both hands, looking at us across the wet cup, making the sound.

" Look at Nancy," Jason said. " Nancy can't cook for us now. Dilsey's got well now."

" You hush up," Dilsey said. Nancy held the cup in both hands, looking at us, making the sound, like there were two of them: one looking at us and the other making the sound. " Whyn't you let Mr. Jason telefoam the marshal? " Dilsey said. Nancy stopped then, holding the cup in her long brown hands. She tried to drink some coffee again, but it splashed out of the cup, onto her hands and her dress, and she put the cup down. Jason watched her.

" I can't swallow it," Nancy said. " I swallows but it won't go down me."

" You go down to the cabin," Dilsey said. " Frony will fix you a pallet and I'll be there soon."

" Won't no nigger stop him," Nancy said.

" I ain't a nigger," Jason said. " Am I, Dilsey? "

" I reckon not," Dilsey said. She looked at Nancy. " I don't reckon so. What you going to do, then? "

Nancy looked at us. Her eyes went fast, like she was afraid there wasn't time to look, without hardly moving at all. She looked at us, at all three of us at one time. " You member that night I stayed in yawl's room? " she said. She told about how we waked up early the next morning, and played. We had to play quiet, on her pallet, until Father woke up and it was time to get breakfast. " Go and ask your maw to let me stay here tonight," Nancy said. " I won't need no pallet. We can play some more."

Caddy asked Mother. Jason went too. " I can't have Negroes sleeping in the bedrooms," Mother said. Jason cried. He cried until Mother said he couldn't have any dessert for three days if he didn't stop. Then Jason said he could stop if Dilsey would make a chocolate cake. Father was there.

" Why don't you do something about it? " Mother said. " What do we have officers for? "

" Why is Nancy afraid of Jesus? " Caddy said. " Are you afraid of Father, Mother? "

" What could the officers do? " Father said. " If Nancy hasn't seen him, how could the officers find him? "

" Then why is she afraid? " Mother said.

" She says he is there. She says she knows he is there tonight."

"Yet we pay taxes," Mother said. "I must wait here alone in this big house while you take a Negro woman home."

"You know that I am not lying outside with a razor," Father said.

"I'll stop if Dilsey will make a chocolate cake," Jason said. Mother told us to go out and Father said he didn't know if Jason would get a chocolate cake or not, but he knew what Jason was going to get in about a minute. We went back to the kitchen and told Nancy.

"Father said for you to go home and lock the door, and you'll be all right," Caddy said. "All right from what, Nancy? Is Jesus mad at you?" Nancy was holding the coffee cup in her hands again, her elbows on her knees and her hands holding the cup between her knees. She was looking into the cup. "What have you done that made Jesus mad?" Caddy said. Nancy let the cup go. It didn't break on the floor, but the coffee spilled out, and Nancy sat there with her hands still making the shape of the cup. She began to make the sound again, not loud. Not singing and not unsinging. We watched her.

"Here," Dilsey said. "You quit that, now. You get aholt of yourself. You wait here. I going to get Versh to walk home with you." Dilsey went out.

We looked at Nancy. Her shoulders kept shaking, but she quit making the sound. We watched her. "What's Jesus going to do to you?" Caddy said. "He went away."

Nancy looked at us. "We had fun that night I stayed in yawl's room, didn't we?"

"I didn't," Jason said. "I didn't have any fun."

"You were asleep in Mother's room," Caddy said. "You were not there."

"Let's go down to my house and have some more fun," Nancy said.

"Mother won't let us," I said. "It's too late now."

"Don't bother her," Nancy said. "We can tell her in the morning. She won't mind."

"She wouldn't let us," I said.

"Don't ask her now," Nancy said. "Don't bother her now."

"She didn't say we couldn't go," Caddy said.

"We didn't ask," I said.

"If you go, I'll tell," Jason said.

"We'll have fun," Nancy said. "They won't mind, just to my house. I been working for yawl a long time. They won't mind."

"I'm not afraid to go," Caddy said. "Jason is the one that's afraid. He'll tell."

"I'm not," Jason said.

"Yes, you are," Caddy said. "You'll tell."

"I won't tell," Jason said. "I'm not afraid."

"Jason is going to tell," Caddy said. The lane was dark. We passed the pasture gate. "I bet if something was to jump out from behind the gate, Jason would holler."

"I wouldn't," Jason said. We walked down the lane. Nancy was talking loud.

"What are you talking so loud for, Nancy?" Caddy said.

"Who, me?" Nancy said. "Listen at Quentin and Caddy and Jason saying I'm talking loud."

"You talk like there was five of us here," Caddy said. "You talk like Father was here too."

"Who; me talking loud, Mr. Jason?" Nancy said.

"Nancy called Jason 'Mister,'" Caddy said.

"Listen how Caddy and Quentin and Jason talk," Nancy said.

"We're not talking loud," Caddy said. "You're the one that's talking like Father — "

"Hush," Nancy said; "hush, Mr. Jason."

"Nancy called Jason 'Mister' aguh — "

"Hush," Nancy said. She was talking loud when we crossed the ditch and stooped through the fence where she used to stoop through with the clothes on her head. Then we came to her house. We were going fast then. She opened the door. The smell of the house was like the lamp and the smell of Nancy was like the wick, like they were waiting for one another to begin to smell. She lit the lamp and closed the door and put the bar up. Then she quit talking loud, looking at us.

"What're we going to do?" Caddy said.

"What do yawl want to do?" Nancy said.

"You said we would have some fun," Caddy said.

There was something about Nancy's house; something you could smell besides Nancy and the house. Jason smelled it, even. " I don't want to stay here," he said. " I want to go home."

" Go home, then," Caddy said.

" I don't want to go by myself," Jason said.

" We're going to have some fun," Nancy said.

" How? " Caddy said.

Nancy stood by the door. She was looking at us, only it was like she had emptied her eyes, like she had quit using them. " What do you want to do? " she said.

" Tell us a story," Caddy said. " Can you tell a story? "

" Yes," Nancy said.

" Tell it," Caddy said. We looked at Nancy. " You don't know any stories."

" Yes," Nancy said. " Yes I do."

She came and sat in a chair before the hearth. There was a little fire there. Nancy built it up, when it was already hot inside. She built a good blaze. She told a story. She talked like her eyes looked, like her eyes watching us and her voice talking to us did not belong to her. Like she was living somewhere else, waiting somewhere else. She was outside the cabin. Her voice was inside and the shape of her, the Nancy that could stoop under a barbed wire fence with a bundle of clothes balanced on her head as though without weight, like a balloon, was there. But that was all. " And so this here queen come walking up to the ditch, where that bad man was hiding. She was walking up to the ditch, and she say, ' If I can just get past this here ditch,' was what she say . . ."

" What ditch? " Caddy said. " A ditch like that one out there? Why did a queen want to go into a ditch? "

" To get to her house," Nancy said. She looked at us. " She had to cross the ditch to get into her house quick and bar the door."

" Why did she want to go home and bar the door? " Caddy said.

IV

Nancy looked at us. She quit talking. She looked at us. Jason's legs stuck straight out of his pants where he sat on Nancy's lap. " I don't think that's a good story," he said. " I want to go home."

" Maybe we had better," Caddy said. She got up from the floor. " I bet they are looking for us right now." She went toward the door.

" No," Nancy said. " Don't open it." She got up quick and passed Caddy. She didn't touch the door, the wooden bar.

" Why not? " Caddy said.

" Come back to the lamp," Nancy said. " We'll have fun. You don't have to go."

" We ought to go," Caddy said. " Unless we have a lot of fun." She and Nancy came back to the fire, the lamp.

" I want to go home," Jason said. " I'm going to tell."

" I know another story," Nancy said. She stood close to the lamp. She looked at Caddy, like when your eyes look at a stick balanced on your nose. She had to look down to see Caddy, but her eyes looked like that, like when you are balancing a stick.

" I won't listen to it," Jason said. " I'll bang on the floor."

" It's a good one," Nancy said. " It's better than the other one."

" What's it about? " Caddy said. Nancy was standing by the lamp. Her hand was on the lamp, against the light, long and brown.

" Your hand is on that hot globe," Caddy said. " Don't it feel hot to your hand? "

Nancy looked at her hand on the lamp chimney. She took her hand away, slow. She stood there, looking at Caddy, wringing her long hand as though it were tied to her wrist with a string.

" Let's do something else," Caddy said.

" I want to go home," Jason said.

" I got some popcorn," Nancy said. She looked at Caddy and then at Jason and then at me and then at Caddy again. " I got some popcorn."

" I don't like popcorn," Jason said. " I'd rather have candy."

Nancy looked at Jason. " You can hold the popper." She was still wringing her hand; it was long and limp and brown.

" All right," Jason said. " I'll stay a while if I can do that. Caddy can't hold it. I'll want to go home again if Caddy holds the popper."

Nancy built up the fire. " Look at Nancy putting her hands in the fire," Caddy said. " What's the matter with you, Nancy? "

" I got popcorn," Nancy said. " I got some." She took the popper from under the bed. It was broken. Jason began to cry.

" Now we can't have any popcorn," he said.

" We ought to go home, anyway," Caddy said. " Come on, Quentin."

" Wait," Nancy said; " wait. I can fix it. Don't you want to help me fix it? "

" I don't think I want any," Caddy said. " It's too late now."

" You help me, Jason," Nancy said. " Don't you want to help me? "

" No," Jason said. " I want to go home."

" Hush," Nancy said; " hush. Watch. Watch me. I can fix it so Jason can hold it and pop the corn." She got a piece of wire and fixed the popper.

" It won't hold good," Caddy said.

" Yes it will," Nancy said. " Yawl watch. Yawl watch. Yawl help me shell some corn."

The popcorn was under the bed too. We shelled it into the popper and Nancy helped Jason hold the popper over the fire.

" It's not popping," Jason said. " I want to go home."

" You wait," Nancy said. " It'll begin to pop. We'll have fun then." She was sitting close to the fire. The lamp was turned up so high it was beginning to smoke.

" Why don't you turn it down some? " I said.

" It's all right," Nancy said. " I'll clean it. Yawl wait. The popcorn will start in a minute."

" I don't believe it's going to start," Caddy said. " We ought to start home, anyway. They'll be worried."

" No," Nancy said. " It's going to pop. Dilsey will tell um yawl with me. I been working for yawl long time. They won't mind if yawl at my house. You wait, now. It'll start popping any minute now."

Then Jason got some smoke in his eyes and he began to cry. He dropped the popper into the fire. Nancy got a wet rag and wiped Jason's face, but he didn't stop crying.

" Hush," she said. " Hush." But he didn't hush. Caddy took the popper out of the fire.

"It's burned up," she said. "You'll have to get some more popcorn, Nancy."

"Did you put all of it in?" Nancy said.

"Yes," Caddy said. Nancy looked at Caddy. Then she took the popper and opened it and poured the cinders into her apron and began to sort the grains, her hands long and brown, and we watching her.

"Haven't you got any more?" Caddy said.

"Yes," Nancy said. "Yes. Look. This here ain't burnt. All we need to do is — "

"I want to go home," Jason said. "I'm going to tell."

"Hush," Caddy said. We all listened. Nancy's head was already turned toward the barred door, her eyes filled with red lamplight. "Somebody is coming," Caddy said.

Then Nancy began to make that sound again, not loud, sitting there above the fire, her long hands dangling between her knees; all of a sudden water began to come out on her face in big drops, running down her face, carrying in each one a little turning ball of firelight like a spark until it dropped off her chin. "She's not crying," I said.

"I ain't crying," Nancy said. Her eyes were closed. "I ain't crying. Who is it?"

"I don't know," Caddy said. She went to the door and looked out. "We've got to go now," she said. "Here comes Father."

"I'm going to tell," Jason said. "Yawl made me come."

The water still ran down Nancy's face. She turned in her chair. "Listen. Tell him. Tell him we going to have fun. Tell him I take good care of yawl until in the morning. Tell him to let me come home with yawl and sleep on the floor. Tell him I won't need no pallet. We'll have fun. You member last time how we had so much fun?"

"I didn't have fun," Jason said. "You hurt me. You put smoke in my eyes. I'm going to tell."

V

Father came in. He looked at me. Nancy did not get up.

"Tell him," she said.

"Caddy made us come down here," Jason said. "I didn't want to."

Father came to the fire. Nancy looked up at him. "Can't you go to Aunt Rachel's and stay?" he said. Nancy looked up at Father, her hands between her knees. "He's not here," Father said. "I would have seen him. There's not a soul in sight."

"He in the ditch," Nancy said. "He waiting in the ditch yonder."

"Nonsense," Father said. He looked at Nancy. "Do you know he's there?"

"I got the sign," Nancy said.

"What sign?"

"I got it. It was on the table when I come in. It was a hogbone with blood meat still on it, laying by the lamp. He's out there. When yawl walk out that door, I gone."

"Gone where, Nancy?" Caddy said.

"I'm not a tattletale," Jason said.

"Nonsense," Father said.

"He out there," Nancy said. "He looking through that window this minute, waiting for yawl to go. Then I gone."

"Nonsense," Father said. "Lock up your house and we'll take you on to Aunt Rachel's."

"'Twon't do no good," Nancy said. She didn't look at Father now, but he looked down at her, at her long, limp, moving hands. "Putting it off won't do no good."

"Then what do you want to do?" Father said.

"I don't know," Nancy said. "I can't do nothing. Just put it off. And that don't do no good. I reckon it belong to me. I reckon what I going to get ain't no more than mine."

"Get what?" Caddy said. "What's yours?"

"Nothing," Father said. "You all must get to bed."

"Caddy made me come," Jason said.

"Go on to Aunt Rachel's," Father said.

"It won't do no good," Nancy said. She sat before the fire, her elbows on her knees, her long hands between her knees. "When even your own kitchen wouldn't do no good. When even if I was sleeping on the floor in the room with your chillen, and the next morning there I am, and blood — "

" Hush," Father said. " Lock the door and put out the lamp and go to bed."

" I scaired of the dark," Nancy said. " I scaired for it to happen in the dark."

" You mean you're going to sit right here with the lamp lighted? " Father said. Then Nancy began to make the sound again, sitting before the fire, her long hands between her knees. " Ah, damnation," Father said. " Come along, chillen. It's past bedtime."

" When yawl go home, I gone," Nancy said. She talked quieter now, and her face looked quiet, like her hands. " Anyway, I got my coffin money saved up with Mr. Lovelady." Mr. Lovelady was a short, dirty man who collected the Negro insurance, coming around to the cabins or the kitchens every Saturday morning, to collect fifteen cents. He and his wife lived at the hotel. One morning his wife committed suicide. They had a child, a little girl. He and the child went away. After a week or two he came back alone. We would see him going along the lanes and the back streets on Saturday mornings.

" Nonsense," Father said. " You'll be the first thing I'll see in the kitchen tomorrow morning."

" You'll see what you'll see, I reckon," Nancy said. " But it will take the Lord to say what that will be."

VI

We left her sitting before the fire.

" Come and put the bar up," Father said. But she didn't move. She didn't look at us again, sitting quietly there between the lamp and the fire. From some distance down the lane we could look back and see her through the open door.

" What, Father? " Caddy said. " What's going to happen? "

" Nothing," Father said. Jason was on Father's back, so Jason was the tallest of all of us. We went down into the ditch. I looked at it, quiet. I couldn't see much where the moonlight and the shadows tangled.

" If Jesus is hid here, he can see us, can't he?" Caddy said.

" He's not there," Father said. " He went away a long time ago."

" You made me come," Jason said, high; against the sky, it looked like Father had two heads, a little one and a big one. " I didn't want to."

We went up out of the ditch. We could still see Nancy's house and the open door, but we couldn't see Nancy now, sitting before the fire with the door open, because she was tired. " I just done got tired," she said. " I just a nigger. It ain't no fault of mine."

But we could hear her, because she began just after we came up out of the ditch, the sound that was not singing and not unsinging. " Who will do our washing now, Father? " I said.

" I'm not a nigger," Jason said, high and close above Father's head.

" You're worse," Caddy said, " you are a tattletale. If something was to jump out, you'd be scairder than a nigger."

" I wouldn't," Jason said.

" You'd cry," Caddy said.

" Caddy," Father said.

" I wouldn't! " Jason said.

" Scairy cat," Caddy said.

" Candace! " Father said.

— From *These Thirteen*, 1931. Reprinted
by permission of Random House, Inc.

THE NEGRO IN THE WELL

By Erskine Caldwell

JULE ROBINSON was lying in bed snoring when his foxhounds struck a live trail a mile away and woke him up with a start. He jumped to the floor, jerked on his shoes, and ran out into the front yard. It was about an hour before dawn.

Holding his hat to the side of his head like a swollen hand, he listened to the trailing on the ridge above the house. With his hat to deflect the sound into his ear, he could hear the dogs treading in the dry underbrush as plainly as his own breathing. It had taken him only a few seconds to determine that the hounds were not cold-trailing, and he put his hat back on his head and stooped over to lace his shoes.

"Papa," a frightened voice said, "don't go off again now — wait till daybreak, anyway."

Jule turned around and saw the dim outline of his two girls. They were huddled together in the window of their bedroom. Jessie and Clara were old enough to take care of themselves, he thought, but that did not stop them from getting in his way when he wanted to go fox hunting.

"Go on back to bed and sleep, Jessie, you and Clara," he said gruffly. "Those hounds are just up on the ridge. They can't take me much out of hollering distance before sunup."

"We're scared, Papa," Clara said.

"Scared of what?" Jule asked impatiently. "There ain't a thing for two big girls like you and Jessie to be scared of. What's there to be scared of in this big country, anyway?"

The hounds stopped trailing for a moment, and Jule straightened up to listen in the silence. All at once they began again, and he bent down to finish tying his shoes.

Off in the distance he could hear several other packs of trailing hounds, and by looking closely at the horizon he could see the twinkle of campfires where bands of fox hunters had stopped to warm their hands and feet.

"Are you going anyway, Papa?" Clara asked.

"I'm going anyway," he answered.

The two girls ran back to bed and pulled the covers over their heads. There was no way to argue with Jule Robinson when he had set his head on following his foxhounds.

The craze must have started anew sometime during the holidays, because by the end of the first week in January it looked and sounded as if everybody in Georgia were trading foxhounds by day and bellowing "Whoo-way-oh!" by night. From the time the sun went down until the next morning when it came up, the woods, fields, pastures, and swamps were crawling with beggar-liced men and yelping hound-dogs. Nobody would have thought of riding horseback after the hounds in a country where there was a barbwire fence every few hundred yards.

Automobiles roared and rattled over the rough country roads all night long. The fox hunters had to travel fast in order to keep up with the pack.

It was not safe for any living thing with four legs to be out after sundown, because the hounds had the hunting fever too, and packs of those rangy half-starved dogs were running down and devouring calves, hogs, and even yellow-furred bobcats. It had got so during the past two weeks that the chickens knew enough to take to their roosts an hour ahead of time, because those packs of hunt-hungry hounds could not wait for sunset any more.

Jule finished lacing his shoes and went around the house. The path to the ridge began in the back yard and weaved up the hillside like a cowpath through a thicket. Jule passed the well and stopped to feel in his pockets to see if he had enough smoking tobacco to last him until he got back.

While he was standing there he heard behind him a sound like water gurgling through the neck of a demijohn. Jule listened again.

The sound came even more plainly while he listened. There was no creek anywhere within hearing distance, and the nearest water was in the well. He went to the edge and listened again. The well did not have a stand or a windlass; it was merely a forty-foot hole in the ground with boards laid over the top to keep pigs and chickens from falling into it.

" O Lord, help me now! " a voice said.

Jule got down on his hands and knees and looked at the well cover in the darkness. He felt of the boards with his hands. Three of them had been moved, and there was a black oblong hole that was large enough to drop a mule through.

" Who's that? " Jule said, stretching out his neck and cocking his ear.

" O Lord, help me now," the voice said again, weaker than before.

The gurgling sound began again, and Jule knew then that it was the water in the well.

" Who's down there muddying up my well? " Jule said.

There was no sound then. Even the gurgling stopped.

Jule felt on the ground for a pebble and dropped it into the well. He counted until he could hear the *kerplunk* when it struck the water.

" Doggone your hide, whoever you are down there," Jule said. " Who's down there? "

Nobody answered.

Jule felt in the dark for the water bucket, but he could not find it. Instead, his fingers found a larger pebble, a stone almost as big around as his fist, and he dropped it into the well.

The big rock struck something else before it finally went into the water.

" O Lord, I'm going down and can't help myself," the voice down there said. " O Lord, a big hand is trying to shove me under."

The hounds trailing on the ridge swung around to the east and started back again. The fox they were after was trying to back-trail them, but Jule's hounds were hard to fool. They had got to be almost as smart as a fox.

Jule straightened up and listened to the running.

" Whoo-way-oh! " he called after the dogs.

That sent them on yelping even louder than before.

" Is that you up there, Mr. Jule? " the voice asked.

Jule bent over the well again, keeping one ear on the dogs on the ridge. He did not want to lose track of them when they were on a live trail like that.

" This is only Bokus Bradley, Mr. Jule," he said.

" What you doing down in my well muddying it up like that, Bokus? "

" It was something like this, Mr. Jule," Bokus said. " I was coming down the ridge a while ago, trying to keep up with my hounds, and I stumbled over your well cover. I reckon I must have missed the path, somehow or other. Your well cover wouldn't hold me up, or something, and the first thing I knew, here I was. I've been here ever since I fell in. I reckon I've been down here most of the night. I hope you ain't mad at me, Mr. Jule. I just naturally couldn't help it at all."

" You've muddied up my well water," Jule said. " I ain't so doggone pleased about that."

" I reckon I have, some," Bokus said, " but I just naturally couldn't help it none at all."

" Where'd your dogs go to, Bokus? " Jule asked.

" I don't know, Mr. Jule. I haven't heard a sound out of them since I fell in here. They was headed for the creek when I was coming down the ridge behind them. Can you hear them anywhere now, Mr. Jule? "

Several packs of hounds could be heard. Jule's on the ridge was trailing east, and a pack was trailing down the creek toward town. Over toward the hills several more packs were running, but they were so far away it was not easy to tell whom they belonged to.

" Sounds to me like I hear your dogs down the creek, headed for the swamp," Jule said.

" Whoo-way-oh! " Bokus called.

The sound from the well struck Jule like a blast out of a megaphone.

" Your dogs can't hear you from way down there, Bokus," he said.

" I know they can't, Mr. Jule, and that's why I sure enough want to get out of here. My poor dogs don't know which way I want them to trail when they can't hear me talk to them."

" Whoo-way-oh! " Bokus shouted. " O Lord, help me now! "

Jule's dogs sounded as if they were closing in on a fox and Jule jumped to his feet.

" Whoo-way-oh! " he shouted, cupping his hands around his mouth. " Whoo-way-oh! "

" Is you still up there, Mr. Jule? " Bokus asked. " Please, Mr. Jule, don't go away and leave me down here in this cold well. I'll do anything for you if you'll just only get me out of here. I've been standing neck-deep in this cold water near about all night long."

Jule threw some of the boards over the well.

" What you doing up there, Mr. Jule? "

Jule took off his hat and held the brim like a fan to the side of his head. He could hear the panting of the dogs while they ran.

" How many foxhounds have you got, Bokus? " Jule asked.

" I got me eight," Bokus said. " They're mighty fine fox trailers, too, Mr. Jule. But I'd like to get me out of this-here well before doing much more talking with you."

" You could get along somehow with less than that, couldn't you, Bokus? "

" If I had to, I'd have to," Bokus said, " but I sure enough would hate to have fewer than my eight dogs, though. Eight is just naturally the right-sized pack for me, Mr. Jule."

" How are you figuring on getting out of there? " Jule said.

" I just naturally figured on you helping me out, Mr. Jule," he said. " Least-aways, that's about the only way I know of getting out of this-here well. I tried climbing, but the dirt just naturally crumbles away every time I dig my toes into the sides."

" You've got that well so muddied up it won't be fit to drink out of for a week or more," Jule said.

" I'll do what I can to clean it out for you, Mr. Jule, if I ever get up on top of the solid ground again. Can you hear those hounds of mine trailing now, Mr. Jule? "

" They're still down the creek. I reckon I could lower the water bucket, and I could pull a little, and you could climb a little, and maybe you'd get out that way."

"That just naturally would suit me fine, Mr. Jule," Bokus said eagerly. "Here I is. When is you going to lower that water bucket?"

Jule stood up and listened to his dogs trailing on the ridge. From the way they sounded, it would not be long before they treed the fox they were after.

"It's only about an hour till daybreak," Jule said. "I'd better go on up on the ridge and see how my hounds are making out. I can't do much here at the well till the sun comes up."

"Don't go away and leave me now, Mr. Jule," Bokus begged. "Mr. Jule, please, sir, just lower that water bucket down here and help me get out of here, Mr. Jule. My dogs will get all balled up without me following them. Whoo-way-oh! Whoo-way-oh!"

The pack of fox-trailing hounds was coming up from the creek, headed toward the house. Jule took off his hat and held it beside his ear. He listened to them panting and yelping.

"If I had two more hounds, I'd be mighty pleased," Jule said, shouting loud enough for Bokus to hear. "Just two is all I need right now."

"You wouldn't be wanting two of mine, would you, Mr. Jule?" Bokus asked.

"It's a good time to make a trade," Jule said. "It's a mighty good time, being as how you are down in the well and want to get out."

"Two, did you say?"

"Two is what I said."

There was silence in the well for a long time. For nearly five minutes Jule listened to the packs of dogs all around him, some on the ridge, some down the creek, and some in the far-off hills. The barking of the hounds was a sweeter sound to him than anything else in the world. He would lose a night's sleep any time just to stay up and hear a pack of foxhounds live-trailing.

"Whoo-way-oh!" he called.

"Mr. Jule!" Bokus shouted up from the bottom of the well.

Jule went to the edge and leaned over to hear what the Negro had to say.

"How about that-there trade now, Bokus?"

"Mr. Jule, I just naturally couldn't swap off two of my hounds. I just sure enough couldn't."

"Why not?" Jule said.

"Because I'd have only just six dogs left, Mr. Jule, and I couldn't do much fox hunting with just that many."

Jule straightened up and kicked the boards over the top of the well.

"You won't be following even so few as one hound for a while," he said, "because I'm going to leave you down in the bottom where you stand now. It's another hour, almost, till daybreak, and I can't be wasting that time staying here talking to you. Maybe when I get back you'll be in a mind to do some trading, Bokus."

Jule kicked the boards on top of the well.

"O Lord, help me now!" Bokus said. "But, O Lord, don't make me swap off no two hounds for the help I'm asking for."

Jule stumbled over the water bucket when he turned and started across the yard toward the path up the ridge. Up there he could hear his dogs running again, and when he took off his hat and held it to the side of his head he could hear Polly pant, and Senator snort, and Mary Jane whine, and Sunshine yelp, and the rest of them barking at the head of the trail. He put on his hat, pulled it down hard all around, and hurried up the path to follow them on the ridge. The fox would not be able to hold out much longer.

"Whoo-way-oh!" he called to his hounds. "Whoo-way-oh!"

The echo was a masterful sound to hear.

— From *Southways*, 1938. Reprinted by permission of Duell, Sloan, and Pearce, Inc.

A PROUDFUL FELLOW

The Black People Called Him Ut Wine

By Julia Peterkin

His name was Earth Wine—Earth for the earth itself, that he might have long life, and Wine for the family to which he belonged. His black mother and all the other black people on the plantation called him Ut Wine. He called himself that.

Ut could not bear to live like the rest of his people. The climate was warm; most of the days were brilliant and fine; the tottering old Quarter houses which had sheltered Ut's black kin ever since the first of them were brought up the river, long ago, to work as slaves alongside the mules in the cotton and corn fields, gave shelter enough, all the shelter Ut ever needed from rain or sun or cold.

Ut really loved the old houses and the great old moss-draped oaks that shaded them, but he wanted to own a piece of land and have a home of his own. This may have been because he was not altogether black. His mother was, but his father was white.

White blood has a strange way of poisoning men so that they cannot rest unless they own things. Sometimes they crave land, sometimes houses, sometimes people. Ut craved all three, for he felt that Harpa, his young wife, was his the same as his faithful dog Sounder, or his cow, or his mule.

His mother argued with him and tried to show him that he was foolish and proudful; that while men may think they own land because they pay taxes on it and plow it and salt it with sweat to make it give them grain or cotton, the truth is that the land owns them all the time; and when it has worn them out with struggling and striving, it takes them and turns them back into dust to feed its trees and grass and weeds.

Ut was a fool to turn his back on things that were good enough. He had good clothes and a roof over his head; he could rest or pleasure himself from dusk until dawn every night God sent. He ought to thank God and be satisfied.

In spite of her warning that he was tempting fate when he stepped out alone, for himself, Ut bought a piece of thick-wooded land some miles away where a lonely hill bulged out, making the sullen yellow river crook sharply into a bend that was called the Devil's Elbow. It had always been a bad-luck place, for the river swamp below it was filled with hoot owls and barking snakes and spirit dogs and ugly things bred in slime and black moon-shadows.

Ut's land was rich enough, but its richness fed weeds and grass as freely as it fed his crops, and it took a brave heart and tough sinews to rule it and keep it smooth and clean.

If Ut had wanted to run a still and make corn whiskey to sell, his mother would not have minded, for easy money can be made so, and no better place could be found for such work than the deep shady cove on the side of that hill where the great trees and thick undergrowth hide the sky from the earth.

Or if Ut had done something wrong and wanted to hide from the law, she would have been glad for him to stay in the swamp below the hill, for it is a roadless jungle and the river's broad stream runs clear to the sea and could take him to safety without leaving a single telltale track behind.

But Ut wanted only a bit of land and a home, and a chance to make something of himself. He built his house out of pine poles with the cracks carefully daubed with mud; and the chimney was made out of sticks and clay, but it was solid and strong, a good enough house for anybody to live in.

Then he planted patches of peas and potatoes and vegetables, and got a cow, a flock of chickens, and put a shote into a pen to grow into a big hog by fall. He aimed to have plenty to eat, not only for himself and Harpa, but for Joe, his younger brother. Next to Harpa he loved Joe better than anybody in the world.

All these things kept him working early and late, Saturdays the same as other days, although everybody else in the whole country rested from Friday night until Monday morning.

Sometimes Harpa complained that Ut had forgotten all about pleasure; but he always claimed that he got his joy out of owning his home. He went hunting and fishing now and then. The river was full of fish to be had for the taking, the woods full of game; Sounder had a sure nose and Ut was a good shot. His old double-barreled gun was so well trained it could shoot straight and kill almost without his ever aiming it.

Ut had a tender heart and he hated to kill the free wild things; but he had hard strength-taxing work to do, and the flesh of the forest creatures makes food that hardens a man's sinews and reddens his blood far better than corn meal and butts-bacon can ever do.

Instead of taking a smart black wife from the Quarters, Ut had gone to the village, ten miles away, and married Harpa, a slender slim-footed girl, even lighter in color than himself. For in spite of his white blood, Ut was dark. He had his mother's crinkly hair and her stout stocky body, but instead of her wide flattened nostrils and thick lips he had his white father's straight mouth and narrow nose, and big soft eyes that were full of tawny light.

Harpa's skin was warm yellow and her eyes blue-green; her straight black hair was shiny and her purple lips were made for laughing. To Ut she was everything lovely and sweet. Little slim yellow Harpa. She did not like work, but Ut felt that her slender body was not meant for work. One morning she tried jerking a hoe through the tough grass roots, and in no time both her palms were blistered. Her hands were too small and tender to stand the rasping of a rough hoe-handle.

Harpa hated to cook. Greasy black pots and ugly dishwater made her feel sick. But Ut ate most of the victuals, and he had far rather cook them than to have Harpa scorching her face in front of the open fireplace where the cooking had to be done.

❦ ❦ ❦

One hot summer evening Ut came in from the field, weary and drenched with sweat. He found Harpa sitting on the doorstep laughing and talking with Joe, and watching the full moon rise. She had on a cool white dress, and a bow of red ribbon tied her hair at one side. When she drew her clean skirts aside to keep Ut from touching them, Joe grunted and frowned. "You don' jump up an' wait on you' husban', Harpa?" he asked. "After he works hard all day, you sets still when he comes home at night? Gal, you ought to be shame. If you was my wife, I declare to Gawd, I'd lick you 'til you would'n eenjoy settin' down."

Ut stopped short in his tracks. "You hush, Joe. You ever did run you' mouth too fast."

Joe got to his feet, talking faster than ever, protesting he had not meant to hurt Ut's feelings. That was the last thing he'd ever do in the world. Ut was the best old brother any man ever had, and the best husband any woman ever had, too. Harpa ought to be glad to wait on him and cook for him. If she would stick at the field work her hands would get tough and used to it.

Ut listened gravely, but his tone was sharp when he answered that what Harpa did was none of Joe's business. Harpa was not a cook or a field hand. She washed and ironed and sewed and patched, and that was her full share of the work. Joe had better learn to keep his mouth out of other people's business.

Joe grinned good-naturedly. He had not meant to meddle. But he would tell the world that when he took him a wife she would never spend his good money buying red stockings and shiny shoes. Those shoes Harpa had on must have cost as much as a whole week's rations. Instead of being vexed at what Joe said discounting her ways, Harpa's white teeth flashed in a laugh so bright, so lovely, that Ut's steady heart fairly turned over. Blessed little Harpa. When she looked like that Ut felt he would work his fingers to the very bone to buy her red stockings and shiny shoes, or anything else she wanted.

Now she tilted her head sideways and with her soft husky voice full of teasing and bantering fun, she asked Joe:

"How 'bout red ribbons, Joe? Would you buy you' wife a piece o' red ribbon?"

Instead of answering Harpa's question Joe's bold eyes looked up at the big white moon while his fingers softly stroked the strings of his battered guitar.

Ut smiled. Harpa knew how to get the best of Joe. Precious little

Harpa, so worthless and yet so merry. Always ready for a laugh or a dance or a song. New shoes never did hurt her feet. When his land was paid for she should have everything in the world she wanted. She should take a trip to town and buy cloth in the stores; and go on the train excursions to Charleston. If he got up a little earlier and worked a little harder and took less time at noon, maybe he could make a bit more money for Harpa.

Ut had helped to raise Joe from a baby; in fact Ut was still trying to raise him. Joe had plenty of sense; he was able, but he wasted his time drinking, gambling, frolicking, singing. Still when Joe had a drink or two his singing was so beautiful that it made Ut's heart open and shut like a book.

Ut often pleaded with Joe to settle down to some kind of steady work; but Joe laughed at the idea. Nobody would ever catch him getting up at dawn to plow a stumpy field. Ut knew nothing about pleasure, and he had never tried loafing or gambling or drinking, or looked at any woman but Harpa. Ut knew Joe pitied him for such ignorance, such stupid ambition and pride. Now Joe's lean black face shone with amusement. His sharp teeth grinned and his black eyes twinkled as he boasted that he was no proudful fellow, thank God. If he could be the richest man in the whole world he would never spend his good days sweating in a piece of new ground, tied to one lone woman. God made his legs too long to walk all day behind a slow-poking mule. They were made to dance and roam after liquor and good-looking women. His fingers itched when they were not picking a box (guitar) or shooting craps. When he got too old for pleasure then he might settle down; but as long as his body was full of good red blood he would never waste himself working. He had too much sense for that.

"How 'bout it, Harpa? Ain' I right?" Joe asked suddenly.

To Ut's astonishment Harpa hesitated, then said there were two sides to everything. Men ought not to forget everything else but work. Once she heard a preacher read out of the Book at church how lilies and grass and beasts never do a single lick of work, yet they have what they need. Joe had clothes and food and pleasure even if he had no land or house or wife.

❦ ❦ ❦

The next morning, Friday, was Harpa's washday. After Ut had filled the washpots with water and built a fire under them and carried the clothes down the hill for Harpa, he walked around looking at his things — noting how the cotton and corn throve and were clean of grass, how the potato vines met in their rows, how the peas were bearing. Now he had every right to be proudful. His work was bearing fruit and proving he had not out-reckoned his strength.

Harpa was up and washing by now; he would go tell her how well everything did.

Hurrying down the narrow path to the spring which ran cool and clear out from under the hill, he soon came to Harpa and the washpots and tubs; but instead of Harpa's bending over the washboard fighting the dirt in the clothes with her two hands, or beating it out with the stout oak paddle, she sat on the ground mournful and cheerless.

"Washin' don' agree wid me, Ut. My back is all but broke," she moaned forlornly.

"Po' li'l gal," he pitied, "it's dem big bedsheets; dey is too heavy fo' you to rule, Honey. Le's stop havin' bedsheets. Quilts won' dirty so fast."

Harpa shook her head. "De bedsheets ain' so bad as dem overalls o' you' own. I can' get 'em clean, not to save my life." She shuddered as she looked at the tub where his offending garment hid under the foamy white soapsuds.

"Lemme wash 'em, Honey; you set still an' rest!"

He took up the long wooden paddle and stirred the things round and round, shirts, undergarments, overalls, bedsheets. Hot lye-scented steam rose in his face — sickening smell. No wonder Harpa hated it. She looked sick sure enough. Her warm skin was pale and ashy, her eyes big and hollow. Maybe — maybe his great wish, his wish for a son, a boy-child, was going to come to pass. His heart jerked at the strings that held it in place, joy flooded him so.

A sudden happy idea came into his mind. "Listen, Honey, lemme hitch up de mule an' wagon an' go to de Quarters an' git Mocky to come an' do dis washin'. Mocky is strong as a ox. She'll come every Friday an' help you do de clothes. I'll pay her."

He lifted Harpa up and stood her on her feet. "Honey, don' look so sorrowful. It makes me pure weak as branch water. If you don' smile I would'n be able to walk home up de hill."

Then Harpa's laughter rippled out bright as the sunshine that pierced the hot shade, and Ut put an arm around her shoulders and together they went up the path.

Mocky came gladly. Washing those few clothes was an easy task for her; she had strength enough in her big arms to break Harpa's body in two; the skin on her black hands was like leather. By noon the clothes were washed and hanging on the line in the sun.

Although Mocky was fat, she turned on her feet light as air, and she was full of fun; but Ut noticed that few words passed between her and Harpa.

❦ ❦ ❦

That night at supper Ut praised the whiteness of the cloth on the table, but instead of joining in, to his amazement Harpa's blue-green eyes darkened and narrowed and her lips tightened into a thin purple line.

"You ought to had married Mocky 'stead o' me, Ut."

"Why, Honey, I would'n gi' you for forty Mockys." Ut's happiness was completely gone.

Harpa carelessly stretched out her slender limbs and drawled, "Joe says Mocky was ever ravin' 'bout you, an' you use to take her to prayer-meetin's every Sunday night, when you an' her was agrowin' up."

Ut laughed and leaning closer to her whispered tenderly, "If you knowed how pretty you looks wid dat li'l red bow a tyin' you' hair, you would'n talk so, Harpa. Whe'd you git dat red ribbon anyhow? Did Joe fetch 'em to you?"

"No," Harpa answered, and her eyes glittered bright and cold as she said it.

A step suddenly sounded in the shadows, and Joe's voice called in blithely, "Yunnuh better stay in de house. Dis moonshine is dang'ous. It's done gone to my head."

"Come on in, Joe." Ut got up to meet him. "Pick us de bes'

tune you know. Sing us de foolishes' song. Harpa's gone an' got sad tonight."

"I ain' sad," Harpa declared. "Ut's de one. Ut is sad 'cause he married me when he might'a married Mocky. She could'a worked in de field an' cooked an' washed an' ironed, an' had de chillen an' patched an' sewed an' had plenty o' time to go to prayer-meetin's too."

Ut said no more; he knew that tone of Harpa's; but Joe's plunk-plunking grew louder, steadier, until a gay song began twanging clearly. Then Harpa's anger was gone, all of a sudden. She was little more than a child, after all; and Ut tried to have patience, long patience, with her babyish ways.

She had eaten very little these last hot days, and now she looked so slight, so slender in the moonlight; he felt almost afraid for her strength. Little slim sweet Harpa.

If he went now and set a trap in the river, he might catch some fish for breakfast. Harpa liked fish, and she ought to eat more than she did.

Neither Joe nor Harpa noticed when he got up off the step and went inside to mix up some corn meal and cotton for fish-bait to put in the trap. When he came back and said, "I'm gwine down to de river, but I'll be back in a minute," Joe said, "All right, old socks." But Harpa answered not a word. She was still cross with him, but she would be over that by morning. She never held her mad long. Easy hurt, easy over. Easy sad, easy glad, that was Harpa's way.

As Ut ran down the shadowy path with old Sounder following close at his heels, a cool night wind sprang up and high pines over-head began moaning. The frogs and crickets cheeped lonesomely, but the night birds had little to say.

When a falling star made a bright spark across the sky, Ut stopped to watch it, for that star made a path for somebody's soul. When he reached the sand bar by the river an owl flopped out from a hollow tree and whoo-whooed a mournful death call. Ut was startled. Two death signs. Two people were going to die. The star and the owl both said so.

He watched the dark bird's shadow float over the swamp on the tops of the moonlit trees, but the wet sand sucked at his feet. It wanted to swallow him up, but he was not so easily caught. He quickly set the trap, then slowly and thoughtfully mounted the path toward home. Not a sound came from the cabin. Everything was silent except a harsh crackle of dry leaves fretted by the wind.

Joe and Harpa must have gotten tired waiting for him and gone to bed. He would go to sleep too and be up early to get the fish for breakfast, for Mocky was coming to finish the ironing, and if the trap had luck it would catch plenty of fish for her too.

❦ ❦ ❦

Dawn barely hid the stars the next morning when Ut eased stealthily out into the yard. He must feed the things and milk the cow, but he must not wake Harpa.

"Eat a plenty and lay," he murmured softly to the hens as he scattered their corn on the ground. "Harpa likes a lot o' eggs in de bread." When he put a great armful of hay and a dozen ears of corn in the mule's trough, he looked at the beast's huge belly. This was Saturday, the day to go to town for the week's rations. The road was long and the wagon heavy. He would put some extra ears in the trough.

"Take time and chaw, old man. Git some meat on you' ribs. You' Missus hates to ride behind a pack o' bones," he said gently as he patted the mule's bony sides.

The pig grunted impatiently and peeped at him between the cracks of the rail pen. Ut laughed at such greediness, but he chided him in a whisper, "Don' squeal so loud, son; you'll wake Harpa. Eat you' breakfast. Fatten all you can. Make us a whole tub full o' lard by Christmas."

Ut was glad for the day. Every sound was good against the stillness — the cock's proudful crowing, the hens' proudful clucking as they woke up the biddies, the moaning of the wind through the pines.

Smoke and sparks were rushing up out of the cabin chimney, for Mocky had come. She had the fish fried, the bread baked, the coffee boiled, the table set, and the kettle on the hearth singing and breathing out a cloud of steam over the row of flatirons heating by the fire's red blaze. But Harpa was not up and dressed yet.

With a pile of sprinkled clothes rolled tight to hold the moisture, on a chair beside her, Mocky bent over the ironing board, humming a tune and running a hot iron swiftly, deftly, over the starched bosom of Ut's white Sunday shirt. Drops of sweat ran down her shiny fat face and fell with tiny hissing pats on the iron. When she looked up to say good morning to Ut, her thick mouth smiled a little but her eyes were full of sulky darkness. "Breakfast sho' smells good, Mocky," Ut praised.

"Harpa's de lazies', triflines' woman I ever seen in my life," Mocky answered.

"Oh no, Mocky. Harpa ain' dat. She jus' don' like to wake up soon. Dat's all. You womenfolks sho' is hard on one another, enty Joe?" Ut tried to laugh good-naturedly as he said this, although Mocky's brazen talk about Harpa did sting him.

"Le's eat," Joe suggested. "I'm hongry."

"We may as well. Harpa's mos' ready anyhow."

The three of them sat down and had their pans helped when Harpa came out of the shedroom; but instead of sitting down with them she stood by the chair and shook her head, "I can' stan' de hotness in dis room, Ut. It would cook a egg. Dat fish smells so sickenin', too. I'm gwine to de spring an' git me a cool drink o' water."

Ut got to his feet, with his mouth full of food, "I'll go wid you, Honey," he mumbled. But Joe dropped his spoon with a click in his pan, and pushed back his chair, "You set down, Ut, and finish you' breakfast. I'll go wid Harpa. I ain' in no hurry to eat. You set down."

Joe took an empty water bucket off the shelf and followed Harpa out into the yard. It was just as well. A walk in the fresh air would do Harpa good, for the room was too hot and steamy for comfort. Ut helped himself to another piece of fish, then passed the pan to Mocky.

"Take another piece, Mocky. Dis fish is sweet as can be," he said.

Mocky's eyes were two hard black beads, and her mouth was twisted into an ugly pout.

"How come you's such a fool dese days, Ut? You used to have good sense."

Ut could scarcely believe his ears. What did Mocky mean?

"I mean you mus' be blind as a bat. Dat's what I mean," she declared bitterly.

All of a sudden Ut knew what Mocky meant. She was intimating an ugly thing about Harpa and Joe. She was jealous of Harpa. She always had been jealous of any girl he liked, and now she wanted him to believe a filthy lie about his wife. Hot blood made a red glow before his eyes, and he seized Mocky's arm in a grip too tight to be loosened.

"Listen, Mocky," — blind fury almost strangled him — "if you crack you' teeth about Harpa, I'll kill you. I ought to choke you' tongue out right dis minute. You mean, lyin' hussy —"

"Choke! Go on an' choke. Cuss me much as you want to, but dat ain' gwine change Harpa none." Mocky shook all over.

"Gal, if you call Harpa's name one more time I'll wring you' neck same as a chicken —" Ut felt his fingers tightening on Mocky's flesh, but she did not move a muscle. She knew him too well not to yield now. She had to shut her mouth.

The cabin was still as a grave except for the crackling fire. Two bright tears hung in Mocky's eyes, and her lips shook with unspoken words. Then the doorstep creaked sharply, and two black shadows fell across the door. There they lay side by side, still and stiff as the headstones of two graves. Joe and Harpa had come back — were listening — they may have heard every word.

Ut's head was dizzy, his heart sick, his blood full of fever. He staggered out past them into the yard, down the path to the river where he fell prone on the moist bank. There he lay, his face downward on his crossed arms, the hot sun beating on his back, while poisoned thoughts raced through his brain.

Mocky was like all the rest of those black Quarter women — mean, jealous, vain; unhappy, unless they were strewing somebody's name about, dragging it in the dirt. None of them had ever liked Harpa; now they'd be glad to spread a filthy tale about her. Certainly Harpa liked Joe, and Joe liked Harpa too, even if he had never praised her once in his life; but if Mocky ever said one ugly word about them again he'd kill her as quickly as he'd kill a poison snake that threatened them. Mocky hated to see him lawfully married to Harpa and living in a decent way, making something of himself. He knew she would have taken him and not cared one bit whether the preacher ever read out of the Book and prayed over them or not. Mocky was black, her ways and her heart were black. She would be glad to tear down all he had worked and striven to build up. He wouldn't let her. He'd go send her home, make her get out of his house, right now.

Before he got halfway up the hill, he met Harpa coming to call him to dinner. Her face and dress were wet with sweat, and her narrow brows were drawn together with a black frown.

"How come you went an' hurt Mocky's feelin's so bad, Ut?" she scolded. "If I was you I'd be shame. I declare to Gawd, you' patience is too short for you to be a big grown man like you is."

"But, Honey—"

"Don' be honeyin' me, now. Mocky cried so hard Joe had to take 'em home. I had to finish de ironin' and cook de dinner too, all by myself. I'm weary enough to die."

Her eyes looked big and hollow, and dark shadows lay underneath them.

"I'm too sorry, Harpa. Whyn't you call me?"

"Call you? How'd I know whe' you was?"

They walked on without speaking until Harpa added sorrowfully, "I was countin' on gwine to town wid you dis evenin', an' now I'm too wore-out. I can' go."

"De ride would do you good."

"Good! Ridin' in dat old rough ramshackle wagon would'n do nobody good. My bones would sure be shook to pieces. My back's mos' broke now."

Poor little Harpa, so thin and frail, and sometimes so strangely sad.

While Ut ate the dinner she had cooked for him, Harpa sat down by the window so that the light from the overcast sky could fall on the faded, freshly washed and ironed overalls which she had started to mend stitch by stitch.

Her eyes lifted from her sewing now and then to rest on the faint blue hills far across the river swamp. She and those hills were in some way alike now; both so softly curved, so tender and lovely, both so far away from him, so out of his reach. All his life those mysterious hills over the river yonder had stood for better things than anything he had ever known on earth, as if they were a part of heaven itself. Yes, Harpa was like them.

He went and stood by her trying to think of some suitable word to say. Poor little tired Harpa, mending and mending, working for him, placing the small industrious stitches side by side. He bent over and kissed the back of her slender neck, then gave one little hand a gentle pat; but the needle it held pricked him sharply, as the hand jerked away from his caress.

"You better hurry an' go on to town, Ut. I see a cloud a-risin' yonder over the river."

He followed the look her blue-green eyes flashed up at the sky, where in truth, ragged clouds were piling. She was right. He must be going.

"I hate so bad to leave you by you'self, Harpa."

"Sounder'll be here wid me."

"I'll hurry back quick as I can, Honey. What must I fetch you from town?"

"I don' want nuttin."

"Not nuttin."

Harpa was out of sorts, downhearted for truth; but he would fetch something for her. Maybe he could find her a string of red glass beads to wear with her pretty red stockings. They'd be beautiful around her slim neck, against her warm yellow skin.

"Good-by, Harpa."

"Good-by, Ut."

"Don' git lonesome, Honey."

Harpa did not answer.

"I'm too sorry you ain' gwine wid me."

No answer again.

As Ut went down the steps Harpa called to him, "You better go by an' see you' Ma! You ain' seen 'em not since week befo' las'!"

Harpa was right, he must not forget his kind old mother. When he bought Harpa's beads he might buy his mother a little present too, maybe a red and white head-kerchief to tie on her head for Sunday.

"Good-by, Harpa!"

"Good-by, Ut!"

❦ ❦ ❦

The mule was slow and the cloud and night both caught Ut on the way home. The steady rain cut clear through his clothes and reached his skin, cold and wet. He went by the Quarters to give his mother the pound of sugar he had bought for her to make sweetened bread; since Harpa's beads had cost so much he had not had enough money left for a head-kerchief.

She pleaded with him to stop long enough to dry his clothes, but he wouldn't, for Harpa was by herself except for Sounder. When he jerked up the rope lines and urged the mule to hurry, the foolish old beast, remembering his old home at the Quarters, would not budge. Ut bawled at him sternly, then doubled back a rope line and gave him some loud wallops; but the tough-mouthed, hard-headed old creature lifted his head, and stretching out his neck gave a long mournful "hee-hee-a haw-haw-haw," as if sorrow were breaking his heart. Instead of moving he took one unwilling step forward, then he stumbled and almost fell, for his forefoot had picked up a nail. A mean, ugly, crooked, rusty nail which had dug through his hoof clear down to the bone.

Those old Quarter houses were always dropping rusty nails out of their rotten sides, and now one had crippled the mule's foot and he could not walk another step. Ut would have to leave the wagon and rations with his mother, and walk home to Harpa.

A wet gray moon gave out a poor dim light as he took a short cut through the woods; but he knew the way well, and in a little while he was climbing the hill through the pattering rain to the solid black blur which was home. He thought Harpa would have had a bright fire burning, and be standing in the door watching for him; but the cabin was dark and still. She must have gotten tired and gone to sleep.

That was good. He would surprise her. He would tiptoe in and lay the beautiful glass beads in her hand. They would wake her.

Precious little Harpa. When Sounder came sniffling and whining to meet him, Ut hushed him with a pat. Sounder must be quiet so that Harpa would not wake until the time came.

The rain sang gaily as it fell off the cabin roof and splashed down off the eaves. But the bed and the chairs in the big room were empty. Harpa must be asleep in the shedroom. A loose board squeaked sharply under Ut's weight, and Harpa cried out of the blackness in the shedroom, "Great Gawd! What is dat?"

The pitiful terror in her voice made Ut smile. But before he could tell her it was he, Ut, her own husband, Joe was saying with a laugh, "Don' be so scary, gal. Po' ole Ut ain' halfway home, not yet."

Ut's horrified ears seized the whispered words and he tried to yell; but his frozen tongue could make no sound. His ears began roaring like the river in a flood. He could not think for its noise. But through the clear darkness his eyes saw his gun standing in the corner. It would tell them in one word that he was home.

Joe must have heard the trigger click, for he struck a match. Then he leaped up, dropping it right in the folds of Harpa's flowered dress, which lay crumpled and empty on the foot of the bed.

"Ut — you fool — put down dat gun!" Joe shouted between chattering teeth. But the gun spoke one loud short word that answered him forever.

The weak flame of the match sputtered and threatened to die, then it seized avidly on the thin cotton cloth, flaring up bright.

Harpa slid to the floor, shivering, tottering, on her bare feet — then she fell on her knees. "Ut — for Christ's sake — Ut!" she quavered. But some devil inside Ut made him laugh. He told her to pray to her Maker, and not to him now.

Harpa took in one long gasping breath then let it out in a thin wild shriek, "Oh-h-ee — !" She tried to wrench the gun from his hands, but he gave her a hard backward shove toward the bed.

Ut was not certain what happened. The gun must have aimed at her and fired before he let it fall; for red blood, red flesh, hid her breast.

Burning cloth made a bitter stench. The whole room was afire;

bed, walls, floor — all fed the growing flames as they sputtered and roared up toward the ceiling.

He must go. But go where? His old lame mule had a stall, but he had no place in the world now.

Looking back once more he saw Harpa's two little empty shoes standing bravely side by side on the floor. Slamming the door hard behind him, he rushed out of the cabin into the yard where red shadows flew about thick in the air. They ran under his feet, tripping him, blinding him; red flames stuck thin long fingers through the cracks of the cabin, pointing at him, reaching for him, making him stumble. Before he knew what he was about, he had fallen on his knees and prayers were slipping through his lips.

"Do, Jesus — Master — look down on dis poor meeked man — I'm done ruint — ruint —"

A sheet of fire lifted the cabin roof, sparks flew clear up to the sky. "Lawd, Jesus, please, suh, have mussy on me —"

A light touch fell on Ut's throat; then another and another, inch by inch. He held his breath to be certain it was there; then a long cold shudder shook him. Praying would do no good now. His time had come. A measuring-worm was marking the size of his neck; it had already crawled up his back and measured his length for its master, Death. The gallows would hang him, the earth would take his body, and his lost soul would fly on and on until Satan caught it and put it in hell.

He had stripped himself bare. He had nothing left but a rope — a shroud, and a new cold grave.

— From *Century*, May, 1928.
Reprinted by permission.

HOW WILLIE PROUDFIT CAME HOME

By Robert Penn Warren

HIGH UP, on the bluffside of the hill, a spring poured out of an archway of stone. In its basin there, the perfectly clear water eddied ceaselessly, braiding and swelling, swaying the young fronds of fern and the grass which trailed lushly down to the surface, spilling over the lip of stone and plunging down the slope to join the creek below. "Soon's I laid eyes on hit," Willie Proudfit would say, "come-en slide-en down that rock that a-way, I says, thar my house will set. Sometimes a-nights I lays in bed and I kin hear hit. I lays in bed and I kin recollect the times out in the dry country I laid out a-nights and studied on water. In this country the Lord's done give a man water whichever way he turns, fer drinken and washen, hit looks lak, and a man don't know how hit is in the dry country, and the thirsten. But even here ain't ever man got him a spring come-en right outer the top of a hill, lak me, and fall-en so he kin lay and hear hit. Nor ever man got him a cold-air cave to keep his milk sweet to his mouth."

He had built his house right at the creek bank, with the little branch from the falls running into the creek just behind it. And the cave, where the moisture dripped from the pelt-thick green moss, was at the foot of the bluff, just beside the house. Inside the cave, in the chill shadow, the crock jars of milk stood in rows. Willie Proudfit's wife would set her candle on a shelf of stone, for even at noon a candle was needed, and dip up the milk with a tin dipper and pour it into her big blue pitcher. Then, from another crock, she would take a pat of butter. Holding the heavy pitcher in one hand, but out from her body strongly and easily, she would move across the patch of grass toward the house. She would set the pitcher on the table, by her husband's plate, and smile. "Willie, now he's the beatenest," she would say, "fer milk."

"Now I thank you," he might say, and pick up the pitcher; or he might only look up at her, not quite smiling, and say nothing, for he was not a man to talk much except on those rare occasions, in the evenings usually, when, lying stretched out like a cat on the boards of the little porch, he would reach back into his mind for some incident out of those years he had spent on the plains. He would tell it, not exactly for us, it seemed, but for the telling, speaking slowly and tentatively. Reaching back into those past times, he was like a man who, in a dark closet, runs his fingers over some once-familiar object and tries, uncertainly, to identify it. "They's a passel of things," he would say, "on God's earth fer a man to study about, and ain't no man e'er seen 'em all. But I seen some. I seen gullies so deep and wide, you could throw that-air hill in hit, lick-stock and barr'l, and ne'er no difference to a man's sight. And the gully with colors spread out in the light, far as air eye could see, lak a flag. Colors lak the colors in the sky at sun, and layen thar on the ground, lak the sky had come a-fall-en down." Then he might pause. His wife, Adelle, and her niece and nephew and I would be sitting in chairs propped back against the wall, with Willie Proudfit lying there on the floor, scarcely visible in the darkness. We would wait for him, not saying anything. If the season was right, the frogs would be piping down the creek, in the place where the ground gets marshy.

"The Indians taken them colors outer the earth," he would say, "and paint theirselves." And he would pause again, and there would only be the night sounds. Then he would say, "When they dance."

"Heathen," the nephew, Sylvestus, said in the darkness, for he was a pious man.

"Heathen," Willie Proudfit said in his soft, slow voice, "heathen, in a way of speaken." Then he fell silent, brooding backward into those times. Then he said: "But them dance-en, hit ain't just frolic and jollification." Then, later: "They's a passel of things, and the Lord God, He made ever one. In His mighty plan, and ain't a sparrow falleth."

But some evenings, he didn't speak a word.

He was a medium-sized man. His face was thinnish, and it had lines in it, tiny lines that meshed multitudinously in the leathery-looking skin, but it was neither an old nor a young face. The skin was brown like an oak leaf, so brown that against it the bluish-green eyes looked pale, and the very blond hair silvery like the hair of an old man. He wore his hair longer than any man I had ever seen, down to his neck behind and cut off square. Sometimes on Sunday mornings, just after breakfast, he would sit out on the chunk of limestone that formed the back step, and his wife would cut his hair. She had a pair of big clumsy-looking shears she used for that, and when the blades engaged on his thick hair, they made a sound like a heel on sand. He was a quiet and smooth-tempered man, even when times got bad and it looked like he was going to lose his place, and even when he knew he would lose it. He did lose it, and moved away. Before he lost it, he talked once or twice about going back west, like he had when he was a boy. One night, lying there on the porch boards, he suddenly said, quietly and offhand, " Oklahoma," like the answer to a question somebody had asked him. But nobody had said anything for quite a while.

" Oklahoma," the nephew said, and added, " they say a man kin git a start out thar."

" A long time since I seen hit," Willie Proudfit said. He shifted a little, and the boards of the porch floor creaked in the dark. Then he said: " Folks was goen in, then. To git a start. And fer one reason or 'nuther. Some just a move-en kind of folks, just move-en on. Lak I was, them days. The buffalo petered out, and they wasn't no more, whar I'd seen 'em black the ground off yander when a man looked. So I moved on, west. But I come back here. But a lot of folks, they ne'er come back, no-whar."

He waited a while, then he said: " I come back, and left the dry country. But a man ne'er knows. Maybe I'll be goen back. To Oklahoma, maybe."

" Sweat fer nuthen," the nephew said, " in this country."

" Maybe I'll be goen agin," Willie Proudfit said, " and the time comes. If they's a place for a man to go nowadays. My pappy up and left here, and he ne'er aimed to, till the time come. Hit was in 'sixty-one and the war a-starten. My pappy wasn't easy in his mind. He never was no Bible-man exactly, but he studied on the shooten and the killen, and he prayed the Lord to show him which side to take. Which was the Lord's side. One mornen he said, 'I ain't a-stayen in this country, on-easy in my mind and with my neighbors.' He said, 'I'm a-leave-en.'

"So he got shet of what he had, land and gear, what he couldn't git on a wagon. And he put two span oxen to the wagon, and we all hit out towards north Arkansas. Pappy had a cousin in north Arkansas who wrote him a letter sayen north Arkansas was air man's country, free fer the gitten, a fair land and flowen. We went down west Tennessee, whar hit was cotton, ever whar a man looked. And to Memphis. We got on a steamboat at Memphis and went down the Mississippi and up the Arkansas, the country flat lak a man's hand, and the ground black and greasy-looken, and dead tree trunks standen in some fields, black with fire whar folks had been ringen and burnen to clear, and the cotton come-en on a-tween. But the good ground was all took. Been took a long time. Then we come to Little Rock. We stayed in Little Rock nigh onto three weeks waiten fer Pappy's cousin. And me, I got so I knowed my way all over the hull town, you know how a kid is, a-pryen and a-prowlen. We was campen down on a little crick, and Pappy was a-fretten and a-fume-en to be gitten on, and the season wearen. He wanted to be gitten some ground broke, even if hit was late, and a house up fore winter. And the drinken water in Little Rock, hit wasn't so good and Pappy one to be cantankerous about drinken water. They's water in that country, but hit ain't good water lak the water here. Lots of folks them days had the flux in Little Rock, they said, and hit was the drinken water. I ain't ne'er been back in Little Rock, not since I went on outer Arkansas west, but I seen a man not more'n five years back, come from Arkansas, and I says to him, how's the drinken water in Little Rock now? They git right good water now, he said. But not them days. And Pappy was a-fume-en to git on.

"But me, I was ten-'leven year old, and ever day Sunday. I'd go up and see the men drillen and gitten ready, some of them drillen with sticks, not have-en no guns yit. One day I says, 'Pappy, ain't you gonna be a sojer?' 'Sojer,' he said, 'you stay away from them sojers, or I'll whale the tar.' But I'd slip off and go watch them sojers, lak a kid will. I had ne'er seen sich.

"Then Pappy's cousin come. 'Amon,' he said to my pappy, fer Amon was his name, 'I been slow a-gitten here, but sumthen crost my path.' He taken a piece of paper outer his pocket, and he had drawed a map on hit, with ever thing marked good. My pappy studied on the map, then he said, 'Ain't you goen back?' 'Naw, Amon, I ain't,' Pappy's cousin said, 'I'm a sojer now.'

"'Sojer,' my pappy said, and looked at him.

"'Sojer,' Pappy's cousin said, 'but I ain't a family man, lak you.'

"Pappy shook his head, slow. 'Naw,' he said, 'hit ain't that. I had me a good place in Kentucky. And my wife, she's a clever woman and foreminded. I'll lay her agin air woman I e'er seen. She and my boys, they could run my place, and I could been a sojer. If I had hit in my mind and heart. But I ain't clear and easy in my mind, this rise-en and slayen and a man not knowen.'

"So Pappy taken the map, and we loaded up the wagon, and put the oven in, and crost over the river. That same, blessed day. Fer north Arkansas.

"Hit was air man's country, and the Lord's truth. Fair and flowen, lak Pappy's cousin done said. Pappy found him a place in a fork of two cricks, bottom ground and high ground layen to a man's use-en, and a spring outer the ground, and timber standen, scalybark and white oak and cedar and yaller poplar and beech. And squirrels so thick they barked to wake you up of a mornen. 'Lord God, Lord God,' Pappy said real soft, just standen there looken, after he'd done settled his mind on a spot to set his house. Then he said to Ma, right sharp and sudden: 'Henrietta, gimme that axe!' And Ma done hit.

"Some of the folks round there went off and went to the war, like Pappy's cousin, but Pappy never the hull duration. Folks would be a-talken, and a man mought name the war, and Pappy, he'd just git up and walk off. Then word come the war was over. I was a big feller then, goen on sixteen, and handy if I do say so. Us boys worked with Pappy round the place, and we done right well. Hit was a good country, fer fair. Ever fall we'd go down to Little Rock and do our big trade-en. Down at Mr. Wolff's wagon yard. When the time come on, Pappy would cast round, and load up what hides layen round, and what tallow they was we didn't need, and sich truck, and honey — Lord God, the honey, you'd go out and knock over a bee tree, and honey to spare — and we'd start down to Little Rock. They wasn't nuthen Mr. Wolff wouldn't buy off'n a man, and give him cash money or swap outer his wholesale store. We done swappen fer the majority, fer you taken cash money and give it right back to Mr. Wolff fer what you was gitten. So Pappy'd swap, and load up the wagon with plunder, and we'd start on back home.

"Time come I was goen on nineteen, and I said to Pappy, 'Pappy, I been studyen about goen up to Kansas.'

"And Pappy said, 'Boy, I been notice-en you sorter raise-en yore sap.'

"So I taken out fer Kansas. Pappy gimme a horse and saddle and fifty dollars and hit gold. I figgered I'd go to Kansas and be a buffalo hunter, lak I'd heared tell. I figgered I was handy with a rifle as the next man. Many's the time, shooten fer a steer, I'd took hind quarter, hide, and tallow, that being top man. Fellers would put up fifty cents a-piece and buy a steer and shoot fer choice, high man hind quarter, hide, and tallow, next man, hind quarter, and next man, fore quarter and head, and next man, fore quarter. Shoot at a shingle and a little heart drawed on hit in white clay, forty paces free style or sixty paces layen to a chunk.

"Hit was in Hays City I taken up with a feller named Mingo Smith. He was a Yankee and he fit the war. He got mustered out and he come to Kansas. He'd been a muleskinner down to Santa Fe, and a bullwhacker out Colorado way, and a boss layen the Kansas Pacific railroad, and he'd hunted buffalo fer the railroad, too, to feed the men; they wasn't nuthen he hadn't took a turn to, hit looked lak. He was a long skinny feller, didn't have no meat on his bones to speak of, and his face was all yaller and he didn't have no hair to his head, and hit yaller, too. And him not more'n thirty. 'Some day, I'll shore be a disappointmint to a Cheyenne,' he'd say, and rub his hand over whar his hair oughter be. He figgered he'd take one more turn, the price on hides goen up lak hit was. Men come-en out to Hays City to buy hides, and all. Mingo, he had some money he'd got fer freighten up from Fort Sill, and a old wagon, and he bought and paid fer what all we needed, and said I could pay him my part outer what we took. So I thanked him kindly, and we hit out, him and me.

"Seven-eight year, and durn, we was all over that-air country, one time and ernuther. North of Hays City to the Saline, and up Pawnee Crick and the Arkansas, and down in the Panhandle on the Canadian, and down to Fort Sill. They had been a time a man couldn't git nuthern fer a hide not seasonable, with the fur good, and summer hunten didn't pay a man powder and git. But we come in to Hays City our first trip, loaded down, and figgeren on what to do till the cold come, and a feller what bought hides for Durfee, over to Leavenworth — give us two dollars and a dime fer prime bull, I recollect — he says, 'Boys, just belly up quick, and quench yore thirst, and hit out agin, I'm buyen now, summer or winter, rain or shine!' 'Is that a fact,' Mingo says, 'summer hide?' 'Hit's a fact,' that feller says.

"Mingo up and buys ernuther wagon, and hires two feller to skin — Irish, they was, the country was plumb full of Irish — and a feller to cook and stretch, and I says to him, 'Lord God, Mingo, you act lak we was rich.' And he says, 'We ain't, but Lord God, we gonna be. And I'm durn tired of skinnen, durned if I ain't. I don't mind shooten, but I hate to skin. One thing hit was, shooten rebels, a man ne'er had to skin 'em. Hit's gonna be shooten now, like a gentleman, till the barr'l hots.'

"And durn if he didn't say the God's truth. The barr'l hot to a man's hand. The day a still day, and the smoke round a man's head like a fog, and yore ears ringen. If'n you got a stand — the buffalo standen and graze-en — and drapped the lead one, the others mought just sniff and bawl, and not stampede. If you was lucky. Nuthen to hit then, keep on shooten fer the outside ones that looked lak they mought git restless, take hit easy and not git yore gun barr'l too hot. That next year, I mind me we got two good stand, Mingo one and me one. I was come-en up a little rise south of a crick runnen in the Pawnee, and I raised up my head, keerful, and thar they was, a passel of 'em. Bout a hundred and fifty paces off yander, and me down wind. I propped my Sharp's to my prong-stick, and cracked down. I started to git up — a man would git up and run to git him his next shot — and got on one knee, and I see they wasn't no buffalo down. I figgered I'd missed, and a easy shot, and I laid back down fer a try. Then I seen a buffalo just lay down, and the rest standen thar, not move-en. I shot agin, and a buffalo come down, and the rest a-standen. And agin. I said, 'Lord God,' I said, 'I do believe hit's a stand!'

"A stand hit was. I laid thar, looken down the barr'l of my Sharp's and the buffalo standen. I laid thar, counten out loud be-twixt shots not to go too fast and hot the gun. A long time, and I could see 'em come down, slow, to the knees, when the ball found. Then keel over and lay. And the rest standen round, sniffen and bawlen. A man lays thar, the sun a-bearen down, and keeps on a-pullen on the trigger. He ain't lak his-self. Naw, he ain't. Lak he wasn't no man, nor nuthen. Lak hit ain't him has a-holt of him. Lak he mought git up and walk off and leave them buffalo down the rise, a-standen, and leave the gun lay, and the gun would be shooten and a-shooten, by hitself, and ne'er no end. And the buffalo, down the rise, standen and bawlen. Hit comes to a man that a-way.

"Seventy-two buffalo I shot that afternoon, layen thar, a-fore they broke and run. Gitten on to sun, they broke. I laid thar, and seen 'em go, what was left, not nigh a score, and the dust a-rise-en behind 'em. They run north. I seen 'em past sight, but I kept on a-layen thar, lak I couldn't uncrook my hand-holt off'n my Sharp's, and the barr'l hot to a man's flesh. I laid thar, lak a man past his short rows.

"'Durn,' Mingo said, 'them buffalo down thar, and you a-layen here lak hit wasn't nuthen!' I ne'er heared him come-en. 'Boy, go git them Irish,' he said, 'hit's gonna be night work, a-skinnen.' I didn't say nuthen, I taken out fer the wagons to git them skinners when they done got done with the ones they was skinnen. We got back hit was night, and Mingo down thar, skinnen and cussen. But the moon come up, red and swole layen thar to the east, bigger'n a barn. Ain't no moons in this country lak them moons in west

Kansas. We skinned by the moon. Didn't nobody say nuthen. Nary a sound but a man grunten, or a knife whetten on a stell, maybe, soft and whickeren lak when hit's a good temper to the blade, and the sound hit makes when the hide gives off'n the meat to a good long pull. Then, off a-ways, the coyotes singen, and come-en closter.

"We skinned 'em all, all seventy-two, and taken the tongues. And the mops off'n the bulls. We loaded the wagon, and started up the rise, not have-en et, and plumb tuckered. Nigh halfway up the rise, I recollect, I looked back. The moon was ride-en high, and the ground down thar looked white lak water, I recollect, and them carcasses sticken up lak black rocks outer water.

"But a man didn't make him a stand ever day. Not by a sight, I kin tell you. He'd try the wind and git down wind, and start move-en in, slow and keerful, crawlen a good piece maybe. They started move-en, and hit was time. Two hundred paces and you was lucky. But a Sharp's will shoot lak a cannon. Hit's a fact. Three quarter mile ain't nuthen fer a Sharp's, not even on a bull buffalo, if'n you kin hit him. Which you caint. But two-fifty, three hundred paces, a man kin. And under the hump. You shoot, and the herd breaks and runs, and stops, and you run to ketch up, and lay and shoot. And they run agin. That a-way, till they done left you. Or you kin ride with 'em, shooten alongside with a carbeen. A Spencer, I had me. But we ne'er done that but to be a-doen. Hit was a sporten man's way, you might say. And the way with the Indians. Only they used a bow and arrow, ride-en alongside, and one arrow doen hit sometimes. Or two.

"But one way and ernuther, by and large we taken our share, Mingo and me. Winter and summer. And not us only. In Charlie Rath's sheds in Dodge City, many's the time with my own eyes I seen fifty-sixty thousand hides baled up and waiten, and his loaden yard so thick with wagons a man could nigh cross hit and ne'er set foot to ground. Wagons standen nigh hub to hub, and loaded, and fellers just in and likkered up and rare-en and cussen, waiten to git shet of their take. A time hit was, with money free lak sweat on a nigger, and men outer the war and from fer countries, and the likker runnen lak water. A power of meanness, and no denyen. But a man could git a-long, and not have him no trouble to speak on. If'n he tended to his business, and was God-fearen, and ne'er taken no back-sass off'n no man.

" We got our'n and didn't reckon on no end, hit looked lak. But a man's that a-way. He sees sumthen, and don't reckon on no end, no way, and don't see hit a-come-en. They's a hoggishness in man, and a hog-blindness. Down off'n Medicine Lodge Crick, one time, I was a-standen on a little rise, in the spring, and the buffalo was a-move-en. North, lak they done. All the buffalo trails run north-south, and hit was spring. They was move-en north, and fer as a man could see, hit was buffalo. They was that thick. No pore human man could name their number, only the Lord on high. That a-way, and no man to say the end. But I seen 'em lay, skinned and stinken, black-en the ground fer what a man could ride half a day. A man couldn't breathe fresh fer the stinken. And before you knowed hit, they wasn't no buffalo in Kansas. You could go a hull day and see nary a one. ' Hit's me fer Oklahoma,' Mingo said, ' whar thar's buffalo yit. Down Cimarron way, or Beaver Crick.'

" ' Hit's Indian country,' I said, ' I ain't a-relishen no Indians.'

" ' They's fellers been down thar and done right good,' Mingo said. ' I heared tell of a feller come out with nigh onto a thousand hides, and not down thar no time.'

" ' And fellers been down thar and ain't come back,' I said.

" ' Indians,' Mingo said, ' I fit Indians down in Oklahoma, when I was freighten. Hit ain't nuthen to brag on. They ain't got nuthen lak this-here.' And he give his Sharp's a little h'ist. ' The guns they got, ain't no white man would have 'em.'

" ' I ain't skeered,' I said, ' but hit ain't the law. Hit's Indian country down thar, by law.'

" ' Indian country,' and Mingo give a spit, ' hit ain't Indian country fer long. A feller from Dodge City said they's a gang gitten ready to go down fer buffalo, all together. Said Myers was gonna go down and buy hides and set up to do business right thar, down in Oklahoma, or maybe Texas toward the Canadian. Hit's big doens.'

" ' You figgeren on goen down with 'em? ' I ast him.

" ' Naw,' Mingo said, ' folks gits under my feet.'

" We went down to Oklahoma, just us and our skinners. New

skinners, they was, our old skinners quitten, nor wanten to go to Indian country. We got two new ones, a French feller and a nigger. We had to give 'em eighty dollars a month and found, because hit was Indian country. We went down thar. 'Seventy-four, hit was, and a drout year with the cricks dryen. And they was grasshoppers come that year, I recollect. But we made out, and they was buffalo thar. Hit was lak a-fore, the buffalo move-en and fillen the land. Hit was lak new country. Fer a spell. And we worked fast and fer. But a man had to keep his eyes skinned, looken fer Indians. And somebody watchen all night, turn about. We ne'er seen none till we got our first take out, up to Dodge City, and come back. Then we seen some, one time. The nigger was down a little draw, skinnen some buffalo Mingo shot, and French was at the wagon, stretchen hides, and Mingo and me was move-en out in the open. They come over a rise, between the draw and the wagons, and we seen 'em. We high-tailed fer home, and beat 'em to the wagons, and started shooten. 'Whar's the nigger?' Mingo said.

"'He ain't here,' French said.

"'God dammit,' Mingo said, layen thar shooten, 'that black bastud lets 'em slip up and git him, and me with a dislak fer skinnen lak I got. Hit's the thanks a man gits fer fighten rebels four years to set a nigger free.'

"We laid thar a-shooten at 'em all afternoon. French loaden, and Mingo and me shooten. When they was a-way off, we used our Sharp's, and when they come ride-en in clost, we used our carbeen and Colt guns. A Spencer carbeen shoots twelve times without stoppen, and heavy lead. Hit was that a-way all afternoon, and hit was a clear night and they couldn't git in clost and us not see. They tried hit, but we seen 'em ever time. They left a-fore day.

"Hit come day, and they was gone. They was some ponies layen off here and yander, and clost in, not more'n fifteen paces, a Indian. I ne'er knowed one got that nigh, but night time'll fool you. If'n we got airy other, they carried him off. But this one was too clost. We walked out to whar he was a-lyen. 'Tryen to make a *coup*,' Mingo said, 'come-en in clost, that a-way. Wanted to git to be a chief.' He was a young Indian, and he was shot in the guts. 'The durn fool,' Mingo said. He poked him with his foot. 'Kiowa,' he said. Then he squatted down and taken out his knife.

" 'What you aim to do?' I ast him.

" 'Git me a scalp,' Mingo said.

" 'Hit ain't Christian,' I said.

" 'Hell,' he said, 'I knowed Christians as skinned Indians. I knowed a feller made him a baccy sack outer squaw-hide. But hit didn't do so good,' he said, and started cutten, 'hit wore out right off. But a scalp now, hit's diff'rent, hit's a keepsake.'

" He scalped him, then we looked down the draw fer the nigger. Thar he was, but they'd done taken his scalp. 'They made a pore trade,' Mingo said, 'a nigger's scalp ain't no good, hit ain't worth beans. Hit ain't much better'n mine.'

" Them was the only Indians we had trouble with that year, but them fellers went down from Dodge City all together, they had plenty trouble over in Texas. They had a big fight down at a place called 'Dobe Walls, and some got killed, and a passel of Indians. But the Indians was still bad on south a-ways. They was fighten at Anadarko with the sojers, and killen and scalpen here and yander. And raiden down to Texas. And the Kiowas caught a supply train — hit was Captain Lyman's wagons, I recollect — and give 'em a big tussle. We was down to Fort Sill the next spring, and we heared tell from the sojers. How they laid out four days in holes they dug, a-thirsten and no water, and the Indians all round, a-ride-en and a-whoopen and a-shooten. They was one Indian tied a white sheet round him and come ride-en through the sojers four times, and back agin, and lead cut that-air sheet off'n him, but ne'er a slug teched him. Doen hit made him a big chief, and they give him a new name fer hit, lak they done. But hit's done left me now, and I caint name hit to you. All them days them sojers laid thar, thirsten. Then the rain come, heavy lak when the drout breaks in that-air country, and hit durn nigh drowned 'em layen thar in them holes they dug. But a scout got through to Camp Supply, and more sojers come.

" Hit was a bad year, and no denyen, and the Gin'al over to Fort Sill — hit was Gin'al Sheridan as fit in the war — a-gitten ready and sot to stomp 'em out. And he done hit. They was run here and yander, lak a coyote and the dogs on him. They run 'em and ne'er give no breathen. Some of 'em come in and give up, but some of 'em kept on a-runnen and a-fighten, the wildest what went with the war chiefs Lone Wolf and Maman-ti and sich. But they come in, too, a-fore hit was done. I seen 'em. Hit was at Fort Sill I seen 'em. They was another chief, named Kicken Bird, what got 'em in. He seen how hit would be, and he said hit to his people, and he made 'em come in. I seen 'em at Fort Sill. They put them Indians in the corrals — they was stone corrals — and the bad chiefs locked up in the jail, and chained, and in the stone ice house they was a-builden. Ever day the wagons with meat come, and they throwed the meat over the wall — raw meat and in chunks lak you was feeden a passel of painters. They taken what stock the Indians had and drove 'em outside and shot 'em and let 'em lay, stinken. Hit was lak the stink when they'd been shooten buffalo and skinned 'em. Git a west wind, and couldn't no man in Fort Sill git the stink of them ponies outer his nose, wake-en nor sleepen. And hit ne'er helped no man eat his vittles.

"They was gonna send the bad chiefs off and git shet of 'em. A fer piece, to Florida. Kicken Bird, they was gonna let him pick out the ones to go, the ones he knowed was dead-set agin the white folks. And he done hit. He named Lone Wolf and Maman-ti, and a passel more, and said they would ne'er have hit in their hearts not to scalp a white man. The time come to git shet of 'em, and I seen hit. Them army wagons was standen thar by the ice house, and sojers drawed up with guns, and they taken out the Indians from the ice house. They had chains on 'em. And thar Kicken Bird come ride-en on his big gray stallion — a man he was to look on, tall and limber, and he could evermore set a hoss, a sight to see. He got off, and come up close to Maman-ti and Lone Wolf and them was standen thar. 'Hit's time,' he said, 'and my heart is full of a big sadness. But it will be. I love you, but you would not take the right road. But I love my people. I send you away because I love my people, and you would make them kill theirselves a-beaten their head agin the stone. Fighten the white man is lak beaten your head on a stone. When yore hearts is changed, you kin come back to yore people, and you will find love in my heart for you.' That's what they said he said, fer I didn't know no Kiowa talk to speak of.

"The chiefs standen thar, the chains a-hangen off'n 'em, didn't say nuthen. They just looked at Kicken Bird. Then Maman-ti, he said: 'You think you are a big chief, Kicken Bird. You think you have done a good thing. The white men talk to you and puff you up, Kicken Bird. But you are lak a buffalo cow, dead and layen in the sun and swole with rot-wind. Indians ought to be a-dyen together, but you would not die with us, Kicken Bird. Now you will die by yoreself, Kicken Bird. You are dyen now, Kicken Bird, and the rot-wind is in you.' The wagons started rollen, the black-snakes a-cracken, off toward Caddo crossen. Kicken Bird stood thar, and watched 'em go. The sojers marched off, but Kicken Bird kept on a-standen thar, looken whar the wagons done gone.

"They's things in the world fer a man to study on, and hit's one of 'em. What come to Kicken Bird. He stood thar, a-looken, and then he went to his lodge, down on Cache Crick, nigh Sill. They say he just set thar, not give-en nuthen to notice, to speak of. He et a little sumthen, but he didn't relish nuthen. He ne'er taken his eyes off'n the ground. Five days that a-way, and come the fifth mornen and he keeled over and died. 'I done what come to me,' he said, layen thar, 'and I taken the white man's hand.' Then he was dead. Nary a mark on him, and him in the prime.

"But they ain't no tellen. Some said as how Maman-ti, when the wagons camped outer Sill, prayed and put a strong medicine on Kicken Bird to die. Then he died his-self fer putten medicine on ernuther Kiowa. But agin, maybe his heart was broke in two. Maybe Kicken Bird's heart broke in two lak a flint rock when you put hit in the hot fire. They ain't no tellen. But hit's sumthen fer a man to study on.

"Hit was in May they taken them Indians away from Sill, and me and Mingo hit out agin. Buffalo hunten agin. But we didn't do so good that year. They was peteren out. That's what made them Indians so durn bad, some folks said, them buffalo goen. They didn't git no vittles then, but what the gov'mint give 'em, and hit spiled more'n lak. We taken what we could find, but the time was goen in Oklahoma. We heared tell they was buffalo down Brazos, and Charlie Hart's boys a-gitten 'em, so hit was down Brazos and up Pease River. We done what we could, but the time was a-goen. Mingo got lak I'd ne'er seen him git a-fore. We'd sight buffalo, and he'd go nigh loco. ' Durn, God durn,' he'd say, his voice lak a man prayen ' God durn the bastuds.' And his eyes with a shine in 'em lak a man got the fever. ' Durn,' he'd say, ' what you a-waiten fer, you Kentuck bastud,' and we'd move out on 'em. Light or dark, he'd be at hit. Past sun, I seen him, and not light fer a man to aim by. Him a-waste-en lead, and them Sharp's evermore et lead lak a hog slop. Two ounce the slug, and powder to back hit. ' Mingo,' I says, to him, ' hit's a willful waste.' ' I'll cut yore scaggly thote,' he said, and ne'er said one more word all night.

"We come outer Brazos and up Kansas way. 'They's buffalo north,' Mingo'd say. Days, and we'd see a old bull, maybe, and a couple of cows. And bones layen white on the ground, fer as a man's sight, white lak a salt flat. The wagon wheel went over 'em, cracken. We come to Dodge City. They was bones piled and ricked up thar, a sight of bones. Them nesters and 'steaders done picked up and brung 'em in to sell 'em. They was buyen 'em back east to make fert'lizer to put on the wore-out ground. Bones picked up thar along the Santa Fe, a-waiten, you ne'er seen sich. They was fellers in Dodge City, but not lak a-fore. Fellers was setten round didn't have a dime, what had been throwen round the green lak a senator. Bones and broke buffalo hunters thar, them days. We was in Dodge City, and Mingo ne'er outer spitten-range of a bottle. ' Buffalo gone,' he said, ' durn, and hit'll be whiskey next, and no country fer a white man.' But they shore-God wasn't no drout in sight yit. Not with Mingo.

"We was in Dodge City, and word come the Santa Fe was payen out good money fer men to fight the Denver and Rio Grande fer putten the track through where the Arkansas comes outer the mountains, out in Colorado. Mingo come and said to git ready, we was goen. But I said, naw, I wasn't gonna be a-shooten and killen no human man, not fer no railroad, no way. ' Me,' Mingo said, ' I kilt plenty fer the gov'mint goen on four years, and kill a man fer the gov'ment, I shore-God oughter be willen to kill me one fer anybody else. Even a railroad.' But naw, I said. But Mingo went on and done hit, and me waiten in Dodge City. Then he come on back, and money he had. ' Hit'll be Santa Fe line,' he said, ' and Irish fer cross-ties.'

"Then Mingo said: 'Yellowstone, up Yellowstone and they's buffalo lak a-fore. Hit's the word. Git ready.' But I ne'er said nuthen. 'What you setten thar fer?' he said. 'Git ready.' Then I said I wasn't aimen to go. 'What you aimen to do?' Mingo said. I said I couldn't rightly name hit, but hit would come to me. I said I might take me out some ground, have-en a little money left to git me gear and a start. Mingo looked at me lak he ne'er laid eyes on me a-fore, and he give a spit on the ground. 'A fool hoe-man,' he said, 'you be a durn fool hoe-man.' 'Maybe,' I said, 'if'n hit comes to me.' 'A bone-picker,' he said. He give me a look, and that's the last word I e'er heard him say. 'Bone-picker,' he said, and give me a look, and walked off. He was gone, a-fore sun next mornen. Yellowstone way, they said.

"I taken me a claim, lak I said. Up in Kansas. And I done well as the next one, I reckin. I ne'er minded putten my back to hit, and layen a-holt. And I had me money to git a start, gear and stock and sich. Two year, goen on three, I stayed. I was a-make-en out, that wasn't hit. Hit was sumthen come over me. I couldn't name hit. But thar hit was, sleepen and wake-en. I sold my stock and gear. I said to a man, 'What'll you gimme fer my stock and gear?' And he named hit. Hit wasn't nuthen, not to what a man could a-got. But I taken hit, and hit was ample. To git me a outfit. And I started a-move-en. Down through Oklahoma, and west. West, lak a man done them days when hit come over him to be a-move-en.

"I went down the way I'd been a-fore, and hit was diff'rent a-ready. But not diff'rent lak when I come back in 'ninety-one on my way back here. The Indians was dance-en then, when I come back through, tryen to dance the buffalo back. They'd been gone a long time then, and the bones. Them Indians was a-tryen to dance 'em back. And Indians ever whar, I heared tell, up in Dakota and west. The ghost-dance, they named hit. They was make-en medicine and tryen to dance back the good times, and them long gone. Hit would be a new world, and fer Indians, they claimed. A new earth was a-come-en all white and clean past a man's thinken, and the buffalo on hit a-move-en and no end. Lak that time I stood on a rise near Medicine Lodge Crick and seen 'em a-move-en, and ne'er reckined on the end, how hit would be. That-air new earth was a-come-en, they figgered, a-slide-en over the old earth whar the buffalo was done gone now and the Indians was dirt, a-blotten hit out clean, lak a kid spits on his slate and rubs hit clean. And thar all the Indians would be, all the nations a-standen and callen, all them what had died, on that-air new white earth. The live ones was dance-en to bring hit.

"They was them as had seen hit. They was them as fell down in the dance and had died, lak they named hit, when they was a-dance-en, and laid on the ground stark and stiff lak dead. They was the ones as had seen hit, the new land. They'd come to, lak a man wake-en, and tell as how they had seen hit. They seen the new earth, all white and shine-en, and the dead ones thar, happy, and beckonen with the hand, and they talked to 'em. Squaws what had chil'en what was dead, they'd see 'em. And they'd git busy a-make-en moccasins and toys, lak hummers and bull-roars and sich, and bring 'em to the dance next time to have 'em ready to give to the chil'en when they seen 'em. They'd see 'em, and give 'em the toys and sich. Then they'd come round, layen thar, and thar'd be that-air truck they'd done fixed fer the chil'en. Layen thar on the ground. They didn't know what to make on hit. See-en hit thar.

"They was some folks as was laughen and scornen. Said them Indians was gone plumb crazy. But not me. One time, long a-fore, when I was young and sallet-green, I mighter scorned. But not then, in 'ninety-one, when I was a-come-en back, after what hit was I'd seen. I'd laid dead lak them Indians, and seen hit come to me. Hit was how I was a-come-en back. In 'ninety-one.

"But them Indians. They come together in a big ring, a dance-en. Round and round, and a-singen. Them songs they made up, how they'd been dead and what they seen in that-air new land a-come-en. And the medicine man, he was in the middle, a-shake-en his eagle feather, and them Indians move-en round, and a-singen. Then somebody starts to feel hit a-come-en and starts a-shake-en and shudderen, lak the chill. And the medicine man, he waves that-air eagle feather a-fore his face what's a-shake-en, and he blows out his breath at him and says, 'Hunh, hunh, hunh, hunh!' And that feller comes outer the ring in the middle, lak the blind-staggers, and the medicine man waves the feather a-fore him, and ne'er stops and says, 'Hunh, hunh, hunh!' Till that-air feller gits the jerks, lak a man when the Gospel hits him. Then the jerks is gone, and him a-standen, stiffer'n a man on the coolen boards and eyes a-stare-en lak a-fore the pennies is put. He stand thar, how long hit ain't no tellen, and them dance-en and singen, and hit come-en on more Indians, too, and them a-fall-en. They lays on the ground thar, lak dead, and broad daylight, maybe. And the singen and dance-en not stoppen.

"But that was in 'ninety-one, when I was come-en back, not when I was a-goen. A-goen, I was headed west, lak I said, lak a man them days when hit come on him to be move-en. I was down in Santa Fe and seen hit. I went to the middle of town, and seen the folks a-move-en and doen, and I figgered I'd lay over and rest up, maybe. Then hit come on me. Naw, I said, I ain't a-stoppen, hit's on me not to be a-stoppen. I didn't tarry none, only to git me grub and sich. A feller said to me, 'Whar you goen?' I said I didn't know, and he said, 'God-a-mighty, stranger, goen and don't know whar!' And I said, 'Naw, I don't know, but hit'll come to me when I git thar.' And he said, 'God-a-mighty!' And I went on.

"I come into the mountains. Them mountains wasn't lak no mountains you e'er seen. Nor me. Not lak them hills in Arkansas or in this-here country in Kentucky. That-air country was open and high, and the mountains rise-en outer hit. Hit was June when I come in the high country, and they was flowers ever whar. I ne'er seen sich. Greasewood with blooms plumb gold, and little flowers on the ground. And the cactus, flowers a-bloomen fer as a man's sight. But no smell. Put yore nose to hit, but they ain't no smell, fer all the brightness.

"I went on to the high mountains. Cedar and juniper I come to, but scrub and not fitten fer nuthen. Then up higher, piñons, then oak but hit scrub. Then high up in them mountains, the big pines standen, and no man e'er laid axe. Look down and the land was all tore up down below, ever which way, tore up and a-layen on end. And the ground with colors lak the sky at sun. Look up, and snow was still layen when I come, and the sun white on hit, lak on cloud-tops in summer. The wind come down off'n the snow, cold to yore face and the sun shine-en.

" I come in that-air country, and ne'er ast no man the way. Outer Santa Fe I seen folks a-goen and come-en, then they wasn't none to speak on. In the high country I seen Indians sometimes, ride-en along, or standen, and I made 'em signs and them me, but I ne'er ast 'em the way. A man could be in a place in that-air country and they'd be Indians live-en thar, not a pistol-shot, and him ne'er knowen. Not the way they fixed them houses, dirt piled up round looken lak a hump outer the ground. Hogans, they named them houses. The cold come or hit git dry and the grass give out, and they'd up and move and build 'em a new house. One day, sun to sun, and hit was built.

" Summer I was in the mountains, high up. The cold come, and I moved down and built me a house, lak them Indian houses, only mine set south, backed up under a hunk of rock. Them Indian houses sets east, ne'er no other way. Hit's agin their religion. And I fixed me a shed fer my ponies. That winter I laid up thar. I lived off'n the land. A man kin do hit, put to hit, what with a rifle and snare-en. But I traded the Indians fer some corn, now and agin. But two-three months, and I ne'er seen nobody, hair nor hide. I didn't miss hit, somehow. I'd a-come thar, and thar I was. Hit's past name-en, how the Lord God leads a man sometime, and sets his foot. Thar I was, and I knowed they was a world of folks off yander, down in the flat country. A-gitten and a-begetten, and not knowen the morrow. I knowed how they'd been war and killen in the country, and folks rise-en in slaughter, brother agin brother. And men was dead and under the earth, as had walked on hit, standen up lak me or airy breathen man. And no man to name the reason. Only the Lord God. I minded me on the power of meanness I'd seen in my time. And done, to speak truth. A man does hit, some more, some less, but he's got hit to think on.

" Hit looked lak my head was full, one thing and ernuther. Sometimes hit was lak I could see, plain as day, ever-thing and ever-body I'd e'er knowed layen out a-fore me, all at one time. They ain't no tellen how hit was, but hit was that a-way. All together, lak a man lived his life, and the time not a-passen while he lived hit. Hit's past sayen, and they ain't no word fer me to say hit, but hit was that a-way. A-fore God. Hit's sumthen to study on. Then a man feels clean, hit's ne'er the same.

"Summer come, and the snow gone, and I started up to the high mountains. I seen Indians a-move-en, too. They made me signs, and I taken up with 'em. They had 'em sheep and ponies, and was goen whar the grass was good. They was two or three of 'em knowed our talk, not good but some. All summer I was with them Indians, off and on. The grass gone and time to be a-move-en, and they ast me to move too, and I done hit. A man could git along with them Indians if'n he had a mind to. I done hit. They ne'er had nuthin agin me, nor me agin them. Hit come cold, and they was a-move-en down low, and I went with 'em. They helped build me a winter hogan, lak their'n, and they rubbed corn meal on the posts, the way they done fer luck, and sprinkled hit on the floor, and said the words they says to make the live-en in the house be good live-en. They throwed a handful on the fire they'd built under the smoke hole, and said the words. They fixed vittles, and we set on the floor, on sheepskins, and taken sop, side by side. They made cigarettes, lak they do, outer corn shucks and terbaccer, and set thar smoke-en and talken. Hit was lak a log-raise-en in this-here country, and folks jollifyen.

"Five year, and hit was that a-way. Hit was a way of live-en, if'n hit's in a man's heart. And I ne'er had no complaint. I was easy in my heart and mind, lak ne'er a-fore in my time of doen and strive-en. I'd a-been thar yit, I reckin, if'n I had'n a-took sick, and hit bad. Hit was in the summer of 'ninety, and we was in the high country, but hit looked lak sumthen went outer me. I wasn't good fer nuthen. Looked lak I couldn't raise my hand, the pith gone out of me. I'd jist set on the ground, and look up at the sky, how thin and blue hit was over them mountains. Then the fever come. Hit taken me, and I said, 'Willie Proudfit, you gonna die.' That's what I said, and the words was in my head lak a bell. Then hit come to me, how other men was dead; they taken hit the best they could and the bitterness, and I said, 'Willie Proudfit, what air man kin do, you kin do.' But the fever come again, and I said, 'You gonna die, and in a fer country.'

" The Indians done what they could. They give me stuff to drink, black and bitter hit was, outer yerbs and sich, but hit ne'er done no good. I'd burn up with fever, then I'd lay and look and ever thing in the world was diff'rent to me. Wouldn't nuthen stay on my stomach, looked lak. And then the fever agin. The Indians treated me good. A man couldn't a-ast more. They give me them yerbs and sich, and hit ain't all foolishness. They knows what grows outer the earth in their country, hit's use the Lord give hit. I seen some mighty sick Indians them years I was thar, and seen 'em get well and walken. But the Lord had laid a powerful sickness on me, and I said, ' Willie Proudfit, you gonna die.'

" But no, ain't no man knows what the Lord's done marked out fer him. And many's the pore, weakid man done looked on the face of blessedness, bare-eyed, and ne'er knowed hit by name. Lak a blind man a-liften his face to the sun, and not knowen. Hit was a blessen the Lord laid on me, and I praise hit.

" Them Indians seen I was witheren up, lak a tree in the sun done had the axe at hit's root. Because they done called me brother and give me a name, they done ever thing they could. They built the medicine house, made a fire thar, and set me in the medicine house, and tried to take out the evil. Not jist one day, they was tryen to git the evil out. They set in thar and some of 'em had their faces covered up with masks made outer leather and painted, and they waved eagle feathers on me to bring out the evil, and sometimes they put stuff on my head and my feet and my knees and my chist, stuff they done mixed up, and sometimes corn meal. Sometimes hit was sand on my head. And sometimes they washed me with suds, they done made outer yerbs, and done dried me with corn meal. And agin they done put pine branches on me, and put stuff on the fire fer me to breathe and one thing and ernuther, and me too nigh gone to keer. And sometimes they done made pictures outer colored sand on the floor, and feathers and beads and sich, and they was singen and hooten, sometimes. To git out the evil. And they put me in them sweat houses, little houses not much bigger'n fer a man to lay in, and covered with dirt and sand, and pictures in colored sand, and a curtain outer deerskin fer a door. But hit had to be skin off'n a deer they done run down and smother with a man's hand, not shot or cut fer the killen. They put me in hit, and rocks they done got red hot, and sweated me. And one night they was dance-en all night hit looked lak, and singen, naked and painted white, I recollect, and the fires was burnen big.

" But the fever done had me sometimes, and hit was lak a dream. I was a-goen, and nuthen to lay holt on. And I didn't keer. The time comes and a man don't keer. They taken me out and laid me on the ground. Hit was night. I knowed that, then I was a-goen. I might been gone, fer all I know. They ain't no sayen.

" I might been gone, when hit come to me, what I seen. I seen a long road come-en down a hill, and green ever whar. Green grass layen fresh, and trees, maple and elm and sich. And my feet was in the road, and me a-move-en down hit. They was a fire in me, thirsten. Hit was a green country, and the shade cool, but the fire was in me. I come down the hill, and seen houses setten off down the valley, and roofs, and the green trees standen. I taken a bend in the road, and thar was a little church, a white church with a bell hangen, and the grass green a-fore hit. Thar was a spring thar, by the church, and I seen hit and run to hit. I put my head down to the water, fer the fire in me, lak a dog gitten ready to lap. I didn't take no water in my hand and sup. Naw, I put my face down to the water, and hit was cool on me. The coolness was in me, and I taken my fill.

" No tellen how long, and I lifted up my head. Thar a girl was sitten, over thar nigh the spring, and she was a-looken at me. I opened my mouth but nary a word come out. Hit looked lak the words was big in me to busten, and none come.

" Then hit was finished and done, and I'd ne'er spoke. The dream, if'n hit was a dream. No tellen how long I laid thar, but I come to, hit was mornen light, gray, fer the rain was fall-en. I didn't have no fever. I laid thar, and my head was full of what all I'd been a-dreamen. They taken me in, and a-fore night I et a little sumthen, and hit stayed on my stomach. My strength come back, not fast, but hit come. All the time I was a-thinken what I'd seen, the church and the green trees standen, and the spring. Ever day. I'd seen hit, I knowed I'd seen hit, but I couldn't give hit the name. Then I knowed. Hit was the road come-en down to Thebes, in Kentucky, when I was a kid thar, and the church setten thar whar hit takes a bend. I ne'er seen hit since Pappy done up and taken outer Kentucky fer Arkansas when the war come and he was on-easy in his mind, but hit come to me plain as day, and I said, 'I'm a-goen thar.'

"My strength come, and I done hit. I told them Indians good-by, and they taken my hand. I come to Santa Fe, and up Oklahoma, lak I said, and on to Arkansas. I was gonna see my pappy, and my mammy, if'n the Lord had done spared 'em. I come in Arkansas at Fort Smith, and on east, whar my folks had been. My mammy was dead. Been dead a long time, folks said. And my pappy, he was dead too, but not more'n goen on a year. He was kilt, with a knife. A feller from up Missouri kilt him. He was settin down at a store one night, at the settlement, and ever-body was talken and goen on. They was a-talken about the war, and how hit come. The feller from up Missouri, he was cussen the rebels, and my pappy said, naw, not to be a-cussen 'em that a-way, they didn't do hit, no more'n no other man. They had a argument, and the feller from up Missouri, he cut my pappy, and him a old man. The feller from up Missouri taken out, and was gone, no man knowed whar. And my pappy died, layen thar on the floor. I seen the place he was buried, and my mammy. Nobody knowed whar my brothers was gone, been gone a long time. Strange folks was a-live-en in the house my pappy'd built long back, the house I'd seen him start builden that day he'd stood thar and looked whar hit was gonna set, sayen, 'Lord God, Lord God,' right soft, and then sudden-lak, to Ma, 'Henrietta, gimme that-air axe!' I seen hit, the logs notched clean and set tight, and the chimney true, ne'er sunk nor slipped yit.

"I sold the place fer what I could git. I ne'er hemmed and hawed. Then I come on, on here to Kentucky, acrost Tennessee. I come on to Thebes. Hit was a hot day, when I come, but summer not on good yit. I come over the hill, down the road, and thar was the grass and the trees standen green. Lak hit is, and lak hit come to me that time. I taken the turn in the road, and thar was the church. New Bethany church, hit is. And the spring, and I run to hit, on-steady and nigh blind, with what come on me when I seen hit. I put my face down to the water. I taken my fill.

"I lifted up my head, slow. And thar she set."

His voice stopped. In the silence, in the marshy ground down the creek the frogs were piping. Then he said: " Hit was Adelle."

" Yes," his wife's voice said, quietly, from the shadow where her chair was, " I was setten thar, in the shade of a sugar-tree, and I seen him come down the hill."

— From the *Southern Review*, Fall, 1938. Reprinted by permission.

THE CAPTIVE

By Caroline Gordon

We were up long before daybreak and were loading the horses at first dawn streak. Even then Tom was a mind not to go.

" This ginseng it don't have to get to the station," he said, " and as for the money it'll bring, we can git along without that."

" We've been without salt for three weeks now," I told him.

" Thar's worse things than doing without salt," Tom said.

I knowed if he got to studying about it he wouldn't go and I was bound he should make the trip, Indians or no Indians. I slapped the lead horse on the rump. " G' long," I said, " I'd as soon be scalped now and have done with it as keep on thinking about it all the time."

Tom rode off without saying anything more, and I went on in the house and set about my morning work. The children was all stirring by that time. Joe, he felt mighty big to be the only man on the place and he was telling 'em what he'd do if any Indians was to come.

" You better hush that up," I says. " Can't you git your mind off them Indians a minute? "

All that morning, though, I was thinking about what Tom had said and wishing he hadn't had to go. Seems like I was riding with him most of the day.

" Now he's at West Fork," I'd say to myself, and then after I'd done some more chores, " He'll be about at the crossroads now or maybe Sayler's tavern." I knowed, though, it warn't much use to be following him that way in my mind. It'd be good dark before he could git home, and my thinking about it wouldn't hurry him none.

It was around ten o'clock that I heard the first owl hooting. Over on the mountain it seemed like. Joe was in the yard feeding the chickens and he stopped stock-still when he heard it and throwed back his head.

"You hear that, Mammy?" he said.

I knowed then thar must be something wrong with the call, or a boy like Joe wouldn't have noticed it.

I spoke up sharp, though. "I heard it," I says, "and I could hear a heap of other things ef'n I had time to stand around with my years open. How long you reckon it's going to take you to git them chickens fed?"

We both went on about our business without more talk, but all the time I was saying to myself that ef'n I could git through this day and see Tom Wiley riding in at the gate one more time I'd be content to bide without salt the rest of my natural life. I knowed it wouldn't do to let down before the children, though, and I kept 'em all busy doing one thing and another till dinner time. It began to rain while we was eating our dinner and it rained a long time. After it stopped raining the fog settled down, so thick you could hardly see your hand before you. And all the time the owls was calling. Calling back and forth from one mountain to the other. My littlest girl, Martha, got scared; so I made all the children stay in the house and play by the fire whilst I started in on a piece of cloth I'd had in the loom a long time and never could seem to finish. Red it was with a stripe running through it. I aimed to make both the girls a dress out of that piece before the winter set in.

By that time the fog had risen as high as the top of the ridges and the whole house was swallowed up in it. The children kept teasing, saying it was good dark now and couldn't they have a candle.

"Yes," I said, "we here all by ourselves and you want to go lighting candles, so they can't help finding the house."

One of the gals got to crying. "Who's coming?" she said. "Mammy, who you think's coming?"

I seen then I'd got 'em stirred up and I'd have to settle 'em, for seems like I couldn't stand to be worrying like I was and the children crying too. I give them all a lump of sugar around and got 'em started on a play-party. I made out I had the headache and if they was going to sing they'd have to sing low. Hog-Drovers it was they was playing.

> " Hog-drovers, hog-drovers, hog-drovers we air,
> A-courtin' your darter so sweet and so fair.
> Kin we git lodgin' here, O here,
> Kin we git lodgin' here? "

I got 'em started to frolicking and playing and then I went back to my work. But I couldn't git my mind off something a man said to me once when we was out hunting on the Hurricane, and I made him go right in on a bear without waiting for the other men folks to come up.

" You're brash, Jinny," he said, " you're brash and you always been lucky, but one of these times you going to be too brash."

Sitting there listening to them owls calling, and wondering how much longer it'd be before Tom got home, I got to thinking that maybe this was the time I was too brash. For I knowed well thar warn't another woman in the settlements would have undertook to stay on that place all day with nothing but a passel of children. Still I said to myself it's done now and thar ain't no undoing it. And the first thing I know Tom will be back, and tomorrow morning it'll fair up, and I'll be thinking what a goose I was to get so scared over nothing.

The children was still singing.

> " Oh, this is my darter that sets by my lap.
> No pig-stealin' drover kin git her from pap.
> You can't git lodgin' here, O here,
> You can't git lodgin' here."

I got up and looked out the window. Seemed to me the fog was lifting a little. A man was coming up the path. I knew it was a white man by the walk, but I didn't know it was John Borders till he stepped up on the porch.

The first thing he asked was where was Tom.

" Gone to the station with a load of ginseng," I told him. " I'm looking for him back now any minute."

He stood there looking off towards the mountain. " How long them owls been calling? " he asked.

"Off and on all evening," I said, "but owls'll hoot, dark days like this."

"Yes," he said, "and some owls'll holler like wolves and gobble like turkeys and ever' other kind of varmint. Jinny, you better git them children and come over to our house. Ain't no telling when Tom'll be back."

Just then an owl hooted and another one answered him from somewhere on top of the ridge. We both listened hard. It sounded like a real owl calling to his mate, but I was good and scared by that time and I thought I'd best go over to the Borderses'. It was my judgment, though, that thar warn't any hurry. Indians hardly ever come round before nightfall.

I told John that if he'd wait till I'd fastened up the stock I'd go back with him. He said that while I was doing that he'd walk out in the woods a little way. He'd been looking all day for some strayed sheep and hadn't found no trace of them, but he thought they might be herded up in that gulley by the spring. He went off down the path and I fastened the front door and went out the back way. I didn't fasten the back door, but I kept my eye on it all the time I was worrying with the cattle. Joe, he was along helping me. The cow was standing there at the pen; so I stopped and milked her while Joe went up in the triangle to look for the heifer. He found her all right and brought her up to the cowpen just as I finished milking. We fastened both cows up in the stable and Joe went over and saw that all the chickens was up and fastened the door on them. Then we started back to the house with the milk.

We were halfway up the path when we heard the Indians holler. We started for the house on a dead run. I could see Indians in the yard, and one Indian was coming around to the house to the back door. I ran faster and slipped in the door ahead of him. Joe was right behind me. The room was so full of Indians that at first I couldn't see any of my children. The Indians was dancing around and hollering and hacking with their tomahawks. I heard one of the children screaming but I didn't know which one it was. An Indian caught me around the waist but I got away from him. I thought, I have got to do something. I fell down on my knees and crawled around between the Indians' legs, they striking at me all the time, till I found Martha, my littlest one, in the corner of the loom. She was dead and I crawled on a little way and found Sadie. She was dead, too, with her skull split open. The baby was just sitting there holding on to the bar of the loom. I caught him in my bosom and helt him up to me tight; then I got to my feet. Joe was right behind me all the time and he stood up when I did. But an Indian come up and brained him with a tomahawk. I seen him go down and I knowed I couldn't git any more help from him. I couldn't think of anything to do; so I worked my way over towards the door, but there was two or three Indians standing on the porch and I knowed there was no use running for it. I just stood there holding the baby while the Indians pulled burning logs out of the fire on to the floor. When the blaze had sprung up they all come out on to the porch.

I made a break and got some way down the path, but an Indian run after me and caught me. He stood there, holding me tight till the other Indians come up; then he laid his hand on my head and he touched the baby too. It seemed he was claiming me for his prisoner. He had rings on his arms and ankles, and trinkets in his ears. I knew he was a chief and I thought he must be a Shawnee. I could understand some of what he said.

He was telling them they better hurry and git away before Tice Harman come home. Another Indian stepped up. I knew him — a Cherokee that come sometimes to the station. Mad Dog they called him. Tice Harman had killed his son. It come to me that they had been thinking all along that they was at Tice Harman's. I jerked my arm away from the Shawnee chief.

"You think you're burning Tice Harman's house," I said. "This ain't Tice Harman's house. It's Tom Wiley's. Tom Wiley. Tom Wiley never killed any Indians."

They looked at each other and I think they was feared. Feared because they had burned the wrong house, but feared too of Tice Harman. Mad Dog said something and laid his hand on his tomahawk, but the old chief shook his head and took hold of my arm again. He spoke, too, but so fast I couldn't tell what he was saying. The Cherokee looked mad but he turned around after a minute and called to the other Indians and they all left the house and started off through the woods. Mad Dog went first and half a dozen young Indians after him. The old chief and I came last. He had hold of my arm and was hurrying me along, and all the time he kept talking, telling me that he had saved my life, that I was to go with him to his town to be a daughter to him to take the place of a daughter that had died.

I didn't take in much that he was saying. I kept looking back towards the burning house, thinking maybe they wasn't all dead before the Indians set fire to it. Finally I couldn't stand it no longer and I asked the old Shawnee. He pointed to one of the young Indians who was going up the ridge ahead of us. I seen something dangling from his belt and I looked away quick. I knowed it was the scalps of my children.

2

We went up over the ridge and then struck north through the woods. I didn't take much notice of where we was going. I had all I could do to keep Dinny quiet — he warn't but ten months old. I let him suck all the way but it didn't do much good. We went so fast it'd jolt out of his mouth and he'd cry louder than ever. The Shawnee would grab my arm and say the other Indians would kill him sure if he kept that up. Finally I got his head down inside the waist of my dress and I helt him up against me so tight he couldn't cry, and then I was scared he'd smother, but the Shawnee wouldn't let me stop to find out.

We went on, up one valley and down another, till finally we come out on level land at the foot of a mountain. The old chief made me go first, right up the mountainside. It was worse there than it was in the woods. The laurel and the ivy was so thick that sometimes he'd have to reach ahead of me and break a way through. My arms got numb and wouldn't hold the baby up. It was lucky for me I was crawling up a mountain. I would put him up ahead of me and then crawl to him, and in this way my arms would get a little ease of the burden. The old chief didn't like this, though, and ever' time it happened he'd slap me and tell me to go faster, go faster or they would surely kill the baby.

We got to the top of the mountain, somehow, and started down.

My legs were hurting me now worse than my arms. It was going so straight down the mountainside. The back of my legs got stiff and would jerk me up every time I set my foot down, what they call stifled in a horse. I got on, somehow, though, all through that night and for most of the next day. It was near sundown when we stopped, in a rockhouse [1] at the head of a creek. The Indians must have thought they was too far for any white men to follow them. They made up a big fire and walked around it pretty careless. Two of the young Indians went off in the woods. I heard a shot and they come back dragging a little deer. They butchered it and sliced it down the middle, and slung the two haunches over the fire on forked sticks. The tenderer parts they broiled on rocks that they heated red-hot in the coals. A young buck squatted down by the fire and kept the venison turning. Soon the smell of rich meat cooking rose up in the air. The juices begun dripping down into the blaze and I thought it was a shame for all that gravy to go to waste. I asked the Shawnee to lend me a little kittle he had, and I hung it on a forked stick and caught the juices as they fell, and then poured them back over the meat. When they turned brown and rich I caught the gravy in the little kittle and sopped my fingers in it and let the baby suck them.

The old chief, Crowmocker, smiled like he thought a lot of me. "White woman know," he said. "White woman teach Indian women. You make rum?"

I said I didn't know how to make rum, but there was plenty in the settlements and if he would take me back, take me just within a mile or two of the clearing, I'd undertake to furnish him and his men with all the rum they could drink.

He laughed. "White people promise," he said. "You in your cabin you forget poor Indian."

The Cherokee, Mad Dog, had been sitting there broiling the deer nose on a rock that he had got red-hot in the flames. When it was brown he brought it over and gave it to me. Then he went back and sat down, sullen like, not saying anything. The fire shone on his black eyes and on his long beak of a nose. When he moved, you could see the muscles moving, too, in his big chest and up and

[1] A rockhouse is not a cave, but a place sheltered by an overhanging ledge of rock.

down his nekkid legs. An Indian woman would have thought him a fine-looking man, tall and well formed in every way, but it frightened me to look at him. I was glad it was the old chief and not him that had taken me prisoner. I was glad, too, that the chief was old. I'd heard tell how particular the Indians was about things like that. I thought the old chief would likely do what he said and keep me for his daughter, but if it was Mad Dog he would have me for his wife.

I thought the meat never would get done, but it finally did. The Indians give me a good-size piece off the haunch and I ate it all, except a little piece I put in Dinny's mouth. He spit it out, but I kept putting it back till he got some good of it. Then I took him down to the creek and scooped up water in my hands for him. He'd been fretting because my milk was giving out, but the water and the juice from the meat quieted him a little. After we'd both had all the water we could drink I went back up the hill and sat down on a log with Dinny laying across my knees. It felt good to have his weight off my arms, but I was afraid to take my hands off him. I was feared one of them might come up and snatch him away from me any minute.

He laid there a while a-fretting and then he put his little hand up and felt my face.

"Sadie . . . ," he said. "Sadie . . ."

Sadie was the oldest girl. She played with him a lot and fondled him. He'd go to her any time out of my arms.

I hugged him up close and sang him the song Sadie used to get him to sleep by. "Lord Lovell, he stood at the castle gate," I sang and the tears a-running down my face.

"Hush, my pretty," I said, "hush. Sadie's gone, but Mammy's here. Mammy's here with baby."

He cried, though, for Sadie and wouldn't nothing I could do comfort him. He cried himself hoarse and then he'd keep opening his little mouth but wouldn't no sound come. I felt him and he was hot to the touch. I was feared he'd fret himself into a fever, but there wasn't nothing I could do. I helt his arms and legs to the blaze and got him as warm as I could, and then I went off from the fire a little way and laid down with him in my arms.

The Indians kept putting fresh wood to the fire till it blazed up and lit the whole hollow. They squatted around it, talking. After a while half a dozen of them got up and went off in the woods. The light fell far out through the trees. I could see their nekkid legs moving between the black trunks. Some of them was dragging up down timber for the fire and some kept reaching up and tearing boughs off the trees. They come back trailing the green boughs behind them. Two or three other Indians come over and they all squatted down and begun stripping the leaves off the switches and binding them into hoops. An Indian took one of the scalps off his belt — Sadie's light hair, curling a little at the ends and specked now all over with blood. I watched it fall across the bough of maple. I watched till they began stretching the scalp on the hoop and then I shut my eyes.

After a while Crowmocker come over and tied me with some rawhide thongs that he took off his belt. He tied me up tight and it felt good to have the keen thongs cutting into me. I strained against them for a while and then I must have dropped off to sleep. I woke myself up hollering. I thought at first it was the Indians hollering, and then I knew it was me. I tried to stop but I couldn't. It would start way down inside me and I would fight to hold it in, but before I knew it my mouth would be wide open and as soon as I'd loose one shriek another would start working its way up and there wasn't nothing I could do to hold it back. I was shaking, too, so hard that the baby rolled out of my arms and started crying.

The old chief got up from where he was sleeping and come over. He stood there looking down at me and then he lighted a torch and went off in the woods a little way. He brought some leaves back with him and he put them to boil in his little kittle. He made me drink some tea from the leaves and he gave the baby some too, and after a while we both went off to sleep.

3

I woke with the old chief shaking me by the arm and telling me it was time to get up. I was still sort of lightheaded and for a minute I didn't know where I was. It was raining hard and so dark you couldn't tell whether it was good day. The Indians had built a fire up under the ledge and was broiling the rest of the venison. I laid there and I saw the light shine on their nekkid legs and the tomahawks hanging from their belts, and I knew where I was and all that had happened.

The old chief untied the thongs and I stood up with Dinny in my arms. They gave me a little piece of venison and some parched corn. My lips was so swelled I couldn't chew, but I swallowed the corn and I put the meat in my mouth and sucked it till it went away. I felt milk in my breasts and I was glad for the baby. I gave him his dinny but he wouldn't suck. He wouldn't hardly open his eyes. I thought that was from the tea the old Indian had given us and I feared he'd got too much. He was still hot to the touch and I thought he might have got a fever from laying out all night in the rain. I tore off part of my top skirt and I made a sort of sling that I put around my shoulders to carry him in; and I made a cover, too, out of part of the cloth to keep the rain off his little face.

Soon as we had finished eating, the Indians stomped out the fire and scattered the ashes so you couldn't have told there had ever been a camp there, and we started off through the woods.

We hadn't gone far before two of the young Indians left us. I thought they was most likely going back over the trail to watch if anybody was following us. I heard them saying that the folks at the settlement would be sure to send out a party. Some of the Indians thought it wouldn't do no good because the heavy rains had washed out the trail so nobody could find it. But Mad Dog said Tice Harman could follow any trail. I never knew before the Indians was so feared of Harman. They said he was the best hunter among the Long Knives, that he could go as far and stand as much as any Indian, and that they would like for him to come and live with them and be one of their warriors. Mad Dog said now that the only thing was to go so fast and go so far that even Tice Harman couldn't come up with us. He said "O-hi-yo" several times and I judged they meant to make for one of the towns on the river.

It stopped raining after a while but it didn't do much good. It was level ground we was traveling over and the water was standing everywhere, so that half the time you was wading. I knew we was some place high up in the hills, but afterwards I couldn't have told what country I had passed over. I went with my head down most of the time, not seeing anything but the black trunks of the trees going by and the yellow leaves floating in the puddles. Beech woods we must have been in because the leaves was all yellow and little.

We went on like that all day, not stopping to eat anything except some parched corn that the old chief took out of his bag and handed around to us still traveling. Late that evening we come to a water hole. One of the Indians shot a bear and we stopped and built a fire under a cliff. The Indians hadn't no more'n butchered the meat when two scouts come running into camp. They said that white men were following us, on horseback. The Indians all looked scared at this. Crowmocker stood there talking to Mad Dog about what we had best do. I went over and stood by them. Mad Dog said that they ought to kill the child and change the course, that they would have to go faster then ever now and I couldn't keep up, carrying the baby. Crowmocker showed him the sling I had made and said the baby wasn't no burden to me now. He said he had brought me this far and was going to carry me on to his town to teach his women how to weave cloth like the dress I had on.

He told Mad Dog that and then he motioned to me and said "Go!" I started off, top speed, through the trees. Behind me I could hear the Indians stomping around in the leaves to cover up the signs of the fire. I went on as fast as I could, but every now and then an Indian would shoot past me. Pretty soon they was all ahead except the old chief.

We went down hill towards a hollow that had a little branch running through it. Mad Dog was in the lead, the other Indians right on his heels, jumping over down logs and bushes quick as cats. The old chief stayed by me, and when I'd slow up getting over a log or fall down in the bushes he'd jerk me on to my feet again.

The branch was narrow but running deep with the rains. Mad Dog started wading downstream and the other Indians after him, single file. They hadn't slowed up much and water splashed high. I could see their legs moving through the splashing water. The old chief by my side was breathing hard. I knowed he was winded but I thought he would wind quicker than the others. I thought I would keep moving as long as I saw the Indians' legs going on.

The Indian that was in front of me stepped in a hole up to his waist. When he come out of it he took two three steps and stood still. I knowed then that Mad Dog had stopped and I knowed he would be coming back down the line. I looked up, but the sides of the gulley was too steep. I turned and ran back upstream fast as I could. I heard the breathing close behind me and I knowed it was the old chief, and then there was a big splashing and I knowed Mad Dog was after me.

I left the water and ran sideways up the gulley. The breathing was closer now. I tried to run faster and I caught my foot in a root. They was on me as soon as I went down. Mad Dog grabbed me by both arms. Crowmocker got there a second after, but Mad Dog already had hold of Dinny. I caught at his legs and tried to push them out from under him but he kicked me away. I got up and went at him again but he kicked me down. He kicked me again and then he went on up the side of the gulley till he come to a big tree and he held the baby by the feet and dashed his brains out.

I rolled over on my face and I laid there flat on the ground till the old chief come up. He pulled me to my feet and said we would have to run on fast, that the white men were following us on horses. I said no, I wouldn't go, I would stay there with my baby; but he and another Indian took me by the arms and drug me down the stream spite of all I could do.

We went on down the branch a good way. Towards dark we came out on the banks of a river. Water was standing halfway up the trunks of big trees. I saw the current, running fast and covered with black drift, and I didn't believe even an Indian could get across that raging river. But they didn't stop a minute. Crowmocker fell back and two young Indians took hold of my arms and carried me out into the water. The current caught us and swept us off our feet. I couldn't swim much on account of my clothes, but the two young Indians held on to my wrists and carried me on between them. The other Indians come right in after us. They held their guns up high over their heads and swum like boys treading water. I could see their heads bobbing all around me through the black drift and I couldn't see nothing to keep all of us from drowning. They managed to keep out of the drift somehow, though, and all the time they was working towards the other bank till finally we come out in dead water at the mouth of a creek. The Indians that was holding me up stopped swimming all of a sudden, and I knowed then that we must have got across. It was so dark by that time that I couldn't see nothing hardly. I got out of the water as best I could and a little way up the creek bank. I fell down there 'mongst some willows. I saw the Indians come up out of the water shaking themselves like dogs, and I saw them falling down all around me, and then my eyes went shut.

4

The old chief woke me up at the first dawn streak. I heard him and I felt him shaking me, but I didn't get up. As soon as I opened my eyes the pain in my feet started up. I touched one foot to the ground and it throbbed worse'n toothache. I knew I couldn't travel any that day and I didn't care. I turned over on my back and laid there looking up at the sky. It had cleared off during the night and the stars was shining. The sky was all a pale gray except for one long sulphur-colored streak where day was getting ready to break. Behind me the Indians was looking to their guns and settling their tomahawks in their belts. I watched their heads and shoulders moving against that yellow light, and I saw one of them take his tomahawk out and heft it and then try the blade with his finger. I thought that if I just kept on laying there that maybe he would be the one to finish me off, and then I thought Mad Dog was quicker and would beat him to it.

The old chief was still shaking me. "Get up, Jinny. Day come."

"No," I said, "I ain't going to get up."

He took me by the shoulders and tried to pull me to my feet but I slimped back on the ground. I spoke to him in Shawnee.

"My feet bleed and I cannot travel. Let me die."

He leaned over and looked at my feet and then he called to one of the young Indians to bring him some white oak bark. When the bark come he boiled it over the fire and then he took the liquor from the bark and cooled it with more water and poured it over my feet.

The other Indians had finished scattering the fire and was starting out through the willows, but Crowmocker just sat there pouring that stuff on my feet. I could feel the swelling going down and after a while I touched my feet to the ground. It didn't hurt nothing like it had, and I got up and we started off. He give me some parched corn and I ate it, walking. He said we would have to travel fast to catch up with the other Indians. I asked him if the white people was still following us and he laughed and said no white men could get across that river. I owned to myself that they couldn't, and I didn't think any more about them coming after me. I thought the Indians would probably take me so far away that I'd never again see a white face.

We caught up with the other Indians towards dark. That night we slept in a canebrake by a little river. A buffalo was wallowing in the river as we come up. One of the Indians shot him. They butchered him there in the water and drug big slabs of the meat up the bank with ropes cut from the hide. We must have been in Indian country by this time. They didn't seem to think it made no difference how much noise they made. They made up a big fire to one side of the brake and they was half the night cooking the meat and eating. I went to sleep under a tree with them singing and yelling all around me.

When I woke up the next morning they was having a council. They talked till the sun was high and then they split up into two parties. Mad Dog and three of the young bucks left us and swum across the river. The rest of us kept on up the bank. We traveled all that day through the cane and then we struck a divide and followed it into another valley. We had run out of everything to eat by this time except the strings of jerked meat that they all carried slung around their necks. We stayed two three days at a buffalo lick, hoping to kill some game, but none came and we went on.

Most of the leaves was off the trees by this time and the nights was real cold. I knew it was some time in October that the Indians come and burned our house, but I didn't know how long we'd been on the trail and I didn't have no idea what country we was in.

One morning we come out in some deep narrows just above where two creeks flowed together. A wild-looking place with tumbling falls and big rocks laying around everywhere. I looked up at the cliffs over our heads and I couldn't believe my eyes. They was *painted:* deer and buffalo and turtles big as a man, painted in red and in black on the rock. Some of the young Indians acted like they had never been there before either. They would keep walking around looking at things and sometimes stand and stare at the pictures of wild beasts that was painted everywhere on the smooth rock.

The old chief took a way up the side of the cliffs, the rest of us following. The young Indians went up like deer, but I had to pull myself up by the laurel and ivy that grew down in between the rocks. We walked along a narrow ledge and come to a rockhouse. It was the biggest rockhouse ever I seen, run all along one side of the cliff. The old chief uncovered an iron pot from where it was hid in a lot of trash in one corner of the cave and showed me how to set it up on forked sticks. He said that I would have to do all the work around the camp from now on the way Indian women did, and when the spring rains come and melted the snows he would take me to his town on the Tenassee and I would learn more about Indian ways and be adopted into the tribe in place of his dead daughter.

I thought if he took me there I would never get away and I had it in mind to make a break for it first chance I got. I got hold of two strings of jerked meat and I kept them tied around my waist so I'd be ready when the time came. I thought I would wait, though, and maybe I would find out how far it was to the settlements. I would lie there in my corner of the cave at night, making out I was asleep and listen to them talking around the fire. I heard them call the names of the creeks that flowed through that valley — Big Paint and Little Mudlick; and further off was another creek, Big Mudlick, where they went sometimes to hunt. The names was strange to me and I never could tell from their talk how far it was to the settlements or even which way to go. I had an idea that the place I was in was secret to the Indians, for it was a wonder to see and yet I had never heard any white body tell of it. I asked Crowmocker what the pictures of deer and buffalo and bear was for and he said they was the Indians' fathers and that I would learn about them when I was adopted into the tribe. Once he pointed some mounds out to me and said they was graves. He said that he and his people always stopped when they come this way to visit the graves of their fathers that was all over the valley.

A spell of fine weather come, late in the fall. Indian summer they call it. We looked out one day and bees was swarming on the cliff-side. Crowmocker was mad when he saw them. He said it meant that the white people were coming; that when bees swarmed out of season they was running away from the white people who had scared all the game out of the country and made it so that even bees couldn't live in it. I asked would the white people find their way into this valley and he said they couldn't — that it was a way known only to Indians; that if a white man ever set foot in it the great bear would come down off the wall and crush him in his paws. He said, though, that there would be fighting soon over all the land and a lot of bloodshed.

I knowed that was all foolishness about the bear, but I thought likely as not there would be fighting and I wanted to get away worse than ever. One morning I was down in the hollow by myself, gathering wood, and I thought that was the time. Three of the Indians had gone off hunting and I knowed the others was laying up in the cave asleep. I didn't think anybody would be following me, for a while, anyhow. I started off, slipping from tree to tree, and I got quite a ways up the hollow. I knowed wasn't nobody following me, but I would keep looking back over my shoulder all the time. I got to thinking. I didn't have no way to kill no game, and nothing to eat but them two strings of jerked meat. I didn't even know how far I'd have to go before I came to any settlement. Worst of all, I didn't even know which way to take. Likely as not I'd starve to death in the woods, or freeze if the weather turned. I'd better stay with the Indians, where at least I could sleep warm and eat, if it wasn't nothing but parched corn. I picked up my load of wood and I got back to camp quick as I could, and didn't none of them ever know I'd been away.

I never tried it again, but sometimes I'd sit there on the edge of the cliff and pick out the way I'd take if I did go. There was a ridge covered with black pines rose up right in front of the rock-house. I thought if I could once get up there I could get down into the valley easy. I hadn't never been over there, but I knew what the country would be like. I saw myself slipping along through that divide, around the foot of the mountain and over some more mountains till I'd come out on a clearing. I'd slip up to some cabin, towards dark. They'd think I was an Indian at first, maybe, and then they'd see my eyes was light and they'd take me in and keep me till I could get back to my own folks again.

We stayed in that rockhouse a long time. The leaves all fell off the trees, and one or two light snows fell, but the real cold weather was late coming. The Indians hunted just enough to keep us in meat. They said the pelts was thin that year and not worth taking. Sometimes they would take me along to bring in the game, but mostly they left me to work by myself. When cold weather set in we built big fires in the cave and it was warm inside like a house. When the Indians wasn't hunting they would lie around on buffalo skins and sleep. The smoke was terrible and the smell of Indians was all over everything. At first it bothered me, but after a while I got so I didn't notice it.

I wasn't in the cave much, even in bad weather. I had to gather all the firewood. The Indians didn't have no axe and I couldn't get nothing but dead branches. There wasn't much down timber on the cliffside; so I'd mostly go up over the cliffs when I was hunting wood. There was a barren there, flat as the palm of your hand and covered with a thin kind of grass. It had plenty of trees on it but they was all twisty and stunted by the wind. The only sizable tree was a big elm. It was peeled for thirty or forty feet and had a rattlesnake painted on it — a monster snake coiling up around the trunk. You could see that snake from everywhere on the barren. I was feared to look at it. The Indians seemed to think a lot of it. Sometimes they would go up there at night and I would hear them singing and dancing and calling to the snake.

Somewhere on the barren there was lead mines. The Indians never let me go to them, but they would go off and stay two-three hours and come back with big balls of lead. They made me smelt it out for bullets. I had to have a mighty fire. It would take me days and days to get up enough wood. I would heap it up in a big pile and then I would kindle the fire and keep it going for hours. When the lead melted, it ran down through little ditches into holes that I had dug to form the bullets. It would take the lead a long time to melt. Sometimes I would be up on the barren from sunup to sundown.

I would sit there and think about my husband and my children. I would wonder whether Tom went out in the woods hunting ginseng the way he used to do, and was he still looking for me or had give me up for dead. When I thought of Tom the house would be there, too, not burning down the way it was last time I saw it, but standing with the rooms just the way they always was. I could see both rooms plain, even to the hole that was burnt in the floor when a big log fell out one night. The children would be playing in and out of the house like they did. It was like they was all living; it was only me that was gone away.

I would think back, too, over things that happened long before ever I was grown and married to Tom Wiley. There was a man named Rayburn stayed at the settlement one winter. Lance Rayburn. A big, strong man and a mighty hunter. We ate bear of his shooting all that fall. He was handy with snares too, and took over a hundred beaver down in the bottom. He courted me some that winter, sitting in front of the fire after the old folks was in bed. I laughed and went on with him, but Tom Wiley had just started a-courting me and all the time my mind was on him more'n it was on the stranger.

Come time for Rayburn to pack up his pelts to take to the station, he saved one out for me. Beaver, and extra fine and soft. He give it to my sister, Sarah, and told her to hand it to me when I come to the house. She made one of the children bring it down to the creek where I was boiling clothes. I laid it there on the grass and I would stop and look at it as I went back and forth with my clothes, and sometimes I would wipe my hands dry and lay them on the soft fur for pleasure in the feel. But all the time I knowed I wasn't going to keep it. When Rayburn come towards me through the willows I went to meet him with the pelt in my hands.

"Keep this," I said, "and give it to some girl where you're going."

"Don't you want it?" he asked.

"I ain't taking nothing from you."

He stood there looking at me and all of a sudden his eyes narrowed up like a cat's. "You're full young to be marrying," he said.

"I ain't too young to know my own mind," I told him and before I thought I laughed.

He come towards me, and before I knowed what he was up to he was on me and trying to bear me to the ground. He was a strong man but I was stout, too, and I stood up to him. We was rassling around in the bushes quite some while before he got me down, and then he had to keep both his hands on my chest. I laid there right still, looking up at him.

"What you reckon my pappy'll say when I tell him about this?" I asked.

He laughed. "I ain't a-feared of no Sellards that ever walked," he said, "but that Tom Wiley ain't no manner of man for you," he said.

"You can talk against Tom Wiley and you can hold me here till Doomsday," I told him, "but it ain't going to do you no good. I ain't going to have none of you no matter what happens."

His face kind of changed. Looked like it hurt him to hear me say it. He got up off me right away and he picked the beaver pelt up from where it lay in the grass and he throwed it hard as he could into the creek.

"It'll git to my girl that way fast as any other," he said.

I watched the pelt floating down the water and on to a rock and then off again. When I turned around he was out of sight and he was gone when I got back to the house. He stayed at the station a while and then he went off in the mountains hunting bear and wasn't never heard of again. Some said he was killed by wild beasts. A rifle and a cap that they said was his'n was found up in the hills. The man that found the rifle kept it, but they give the cap to the Borderses. Wouldn't nobody wear it, and Sally hung it up in the dog alley. I used to look at it ever' time I passed and wonder whether it had ever been on Lance Rayburn's head and was he dead or still living. And sometimes I'd wonder how it'd been if I'd married him instead of Tom, but I knowed all the time I wouldn't never have married nobody but Tom because he was the one I fancied from the time I was a chap, living neighbor to the Wileys, back in the Roanoke country.

I thought about Lance Rayburn and I thought about a lot of other folks that had come to the settlement and stayed and then gone on and wouldn't anybody know whether they was living still or dead. And I thought about people dead long ago, my old granny back in Carolina, ninety-eight years old and turned simple. She'd sit in the chimney corner all day long singing, the likeliest tunes!

"Pa'tridge in the pea patch," she'd sing and call me to her and fondle me, liking gals, she said, always better than boys.

> "Pa'tridge in the pea patch
> Pickin' up the peas.
> Long comes the bell cow
> Kickin' up her heels . . ."

"Oh . . . h, the bell cow," she'd sing and catch me by my little shimmy tail. "O . . . O . . . hh, the bell cow . . ." and hist me up over the arm of her chair. "O . . . O . . . hh, the bell cow, kickin' up her heels. Call the little gal to milk her in the pail."

I used to call those songs to mind when I had to go down to the lick for salt. It was a place I didn't like to go. A deep hollow with three sulphur springs and a lick that covered nigh an acre of ground. The biggest lick ever I seen in my life. The way was white with the bones of beasts, and in between the piled up bones the long furrows that the buffalo made licking the ground for salt. I would walk down those furrows to the spring and fill my bucket with the salty water and go back up the hill to where my kettle was slung between two little birches. Sitting there waiting for the water to boil, I couldn't keep my eyes off the bones. I would take them up in my hand and turn them over and over, wondering what manner of beasts they had belonged to.

Once I made myself a little beast, laying all the bones out on some lacy moss, the front feet stiff like it was galloping off in the woods, the hind legs drawn up under him. A hare it might have been or a little fawn. Or maybe a beast that nobody ever heard of before.

They was beasts come to that lick one time or another not known to man. Bigger'n buffalo they must have been. One thighbone, I mind, longer'n I was and twice as big around as two good-sized men.

I thought of a man used to be around the station, Vard Wiley, second cousin to Tom. Folks said he was the biggest liar in the settlements. He would stay off in the woods hunting day after day and never bring in no game except maybe a brace of wild turkeys. And he told tall tales about a lick bigger'n any lick around those parts, where the beasts come up in tens of thousands. He would lay up in a tree all day and watch 'em he said, and not take a shot for wonder. There was beasts used there, he said, ten times the size of buffalo. He offered to take anybody there and show them the bones, and when they asked him why he didn't bring them back to the settlement he said couldn't no man carry them, nor no two horses.

Folks laughed at him, and the children round the settlement used to sing a song:

"Vard Wiley's gone west, Vard Wiley's gone east,
A-huntin' the woods for a monster beast.

He'll make him a tent out of the wild beast's hide
And all the king's horses can stable inside.

He'll make him a wagon out of solid bone
And it'll take ten oxen to draw it home."

I called that song to mind and I thought how if I ever saw Vard Wiley again I'd go up to him and say I knew him to be a truth-teller, and all the people would laugh at me maybe, the way they did Vard Wiley, but all the time I would be knowing it was the truth.

I thought, too, of other tales he told and of jokes he played. Of the time he borrowed my dress and sunbonnet and shawl and went and sat on the creek bank when the schoolmaster was in swimming. He sat there all evening with the sunbonnet hiding his face and old Mister Daugherty shaking his fist at him. "You hussy! You brazen hussy! Don't you know I'm nekkid?" and finally when he come up out of the water nekkid as the day he was born Vard took out after him and run him clean to the house. Old Mister Daugherty went around saying they was a woman ought to be run out of the settlements, and Vard would talk to him and make out it was me. But Old Man Daugherty knowed wouldn't none of Hezekiah Sellards' daughters be carrying on like that. He was bound it was a woman from Ab's Valley.

I would think about 'em sitting there and arguing about how the hussy ought to be run out of the settlements, and I would laugh all by myself there in the woods. Throw back my head and laugh and then feel silly when the woods give back the echo.

I done a lot of work while I was with the Indians. It was hard on me at first but I got used to it. It was better after Mad Dog left us. The old chief was like a father to me, and the young ones knowed I belonged to him and didn't bother me none. I slept off by myself in a fur corner of the cave and he would wake me up at daybreak and tell me what there was to do that day. He took pains to show me how to flesh pelts and cure them, and he showed me how to split a deer sinew for thread and how to make a whistle to call deer out of birch bark and sticks. And after I got so I could sew skins good he had me make him a pair of leggings and trim them with porcupine quills — porcupine quills colored with some roots he got out of the woods.

It bothered him the way I looked and he made me paint my face the way the Indians did. Fixed me up some of the red root mixed with bear's grease, and after I'd been putting it on my face for a while you couldn't told me from an Indian woman, except for my light eyes.

He'd stay in the cave with me sometimes all day, his buffalo hide wrapped around him so tight that his knees was up against him like a chair. He'd sit there and rock back and forth on his heels and talk while I worked. Down in the hollow the young braves would be practicing their war whoops. He would listen to them and laugh.

"Our young men give the war whoop loudly to cover up their fear of the enemy. It was not so when I was young. There was joy in the war whoop then."

He said he was a chief but he might have been something better. He might have been a medicine man. He had the gift of it from his grandmother. His own mother died when he was born, he said, and his old granny raised him. He told me about how she would take him into the woods with her looking for yarbs and roots, and how she knew where everything grew and which roots would be good to take and which had no strength in them. He said that after I was adopted into the tribe he would tell some of her secrets to me, but the Spirit would be angry if a white woman knew them.

I asked him wouldn't I still be a white woman after I was adopted into the tribe but he said no, the white blood would go out of me and the Spirit would send Indian blood to take its place, and then I would feel like an Indian and know all the Indian ways and maybe get to be a wise woman like his old granny.

He told me about his youngest daughter and how she come by her death, following what she thought was a fawn bleating. They found her days afterward, three enemy arrows in her. Her death had been paid for with three scalps of warriors, and he would say that he didn't grieve over her, but I knew he did. I got to feeling sorry for him sometimes to have lost his daughter that meant so much to him, and then I would think how I had lost all my children and my husband and I would cry, dropping tears on the skin I was sewing.

I got so after a while that the Indian way of doing things seemed natural to me. I thought nothing of seeing dark faces around me all the time, but in the night sometimes I would dream of white faces. White faces coming towards me through the trees. Or sometimes I would be in a house again and look up all of a sudden and all the faces in the room would be white.

One white face was always coming to me in my dreams: Tice Harman, the man whose house the Indians thought they was burning the day they burned ours. I always thought that if anybody came to save me it would be Tice Harman. I could see him plain in my dreams. A little man, wouldn't weigh more'n a hundred and twenty pounds, but he had a big head. A big head and a big beak of a nose and long yellow hair down to his shoulders. His eyes was blue and in my dreams they glittered like ice. I would dream about Tice Harman and when I waked I would think what I'd heard said of him — how he could go further and stand more than any man in the settlements, and how he loved to fight Indians better'n eat when he was hungry. I would think, too, of how folks said he would bring trouble on the settlements shooting that Indian down when there warn't really no use in it; and I would think that since it was him that brought all my trouble on me, maybe it would be him that would get me away from the Indians. But time went on and nobody came, and after a while I got so I didn't think much about it.

One evening I was gathering wood on the cliffside and I heard a lot of whooping and hollering down near the mouth of the creek. The Indians come out from where they was sleeping back in the cave and stood looking over the falls. A long whoop came and the old chief put his hands to his mouth and answered it. There was more whooping back and forth, and then Mad Dog came up the trail by the falls with about twenty Indians following him. They was painted for war and marched single file, all except the last six or eight. They was in pairs and in the middle of them a white man, walking with his hands tied behind him. A white man? A boy. Couldn't have been more'n eighteen years old.

I had to step out of the path to let them by. The dead branches rustled in my hands. The prisoner turned his head. He looked straight into my eyes. It was like he didn't know I was there. I spoke to him.

"I can't do nothing," I said. "I'm a white woman, but I can't do nothing. Christ!" I said, "there ain't nothing I can do."

He kept on looking at me but he didn't say nothing. They was hurrying him past. I dropped the branches and run after them. Mad Dog called to one of the young bucks and he caught me and held me. I fought him, but he held me till they had all gone up the path.

I went on to the rockhouse and kindled up the fire. After a while Mad Dog come down and told me to cook up some meat quick as I could. There would be singing and dancing he said; they would want meat all night long.

I looked at him. "A present," I said. "A present for Kagahyeliske's daughter. Give me this boy. He is not good for anything but to gather wood."

His eyes was fierce. " Boy? " he said. " He has this day killed my brother." Then he laughed and smoothed my hair. " Jinny," he said, " pretty Jinny."

I made out I had to see to the fire and walked away. I put some bear meat on to boil and I told him I would call him when it was done, and he went on back up the path.

There was a moon coming. I sat there waiting for the meat to boil and watched it rise over the pines. Up on the barren the Indians was dragging up all the dead branches they could find into one pile. After a while I looked up over the rockhouse and saw the sky all light and I knew they had kindled the fire.

The stamping and yelling went on, and every now and then a gun would go off. Then there was running around the tree. You could hear the feet pounding and the long calls. " Ai . . . yi . . . Ai . . . yi . . . Ai . . . yi . . ." One for each man that had died that day. And the sharp cry for the scalp taking. They would act it all out and the boy standing there watching. He was dazed, though; he wouldn't see it for what it was. He wouldn't know what they was doing, might not know what they was going to do. There on the path he looked at me and didn't know me for a white woman. I ought to have found out his name and where he come from. I ought to have done that much. But he wouldn't have answered. And what good would it do his folks . . . if I ever saw white folks again. Mad Dog's hand on my hair. " Pretty Jinny . . . pretty Jinny . . ."

The flames shot up and lit the whole valley. The moon looked cold where it hung over the pines. I kept the fire up under the kittle but I couldn't sit still. I walked back and forth in the rockhouse, back and forth, back and forth, waiting for the shrieks to start.

They was a long time coming. I thought maybe it was already going on. Indians can stand there burning and not make a sound, and there have been white men that could. But this was just a boy . . .

The first shriek was long and then they come short and quick, one right after the other. I got over in a corner of the rockhouse and held on tight to a big rock. After a while I let go of the rock and put both fingers in my ears and then I was feared to take them out, thinking it might not be over yet. The Indians was still yelling and stamping. The young ones kept running down and grabbing up chunks of meat from the boiling pot and carrying them up to the barren. I could see the old chief's shadow where he stood on the edge of the cliff calling to the new moon.

When he came down to the rockhouse Mad Dog was with him. They stood there dipping meat up out of the kettle. Mad Dog talked.

" It is too much. For five hundred brooches I could buy a girl of the Wild-Cats, young and swift, a fine worker in beads. A girl like a moonbeam, daughter of a mighty warrior."

His eyes was black in the circles of paint. His tongue showed bright between his painted lips. The red lines ran from his forehead down the sides of his cheeks to make gouts of blood on his chin.

A devil. A devil come straight from hell to burn and murder. Three white men killed that day and the boy brought back to torture. It was him that killed them, him that yelled loudest when the boy was burning. Him that set fire to my house and burned my children . . .

I saw him running through the woods, white men after him. I saw him fall, a dozen bullets in him. But he wouldn't be dead. He would lay there bleeding and look at me out of his painted eyes, and I would go up and stomp on him, stomp him into the dirt . . .

My hands shook so I dropped the sticks I was carrying. I was up near enough now to hear all they was saying. Mad Dog was taking little silver brooches out of a buckskin bag. He poured them out in a pile on a rock and then counted them. The old chief stood there till he got through counting; then he swept them all up into a bag he took from around his neck.

" Brother," he said, " the woman is yours."

Mad Dog had left the fire and was coming towards me. I ran over and caught hold of the old chief's arm. I called him by his Indian name.

" Kagahye-liske, do not give me to this man. He has killed my children and burned my house."

He looked down at me and it was like he'd never seen me before. His face, not painted, was as cruel as the Cherokee's, the eyes bloodshot and the whole face swollen from the meat he had eaten.

"The war whoop drowns sorrow," he said. "This chief is my brother and a mighty warrior. He has this day killed three white men."

I hung on to his arm. "Keep me for one of the young men of your village," I said. "The Cherokee are old women. You have said so and you have promised. You have promised to take me with you wherever you go."

He shook my hands off. "A promise," he said, "to a white coward! Go to your work."

He turned around like he was going to leave the cave. I run after him and caught hold of his knees, but he broke away. Mad Dog come and tied me up tight with thongs that he cut from buffalo hide, and then they both went on up to the barren where the other Indians was still screeching and stamping.

The screeching and stamping went on far into the night. The fire under the kittle went out and it was dark except for a little light from the moon. I laid there on the floor, listening to the Indians and thinking about how it would be when Mad Dog came down to take me for his wife. I laid there, expecting him to come any minute, but the singing and dancing went on and he didn't come, and after a while I went to sleep.

5

The white boy that they had burned came to me while I was asleep. He came carrying a lamp that was made from the bleached skull of a sheep. The brain hollow was filled with buffalo fat and there was a wick in it burning bright. He came walking between the trees like he didn't have need to look where he was going. His hair was light like I had seen it when he passed me there on the path, but it was long, too, like Tice Harman's. His eyes were the same eyes that had looked at me there on the path.

I said to him what I had said there. "I couldn't do nothing," I said. "There wasn't nothing I could do."

He didn't speak — only made signs for me to follow him. I got up and walked after him. The rawhide thongs was still on me but they didn't bind any more and I moved as easy and as light as he did. He went down by the falls and clomb up over the hill to where the elm tree stood that had the big rattlesnake painted on it. He walked past the elm tree and struck out through the black pines that was all over that ridge. Sometimes he would go so fast that I couldn't keep up with him, and then I would stand still and after a while I would see the light flickering through the trees and I would go on to where he was waiting for me. We went on through the pine woods and started down the side of the ridge. I heard water running somewhere far down below. I thought that would be Mudlick creek, but when I got to it it was a branch I'd never seen before. We crossed it and went on up a path through a clearing. There was little shrubs all around like the ones up on the barren, and in the middle of them was a house. It was my house and yet it wasn't. White all over and the walls so thin you could see the light from the lamp shining through the logs.

People was walking around in the yard and sitting on the door-step. They moved to let me go through the door, but they didn't speak to me and I didn't speak to them.

The men that was sitting in front of the fire playing draughts didn't even look up when I came in. I went over to the hearth and tried to dry out my clothes. I stood there holding out my hands but didn't no heat come. I looked at the logs and they was white like the timbers of the house, and the same light came from them. I saw that the men playing didn't have no lamp and yet there was light all around them.

People kept walking in and out of the cabin, men and women and little children. I would go up to them and look in their faces, but there wasn't nobody there I knew. I walked round and round the room. Every now and then the people would move out of the way and I would catch a sight of the walls. White, with patches of green on them. I put my hand up and felt one of the logs. It was round and cold to the touch. No log at all, but bleached bone. I knew then that all the house was bone, the floor and the walls and the chimney, even the table that the men was playing on, all made from the big bones down at the lick.

One of the men at the table stretched his arm out and pulled me over to him. He had on a beaver cap and his face under it was pale like he'd been in the woods a long time. He looked at me and I saw it was Lance Rayburn. He sang, pulling me up over the arm of his chair:

> "Oh . . . the bell cow, kicking up her heels,
> Call the little gal to milk her in the pail . . ."

Fiddling started up somewhere and all fell to dancing. They danced to one of my old granny's tunes:

> "They was an old lord lived in a northern countree,
> Bowee down, bowee down . . ."

There was bowing back and forth and balancing, and there was figures called, but wasn't no women dancing anywhere. I would see something going by and think it was a woman's skirt, but when I got up to it it would be fur or feathers dangling from a belt and all the faces around was dark, not like they was at first.

The great flames went leaping up the chimney, and all of a sudden I knew that they had built that fire to burn somebody by. I looked around for the one they was going to burn but he wasn't there. I said they will burn me next, and I saw what they would tie me to — the rattlesnake tree, going straight up from the table through the roof.

I went to the door and I saw through the black trunks a light flickering. I run and Mad Dog and the old chief was after me the way they was that day in the hollow. I thought they will kill me now when I go down, and I run faster and then they was both gone away and I was walking through pine woods, the light flickering on ahead of me.

I walked on and come to a creek that ran along between wide banks of cane. The light shone on the water and made it light as mist. I stepped in, not knowing whether it was water or mist, and I could feel it coming up around my knees, water and yet not water. I moved along through it light as the wind till I come to where the creek forked. I could see the two forks and the white trunks of the sycamores along the bank, but I didn't know which way to go.

The light was all around me. I could see it shining on the reeds and on the little leaves of the cane and on the water where it broke on the rocks. Behind me there was voices talking.

"Jinny Wiley . . . Jinny Wiley, that was stolen and lived with the Indians . . ."

And then it was the old chief talking to the new moon:

"The white people . . . The white people are all over the land. The beaver makes no more dams and the buffalo does not come to the lick. And bees swarm here in the ancient village. Bees swarm on the graves of our fathers . . ."

The light that had been around me was gone. It was shining now through the tree trunks down a fork of the creek. I waded towards it through the light water, the voices following, and then they was gone away and I was standing at the foot of a high mountain. I looked up and I saw the light flickering at the top and I clomb towards it, pulling myself up by the scrubs and holly bushes.

I got up on the mountain top but the young man wasn't there. I walked out on to the edge of a cliff and he was by my side. He said "Look, Jinny!" and the flame of his lamp leaped up and lighted the whole valley and I looked across a river and I saw a fort. I saw the roofs of the houses and the stockade and the timber burned back over the rifle range, and I saw men and women walking around inside the stockade.

I said: "I'm a-going over there," but the young man wasn't with me no more, and the dark that was all around was the inside of the rockhouse.

6

When I woke up the next morning the Indians had a big fire going and was all sitting around eating. I laid there and made out I was still asleep. They had found trace of buffalo down at the lick and was making ready for a big hunt. I thought maybe they would take me along to bring in the game the way they did sometimes, and then I heard Mad Dog say they would leave me tied up in the cave till they got ready to start for their town.

I was laying with my face turned up and I was feared they could tell by my eyes that I wasn't asleep. I give a kind of groan and rolled over on my side. I laid there not moving while the talking went on all around me. Once footsteps come over to the corner where I was laying and I heard something slap down on the ground right by me but I didn't give any sign and the footsteps went away.

I laid there so still that I went to sleep again with the talking and the making ready for the hunt still going on. I was waked up by a kind of roaring sound. At first I thought it was the falls and then I knowed the falls wouldn't sound that loud. I opened my eyes. The Indians was all gone and there was a big storm blowing up.

I laid there watching the pine tops lash back and forth in the wind, and the dream I'd had come back into my mind as plain as if it was something that had happened. I thought it was sent to me on purpose to tell me that now was the chance to get away. I knowed that if the Indians come back with any game that night they'd feast high again and was more than likely to take me up on the barren and burn me like they done that boy.

I sat up. A piece of meat was lying on the floor right by me. That meant that the Indians would be all gone all day and maybe another day. If I could only get free of the thongs I might get a long way off before they knew I was gone.

There was a knife stuck in a crack of the rock where they laid the meat. If I could only get hold of that! I rolled over and over till I got to the rock and I managed to get up on my knees, though the thongs cut into me bad. I could see the handle of the knife sticking up out of the crack and I laid my face down flat on the rock and tried to catch hold of it with my teeth. But it was too far down and all I did was get my mouth full of grit and sand. I gave up and laid down again. The wind wasn't as high as it had been, but the rain was coming down hard. It blew way back into the cave. I laid there with the big drops spattering in my face and a thought came to me. I rolled over to where the rain was pouring down off the roof and I laid there till I was soaked through. All the time I kept straining at the thongs and I could feel them giving a little, the way leather does when it's wet. I kept on, getting them looser and looser till finally I worked my way out of them and stood up free.

I listened and I couldn't hear anything but the roaring of the wind and the beating of the rain on the ledge. I tiptoed to the end of the cave and looked down the path. But I couldn't see any sign of living creature. I dug the knife out from between the rocks and I took the piece of cooked meat and a little kittle that the old chief had left laying around, and I went off out of the other end of the cave and along the cliffside.

I kept to the path a little way and then I struck off through the trees down the hillside. The ground was wet and slid from under my feet in big chunks. I caught on to the trees all the way to keep myself from falling. When I got to the bottom I could look back and see where I'd come, as plain as if I'd blazed a trail. I knowed I'd have to strike water. I run in among some pines and come to a wet weather branch. I waded right in. It was swift water and full of holes. I would step in one every now and then and go down, but I kept on as fast as I could. I felt all the time like the Indians was after me. I knowed they had gone south towards the salt lick and I knowed the whole cliffside and the barren was between me and them, but all the time I felt like they was right behind me. When I looked over my shoulder the top boughs of the rattlesnake tree showed from the barren. I was glad when I rounded a bend and it was out of sight.

When I come to where the branch flowed into the creek I didn't know which way to go, and then I thought that in my dream I was following water and I struck right down the stream. It was harder going here than it was in the branch. The snows melting had filled all the dry weather branches, and muddy water kept running in till you couldn't tell nothing about the depth. It was good I was going downstream, but even then the current was a hindrance to me, reaching in and sweeping me off my feet sometimes into a hole that I would have a time getting out of. More'n once I was in danger of drowning.

I kept on like this all day. When it was drawing towards dark I crawled up on the bank under some cedars and I laid there and I ate a good-sized piece of the cooked meat I had brought with me. The rain had fallen off to a light drizzle and there was some color in the sky, sign of a clear day tomorrow. There was a flight of little birds over the water and then round and round the tops of the cedars. Some of them lit in the boughs of the tree I was laying under. I could hear them flying in and out and the quick cries and then the twittering as they settled down to roost. It was dark under the trees but the streak of light stayed on the water. I laid here and watched it fade and I wished I could stay there where the cedar boughs was like a little house. I wished I could stay there and not run no more. I thought I would maybe sleep a few minutes and then I could go on faster. But when I shut my eyes I would think I heard the Indians coming through the trees and after a little I got up and went on again.

I tried wading some more but I couldn't make it in the pitch dark. I got up on the bank of the creek and pushed my way through the bushes as best I could. Sometimes the undergrowth would be so thick I couldn't make it, and then I would have to get down in the water again. All the way I was worrying about losing time following the bending and twisting of the creek, and then I would think that was the only sure way to get out of the hill country and I had best stick to water, spite of all the bending.

Some time during the night I lost my way from the creek and wandered in the pitch dark into a marsh that was all along the creek bottom. More like a bog it was. I couldn't seem to get out of it no matter what I did. I stood there bogged to the knees and I couldn't even hear the creek running — nothing but the wind soughing in the trees. And I thought what a lone place it was and if I came on quicksand, as was more than likely, I could go down and even my bones never be found. And I thought of how Lance Rayburn's bones might have been laying all this time in some hollow of the mountain and nothing maybe but squirrels or deer ever going near the place, and it seemed to me I might better have stayed with the Indians. But I knew it wouldn't be no use going back now. They would put the fire to me sure.

I stood there and I heard some wild thing passing. Pit pat pit pat it went; feet falling on dry ground. I pulled out of the muck and made towards the sound, and a deer or something broke through the thicket and went off through the woods.

I followed and come out on high ground, a slope covered with pine needles. I throwed myself down flat on my face. I must have gone off to sleep. When I come to myself light was growing through the trees, and all around me I could hear twigs snapping and little rustlings. I got up quick, thinking it was the Indians coming, and then I felt foolish, knowing it was only game stirring at break of day. I saw two deer go by, moving slow over the brown pine needles. The air was so still they didn't get a whiff of me till they was out of the thicket. The buck wheeled so quick he almost knocked the doe over, and then they was both clattering off over the hill.

I went down to the creek bank and washed my face and let the water run over my wrists where they was scratched by the branches. I ate the last of my meat sitting there on a rock. When I got ready to go I found out that one of my strings of jerked meat had slipped off during the night. I couldn't hardly believe it at first. I stood up and felt all over my clothes time and again but it warn't there.

"Well," I said, "it's gone and they ain't no use crying over it, but I wish to God it'd a been the little piece."

I got in the water and started wading again. The creek was shallow for about half a mile and then it run into a bigger creek. The two of them run on before me and I didn't know which way to go. I stood there looking. The sun was up and it shone on the water. I watched the riffles break on the black rocks where the sun caught them, and the place was not the same place I had seen in the dream and yet it was the same because of the light that was over everything.

I remembered the way I took in the dream. "Left I'll go," I said, "like it was in the dream, and if it don't turn out right it's no fault of mine."

I went on, wading half the time. All that day I was thinking about something to eat. Seems like everything good I ever had to eat in my life come back to torment me that day. The smell of herring, cooking, bothered me most. I would see myself, a chap, back in the Roanoke country, broiling herrings over the coals the way children did when their mammy wouldn't give them anything else to eat between meals. I would go over it all, time and again, the herrings hanging in rows in the smokehouse, like tobacco in a barn, and us climbing up on a slab of wood to get at them.

"Three," Dinny, that's my oldest brother, 'd say every time. "Three. You might as well get one apiece while you're at it."

I thought, too, about people wasting things, of a woman I knew used to give all her buttermilk to her pig, and I thought how it was shameful to have no mind for them that might be starving. And I thought how if I could have that pig's dinner one time, or even a moldy piece of bread, the kind I'd thrown away many a time as not good enough for the dogs. And yet I'd been as wasteful as any of them in my day — worse, even, with game. I used to go hunting just for the fun of it. Seemed like there warn't nothing I liked better than sighting down a rifle. Warn't none of the Sellards or Damron boys a better shot than I was, and I could throw a knife with the best of them. That time John and Dick and me and the two Damrons went to Sinking Fork on a big hunt I shot eighteen wild gobblers, and when we loaded up and they was more'n we could carry it was me that said to leave them laying, that there warn't no use in breaking yourself down and the woods full of gobblers like they was. I thought about them gobblers more'n once that day and Lord, how I wished I could git my hands on a rifle butt just one more time.

I throwed my knife once or twice at some small game, mostly rabbits, but it was a rusty old thing and not fitted to the hand the way a knife has to be to turn proper. One rabbit that I hit square in the middle got up and skittered off like nothing had happened, and I seed then it was a waste of time to throw at them.

Late that evening I come on some forward wild greens in a sheltered place on the creek bank. I went down on my knees and I gathered every shoot. I found some punk and I went up to a rockhouse on the side of the hill and I built a little fire way in under the ledge the way I'd seen the Indians do. I knowed it was craziness to build a fire, but it might be days before I'd come on any wild greens again. "I'll eat," I said, "varmints or no varmints."

I put my greens on to boil in the little kittle with a piece of the jerked meat and I sat there, thinking about how Indians would go up on a cliff to sight over the country and how the least little smoke curling up would be a sign to them. Once I was on the point of putting the fire out but I couldn't bring myself to do it. I feared to feed it much and yet I'd catch myself putting dead twigs to it. It was a long time before the bubbles started rising up in that little old kittle. I sat there rocking on my heels and talking to them.

"Bile," I said, "bile. God's sake, can't you bile no faster'n that? And me setting here starving."

I ate up ever' mite of the greens and I drank the pot liquor and licked the kittle and then I put out down the hill as fast as I could. I could feel my stomach tight under my waist band and strength coming up in me from the vittles and I run faster than I'd ever run before. It was dark under the trees but there was still light down the water courses. I thought how in some cleared place or in a town it wouldn't be dark for two or three hours yet and I saw myself in such a place, moving around and talking to people but staying always in the light. And I said to myself, if I ever got into such a cleared place again it'd be hard to get me to set foot in the woods.

The creek I was following was a master tumbler. Straight down it went over big rocks and the water white everywhere with its dashing. Once I thought I would leave it and strike out through the woods again, and then I thought falling water'd take me out of the hills quicker'n anything else and I'd best stick to it long as I could.

I went on and then all of a sudden I come upon something that froze my guts cold: the print of a foot by the water. I knowed it would be a moccasin but I stooped down and looked at it good. I told myself it might be a white man — might be a hunter wearing moccasins like most of 'em did; but I went on a little way and there was three-four footprints in some wet sand and all of 'em was moccasins. I thought then the game was up or would be directly, but I run on. I run on. I couldn't think of nothing else to do.

It was still light when I come out on a big rock by some little falls. I stood there looking and I couldn't believe my eyes. A broad river ran there before me and clearings here and there on the bank and right across from the rock I was standing on a fort: a blockhouse with a stockade fence around it and the timber burned back over the rifle range.

I got off the rock and I run down towards the water. A woman and some children was walking along outside the stockade. I called to the woman. She give one look at me and turned and run inside the fort, the children after her. I saw the gate swing to behind them and I knowed they had shot the bolt.

I tore off my petticoat and I waved it over my head and I yelled loud as I could.

"Let me in! Let me in, I tell you!"

I could see heads at the upper story and one somebody standing up on a stump to look over the stockade. But nobody answered and there wasn't no sign of the gate opening.

I looked over my shoulder. The woods was dark behind me and they wasn't no signs of Indians, but I knowed they'd be coming any minute. I felt like I knowed the place in the woods they was at now. I saw them trotting, trotting through the trees, one after another, the way they went.

I thought, I'll have to do something quick or they'll git me sure, after all my trouble. I started in to swim it but I couldn't make no headway against that current. I saw I would be drowning in a minute, and I swum hard and got back to shallow water. It come to me then that the folks in the fort didn't know who I was. I stood up in the water and I yelled, loud as I could.

"I'm Jinny Wiley . . . Jinny Wiley that the Indians stole."

The echo come back to me from the woods, but there warn't no sound from the fort. Then the gate opened a little way and an old man come out with a gun in his hand. He stood there looking at me and he turned around and said something to the folks in the fort and then he started down the path. I watched him coming down over the rifle range, an old man, gray-haired and feeble enough to a been my grandsire. I shouted at him.

"You can't do it. Send some young body over."

He stood on the bank and shouted back at me, his old voice quavering across the water:

"Where'd you come from?"

I jumped up and down and shrieked, top of my voice:

" God's sakes, man, you going to let me die right here before your eyes? I'm white! White, I tell you! "

" All of 'em's gone but me," he said, " and they ain't no canoe."

" Make a raft," I told him.

He nodded his head up and down. I could see his old gray beard a-shaking. " You better be ready to swim for it," he said. " I don't know as I can git across."

He called to the women in the fort and they come and brought an axe. They was a dead mulberry tree on the bank and they went to work felling it. The old man went off in the woods and come back with some grapevine. When the tree fell it split into three logs and he tied them together with grapevine and then he and the women rolled them down to the water. They handed him two rifles and he laid them on the raft and started poling. The current caught him and he was going downstream. Yelling had started behind me somewhere in the woods. The Indians was coming.

I run down the bank till I got even with the raft and I swum out and clomb abroad. The old man poled hard. We got halfway out in the river and then the vines begun to come loose and the raft was spreading apart. I knelt down and held the logs together with my hands as best as I could. The old man fell down on his knees and started praying.

" 'Tain't no use," he said, " we can't make it."

I looked over my shoulder. The Indians was swarming down towards the water. I knowed they'd be swimming directly. The old man was still praying. I took the pole away from him.

" Go on and pray, you old fool," I said. " I'm a-going to git across this river."

I put all the strength I had into it and we made some headway. The yelling was closer now. The Indians was in the water. A shot rung out. I hoped to God one of 'em was hit. I poled harder and I seen some willow boughs ahead of me. I reached out and grabbed hold of 'em and we pulled ourselves to shore.

We went up over the rifle range fast as we could. I looked back once. The Indians had left the water and was standing on the bank. I heard Mad Dog calling:

" Whoopee! . . . whoopee! . . . pretty Jinny! "

We went through the gate. I heard the bolt shoot home and I knowed I was inside the fort. I fell down on the ground and the women and children come crowding. The Indians was still yelling. I sat up and the high stockade fence was all around me.

" Lord God," I said, " I was lucky to git away from them Indians! "

— From *Hound and Horn,* Autumn, 1932. Reprinted by permission.

THE YELLOW DRESS

By Brainard Cheney

You can usually figure out what a nigger is after, but seldom from what he tells you. At least that's powerfully true of Big Bite niggers.

There's a geechee strain here in this river bend, where I been running the Wilkins Day plantation for the last fifteen years. They are blue-gummed and blue-black and the unaccountablest niggers in some ways I ever had to deal with. There ain't no question of their knowing their place and they are good-natured and simple. But when one of them takes a quare, superstitious notion into his head there ain't no gettin' shed of it.

I want to tell you about a hand I got a yellow wedding dress for, or the goods for it. Her name was Lessie. Her pa, Tink, is a cropper on the place now. She got the Goddurndest notion about this dress!

The first I knowed anything was happening, I come by Tink's place on the Saturday afternoon before the wedding was to be on Sunday — and I didn't know what it was all about then, the way it broke out. I was on my way to the river to fish my baskets and I thought I'd get Tink to paddle my boat. I come through the side yard by the scuppernong arbors, heading past his shanty for the swamp road. I was abreast of the house before I slowed down to yell for him and I saw Lessie in that yellow dress shutting the door quick. I stopped her and asked if Tink had got back from town, where I knowed he'd gone with a load of cotton.

She stood there on the inside with the door cracked about a foot. It looked like she didn't aim to speak; then she said, "Naw-suh." Her voice was sort of husky. The sun was gone down behind the ridge of the shanty, but I could see her face. It was stiff and right ashy colored. I glimpsed inside through the door crack at the hinges, as you will looking a thing over. I caught sight of a pair of checked pants on the back of a chair before the fire.

"Anybody home 'sides you?" I asked her. It seemed just as hard for her to get it out the second time, but finally she said, "Nawsuh." Well, I knowed better than that, but I didn't say anything. I just laughed and got going again. I decided she had her man in there gittin' in an afternoon's ruttin' while Tink and Matt and the children were away in town. While I was walking on down to the river, I thought to myself that I'd never seen a nigger gal get so scared over a thing like that before, but I dropped it.

I took four carp and two yellow cat out of one of the baskets and didn't bother the other. I had a mess. Heading for home, I cut through the swamp instead of coming back the road. On the way I saw Lessie again, or thought I did. It was first dark in the swamp and she was a hundred yards away, going crosswise to me along the old Colter field trail. I saw that yellow dress; but you couldn't be sure about a Big Bite nigger at that distance. I hollered at her. She never looked around — just pyertened her step and kept going. She was done out of sight when I crossed the trail.

The reason I knowed that dress so good was, as I said, I bought the material. My wife wanted me to get something she could use for window curtains in the next bolt of goods I got to keep at the commissary. The store clerk said it was dressy stuff and would do for most anything. He called it canary yellow. I liked the color. When Matt come to me for some goods to make her gal a wedding dress out of, I sold her a piece of it. I didn't think it made any special difference to let the nigger have it for that.

I was glad enough to get Lessie married and get her off the place, and it seemed to me that she ought to been glad to go, but she wasn't. The wedding dress and all was Matt's idea. Still I let her have it to help the thing along, because Lessie hadn't been worth her snuff as a hand — not since Lum, her twin brother, left two years before.

She ought to've been glad to get shed of Lum, too, but I tell you, niggers never know what's good for them. Matt had made out some superstition about them: she said they always had to work together, for the Lord meant twins to team up. They were the only pair of twins she had and they looked as much alike as a pair of Hampshire pigs, only stringier. Even when they were younguns, when she sent Lum for a bucket of water, Lessie had to go along with him and help carry it. I never seen one of them come to the field without the other. I remember when Tink started Lum in to learn to plow, he put Lessie at another plow alongside of him, behind an old gray mule.

And they come to make a good work pair. They could chop as much cotton as Tink and Matt, durn near it. The fall before Lum left, Lessie was the best cotton picker of the bunch. I weighed her in at two hundred pretty nigh ever night. But they were gettin' grown and it was time to break that sort of thing up — that twin business.

When Cap'n Day asked me about taking Lum to Dublin with him for a yard boy, I didn't say much. I didn't think these Bite niggers could be broke for no yard use, but I let him take him on.

It had always been my idea that Lessie was the one who had the get-up-and-go about her anyhow. But it look like I was wrong after Lum left. She wasn't half a hand that summer. She spent more time leaning on the hoe-handle than chopping cotton. I know I told her the cotton would be too big to chop before she worked out her row if she didn't make haste. And it looked like every time I went to the water barrel or the spring I found her there, usually just settin' on the ground.

She wasn't no better in the picking season, either. She had picked out ahead of Lum and the rest of the crowd the season before, but she hardly made a hundred pounds a day. I know I come along one morning and found her sittin' on her sack, and I told her if she didn't get up and start picking I was going to run her out of the field.

Tink was picking along on the next row and I stepped over to him — I'd done got dog tired of it then — and I told him she was his gal and he could do what he pleased about her, but if she was mine I wouldn't feed her for the work she was doing. I recollect I told him, "What she needs is a good application of a gallberry whip about twicet a day and half rations."

Tink straightened up and didn't say nothing and there wasn't nothing in his face for a minute, and then he come with a kind of dry smile and said, "I reckon I better try her another season before I do dat."

Matt was picking the row beyond Tink and I reckon she heard what we said, for she come, her hands flying into that cotton like a sewing machine, until she got alongside and then she bounced up and lit into us. She really lit into us. Matt's plain all-nigger. Her face has got the shine as well as the black, and there's plenty of mouth in it. When she's not singing, she's liable to be bellowing or cussing somebody out — she don't never sull.

I recollect the way she put it. "Y'all leave dat poh chile alone," she said, her big lips a-quivverin' a little and her eyes bugged out like a calf being pulled off a cow's teat. "Whut y'all know about her troubles? D'neither one of y'all have yoh twin took away from you — you ain't even never had no twin! Dat's de fuvrest away and de longest apart dey bin since I birthed Lum and, in less'n a minute after, drapped her — eighteen years ago."

Then she looked at Tink, her lips still sticking out beyond her nose, and went on, "You de one responsible for it, you know you is — sending 'im away — and to Dublin! Dublin ain't no place for Big Bite niggers to go and you knows it. You knows what happens to us niggers who goes up dere. Yeah, Big Lum, Big Lum who Lum named a'ter, goes up dere and gets shot to death. And Edd, my own boy, my fust one — Edd didn't tote no chairs at home, he wucked hard — he goes up dere and gets triflin'. Now he on de gang. White people ruined Edd. And heah you playin' up to Cap'n Wilk 'cause he stop and talk wid yuh. He say he need a boy around de place and you say, 'Sho' take Lum.' It'll be de ruination of Lum, too — Dublin! "

She stopped to blow a minute and we just stood there looking at her. Then she wound up, "Lessie know whut Dublin mean. Dat poh chile sick fit to die and don't neither one of y'all so much as touch her! " She put on a show. But it wasn't putting sense in that gal's head.

I guess it was the first of last summer; it was that same day Lessie come brought me a dang buckeye to take to Lum, I remember. That was all she had to send. Come asking me to take a buckeye all the way to Dublin; but Lum had sent her word he needed it, she said. Anyhow, I know that was the first time I saw this nigger Hawtense hanging around her. It looked like then she was a lot more interested in getting that dang buckeye to Lum than she was in Hawtense. I didn't know he was sparkin' her, but after that most any Saturday afternoon or Sunday I happened to go by Tink's I could find that nigger around. And most of the time, it seemed, he was settin' out under the trees by hisself, or talkin' to Matt or one of the boys. Anyhow Matt come to me first of cotton picking season and told me they were going to get law-locked and settle down on the Barnes place. She said as God lived, she was glad. It would be a good thing for Lessie to get away from where she and Lum had been all her life, and Matt wanted to give her a big send-off with a wedding and a dress to go with it. I told Matt, Lessie ought to be glad to get a man of any sort, the way she had acted; and to get one with a crop and a house to put her in, she ought to feel proud. I didn't tell Matt I was glad Lessie was going, but I let her have that yellow goods for what it cost me.

❦ ❦ ❦

I had done forgot about the dress and Lessie and her man, too, after I got back from the river that night, when they come. I was settin' reading the paper with my shoes off and thinking about going to bed when they tromped up on the front porch. They pounded on the door a couple of times before I could get a lamp lit in the front room, and I wouldn't have opened up if I hadn't thought I knew the voice that spoke.

He come inside by hisself, but some stood in the doorway. He was a big stout fellow and had on a double-bill hunting cap. "I want you to show us where a nigger named Lum McRae lives," he said. He looked from a little book in his hand up at me, his eyes squinting together like a pair of scissors shuttin'.

I started off to tell him that Lum had left the Bite, but he stopped me. He said he knew all about that, but he had reason to believe Lum had come back home that day. It was plain that

Lum was in trouble. I asked the man (I couldn't place him but I knowed I'd seen him before in Dublin) what it was, and he said Lum had raped a white girl there.

It sort of shook me up, his saying that, and I couldn't come to the idea right off that Lum or any other Big Bite nigger 'ud do such a thing. I asked him how he knowed it was Lum. There wasn't no doubt, he said. Lum was the only nigger on the place when it happened and the white girl had said it was a nigger in a checked suit. Lum was last seen in Dublin after it happened — though the switchman didn't know about the raping — in the railroad yard, still wearing a checked suit.

I was about to tell him I didn't think Lum would come back home if he did a thing like that, when I recollected those checked pants I seen through the door crack.

There looked to be twenty to twenty-five men in the bunch, when I stepped outside — I couldn't tell so good in the dark. The big fellow in the hunting cap put me in the front car with him. And he told me going over to Tink's that the girl's uncle was settin' on the back seat.

Tink's shanty was plumb cold when we got there. It looked like nobody was home and I would have left this crowd at the gate, but the big fellow wouldn't let me. He took six other men — they all had guns and pistols, but I didn't bring any — and made me come along with them to the house. They surrounded it and then he rapped on the door with his pistol butt and yelled, "Hey, ole nigger!" I didn't go in, but all they found was Matt sick in the bed. They turned the place upside down, but it didn't do any good.

The big fellow, when he come out of the house, yelled, "Hey you men, don't let anything get by you — that nigger's somewhere around here — he's been here tonight." They had been standing quiet under the trees; now they got noisy. They broke up in bunches and searched the outhouses, the cowshed, the barn, the scuppernong arbors. They even threw down the rail fences and climbed up the trees. A couple of 'em broke down the smokehouse door.

It looked like they weren't goin' to find anything when a high-pitch voice hollered from the barn, "Here he is!" A squat fellow and a tall one come through the barnlot gate dragging him between them. There was a moon, but all I could see was somebody being drug. The crowd gathered around and a couple of them said it was Lum, they knew him. I held back, thinking maybe they'd let me go now, but the fellow in the hunting cap made me get in the car with him.

We only went about a mile and turned off the road into an oak grove, where the old Nall house used to stand. Our car pulled over beyond a big low-limbed oak and stopped in what had been the yard once. When we got back to the tree, the two men who found the nigger were standing under it with him, and one of them was holding a railroad lantern. The rest of the crowd was getting out of their cars and coming up.

Just as we got there a man in our bunch — tall thin man with mustaches — stepped out of a sudden and slapped the nigger in the face. The two men holding him had turned him loose and he went down. The big fellow with me grabbed this mustached man by the arm and said, "Hold on Ed, we ain't ready for that yet."

The crowd gathered into a circle around the nigger on the ground and the two men who'd been holding him. I could see now he had on the checked suit. The big man in the hunting cap was sort of running things. He kicked the nigger's foot and told him to get up. The nigger come up slow, the man with the railroad lantern holding his arm.

Somebody played a flashlight on him when he was on his feet. He looked like a man I saw once who took hold of a live wire and couldn't turn it loose, but his eyes were closed. I know I thought, "Poor Lum, your buckeye won't do you no good now" — though I could laugh about that afterward.

Then the big man stepped in the ring and said in a sharp way, "Nigger, you going to meet your Maker in a minute — you better clean your conscience while you can." He waited a while and then he said, "We're giving you this last chance to get right with God."

The nigger stood there like something cut out of clabber. His eyes were still closed and you could only tell he wasn't asleep by his breathing and a sort of fluttering in his throat. There were flashlights playing on him from all around the ring now, and the men who held his arms shook him, but he didn't open his mouth once.

The big man stepped toward him of a sudden and said, "You raped that girl! Didn't you?"

His eyes come open, like when you shove a stick of fire at a fellow's face. They kept staring at the big man, staring at 'im, but that was all.

About that time the man with the mustaches hit the nigger in the face with his pistol butt and kicked him in the privates after he was on the ground. Then the ring broke up and everybody started kicking him. It turned me sick at my stomach and I stepped away and bent over a bush for a minute. The crowd was spreading out from the tree when I come back and the nigger was already swinging from the rope. As I made my way into the circle, I saw he was barefooted. I stood there staring and it come to me about that afternoon Cap'n Day took him off to Dublin. Me and Cap'n had come back from fishing on the river and picked up Lessie at the forks of the swamp road. It wasn't until we got over to Tink's that Cap'n found out — and me too for that matter — we had Lessie and not Lum in the car. Cap'n hollered at our mistake. While this thing was running through my mind the rope slipped on the limb or something and the nigger's body turned. The flashlights were playing on his stretching neck and rumpled checked suit. My eye fixed on the back of his heel. I realized of a sudden that I was looking at a white crooked scar on the nigger's heel: that day trying to get out'n the back of the car and away from us, Lessie had busted open the door and fell out on the ground, splittin' her heel on a piece of glass. I knew that scar — I knew damn well I knew it.

I was so taken, I just lifted my arms and started running toward the nigger without saying a word. I couldn't make words come for a minute. By the time I had got there, several of the crowd had grabbed me. I thought I wasn't never going to make 'em understand. I had to tear off the coat and shirt, too, and show 'em.

It was Lessie all right, but it was already too late when we cut her down. And I'd thought all the time she was wearing that yellow wedding dress.

— Reprinted by permission
of the author.

THE HAUNTED PALACE

By Elizabeth Madox Roberts

The House stood at the head of a valley where the hollow melted away into the rolling uplands. The high trees about the place so confined the songs of the birds that on a spring morning the jargoning seemed to emerge from the walls. The birds seemed to be indoors or within the very bricks of the masonry. In winter the winds blew up the hollow from the valley and lashed at the old house that stood square before the storms. The place was called Wickwood. It had been the abode of a family, Wickley, a group that had once clustered about the hearths there or had tramped over the courtyard or ridden through the pastures.

From a road that ran along the top of a ridge two miles to the east, the House could be seen as a succession of rhomboids and squares that flowed together beneath the vague misty reds of the mass. Or from the valley road to the west, looking up the hollow into the melting hills, in winter it could be seen as a distant brick wall set with long windows, beneath a gray sloping roof. Sometimes a traveler, allured by the name of the place or by the aloof splendor of the walls as seen vaguely from one or the other of these highways, would cross the farm lands by the way of the uneven roads. He would trundle over the crooked ways and mount through the broken woodland to come at last to the House. Leaving his conveyance, he would cross the wide courtyard on the smooth flagstones, and he would hear the strange report his footfalls made as they disturbed the air that had, but for the birds and the wind, been quiet for so great a length of time that it had assumed stillness. He would wonder at the beauty of the doorways and deplore the waste that let the House stand unused and untended. He would venture up the stone steps at the west front and peer through the glass of the side lights. The strange quality of the familiar fall of his own shoe on stone would trouble his sense of all that he had discovered, so that he would at last come swiftly away.

The country rolled in changing curves and lines and spread toward the river valleys where it dropped suddenly into a basin. The farms were owned by men and women who had labored to win them. But among these were younger men who worked for hire or as share-owners in the yield.

❦ ❦ ❦

One of these last, Hubert, lived with Jess, his wife, in a small whitewashed shelter behind a cornfield. Jess spoke more frequently than the man and thus she had more memory. She had been here two years, but before that time she had lived beside a creek, and before that again in another place, while farther back the vista was run together in a fog of forgetting. She had courted Hubert in a cabin close beside a roadway. She remembered another place where there was a plum tree that bore large pink-red fruits, and a place where her father had cut his foot with an axe. Now, as a marker, her own children ran a little way into a cornfield to play. Beyond these peaks in memory, going backward, the life there rested in a formless level out of which only self emerged. She met any demand upon this void with a contempt in which self was sheltered.

Hubert was a share-laborer, but he wanted to be able to rent some land. He wanted to use land as if he were the owner, and yet to be free to go to fresh acres when he had exhausted a tract as he willed. After the first child, Albert, was born, he said to Jess:

" If a person could have ahead, say, four hundred dollars, and against the Dean land might come idle . . ."

His fervor had the power of a threat. He was knotty and bony and his muscles were dry and lean. He had learned at school to write his name and to make a few slow marks that signified numbers or quantities, but later he had used this knowledge so infrequently that most of it was lost to him. He wrote his name painfully, and writing, he drew his fingers together about the pen. His breath would flow hard and fast under the strain, his hand trembling. If there were other men standing about he would, if he were asked to write his name, sometimes say that he could not, preferring to claim complete illiteracy rather than to undergo the ordeal.

"Against the Dean land might come idle . . ." He had a plan over which he brooded, wanting to get a power over some good land that he might drain money out of it. He was careful, moving forward through the soil, taking from it.

When the second child came they lived at the Dean land, behind the cornfield. Jess would fling a great handful of grain toward her hens and they would come with reaching bills and outthrust necks, their wings spread. She would throw ears of corn to the sow and it would chew away the grains while the sucklings would drag milk, the essence of the corn, from the dark udders.

"We ought, it seems, to build the sow a little shed against winter comes," Jess said to Hubert.

"We might eat the sow. I might fatten up the sow and get me another."

"She always was a no-account sow. Has only five or six to a litter. It's hardly worth while to pester yourself with a lazy hog."

"Fannie Burt asked me what was the name of the sow or to name what kind of breed she was. 'Name?' I says. As if folks would name the food they eat!"

Hubert laughed at the thought of naming the food. Names for the swine, either mother or species, gave him laughter. To write with one's hand the name of a sow in a book seemed useless labor. Instead of giving her a name he fastened her into a closed pen and gave her all the food he could find. When she was sufficiently fat he stuck her throat with a knife and prepared her body for his own eating.

Jess yielded to the decision Hubert made, being glad to have decisions made for her, and thus she accepted the flesh of the brood sow. Of this she ate heavily. She was large and often of a placid temper, sitting in unbrooding inattention, but often she flamed to sudden anger and thrust about her then with her hands or her fists. She did not sing about the house or dooryard. Singing came to her from a wooden box that was charged by a small battery. She adjusted the needle of this to a near sending station and let the sound pour over the cabin. Out of the abundant jargon that flowed from the box she did not learn, and before it she did not remember. . . .

Jess had a few friends who came sometimes to see her. They were much like herself in what they knew and in what they liked. She would look curiously at their new clothing.

But one of them, named Fannie Burt, would come shouting to the children as she drove up the lane in a small cart, and her coming filled the day with remembered sayings and finer arrangements. When Fannie came, Jess would call Albert, the oldest child, and send him on his hands and knees under the house to rob the hen's nest if there were not enough eggs in the basket; for the day called for a richer pudding. Fannie had no children as yet and she could be light and outflowing. She went here and there and she knew many of the people.

"Miss Anne mended the cover to the big black sofa in the parlor . . ." She would tell of many things — of tapestry on a wall, blue and gold. Words seemed light when she talked, as being easily made to tell of strange and light matters. Jess was not sure that Fannie knew more of these things than she knew herself since the words conveyed but an undefined sense. The lightness of bubbles floated about Fannie, things for which Jess had no meanings. Fannie had lived the year before at a farm where the owner had been as a neighbor to her. She often went back to call there, staying all day as a friend.

"Miss Anne mended the cover to the sofa where it was worn." Jess laughed with Fannie, and she scarcely knew whether she laughed at the sofa or at the mended place. She herself could not sew, and thus she could not mend any broken fabric of any kind. She laughed, however, Fannie's call being just begun. She was not yet hostile to it. She tried for the moment to stretch her imaginings to see something desired or some such thing as grace or beauty in the person who leaned over the ancient tapestry to mend it. The effort was spent in wonder and finally in anger. Fannie laughed at the sullenness that came to Jess. The sofa had come from Wickwood, she said. It had been given to Miss Anne at her marriage, for she was somehow related to the Wickleys. Laughing, Fannie tossed the least child and settled to tell again. Her tales would be, all together, a myth of houses and families, of people marrying and settling into new abodes. She was gay and sharp, and her face was often pointed with smiles. Or she would be talking now with the children and telling them the one story she had from a book.

"Then a great ogre lived in the place . . . a thing that threatens to get you . . . a great Thing . . . destroys . . . eats up Life itself. Drinks the blood out of Life. It came with a club in its hand. . . . It was a fine place, but had a Thing inside it. . . . That would be when little Blue Wing went to the woods to play. She found this place in the woods . . ."

"What was that?" Jess asked suddenly. "What kind was that you named?"

"A giant. Orgy or ogre. A Thing. Comes to eat up a man and to eat Life itself. . . ."

Fannie would be gone and Jess would be glad to have an end of her. As if too much had been asked of her she would sit now in vague delight, and she would forget to run her radio instrument while she saw Fannie's bright pointed face as something slipping past her. The stories that had been told had become a blend of indistinct mental colorings that would drop out of memory at length, as a spent pleasure no longer wanted. She would reject the visit completely and turn to anger, thrusting Fannie out. Then, complete hostility to the visitor having come to her, she would set roughly upon her tasks. If the children spoke of the stories that had been told she would order them to be quiet.

❦ ❦ ❦

Some of the farms had lost their former owners. A house here and there was shut and still while the acres were farmed by the shifting men who lived in the cabins or in the town. A man came searching for Hubert at the end of the harvest to offer him a part of the Wickley place to farm.

"It's said fine people once lived there," Hubert said when he told Jess of his offer.

"If they're gone now I wouldn't care."

"It's not like any place ever you saw in life. It's good land howsoever."

Other tenants would be scattered over the acres, laborers who would farm by sharing the crops. Hubert would rent the acres about the house and he would live there.

"Is there a good well of water?"

"Two wells there are," he answered her.

"I never heard of two wells."

"One has got a little fancy house up over it."

"What would I do with a little fancy house built up over a well? I can't use such a house." As if more might be required of her than she could perform, Jess was uneasy in thinking of the new place to which they would go. She did not want to go there. "It's a place made for some other," she said. She could not see the women of the place going about their labors. She could not discover what they might carry in their hands and what their voices might call from the doorways, or how they would sleep or dress themselves or find themselves food. In her troubled thought, while she came and went about the cabin room where the least child lay, shapes without outline, the women of the Wickleys, went into vague distances where doors that were not defined were opened and closed into an uncomprehended space.

But the next day Fannie Burt came and there was something further to know. The Wickley farm was called Wickwood, she said. Miss Anne's father had gone there in old Wickley's lifetime. Together these two men had made experiments in the growing of fine animals. Sometimes it would be a horse old Wickley wanted. "Egad!" he would say, or "I'm not dead yet!" Another story running into a comic ending, "A good colt she is, but a leetle matter of interference. Look at her hind feet." Fannie had something that Miss Anne had in mind. It was told imperfectly, thrown out in a hint and retained in a gesture, put back upon

Miss Anne, who could tell with fluent words and meaning gestures. She would be sitting over the last of the dessert in the old, faded dining-room. She would be telling for the pure joy of talking, laughing with the past. "Pappy went over to Wickwood. . . . It was Tuesday. . . . Came Sunday then and we all said, 'Where's Pappy?' Came to find out and he's still over to Wickwood with Cousin Bob. All that time to get the brown mare rightly in foal. And all still on paper."

Fannie would seem to be talking fast, and one thing would seem to be entangled with another, although she spoke with Miss Anne's quiet, slow cadence. In her telling, men would be sitting together in a library. One would be making a drawing of a horse, such a horse as he would be devising. A horse would be sketched on paper before it was so much as foaled. This would be old Robert Wickley, a pen between his thumb and his fingers. "What we want after all is a good Kentucky saddle horse, fifteen hands high and two inches over. Take Danbury II, say, over at Newmarket . . ."

"You take Danbury and you'll plumb get a jackass."

"Pappy laughed over a thing once for a week before he told us," Miss Annie's speaking through Fannie's speaking. "Pappy in a big tellen way one day and he let it be known what he was so amused about."

A man had come in at the door at Wickwood, a hurried man with money in cash saved by. He wanted the Wickley land on which to grow something. He wanted to buy, offering cash.

"Do you think you could live in my house and on my land?" old Wickley asked.

Fannie would be telling as Miss Anne had told and, beyond again, the father who had told in a moment of amusement. Men who came on business were let in at a side door. "Business was a Nobody then," Miss Anne said. Mollie would be off somewhere in the house singing. Carline had run off to get married. Old Wickley, father to Robert, rolling back his shirtsleeves because the day was hot, and walking barefoot out into the cool grass; or he would be standing under the shower in the bathhouse while somebody pumped the water that sprayed over him. Miss Sallie made the garden with her own hands and designed the sundial. They made things for themselves with their hands. Bob Wickley sketching for himself the horse he wanted on a large sheet of manilla paper. His grandmother had, as a bride, set the house twelve feet back of the builder's specifications in order to save a fine oak tree that still grew before the front door. A man wanting to plow his pastures . . . .

"Two hundred dollars an acre for the creek bottom, cash money."

Wickley had called him a hog and sent him away. "Pappy laughed over it for a week. 'You think you could live in my house? Come back three generations from now.' . . . 'And egad, he couldn't,' Pappy said."

"Hogs want to root in my pasture," Bob Wickley said. He was angry. . . . Miss Anne speaking through Fannie's speaking, reports fluttering about, intermingled, right and wrong, the present and the past. Fannie could scarcely divide one Wickley from another. One had gathered the books. One had held a high public office. One had married a woman who pinned back her hair with a gold comb. Their children had read plentifully from the books. Justus, William, and Robert had been names among them. Miss Anne now owned the portrait of the lady of the golden comb. There had been farewells and greetings, dimly remembered gifts, trinkets, portraits to be made, children to be born. . . .

In this telling as it came from the telling of Miss Anne, there was one, a Robert, who danced along the great parlor floor with one named Mollie. Mollie was the wife of Andrew. She had come from a neighboring farm. When they danced, the music from the piano had crashed and tinkled under the hands of Miss Lizette, Robert's mother, or of Tony Barr, a young man who came to visit at Wickwood. Down would fling the chords on the beat and at the same instant up would fling the dancers, stepping upward on the rhythm and treading the air. Mollie's long slim legs would flash from beneath her flying skirts, or one would lie for an instant outstretched while the pulse of the music beat, then off along the shining floor, gliding and swaying with the gliding of Robert, until it seemed as if the two of them were one, and as if they might float out the window together, locked into the rhythms, and thus dance away across the world.

"Where are they now?" Jess asked.

Fannie did not know. Miss Anne had not told her.

"Where would be Andrew, the one that was her husband?" She was angry and she wanted to settle blame somewhere.

He would be beside the wall. He would look at Mollie with delight. His head would move, or his hands, with the rhythm, and his eyes would be bright. Mollie loved him truly.

Sometimes it would be the old fast waltzes that were danced, and then Miss Lizette and old Bob would come into it. Then they would whirl swiftly about the floor and the music would be "Over the Waves." The young would try it, dizzy and laughing, or they would change the steps to their own.

"What did they do?" Jess asked. "I feel staggered to try to know about such a house."

"They had a wide scope of land," Fannie answered her. "They burned the bricks and made the house. They cut the timber for the beams of the house off their own fields."

The House had become an entity, as including the persons and the legends of it. All the Wickleys were blurred into one, were gathered into one report.

"There was a woman, Mollie Wickley. She was the mother of Andrew, or maybe she was his wife," Fannie said. "I don't recall. It's all one. There was a Sallie Wickley. I don't know whe'r she was his daughter or his wife."

"Iffen he couldn't keep it for his children," Jess called out, "why would he build such a place?"

"He lived in the house *himself*."

Jess and Hubert would be going to the place where these had been. All these were gone now. The land was still good. Hubert would be able to take money out of it. He would hold the plow into the soil and his tongue would hang from the side of his mouth in his fervor to plant more and to have a large yield. The people would be gone. Jess dismissed them with the clicking of her tongue. They seemed, nevertheless, to be coming nearer. In Fannie's presence, while she sat in the chair beside the door, they came nearer to flit as shapes about her fluttering tongue while Jess fixed her gaze upon the mouth that was speaking or shifted to look at the familiar cups and plates on the table. Shapes fluttered then over the cups. Vague forms, having not the shapes of defined bodies but the ends of meanings, appeared and went. Fannie knew little beyond the myths she had made, and Jess knew much less, knew nothing beyond the bright tinkle of Fannie's chatter.

"It was the horse then," Fannie said, in part explaining. "Now nobody wants enough horses. . . . Now it's tobacco."

❦ ❦ ❦

Hubert and Jess came to the place, Wickwood, at sundown of an early winter afternoon. Hubert talked of the land, of the fields, growing talkative as their small truck rolled slowly through the ruts of the old driveway. When they had passed through the woodland, which was now in part denuded of its former growth, they came near to the house. It seemed to Jess that there was a strange wideness about the place, as if space were spent outward without bounds. They went under some tall oaks and maples while Hubert muttered of his plans.

A great wall arose in the dusk. The trees stretched their boughs toward the high wall in the twilight. When it seemed that the truck would drive into the hard darkness of the wall that stood before them as if it went into the sky, Hubert turned toward the left and rounded among the trees. Other walls stood before them. Jess had never before seen a place like this. It seemed to her that it might be a town, but there were no people there. The children began to cry and Albert screamed, "I want to go away." Jess herself was frightened.

"Hush your fuss," Hubert said. His words were rough. "Get out of the truck," he said to her. She attended to his short angry speech; it jerked her out of her fear and dispersed a part of her dread of the place. It made her know that they, themselves and their goods, their life and their ways of being, would somehow fit into the brick walls, would make over some part of the strangeness for their own use. He had climbed from the vehicle and he walked a little way among the buildings, stalking in the broad courtyard among the flagstones and over the grass. He looked about him. Then he went toward a wing of the largest house and entered a small porch that stood out from one of the walls. "We'll live here," he said.

She did not know how he had discovered which part of the circle of buildings, of large houses and small rooms, would shelter them. He began to carry their household goods from the truck. Jess found her lantern among her things and she made a light. When the lantern was set on a shelf she could look about the room where they would live.

There were windows opposite the door through which they had entered. Outside, the rain dripped slowly through the great gnarled trees. The rain did not trouble her. A press built into the wall beside the chimney seemed ample to hold many things. Hubert set the cooking stove before the fireplace and fixed the stovepipe into the small opening above the mantel. The children cried at the strangeness, but when the lamp was lighted and food had been cooked they cried no more. When Jess set the food on the table they had begun to live in the new place.

Hubert went away across the courtyard and his step was hollow, amplified among the walls of the building. He came back later, the sound he made enlarged as he walked nearer over the flagstones.

"It's no such place as ever I saw before," Jess cried out.

She had begun a longer speech but she was hushed by Hubert's hostile look. They would stay here, he said. It was the Wickley place. She closed the door to shut in the space she had claimed for their living, being afraid of the great empty walls that arose outside. The beds were hastily set up and the children fell asleep clutching the familiar pillows and quilts. Her life with Hubert, together with her children and her things for housekeeping, these she gathered mentally about her to protect herself from being obliged to know and to use the large house outside her walls. She began to comfort herself with thoughts of Hubert and to court him with a fine dish of food she had carefully saved.

The morning was clear after the rain. Hubert had gone to

bring the fowls from their former abode. Albert had found a sunny nook in which to play and with the second child he was busy there.

"What manner of place is this?" Jess asked herself again and again. Outside the windows toward the south were the great gnarled trees. Outside to the north was the courtyard round which were arranged the buildings, all of them built of red, weathered brick. Toward the west, joined to the small wing in which Hubert had set up their home, arose the great house. There were four rows of windows here, one row above the other.

The buildings about the court were empty. A large bell hung in the middle of the court on the top of a high pole. There was a deep well at the back of the court where the water was drawn by a bucket lifted by a winch. Jess had a great delight in the well, for it seemed to hold water sufficient to last through any drought. Not far from the well stood a large corncrib, holding only a little corn now, but ready for Hubert's filling. She went cautiously about in the strange air.

She had no names for all the buildings that lay about her. She was frightened of the things for which she had no use, as if she might be called upon to know and to use beyond her understanding. She walked toward the west beneath the great wall of the tallest house.

There were birds in the high trees and echoes among the high walls. The singing winter wren was somewhere about, and the cry of the bird was spread widely and repeated in a shadowy call again and again. Jess rounded the wall and looked cautiously at the west side. There were closed shutters at some of the windows, but some of the shutters were opened. In the middle of the great western wall there were steps of stone. They were cut evenly and laid smoothly, one above another, reaching toward a great doorway about which was spread bright glass in straight patterns at the sides, in a high fanshape above.

Jess went cautiously up the steps, watching for Hubert to come with the fowls, delaying, looking out over the woodland and the fields. Hubert had said again and again that this would be the Wickley place, Wickwood, that they would live there, tilling the soil, renting the land. Jess saw before her, on the great lefthand door, a knocker. She lifted and tapped heavily, listening to the sound she made, waiting.

There was no sound to answer her rap but a light echo that seemed to come from the trees. Her own hate of the place forbade her and she dared not tap again. Standing half fearfully, she waited, laying her hands on the smooth door frame, on the fluted pillars and the leading of the glass. A cord hung near her hand and, obeying the suggestion it offered, she closed her fingers about it and pulled it stiffly down. A sound cut the still air where no sound had been for so long a time that every vibration had been stilled. The tone broke the air. The first tone came in unearthly purity, but later the notes joined and overflowed one another.

She waited, not daring to touch the cord again. The stillness that followed after the peal of the bell seemed to float out from the house itself and to hush the birds. She could not think what kind of place this might be or see any use that one might make of the great doorway, of the cord, of the bell. A strange thing stood before her. Strangeness gathered to her own being until it seemed strange that she should be here, on the top of a stair of stone before a great door, waiting for Hubert to come with her hens. It was as if he might never come. As if hens might be gone from the earth.

She saw then that the doors were not locked together, that one throbbed lightly on the other when she touched it with her hand. She pushed the knob and the door spread open wide.

Inside, a great hall reached to a height that was three or four times her own stature. Tall white doors were opened into other great rooms, and far back before her a stairway began. She could not comprehend the stair. It lifted, depending from the rail that spread upward like a great ribbon on the air. Her eyes followed it, her breath coming quick and hard. It rose as a light ribbon spreading toward a great window through which came the morning sun. But leaving the window in the air, it arose again and wound back, forward and up, lost from view for a space, to appear again, higher up, at a mythical distance before another great window where the sun spread a broad yellow glow. It went at last into nothingness, and the ceiling and the walls melted together in shadows.

When she had thus, in mind, ascended, her eyes closed and a faint sickness went over her, delight mingled with fear and hate. She was afraid of being called upon to know this strange ribbon of ascent that began as a stair with rail and tread and went up into unbelievable heights, step after step. She opened her eyes to look again, ready to reject the wonder as being past all belief and, therefore, having no reality.

" What place is this? " she asked, speaking in anger. Her voice rang through the empty hall, angry words, her own, crying, " What place is this? "

At one side of the floor there were grains of wheat in streaks, as if someone might have stored sacks of wheat there. Jess thought of her hens, seeing the scattered grain, and she knew that they would pick up the remaining part of it. They would hop from stone to stone, coming cautiously up the steps, and they would stretch their long necks cautiously in at the doorway, seeing the corn. They would not see the great stairway.

A light dust lay on the window ledges. A few old cobwebs hung in fragments from the ceiling. The dust, the webs, and the wheat were a link between things known and unknown; and, seeing them, she walked a little way from the hall, listening, going farther, looking into the rooms, right and left. She was angry and afraid. What she could not bring to her use she wanted to destroy. In the room to her right a large fireplace stood far at the end of a patterned floor. There were shelves set into the white wall beside the large chimney. She left this room quickly and turned toward the room at the left. There were white shapes carved beneath the windows and oblong shapes carved again on the wood of the doors, on the pillars that held the mantel. Before her a long mirror was set into a wall. In it were reflected the boughs of the trees outside against a crisscross of the window opposite.

She was confused after she had looked into the mirror, and she looked about hastily to find the door through which she had come. It was a curious, beautiful, fearful place. She wanted to destroy it. Her feet slipped too lightly on the smooth wood of the floor. There was no piece of furniture anywhere, but the spaces seemed full, as filled with their wide dimensions and the carvings on the wood. In the hall she looked again toward the stair and she stood near the doorway looking back. Then suddenly without plan, scarcely knowing that her own lips spoke, she flung out an angry cry, half screaming, "Mollie Wickley! Mollie! Where's she at?" The harsh echoes pattered and knocked among the upper walls after her own voice was done. Turning her back on the place, she went quickly out of the doorway.

In the open air she looked back toward the steps she had ascended, seeing dimly into the vista of the hall and the upward lifting ribbon of the stair. A sadness lay heavily upon her because she could not know what people might live in the house, what shapes of women and men might fit into the doorway. She hated her sadness and she turned it to anger. She went from the west front and entered the courtyard. Hubert came soon after with the fowls and there was work to do in housing them and getting them corn.

❦ ❦ ❦

On a cold day in January when his ewes were about to lamb, Hubert brought them into the large house, driving them up the stone steps at the west front, and he prepared to stable them in the rooms there. The sheep cried and their bleating ran up the long ribbon of the stair. They were about thirty in number, and thus the wailing was incessant. Hubert and Jess went among them with lanterns. The ewes turned and drifted about among the large rooms; but as they began to bear their lambs Hubert bedded them here and there, one beneath the stairway and three others in the room to the right where the empty bookshelves spread wide beside the tall fireplace. The night came, dark and cold.

"They are a slow set," Jess said. She wanted to be done and she was out of patience with delaying sheep.

"Whoop! here! Shut fast the door!" Hubert called.

Jess was wrapped in a heavy coat and hooded in a shawl. She went among the sheep and she held a lantern high to search out each beast. If a ewe gave birth to three lambs she took one up quickly and dropped it beside a stout young beast that was giving life to but one, and she thus induced it to take the second as her own. She flung out sharp commands and she brought the animals here and there. The halls were filled with the crying of the sheep. Threats came back upon her from her own voice so that she was displeased with what she did, and her displeasure made her voice more high-pitched and angry. Anger spoke again and again through the room. She wanted the lambing to be easily done, but the days had been very cold and the sheep delayed.

"It was a good place to come to lamb the sheep," she called to Hubert. "I say, a good place." She had a delight in seeing that the necessities of lambing polluted the wide halls. "A good place to lamb. . . ."

"Whoop! Bring here the old nannie as soon as you pick up the dead lamb," Hubert was shouting above the incessant crying of the sheep.

The ewes in labor excited her anew so that she wanted to be using her strength and to be moving swiftly forward, but she had no plan beyond Hubert's. "Whoop, rouse up the young nannie! Don't let the bitches sleep! Whoop, there!"

He was everywhere with his commands. When the task was more than half done he called to Jess that he must go to the barn for more straw for bedding. "Whoop! Shut the door tight after me. Keep the old ewe there up on her legs." He went away, carrying his lantern.

Jess fastened the outer door and she turned back into the parlors. Then she saw a dim light at the other end of the long dark space that lay before her. She saw another shape, a shrouded figure, moving far down the long way. The apparition, the Thing, seemed to be drifting forward out of the gloom, and it seemed to be coming toward her where she stood among the sheep. Jess drove the laboring mothers here and there, arranging their places and assisting their travail with her club. She would not believe that she saw anything among the sheep at the farther end of the rooms, but as she worked she glanced now and then toward the way in which she had glimpsed it. It was there or it was gone entirely. The sheep and the lambs made a great noise with their crying. Jess went to and fro, and she forgot that she had seen anything beyond the sheep far down the room in the moving dusk of white and gray which flowed in the moving light of her lantern.

All at once, looking up suddenly as she walked forward, she saw that an apparition was certainly moving there and that it was coming toward her. It carried something in its upraised hand. There was a dark covering over the head and shoulders that were sunk into the upper darkening gloom. The whole body came forward as a dark thing illuminated by a light the creature carried low at the left side. The creature or the Thing moved among the sheep. It came forward slowly and became a threatening figure, a being holding a club and a light in its hands. Jess screamed at it, a great oath flung high above the crying of the sheep. Fright had seized her and with it came a great strength to curse with her voice and to hurl forward her body.

"God curse you!" she yelled in a scream that went low in scale and cracked in her throat. "God's curse on you!" She lunged forward and lifted her lantern high to see her way among the sheep. "God's damn on you!"

The curse gave strength to her hands and to her limbs. As she hurled forward with uplifted stick the other came forward toward her, lunging and threatening. She herself moved faster. The creature's mouth was open to cry words, but no sound came from it.

She dropped the lantern and flung herself upon the approaching figure, and she beat at the creature with her club while it beat at her with identical blows. Herself and the creature then were one. Anger continued, shared, and hurled against a crash of falling glass and plaster. She and the creature had beaten at the mirror from opposite sides.

The din arose above the noise of the sheep, and for an instant the beasts were quiet while the glass continued to fall. Jess stood back from the wreckage to try to understand it. Then slowly she knew that she had broken the great mirror that hung on the rear wall of the room. She took the lamp again into her hand and peered at the breakage on the floor and at the fragments that hung, cracked and crazed, at the sides of the frame.

"God's own curse on you!" She breathed her oath heavily, backing away from the dust that floated in the air.

Hubert was entering with a load of straw on his back. He had not heard the crash of glass nor had he noticed the momentary quiet of the sheep. These were soon at their bleating again, and Jess returned from the farther room where the dust of the plaster still lay on the air. Hubert poured water into deep pans he had placed here and there through the rooms. He directed Jess to make beds of the straw in each room. Their feet slipped in the wet that ran over the polished boards of the floor.

❦ ❦ ❦

It was near midnight. Jess felt accustomed to the place now and more at ease there, she and Hubert being in possession of it. They walked about through the monstrous defilement. Hubert was muttering the count of the sheep with delight. There were two lambs beside each of the ewes but five, and there were but two lambs dead and flung to the cold fireplace where they were out of the way. There were thirty-two ewes, they said, and their fingers pointed to assist and the mouths held to the sums, repeating numbers and counting profits.

Lamb by lamb, they were counted. There were two to each mother but the three in the farther room and the two under the staircase. These had but one each. "Twice thirty-two makes sixty-four," they said to assist themselves, and from this they subtracted one for each of the deficient ewes, but they became confused in this and counted all one by one. Counting with lantern and club, Jess went again through the halls, but she made thus but forty lambs, for she lost the sums and became addled among the words Hubert muttered. At last by taking one from sixty-four and then another, four times more, in the reckoning they counted themselves thirty-two ewes and fifty-nine lambs. The sheep were becoming quiet. Each lamb had nursed milk before they left it. At length they fastened the great front door with a rope tied to a nail in the doorframe, and they left the sheep stabled there, being pleased with the number they had counted.

HAIR

By Jesse Stuart

IF YOU'VE never been to Plum Grove then you wouldn't know about that road. It's an awful road, with big ruts and mudholes where the coal wagons with them nar-rimmed wheels cut down. There is a lot of haw bushes along this road. It goes up and down two yaller banks. From Lima Whitehall's house in the gap it's every bit of a mile and a half to Plum Grove. We live just across the hill from Lima's house. I used to go up to her house and get with her folks and we would walk over to Plum Grove to church.

Lima Whitehall just went with one boy. I tried to court her a little, but she wouldn't look at me. One night I goes up to her and I takes off my hat and says: "Lima, how about seeing you home?" And Lima says: "Not long as Rister is livin'." Lord, but she loved Rister James. You ought to see Rister James — tall with a warty face and ferret eyes, but he had the prettiest head of black curly hair you ever saw on a boy's head. I've heard the girls say: "Wish I had Rister's hair. Shame such an ugly boy has to have that pretty head of hair and a girl ain't got it. Have to curl my hair with a hot poker. Burnt it up about, already. Shame a girl don't have that head of hair."

Well, they don't say that about my hair. My hair is just so curly I don't know which end of it grows in my head until I comb it. I've prayed for straight hair — or hair of a different color. But it don't do no good to pray. My hair ain't that pretty gold hair, or light gold hair. It's just about the color of a weaned Jersey calf's hair. I'll swear it is. People even call me Jersey.

There was a widder down in the Hollow and she loved Rister. Was a time, though, when she wouldn't look at him. She was from one of those proud families. You've seen them. Think they're better'n everybody else in the whole wide world — have to watch about getting rain in their noses. That's the kind of people they were in that family. And when a poor boy marries one of them girls he's got to step. They are somebody around here and they boss their men. So Rister James went with the woman I loved, Lima Whitehall, when he could have gone with Widder Ollie Spriggs. Widder Ollie wasn't but seventeen years old and just had one baby. Rister was nineteen and I was eighteen. Lima was seventeen. If Rister would have gone with Widder Ollie it would have made things come out right for me. God knows I didn't want Widder Ollie and she didn't want me. I wanted Lima. I told her that I did. She wanted Rister. She told me she did.

Widder Ollie was a pretty girl — one of them women that just makes a good armful — small, slim as a rail, with hair pretty as the sunlight and teeth like peeled cabbage stalks. She'd have made a man a pretty wife. She might not have made a good wife — that's what Effie Spriggs told me. Effie is John Spriggs' mother and Ollie married John when she was fifteen. Effie said Ollie broke a whole set of plates, twelve of 'em, on John's head over nothing in God Almighty's world. And he just had too much honor in his bones to hit a woman with his fist. He just stood there and let her break them. And when she got through, John was kind of addled but he got out of the house and came home to his mother Effie, who is Widder Effie here in the Hollow. (She tried to pizen her man, but he found the pizen in his coffee and left her.) Widder Ollie went to live with Widder Effie later. They had a plenty — a big pretty farm down in the Hollow, fat barns, and plenty of milk cows. They were kindly rich people with heads so high you couldn't reach them with a ten-foot pole.

Widder Ollie, as I said, wouldn't look at Rister at first. She laughed at him when he used to hoe corn for her pappy for twenty-five cents a day. She made fun of poor old Rister's snaggled-toothed mother and said she looked like a witch. She laughed at Rister's pappy and said he looked like old Lonesy Fannin. That was an old bald-headed horse-doctor who used to go from place to place pulling the eyeteeth out of blind horses, saying they would get their sight back. And she said all the children in the James family looked like varmints. She'd laugh and laugh at 'em and just hold her head high. Then suddenly she was after Rister to marry him. But that's the way — pride leads a woman to a fall. And after she gets up, with a little of the pride knocked out of her, she's a different woman.

But I didn't blame Rister for not wanting her when he could get Lima. Lima was the sweetest little black-headed armload you ever put your two eyes on. I was in the market for Lima the first time I ever saw her. And I guess that was when we were babies. But I didn't know how to get her. I think I was a durn sight better-looking boy than Rister. It's funny how a woman will take to an uglier feller that way and just hold on to his coattails whether or not. Hang on just as long as she can. I always thought the reason Lima did that was because she knew Widder Ollie wanted Rister. And if there'd a been another girl around in the district in the market for a man, *she* would have wanted Rister because Lima wanted him and Widder Ollie wanted him.

But nobody was after me. I was left out in the cold — just because of my hair, Mom always told me. Mom said I was a good-looking boy all but the color of my hair, and women wouldn't take to that kind of hair. Of course, it don't matter how ugly a man is, his Mom always thinks he's the best-looking boy in the district.

II

I used to go down past Lima's house last June when the roses were in bloom, and the flags. Them blue and yaller flags just sets a yard off and makes it a pretty thing. Now Rister never saw anything pretty in flowers. He never saw anything pretty in a woman's voice or the things she said, or the shape of her hands. He would watch a woman's legs — and go with them as far as he could. He was that kind of a feller. I knew it all the time. I'd pass Whitehall's house. It would be on a Wednesday when Mom would run out of sugar or salt and I'd have to get on the mule and go to the store and get it. Rister would be down to see Lima on a weekday. Now God knows, when a man is farming he don't have no time to play around with a woman like a lovesick kitten. He's got to strike while the iron is hot. If he don't he won't get much farming done. When

I saw Rister and Lima I reined my mule up to the palings. And I started talking to them as if I didn't care what they were doing. But I did care. I says: "How you getting along with your crop, Rister?"

"Oh, pretty well," he says. "Nothing extra. Terbacker's getting a little weedy on me. Too wet to hoe in it today. Ground will ball up in your hand. Too wet to stir the ground when it is like that."

Well, I knew he was a lying. But I never said anything. I know when ground is wet and when ground ain't wet. I'd been out working in it all morning. It was in good shape to work. Rister used to be a good worker. But you know how a man is when he gets lovesick after a woman. Take the best man in the world to work and let him get his mind on a woman and he goes hog-wild. That was the way with Rister.

While I was there looking over the palings, Lima went right up into his arms. He kissed her right there before me. Mom always says a woman that would kiss around in front of people was a little loose with herself. Well, I would have told Mom she lied about Lima if she'd said that about her to my face. I just didn't want to believe anything bad about Lima. I wanted her for my wife. But, men, how would you like to look over the palings from a mule's back and see your dream-wife in the arms of a man bad after women — right out among the pretty roses and flags — and her right up in his arms, her arms around his neck, and his arms around her waist pulling her up to him tight enough to break her in two. And he would say to her: "Oo love me, oo bitsy baby boopy-poopy oo?" And she would say: "I love U, U bitsy 'itsy boopy-poopy oo. I love my 'ittle 'itsy bitsy turley-headed boopy-poopy oo." God, it made me sick as a horse. It's all right when *you're* loving a woman. It don't look bad to *you*. But when you see somebody else gumsuck around, then you want to get the hell out of the way and in a hurry. It's a sickening thing.

I reined my mule away and I never let him stop till I was a mile beyond the house. I went on to the store and got the sugar. That was Wednesday night and prayer-meeting night at Plum Grove, so I had to hurry back and do up the work and go to prayer-meeting.

I'm a Methodist — I go to church — but God knows they won't

have my name on the Lamb's Book of Life because I saw the fiddle, play set-back, and dance at the square dances. Some of them even say terbacker is a filthy weed and none of it will be seen in heaven. Some won't even raise it on their farms. But I go to church even if they won't have me until I quit these things. I just up and go to see and to be seen — that's what we all go for. It is a place to go and about the only place we got to go.

I hurried and got my work done. I put the mule up and fed him. I helped milk the cows. I slopped the hogs, got in stovewood and kindling. I drew up water from the well — got everything done around the house and I set out to church. Well, when I got down to Whitehall's place, there was Lima and Rister. They were getting ready to go. I gave them a head start and followed after. But I hadn't more than walked out in the big road until here come Widder Ollie and that baby of hers. He was just big enough to walk a little and talk a lot. We started down the road. I said to Ollie: "Rister and Lima's just on ahead of us."

And Ollie says: "They're on ahead? C'mon, let's catch up with them. Take my baby boy, you carry him awhile."

So I took her baby and started in a run with her to catch up with Lima and Rister. You know, a woman will do anything when she loves a man. I could tell Widder Ollie loved Rister. She was all nervous and excited. She had her mind set on getting Rister. And when a woman has her mind set on getting a man she can about get him. That made me think if she could get Rister I'd have a chance to get Lima. That was the only reason I'd be carrying a widder's baby around. I had heard that baby was the meanest young'n in the world. Now I believed it. It had been spiled by them two women — its mother and its grandmother. He would kick me in the ribs and say: "Get up hossy! Get up there! Whoa back, Barnie." And when he would say "Whoa back" he would glomb me in the eyes with his fingers like he was trying to stop a horse. Then he would say: "Get up, hossy, or I'll bust you one in the snoot." And then he started kicking me in the ribs again. I was sweating, carrying that load of a young'n and keeping up with Widder Ollie. I felt like pulling him off my back and burning up the seat of his pants with my hand.

We saw them — Rister had his left arm around Lima's back and she had her right arm around his back. They were climbing up the first hill, that little yaller hill on this side of the haw bushes. It was light as day. The moon had come up and it lit the fields like a big lamp. Pon my word and honor I couldn't remember in all my life a prettier night than that one. You ought to have seen my corn in the moonlight. We had to pass it. I was glad for the girls to go by it and see what a clean farmer I was and what a weedy farmer Rister was. Not a weed in any of my corn. Pretty and clean in the moonlight and waving free as the wind. Lord, I felt like a man with religion to see my corn all out of the weeds and my terbacker clean as a hound-dog's tooth — my land all paid for — not a debt in the world — didn't owe a man a penny. Raised what I et and et what I raised. All I needed was a wife like Lima. She'd never want for anything. And I thought: "What if this baby on my back was mine and Lima's? I'd carry him the rest of my days. I'd let him grow to be a man a-straddle of my back. But if I had my way now, I'd bust his little tail with my hand."

We got right up behind Rister and Lima. And they looked around. Widder Ollie had me by the arm. I had her baby on my back yet. God, it hurt me. But I held the baby while Lima won the battle. You know women are dangerous soldiers. They fight with funny weapons. The tongue is a dangerous cannon when a woman aims it right. We just laughed and talked. We just giggled before Rister and Lima got to giggling at us. I was afraid they'd laugh at me for carrying the baby. They went on up the next hill — us right behind them. We went past the haw bushes and on to church. We just laughed and laughed and went on crazy. That baby on my back, a-making a lot of noise. We went up the hill at the church and the boys said: "Look at that pack mule, won't you?"

Well, to tell the truth I'd ruther be called a pack mule as to be called Jersey. So I just let them whoop and holler to see me with Widder Ollie and carrying her baby. Everybody out on the ground laughed and hollered enough to disturb the Methodist church. Church was going on inside. But there was more people out in the yard than was inside. They could see more on the outside than they could hear going on inside. I just wagged the baby right in the church house. Everybody looked around and craned their necks.

Rister and Lima acted like they were ashamed of us. Tried to sidle out of the way and get us in front so they could dodge us. But we stayed right with them. They set down on a seat. We set right beside them as if we were all together. People looked around. I had Widder Ollie's boy in my lap. He tried to hit the end of my nose. I had a time with him. I could see the girls whisper to one another. They watched us more than they did the preacher. He was telling them about widders and orphans. He was preaching a sermon on that. Rister would flinch every now and then. He wanted to be on another seat. But he couldn't very well move. So he just set there and took it. And I took it from that young'n. But I thought: " There'll be the time when I come back to this church house with a different woman. I'll come right here and marry her. It will be different from what they see tonight."

III

We set right there and listened through that sermon. Boys would come to the winder and point to me from the outside — being with a widder woman who hadn't been divorced from her man very long. Boys around home thinks it's kindly strange to go with a widder woman — but I don't think so. They say a body is in adultery. But when two can't go on loving each other and start breaking plates — twelve at a crack — it's time they were getting apart. Especially when two has to go through life tied together when the mother-in-law tied the knot. I just felt sorry for Widder Ollie. She had always loved Rister and would have married him to begin with if it hadn't been for that mother of hers telling her so many times that she got to believing it that she was better than any man in the Hollow.

Well, they got us in front coming out of the church house. I thought we'd better take advantage of getting out first. So we took the lead going back. Boys just giggled and hollered at me when I come out of the house with the baby on my back. I didn't care. I was seeing ahead. So we just went out the road. The moon was pretty on the fields. A thousand thoughts came into my mind. I didn't want Rister to have Lima. I loved Lima. God, I loved her.

Widder Ollie said to me going home: "Don't think it has done much good for both of us tonight. We'll have to think of something different. I love that boy till it hurts. I could love him forever. I can't get him. Lima don't love him. She holds him because I want him. That is the way of women. You want what you can't get. When you get what you want you don't want it. I have always loved Rister. But my people wanted me to marry John. I married him. My mother married him. Life is not worth while without Rister. And here you've been out carrying my baby around and letting people talk about you so you could help me get Rister and you could get Lima."

That was right. Life was not fair. The night so pretty. The moon above my clean corn. My house on the hill where I would take Lima. I needed a wife. I wanted the woman I loved. I loved Lima Whitehall. And when we passed her home I wouldn't look across the palings at the roses. I remembered the weekday I passed and saw Rister out there with her. I just took Widder Ollie on home. And when we got to the gate I said: "Widder Ollie, I am Rister kissing you. You are Lima kissing me. You are Lima for one time in your life. I am Rister one time in my life. Shut your eyes and let's kiss. Let's just pretend." So we did.

Then I started on the long walk home up the branch. I had to pass Lima's house. Moonlight fell on the corn. Wind blew through the ragweeds along the path. Whip-poor-wills hollered so lonely that they must have been in love with somebody they couldn't get. I went in Lima's yard to draw me a drink of water. And right by the well-gum stood Rister and Lima. They weren't a-saying a word. They didn't see me; I didn't let myself be known; I just stepped back into the moonshade of one of the yard trees. I just stood there and watched. Lima went into the house after kissing and kissing Rister. When Lima left, Rister stood at the well-gum. He looked down at the ground. He kicked the toe of his shoe against the ground. There was something funny about the way he was acting. He kept his eye on the upstairs winder in that house. It had one of them pole ladders — we call them chicken ladders — just one straight pole with little tiny steps nailed across it. It was setting up back of the house — from the ground to the winder.

Then, suddenly, Rister let out one of the funniest catcalls you ever heard. It would make the hair stand up on your head. It wasn't a blue yodel, but it was something like a part of that yodel Jimmie Ridgers used to give. He done it someway down in his throat. It started out like the nip-nip-nipping of scissor blades, then it clanked like tin cans, then like a foxhorn, way up there high, then it went like a bumblebee, then it rattled like a rattlesnake, and ended up like that little hissing noise a black snake makes when it warns you. I never heard anything like it. If it hadn't been for me knowing where it had come from I'd set sail off of that hill and swore it was a speret that made the noise. Rister gave the catcall once — held his head high in the air — no answer. So he gave it again. And from upstairs came the answer — a soft catcall like from a she-cat. So he takes right out in front of me and runs up that ladder like a tom and pops in at the winder.

I thought I'd go home and get the gun and come back and when he came down that ladder I'd fill his behind so full of shot it would look like a strainer. Then again I thought I'd go over and pull the ladder down and make him go down the front way. God, I was mad! But I didn't do neither one. The whole thing made me so sick I just crawled out of the moonshade and sneaked over the hill home. I didn't know what to do. It just made me sick — sick at life. I just couldn't stand it. I couldn't bear to think of Lima in the dark upstairs with Rister.

I thought about taking the gun and going back and blowing Rister's brains out when he came back through that upstairs winder. I could have done it — God knows I could have done it. But they'd have got out the bloodhounds and trailed me home. Lima would have known who did it. I thought there must be a way for me to get Lima yet, and for her to come to her senses. But then I thought, they are up in that dark room together. Lord, it hurt me. Pains shot through and through me. Life wasn't worth the pain one got out of it. I had something for her — a farm, a little money, clean crops, and plenty of food for cold days when the crows fly over the empty fields hunting last year's corn-grains. Rister didn't have nothing to take a woman to but his father's house, and den her with his own father's young'ns.

I went upstairs and got the gun from the rack. I put a shell into its bright blue barrel. Just one shell for Rister. I would kill him. Then I put the gun down. I would not kill Rister. I could see his blood and brains all over the wall. Old Sol Whitehall would run out in his nightshirt. He would kill Lima if he knew. And I wouldn't get Lima. It is better not to let a man know everything—it is better to live in silence and hold a few things than to lose your head and get a lot of people killed. I put the gun back, took the shell out of it, and set it back on the rack. I went to bed. But I couldn't sleep. I could see Lima and Rister in a settee in the front yard, kissing. I could hear that catcall. I memorized it. I said it over and over in bed. It came to me—every funny noise in it. I called it out, several times. It made the hair stand up on my head. It waked Pa up and he said: "I've been hearing something funny in this house or my ears are fooling me. Funniest thing I ever heard. Like a pheasant drumming on a brushpile. Goes something like a rattlesnake too. I can't go to sleep." But Pa went back to sleep. I kept my mouth shet. I just laid there the rest of the night and thought about Rister and Lima.

I didn't eat much breakfast the next morning. I went out and got the Barnie mule and I started plowing my terbacker. I couldn't get Lima off my mind. I prayed to God. I did everything I knew to do. And it all came to me like a flash. It just worked out like that.

So I waited. I just waited about ten hours. I plowed all day, worked hard in the fields. After I'd fed the mule, et my supper, done up the rest of the work, I slipped back up the path that I had come over the night before.

All the lights in the Whitehall house were out. The ladder was up at the winder at the back of the house. Everything was quiet. The old house slept in the moonlight. The hollyhocks shone in the moonlight. Old Buck came around and growled once or twice. But he knew me when I patted his head. He walked away contented. Brown, he was, in the moonlight—like a wadded-up brown carpet thrown among the flowers.

I held my head in the air, threw my chin to the stars, and gave that catcall—just as good as Rister gave it. Lima answered me from upstairs. The dog started barking at the strange sounds. My cap pulled low over my funny-colored hair, I climbed the ladder and went in through the winder. The dog barked below. I was afraid. If Sol Whitehall found me there he would kill me. But I had to do this thing. I just had to.

Lima said: " Oo bitsy 'itsy boopy-poopy oo. My turley-headed baby boy."

I kept away from the streak of moonlight in the room. . . . Well, no use to tell you all. A man's past belongs to himself. His future belongs to the woman he marries. That's the way I look at it. That's the way I feel about it. This is a world where you have to go after what you get or you don't get it. Lima would not stand and say: " Here I am. Come and get me." No. She couldn't say it long as she was free — free without a care in the world. If she was like Widder Ollie, she'd be glad to find a nice young man like me even if I did have hair the color of a Jersey calf and so curly you couldn't tell which end grew in my head. I know that much about women.

When my cap had come off in the moonlight upstairs Lima just screamed to the top of her voice. Screamed like she had been stabbed. I made for the winder. She hollered: " That hair! That hair! " She knew who I was. I went out of that winder like a bird. I heard Sol getting out the bed. I landed on soft ground right in the hollyhock bed, as God would have it. I took down over the bank — circled up in the orchard through the grass so they couldn't track me. I hadn't got two hundred feet when I heard Sol's gun and felt the shot sprinkling all around me in the sassafras like a thick rain falls on the green summer leaves.

I went on to bed that night. I dreamed of Lima. I loved her. I didn't care about Rister and his past with Lima. The way I looked at it, that belonged to them. A girl has the same right to her past that a boy has to his. And when a man loves, nothing matters. You just love them and you can't help it. You'll go to them in spite of the world — no matter what a man has done or a woman has done. That's the way I look at it. Be good to one another in a world where there's a lot of talking about one another, a lot of tears, laughter, work, and love — where you are a part of the world and all that is in it and the world is a part of you. I dreamed about Lima that night. She was in my arms. I kissed her. She was in the trees I'd seen in the moonlight. She was in the wild flowers I saw — the flowers on the yaller bank. She was in my corn and my terbacker. She was in the wind that blows. She was my wife. She wasn't Rister's. She was mine. I loved her.

IV

Well, August ended, and September came along with the changing leaves. Then October when all the world turned brown and dead leaves flew through the air. The wind whistled lonesome over the brown fields. The crows flew high through the crisp autumn air.

The months dragged by. We went to church, but I barely ever spoke to Lima or to Rister. I went with Widder Ollie sometimes. People were talking about Lima. People understood. A woman, with her crooked finger over the paling fence, said: "That poor Lima Whitehall was raised under a decent roof, and in the House of the Lord, a churchgoing girl with as good a father and mother as ever God put breath in. And look how she's turned out. You just can't tell about girls nowadays. They'll fool you — especially when they run around with a low-down boy like Rister James. Curly-headed thing — everybody's crazy about his hair. Look at that bumpy face and them ferret eyes and you'll get a stomachful, won't you?"

And the woman driving home from town with an express and buggy said: "You are right, Miss Fairchild. It's them low-down James people. That boy. He ought to be tarred and feathered, bringing a poor girl to her ruint. She's a ruint girl. Never can stand in the church choir any more with the other girls and play the organ and sing at church. Her good times are over. That James boy won't marry her now. They say he's got to dodging her. Poor thing."

So I went to Widder Ollie and I said: "Everybody's down on old Rister now. You ought to go talk to him. He's down and out. Now is when he needs help. You know what they are accusing him of. I guess it's the truth. Wait till after I see the baby and I might take Lima and the baby. Be glad to get them. If I do, you can grab Rister."

"I'll do it," said Widder Ollie. "I'll spin my net for him like a spider. I'll get the fly. I love that boy. I love him. He's got the prettiest hair you nigh ever see on any boy's head."

The land was blanketed in snow. The cold winds blew. Winter was here. We heard the people talk: " W'y, old Sol Whitehall's going to march that young man Rister right down there at the pint of his gun and make him marry Lima. It's going to be a shotgun wedding. Something is going to happen."

The talk was all over the neighborhood. Everybody in the district knew about Lima. It is too bad when a girl gets in trouble and everybody knows about it. Around home she can never get a man. She's never respected again. For the man it don't matter much. He can go right back to the church choir and sing when they play the organ. Nothing is ever said about the man.

" I won't marry her," said Rister, " and old Sol can't gun me into it. I'll die first. I'll go away to the coal mines and dig coal till it is all over. I'll go where Widder Ollie's pappy is — up in West Virginia."

So Widder Ollie goes to West Virginia after Rister has been there awhile. She leaves her boy with her mother and she goes to stay awhile with her pappy. I thought that was the right move. It just looked like everything was coming nicely to my hands. I had worked hard. I had prayed hard. I had waited. It was time to get something. But what a mess. What a risk to run over a woman. How she had suffered. How I had suffered. The lonely nights I'd gone out to the woods — nights in winter when the snow dusted the earth — when the trees shook their bare tops in the wind and the song of the wind in the trees was long and lonesome and made a body want to cry — lonely nights when a body wondered if life was worth living — white hills in the moonlight — the barns with shaggy cows standing around them and sparrows mating in the eaves. Life is strange. Lima there, and the Lord knew what she'd do the way people were talking in the district. I was just waiting to see. It would soon be time.

The winter left. Birds were coming back from the South — robins had come back. And Rister was gone. Rister was at the mines — had a job — making more money than he'd ever made in his life. He wasn't working for twenty-five cents a day no more. He was working on the mine's tipple for three dollars a day. He was wearing good clothes. He was courting Widder Ollie right up a tree.

And he had her up the tree a-barking at her like a hound-dog trees a possum.

The days went swiftly. April was here — green in the hills and the plow again in the furrows. Mom was there that ninth of April. She was with Lima. Doctor so far away and hard for poor people to get. Lima came through all right. She had the baby. Mom came home the next morning — I was waiting to see. She said: "It's got that funny-colored hair — that Jersey hair with two crowns on its head. But it ain't no Harkreader. It's the first time I ever saw any other person but a Harkreader have hair like that."

I never said a word. I was so happy I couldn't say a word. I had the almanac marked and it had come out just right. So I up and went down to Whitehalls to see the baby. I went in by the bed. I reached over and picked up that baby. It was my baby. I knew it. It was like lifting forty farms in my hands. I kissed it. It was a boy. I never lifted a little baby before or never saw a pretty one in my life. But this baby was pretty as a doll. I loved it. I said: "I'll go to the store and get its dresses right now, Lima."

And she said: "W'y, what are you talking about?"

"Look at its hair," I said. "Only a Harkreader has that kind of hair. You know that."

Fire popped in her eyes — then tears to quench the fire. They flowed like water. "When you get out of bed," I said, "we'll go to church and get married. We'll go right out there where we went to school and where we played together. We'll forget about Rister."

She started out of the bed. I put her back. When a girl is down and out — a girl you love — a girl who is good and who loves as life lets a woman and a man love — I could shed tears. I could cuss. I could cry. But what I did was to run out and chop up that settee. I dug up the green sprouts of the flags and the roses. My daddy-in-law, old Sol Whitehall, ran around the house on me and yelled: "What the devil are you doing? Am I crazy to see you in my yard digging up my flowers?"

And I said: "You are crazy, for I am not here, and you are not Sol Whitehall. You are somebody else."

I dumped the flower roots over the palings. I left Sol standing there, looking at the wind.

I ran toward the store. I said to myself: " I got her! I'll plow more furrows. Clear more ground. Plant more corn. I'll do twice as much work. I got her! And I am going to get my boy some dresses. Hell's fire! He's greater to look at than my farm! "

I got him the dresses. I ran back and told the preacher to be ready soon. She must be mine. And when I got back with the dresses my pappy-in-law said: " And that scoundrel — married. Rister married to Widder Ollie Spriggs. Damn him to hell! God damn his soul to hell and let it burn with the chaff! "

But let them talk. Let them talk. They'll never know.

We went to the church. We were married there. Made Lima feel better to be married there. I could have been married in a barn. Would have suited me.

You ought to see my boy now. Takes after me — long Jersey-colored hair. He's my image. He don't look like his Ma — not the least. He's up and going about.

Rister's back home now. He works for Widder Ollie and her mother. They all live in the house together. Everything came out just fine. We went to church together the other night, all of us. Rister and Widder Ollie walked behind. We went into the church house carrying our babies. I know people thought I was carrying Rister's baby, and that he was carrying the one I ought to carry. The Widder Ollie's brat was digging Rister in the ribs and saying, " Get up, hossy. Get up, hossy, or I'll hit you on the snoot."

And he'd have done it too, if Rister hadn't stepped up a little faster. That kid is twice as big as he was the night I carried him. Ollie says he won't walk a step when she takes him any place. Makes Rister carry him everywhere. People look at us and grin. They crane their necks back over the seats to look at us all together again. Ollie understands. Lima understands. Rister don't understand so well.

And we go back across the hills shining in moonlight. Summer is here again. Corn is tall on the hills. Then I hold my head in the air, throw my chin to the stars, and I give that strange catcall once more. Rister looks a little funny. He understands now better than he did.

— From the *American Mercury*, July, 1936. Reprinted by permission.

SOUTHERN POSSUM HUNT

By Floyd Tillery

SIX YEARS is a pow'ful long time to take to ketch one blackjack possum — 'specially if you've prided yourself all your life on keeping the best possum dawgs in the whole country and you are know'd from one end of the county to the other as Jerry Jones, the Possum Hunter. But that's just how long it taken me and my two boys, Bud and Buck, to ketch "Old Big Foot."

It all started, as I have just said, six years ago this past fall, when early one morning while the two boys was down in the hawg lot, slopping the shotes, Bud called out to me up at the barn, saying, "Lord, Pa! Come quick and see what kind of dam-varmint track this here is!"

With that I put out hard as I could down to where the boys was at, but afore I got there I heard Buck say to his brother, "Hell, it's a bo-coon's track, that's what it is!" When I had got a good look at it, though, I said, "Naw, son, it's a possum track. But it's got the damndest biggest foot I ever seen leave a print on the ground."

Well, nothing would do Bud and Buck but for us to pitch out right after supper that very night and start hunting for what we know'd must be the biggest blackjack in Calhoun county. And, strange thing, but we come dern nigh getting him our first try, too.

We hadn't been in the woods no time afore old Ring and Rattler had treed up a 'simmon sapling what stood not more than fifty yards from a poplar that was five-foot through. Course the boys was just about to bust with excitement, and as we come up to where the dawgs was at, Bud said, "Damn, Pa! What if Old Big Foot had-a made it over there to the Big Poplar!"

"We'd just-a played hell ever ketching him, that's all, ain't it, Pa?" said Buck.

"Yes, son, that's right far as it goes," says I. "But don't never count your possums, Buck, till you've got they tails twixt the split of a stout hickory stick."

In a minute or two my torch was burning good, and I was holding it high over my head, back behind my right shoulder, searching all the limbs on the tree, trying to shine the possum's eyes, when all of a sudden Bud called out, "Lord, Pa! Yonder he is, right yonder, big as all hell!"

And, sho-nuff, it was. I'd a swore the damn thing was a coon, at first. But, no, it was a possum. "Must be Old Big Foot, boys," I finally says.

Bud and Buck wanted to climb for him. But the limbs of a young 'simmon tree are so pow'ful brittle that I said we'd better use the axe. So we did. But, as luck would have it, when we cut the tree down, the two dawgs got into a scuffle and let the damn possum get loose. It wa'n't but a minute or two, though, afore they'd picked up the fresh trail and was running it a beeline to the Big Poplar. And that's how come us first to know where Old Big Foot's den was at.

Soon as I spotted him up in the tree, we seen the fat old rascal scurrying like all hell towards his hole out on the first limb what was big around as a man's belly. As I throw'd my light on him this time, he turnt his head back over his left shoulder and given us a kind of go-to-hell look for a second, then scuttled into the hollow limb. Course we had to give up for that night.

But that was the beginning of the six-year hunt what didn't end till Saddy night, three weeks ago. And during all that time, first and last, I reckon more than a hundred possum hunters taken a hand in trying to help me and the two boys ketch Old Big Foot. They come to my place from all over the county. Fact is, one of the hunts what stands out clearest in my mind is the time when Judge Baker and Dr. Watkins drove down from Centerville and went with us. Something happened on that hunt what proved to me that this particular possum was the damndest smartest animal what ever clumb a tree.

We hadn't been in the woods twenty minutes that night — me and the boys and one or two neighbors and Judge Baker and Dr. Watkins — afore one of the dawgs struck. It was old Ring — you could always tell by his high voice. Next thing we know'd, he was running that trail like hell-and-hallelujah; and old Rattler, the other dawg, was cutting through to join him. The trail got hotter and hotter, and then them there two hounds commenced letting out the prettiest damn music a man's ear ever listened to, coming through the night.

All at once my boy Bud let out one of his whoops that just natcherly set Ring and Rattler on fire! . . . And in less than no time from that, they had treed.

" Talk to him, Ring, old boy! " Bud called out. " Talk to him! "

" Speak to him, Rattler! Speak to him! " Buck shouted, right behind Bud.

And with that the two boys kept on encouraging the dawgs whilst all of us struck up a little trot to hurry and get to them where they was at.

" Bet Old Big Foot didn't make it to his tree this time, Pa! " spoke up Bud, running along 'side of me.

" Hell, naw, you know he didn't! " said Buck. " That poplar's 'cross the branch, and old Ring and Rattler are on this side of the surp mill, ain't they, Pa? "

" That's right, son," says I.

'Bout that time we heard Judge Baker, 'way back behind us, calling for help. " Hell fire, fellows! " he hollowed out. " Y'all wait! I done stumbled into a damn stump hole or Indian grave or sump'n another! "

So we had to stop and go back and help get the Judge out of an old pit where a moonshine still once had been; and that caused us to lose several minutes. Finally we got to the dawgs, though, and they was raising plu-perfect hell — just about to climb up that hickory nut tree and go git the possum.

" Oh, yes, you old rascal, you — you didn't have time to make it to your hole this time, did you, Mister Big Foot! " says I, as I started throwing the light up into the tree, the rest of the crowd circling around to help look.

The hickory being a small tree with no leaves on it to speak of, I thought I'd be able to spot Old Big Foot right now. But I shined and I shined and I shined. Still I couldn't locate no possum no where.

" Hell and damnation! " says I. " I can't figger it all out, fellows. There ain't no vine nor no tree closte enough by for him to have gone into it from this hickory nut, here. And I know these dawgs ain't tearing up stumps like this, for nothing."

" Do you suppose that big-footed old rascal could of gone up this here hickory nut tree, Jerry, and then right back down it — just to trick your dawgs? " one of the men along, what was a mighty good possum hunter hisself, asked me.

" Maybe so, Lem. They's no telling. Old Big Foot's got just about as much human in him as he has possum — I done found that out, and I don't put nothing by him." Then I called off the dawgs.

But in less time than it takes to tell it, old Ring and Rattler had done struck a fresh trail what they taken right down through the hollow, on across the foot-log, and straight to the Big Poplar, just like they know'd it by heart. And when we all got there, bless God if there wa'n't Old Big Foot hisself, setting up there on the first big limb, resting like a fat pig in the sunshine.

All in the same breath, nearly, every one of us said, " Well, I'll be damned! "

After I had throw'd my light on him, good, the old devil rose up on his haunches and forefeet, and given us that go-to-hell look of his'n, then walked unconcerned as you please straight to his den.

" Why don't you cut the tree down, Jerry? " Dr. Watkins asked me.

" Hell, Doc," says I, " it'd take two hours of hard cutting with a couple of axes to fell that tree! Besides, that poplar's worth fifty dollars to me in timber."

" Tell you what, Doc," spoke up Judge Baker, drawling his words out and twisting him off a big chew of tobacco, " I'll pay Jerry, here, for the timber if you'll help cut down the tree."

" Damn if that's so! " Dr. Watkins shot right back at him.

We all laughed. Then Doc said, " Got any more bright suggestions, Judge? "

"Yeah, Doc, come to think of it, I have. Let's all have another drink!"

And with that we all set down and the two boys built up a good fire, and Judge Baker told his nigger what was along to fetch up the little brown jug. Well, we all set there on the ground and drinked liquor and told jokes and shot craps till past two o'clock in the morning.

But as I was saying awhile ago, Old Big Foot learnt me that night that he had more damn sense than any possum what ever clumb a muscadine vine. For that old scoundrel actually did go up that hickory nut tree, then come right back down it, just to throw the dawgs off his track. I wa'n't so sure of it that night, for it was the first time I ever know'd him to do it. But after that, time and time again, when he'd git into a tight place and the dawgs would be crowding him, and he know'd he didn't have time to make it to the Big Poplar, he'd pull that same damn trick on them.

"But just give Old Big Foot plenty of time," I keeps on saying, "and he'll 'ventually do one of two things. Sooner or later he'll either take too big a distance risk, or he'll get careless about his timing."

And that's exactly what finally happened. That, plus the fact that about a year ago I got me a new dawg what I call Top. Without a doubt this Top is the smartest damn possum dawg I ever owned or heard of. Me and the boys has hunted with him all the past fall and not once has he ever disappointed us. And he's the fastest thing on foot I ever seen, too.

But we hunted Old Big Foot for two months or more with Top in the lead, afore we ever had any luck. Then, Saddy night, three weeks ago, we struck the crucial trail what turned out to be the old rascal's last round-up. Top picked up the trail first, and let me tell you what: that hell-raising hound let out a yelp when the trail got hot what sounded like Gabriel's trumpet! When they heard Top, the other dawgs come running in like lightning, and then they all went to it like a pack of July hounds on the final lap of a fox hunt. All of a sudden, though, they took a sharp turn in the woods.

" Aw, hell, Pa! " spoke up Bud in a downhearted voice. " They are heading towards the poplar! "

" Damn! " said Buck, plumb disgusted.

Then we all started on a run for the big tree. But Top and the other dawgs beat us there. They wa'n't right at the trunk of the poplar, but they was barking like hell up a big muscadine vine what swings out about three foot from the tree.

I know'd at once that Old Big Foot had took too big a chance this time. Evidently he had been pushed so closte by Top that he didn't dare risk even the short distance of three foot, but grabbed a-hold of that muscadine vine like a drowning man would a rope — and up it he went. Just high enough, though, to get out of good reach of the dawgs what was leaping six foot up into the air, trying to get him.

Old Big Foot was panting so hard his sides was going in and out like a pair of blacksmith bellows. And he was so closte to the ground we could hear him taking in his breath and letting it out in little short gasps.

" I'll climb up the vine for him, Pa! " said Buck, just a raring to try it, like any eighteen-year-old boy would.

" Yeah, and that damn blackjack'll turn on you and bite hell out of you, too! " said Buck, nearly a grown man, now. " They're mean devils, old blackjacks are, ain't they, Pa? "

" You're right, Buck," says I. " And Old Big Foot's most likely got teeth as long and sharp by now as a wild boar hawg's, too. I believe I can shake him down, boys."

You wouldn't think it, but that possum was so damn near give out that one hard shake of the muscadine vine brought him to the ground into a round heap just like a hot lump of lead. Top was on him like a duck on a June-bug, the second he hit. But that there dawg hadn't so much as broke the hide when I got to him. Old Big Foot was too tired to put up a fight, and old Top was too much of a sport, I reckon, to take advantage of him.

" Let's look at his feet, Pa! " said Buck, first thing.

And, damn, if that there possum's feet wasn't big as half your hand!

" What you going to do with him, Pa — sell him? " asked Buck.

" Hell, naw! Eat him! " says I.

He weighed eleven pounds when he was dressed — fat and tender as a pen-fed turkey. And the best-tasting possum you ever stuck your teeth into. Martha said it taken a heaping peck of sweet taters and two churnings of butter to fix up Old Big Foot in. But it was worth it — all the fellows said so.

You see we had a reg'lar celebration supper over here at the house, and invited all the possum-hunting neighbors to come over and enjoy the feed. Course we had Judge Baker and Dr. Watkins from Centerville, there, too. And the Judge brought along enough corn liquor with him to get the whole bunch of us about three-fourths drunk afore it was all over with. We sho had one big time, I'm telling you!

— From the *Southern Literary Messenger,*
March, 1939. Reprinted by permission.

GAL YOUNG UN

By Marjorie K. Rawlings

THE HOUSE was invisible from the road which wound, almost untraveled, through the flatwoods. Once every five days a turpentine wagon creaked down the ruts, and Negroes moved like shadows among the pines. A few hunters in season came upon them chipping boxes, scraping aromatic gum from red pots into encrusted buckets; inquired the way and whether quail or squirrel or turkey had been seen. Then hunters and turpentiners moved again along the road, stepping on violets and yellow pitcher-plants that rimmed the edges.

The Negroes were aware of the house. It stood a few hundred yards away, hidden behind two live oaks, isolated and remote in a patch of hammock. It was a tall square two stories. The woman who gave them water from her well when the nearby branch was dry looked to them like the house, tall and bare and lonely, weathered gray, like its unpainted cypress. She seemed forgotten.

The two white men, hunting lazily down the road, did not remember — if they had ever known — that a dwelling stood here. Flushing a covey of quail that flung themselves like feathered bronze disks at the cover of the hammock, their first shots flicked through the twin oaks. They followed their pointer-dog on the trail of single birds and stopped short in amazement. Entering the north fringe of the hammock, they had come out on a sandy open yard. A woman was watching them from the back stoop of an old house.

" Shootin' mighty close, men," she called.

Her voice sounded unused, like a rusty iron hinge.

The older man whistled in the dog, ranging feverishly in the low palmettos. The younger swaggered to the porch. He pushed back the black slouch hat from his brazen eyes.

" Never knowed nobody lived in six miles o' here."

His tone was insolent. He drew a flattened package of cigarettes from his corduroy hunting jacket, lighted one, and waited for her to begin scolding. Women always quarreled with him. Middle-aged women, like this one, quarreled earnestly; young ones snapped at him playfully.

" It's a long ways from anybody, ain't it? " she agreed.

He stared at her between puffs.

" Jesus, yes."

" I don't keer about you shootin'," she said. " It's purely sociable, hearin' men folks acrost the woods. A shot come thu a winder jest now; that's all the reason I spoke."

The intruders shifted their shotguns uneasily. The older man touched his finger to his cap.

" That's all right, ma'am."

His companion strolled to the stone curbing of an open well. He peered into its depths, shimmering where the sun of high noon struck vertically.

" Good water? "

" The finest ever. Leave me fetch you a clean cup."

She turned into the house for a white china coffee cup. The men wound up a bucket of water on creaking ropes. The older man drank politely from the proffered cup. The other guzzled directly from the bucket. He reared back his head like a satisfied hound, dripping a stream of crystal drops from his red mouth.

" Ain't your dog thirsty? Here — reckon my ol' cat won't fuss if he drinks outen his dish." The woman stroked the animal's flanks as he lapped. " Ain't he a fine feller? "

The hunters began to edge away.

" Men, I jest got common rations, bacon an' biscuit an' coffee, but you're plumb welcome to set down with me."

" No, thank you, ma'am." They looked at the sun. " Got to be moseyin' home."

The younger man was already on his way, sucking a straw. The other fumbled in his game-pocket.

"Sorry we come so clost upon you, lady. How about a bird fer your dinner?"

She reached out a large hand for the quail.

"I'd shore thank you fer it. I'm a good shot on squirrel, an' turkeys when I got 'em roosted. Birds is hard without no dog to point 'em. I gits hungry fer quail . . ."

Her voice trailed off as the hunters walked through the pines toward the road. She waved her hand in case they should turn around. They did not look back.

❦ ❦ ❦

The man was hunting alone because he had been laughed at. His cronies in the Florida village, to which he had returned after a few years' wandering, knew that he detested solitude. It was alien to him, a silent void into which he sank as into quicksand. He had stopped at the general store to pick up a hunting partner. The men lounging there hours at a time were usually willing to go with him. This time none was ready.

"Come go with me, Willy," he insisted. "I cain't go by myself."

The storekeeper called over his shoulder, weighing out a quarter's worth of water-ground meal for a Negro:

"You'll git ketched out alone in the woods sometime, Trax, an' nobody won't know who 'tis."

The men guffawed.

"Trax always got to git him a buddy."

His smoldering eyes flared at them. He spat furiously across the rough pine floor of the store.

"I ain't got to git me none o' these sorry catbirds."

He had clattered down the wooden steps, spitting angrily every few feet. They were jealous, he thought, because he had been over on the east coast. He had turned instinctively down the south road out of the village. Old man Blaine had brought him this way last week. He hunted carelessly for two or three hours, taking pot shots at several coveys that rose under his feet. His anger made him miss the birds widely. It was poor sport without a companion and a dog.

Now he realized that he was lost. As a boy he had hunted these woods, but always with other boys and men. He had gone through them unseeing, stretching his young muscles luxuriously, absorbing lazily the rich Florida sun, cooling his face at every running branch. His shooting had been careless, avid. He liked to see the brown birds tumble in midair. He liked to hunt with the pack, to gorge on the game dinners they cooked by lake shores under oak trees. When the group turned homeward, he followed, thinking of supper; of the 'shine his old man kept hidden in the smokehouse; of the girls he knew. Someone else knew north and south, and the cross patterns of the piney-woods roads. The lonely region was now as unfamiliar as though he had been a stranger.

It was an hour or two past noon. He leaned his 12-gauge shotgun against a pine and looked about him nervously. He knew by the sun that he had come continuously south. He had crossed and recrossed the road, and could not decide whether it now lay to the right or left. If he missed it to the right, he would come to cypress swamp. He licked his lips. If he picked the wrong road to the left, it would bring him out a couple of miles above the village. That would be better. He could always get a lift back. He picked up his gun and began to walk.

In a few minutes a flat gray surface flashed suddenly from a patch of hammock. He stopped short. Pleasure swept over him, cooling his hot irritation. He recognized the house where he and Blaine had drawn water. He had cursed Blaine for giving a quail to the woman. He wiped the sweat from his face. The woman would feed him and direct him out of the flatwoods. Instinctively he changed his gait from a shuffling drag to his customary swagger.

He rapped loudly on the smooth cypress front door. It had a half-moon fanlight over it. The house was old but it was capacious and good. There was, for all its bareness, an air of prosperity. Clean white curtains hung at the windows. A striped cat startled him by rearing against his legs. He kicked it away. The woman must be gone. A twig cracked in the yard beyond the high piazza. He turned. The woman was stalking around the side of the house to see before she was seen. Her gray face lightened as she recognized him. She laughed.

"Mister, if you knowed how long it's been since I heerd a rap.

Don't nobody knock on my front door. The turpentine niggers calls so's I won't shoot, and the hunters comes a-talkin' to the well."

She climbed the front steps with the awkwardness of middle age. She dried a hand on her flour-sacking apron and held it out to him. He took it limply, interrupting the talk that began to flow from her. He was ugly with hunger and fatigue and boredom.

"How 'bout a mess o' them rations you was offerin' me last week?"

His impatience was tempered with the tone of casual intimacy in which he spoke to all women. It bridged time and space. The woman flushed.

"I'd be mighty well pleased —"

She opened the front door. It stuck at the sill, and she threw a strong body against it. He did not offer to help. He strolled in ahead of her. As she apologized for the moments it would take to fry bacon and make coffee, he was already staring about him at the large room. When she came to him from the kitchen half an hour later, her face red with her hurry, the room had made an impress on his mind, as roads and forests could not do. The size of the room, of the clay fireplace, the adequacy of chairs and tables of a frontier period, the luxury of a Brussels carpet, although ancient, over wood, the plenitude of polished, unused kerosene lamps — the details lay snugly in his mind like hoarded money.

Hungry, with the smell of hot food filling his breath, he took time to smooth his sleek black hair at a walnut-framed mirror on the varnished match-board wall. He made his toilet boldly in front of the woman. A close watching of his dark face, of the quickness of his hands moving over his affectation of clipped sideburns, could only show her that he was good to look at. He walked to the kitchen with a roll, sprawling his long legs under the table.

With the first few mouthfuls of food good humor returned to him. He indulged himself in graciousness. The woman served him lavishly with fried cornbread and syrup, coffee, white bacon in thick slices, and fruits and vegetables of her own canning. His gluttony delighted her. His mouth was full, bent low over his heaped plate.

"You live fine, ma'am, for anyone lives plumb alone."

She sat down opposite him, wiping back the wet gray hair from her forehead, and poured herself a convivial cup of coffee.

"Jim — that was my husband — an' Pa always did say if they was good rations in the house they'd orter be on the table. I ain't got over the habit."

"You been livin' alone quite some time?"

"Jim's fifteen year dead. Pa 'bout six."

"Don't you never go nowheres?"

"I got no way to go. I kep' up stock fer two-three year after Pa died, but 'twa'n't wuth the worry. They's a family lives two mile closer to town than me, has a horse an' wagon. I take 'em my list o' things 'bout oncet a month. Seems like . . ."

He scarcely listened.

A change of atmosphere in her narrative indicated suddenly to him that she was asking him about himself.

"You a stranger?"

She was eager, leaning on the table waiting for his answer.

He finished a saucer of preserved figs, scraping at the rich syrup with relish. He tilted back in his chair luxuriously and threw the match from his cigarette in the general direction of the wood stove. He was entirely at home. His belly well filled with good food, his spirit touched with the unfailing intoxication to him of a woman's interest, he teetered and smoked and talked of his life, of his deeds, his dangers.

"You ever heard the name o' Trax Colton?"

She shook her head. He tapped his chest significantly, nodding at her.

"That's me. You've heard tell, if you on'y remembered, o' me leavin' here a few years back on account of a little cuttin' fuss. I been on the east coast — Daytona, Melbourne, all them places. The fuss blowed over an' I come back. Fixin' to take up business here."

He frowned importantly. He tapped a fresh cigarette on the table, as he had learned to do from his companions of the past years. He thought with pleasure of all that he had learned, of the sophistication that lay over his Cracker speech and ways like a cheap bright coat.

"I'm an A-1 bootlegger, ma'am."

For the time being he was a big operator from the east coast. He told her of small sturdy boats from Cuba, of signal flares on the St. Augustine beach at midnight, of the stream of swift automobiles moving in and out just before high tide. Her eyes shone. She plucked at the throat of her brown-checked gingham dress, breathing quickly. It was fitting that this dark glamorous young man should belong to the rocket-lit world of danger. It was ecstasy, painful in its sharpness, that he should be tilted back at her table, flicking his fragrant ashes on her clean, lonely floor.

He was entirely amiable as he left her. Pleased with himself, he was for a moment pleased with her. She was a good woman. He laid his hand patronizingly on her shoulder. He stroked the striped cat on his way down the steps. This time he turned to lift his hand to her. She waved heartily as long as his lithe body moved in sight among the pines.

An impulse took her to the mirror where he had smoothed his hair, as though it would bring him within her vision again. She saw herself completely for the first time in many years. Isolation had taken the meaning from age. She had forgotten until this moment that she was no longer young. She turned from the mirror and washed the dishes soberly. It occurred to her that the young man had not even asked her name.

The hammock that had been always a friendly curtain about the old house was suddenly a wall. The flatwoods that had been sunny and open, populous with birds and the voice of winds, grew dense and dark. She had been solitary. She had grieved for Jim and for the old man her father. But solitude had kept her company in a warm natural way, sitting cozily at her hearth, like the cat. Now loneliness washed intolerably over her, as though she were drowning in a cold black pond.

The young man's complacency lasted a mile or two. As his feet began to drag, fact intruded on the fiction with which he had enraptured the gray-haired woman. Memories seeped back into him like a poison: memories of the lean years as ignorant hanger-on of prosperous bootleggers; of his peddling to small garages of lye-cut 'shine in ignominious pints. The world for which he considered himself fitted had evaded him. His condition was desperate. He thought of the woman who had fed him, whom he had entranced with his story. Distaste for her flooded him, as though it was her fault the story was a lie. He lifted his shotgun and blew the head from a redbird trilling in a wild plum tree.

❦ ❦ ❦

The storekeeper in the village was the only person who recognized Mattie Syles. The store was packed with the Saturday-night buyers of rations. A layer of whites milled in front of the meat counter; a layer of blacks shifted behind them. At the far grocery counter along a side wall a wedge of Negroes had worked in toward the meal and sugar barrels, where helpers weighed out the dimes' and quarters' worth with deliberately inaccurate haste. Two white women were buying percale of the storekeeper's wife at the dry-goods counter.

The woman came in defiantly, as though the store was a shameful place where she had no business. She looked searchingly from side to side. The storekeeper's wife called, "Evenin', ma'am," and the two white women wheeled to stare and whisper after her. She advanced toward the meat counter. The Negroes parted to let her in. The storekeeper poised his knife over a pork backbone to look at her. He laid it down, wiped his hands with a flourish on his front, and shook hands across the counter.

"If this ain't a surprise! Must be four-five years since you been to town! Meat I been sendin' you by Lantry's been all right? What kin I do fer you? Butchered this mornin' — got fresh beef. How 'bout a nice thin steak?"

She made her purchases slowly and moved to the staples counter. She insisted on being left until the last.

"I ain't in no hurry."

The store was almost empty and ready to close when she gathered her sacks together and climbed into Lantry's wagon, waiting outside the door. As Lantry clicked to his horse and they moved off she did not notice that the man she had hoped desperately to see was just strolling into the store.

"Gimme a couple o' packs o' Camels to tide me over Sunday."

"Fifteen cents straight now, Trax."

" Jest one, then."

The storekeeper spoke across the vacant store to his wife, rolling up the bolts of cloth.

" Edna, you have better manners with the customers, or we'll be losing 'em. Why'n't you take up some time with Mis' Syles? "

" Who? "

" Mis' Syles — Jim Syles' widder — ol' man Terry's daughter — lives four-five mile south, out beyond Lantry's. You know her, Edna. Lantry's been buyin' fer her."

" I never knowed her. How'd I know her now? Why'n't you call her by name, so's I'd of knowed? "

" Well, you keep better track of her if she's goin' to take to comin' to town agin. She's rich."

Trax turned in the doorway.

" You talkin' about that gank-gutted woman left jest now? "

He had avoided going into the store until she left. He had not intended to bring her volubility upon him in public, have her refer to their meal together. He had half-guessed she had come looking for him. Women did.

" She live alone in a two-story house you cain't see from the road? "

" That's her," the storekeeper agreed. " That's Mis' Syles, a'right."

" She's rich? "

" I mean rich. Got her five dollars a week steady rent-money from turpentine, an' three thousand dollars insurance in the bank her daddy left her. An' then lives 'tother end o' nowhere. Won't leave the old house."

" 'Bout time somebody was fixin' to marry all that, goin' to waste."

" She wouldn't suit you, Trax. You didn't git a good look at her. You been used to 'em younger an' purtier."

The man Colton was excited. He walked out of the store without the customary " Well, evenin' " of departure. He hurried to Blaine's, where he was boarding, but did not go in. It was necessary to sit alone on the bench outside and think. His luck had not deserted him. As he leaned his dark head against the wall, the tropical stars glittering over him were the bright lights of city streets. Here and there a fat star flickered. These were the burnished kerosene lamps of the widow Syles. The big room — the fireplace that would heat it on the coolest nights — one by one he drew out the remembered details and tucked them into his plans.

❦ ❦ ❦

The man courted the woman with the careless impatience of his quail hunting. He intended to be done with it as quickly as possible. There was, astonishingly, a certain pleasure in her infatuation. He responded to any woman's warmth as a hound does to a grate fire, stretching comfortably before it. The maternal lavishness of emotion for him was satisfying. Younger women, pretty women, expected something of him, coaxed and coquetted.

On his several visits to the widow before he condescended to be married to her, he sprawled in the early spring nights before the big fireplace. He made it plain that he was not one to sit around the kitchen stove. His fastidiousness charmed her. She staggered into the room with her generous arms heaped with wood: live oak and hickory, and some cedar chips, because Trax liked the smell. From his chair he directed the placing of the heavy logs. A fire must crackle constantly to please him. She learned to roll cigarettes for him, bringing them to him to lick flickeringly, like a snake, with his quick tongue. The process stirred her. When she placed the finished cigarette between his lips and lighted it with a blazing lighter'd splinter; when he puffed languidly on it and half-closed his eyes, and laid his fingers perhaps on her large-boned hand, she shivered.

The courting was needlessly protracted because she could not believe that he would have her. It was miracle enough that he should be here at all in these remote flatwoods. It was unbelievable that he should be willing to prolong the favor, to stay with her in this place forever.

She said, " Cain't be you raly wants me."

" Why not? Ain't a thing the matter with you."

She understood sometimes — when she wakened with a clear mind in the middle of the night — that something strange had happened to her. She was moving in a delirium, like the haze of malaria when the fever was on. She solaced herself by thinking that Trax too might be submerged in such a delicious fog.

When he left her one night in the Blaine Ford he had borrowed, the retreating explosions of the car left behind a silence that terrified her. She ran to the beginning of the pines to listen. There was no sound but the breath of the south wind in the needles. There was no light but the endless flickering of stars. She knew that if the man did not come back again she would have to follow him. Solitude she had endured. She could not endure desolation.

When he came the next day she was ready to go to the village with him to the preacher. He laughed easily at her hurry and climbed ahead of her into the borrowed car. He drove zestfully, with abandon, bouncing the woman's big frame over the ruts of the dirt road.

As they approached the village he said casually, "I keep my money in Clark City. We'd orter do our business together. Where's yours?"

"Mine's there too. Some's in the post office an' some in the bank."

"Supposin' we go git married there. An' reckon you kin lend me a hundred till I add up my account?"

She nodded an assent to both questions.

"Don't you go spendin' no money on me, Trax, if you ain't got it real free to spend." She was alarmed for his interests. "You leave me pay fer things a while."

He drew a deep breath of relief. He was tempted for a moment to get her cash and head for the east coast at once. But he had made his plans to stay. He needed the old house in the safe flatwoods to make his start. He could even use the woman.

When they came back through the village from the city she stopped at the store for supplies. The storekeeper leaned across the fresh sausage to whisper confidentially:

"'Tain't my business, Mis' Syles, but folks is sayin' Trax Colton is sort o' courtin' you. You come of good stock, an' you'd orter step easy. Trax is purely trash, Mis' Syles."

She looked at him without comprehension.

She said, " Me an' Trax is married."

❧ ❧ ❧

The gray of the house was overlaid with the tenderness of the April sun. The walls were washed with its thin gold. The ferns and lichens of the shingled roof were shot through with light, and the wren's nest under the eaves was luminous. The striped cat sprawled flattened on the rear stoop, exposing his belly to the soft warmth. The woman moved quietly at her work, for fear of awakening the man. She was washing. When she drew a bucket of water from the well she steadied it with one hand as it swung to the coping, so that there should be no sound.

Near the well stood bamboo and oleander. She left her bucket to draw her fingers along the satin stoutness of the fresh green bamboo shoots, to press apart the new buds of the oleander in search of the pale pinkness of the first blossoms. The sun lay like a friendly arm across her square shoulders. It seemed to her that she had been chilled, year on year, and that now for the first time she was warmed through to her marrow. Spring after the snapping viciousness of February; Trax sleeping in the bed after her solitude. . . . When she finished her washing she slipped in to look at him. A boyish quiet wiped out the nervous shiftiness of his waking expression. She wanted to gather him up, sleeping, in her strong arms and hold him against her capacious breast.

When his breakfast was almost ready, she made a light clatter in the kitchen. It irritated him to be called. He liked to get up of his own accord and find breakfast smoking, waiting for him. He came out gaping, washed his face and hands in the granite basin on the water-shelf, combed his hair leisurely at the kitchen mirror, turning his face this way and that. Matt stood watching him, twisting her apron. When he was quite through, she came to him and laid her cheek against his.

" Mornin', Trax-honey."

Her voice was vibrant.

" Mornin'."

He yawned again as he dropped into his chair. He beat lightly on his down-turned plate with his knife and surveyed the table. He scowled.

" Where's the bacon? "

" Honey, I didn't think you'd want none with the squirrel an' eggs an' fish."

" My God, I can't eat breakfast without bacon."

" I'm sorry, Trax. 'Twon't take me but a minute now."

She was miserable because she had not fried bacon and he wanted it.

He slid eggs and meat and biscuits to his plate, poured coffee with an angry jerk, so that it spilled on the table, shoveled the food in, chewing with his mouth open. When Matt put the crisp thick slices of white bacon before him, he did not touch them. He lighted a cigarette and strolled to the stoop, pushed off the cat so that he might sit down. He leaned back and absorbed the sun. This was fine.

He had deliberately allowed himself these few idle weeks. He had gone long without comfort. His body needed it. His swaggering spirit needed it. The woman's adoration fed him. He could have had no greater sense of well-being, of affluence, if she had been a nigger servant. Now he was ready for business. His weasel mind was gnawing its hole into the world he longed for.

" Matt! "

She left her dishes and came to stand over him.

" Matt, you're goin' in business with me. I want you should git me three hundred dollars. I want to set up a eight-barrel still back o' the house, down by the branch."

Trax had crashed like a meteor into the flatwoods. It had not occurred to her that his world must follow him. That was detached from him, only a strange story that he had told. She had a sensation of dismay that any thing, any person, must intrude on her ecstasy.

She said anxiously, " I got enough to make out on, Trax. You don't need to go startin' up nothin' like that."

" All right — if you want I should put my outfit some'eres else — "

" No, no. Don't you do that. Don't you go 'way. I didn't know you was studyin' on nothin' like that — you jest go ahead an' put it clost as you like."

"Down by the branch, like I said."

He visioned the layout for her. She listened, distraught. The platform here, for the barrels of mash. There, the woodpile for the slow fire. Here again, the copper still itself. The cover was dense, utterly concealing. The location was remote.

"The idee, Matt," he was hunched forward, glowing, "is to sell yer own stuff what they call retail, see? It costs you fifty, seventy-five cents a gallon to make. You sell by the five-gallon jug fer seven dollars, like they're doin' now, you don't make nothin'. That's nigger pay. But what do you git fer it by the drink? A quarter. A quarter a drink an' a dollar a pint. You let people know they kin git 'em a drink out here any time to Trax Colton's, you got 'em comin' in from two-three counties fer it. You git twenty gallons ahead an' color some up, cook it a whiles underground to darken it, an' you take it to places like Jacksonville an' Miami — you got you real money."

It was as though thunder and lightning threatened over the flatwoods. The darkness of impending violence filled them. She stared at him.

"'Course, if you don't want to invest in my business with me, I got to be gittin' back where I come from."

The smoke from his cigarette drifted across her.

"No, no! It's all right!"

His glamorousness enfolded her like the April sun.

"Honey, anything you want to do's all right."

❦ ❦ ❦

Setting up the still was a week's work. Men began to come and go. Where there had been, once in five days, the silent turpentiners, once in a while the winter hunters, there were now Negroes bringing in cut wood; a local mason putting together brick mortar; a hack carpenter building a roof, men in trucks bringing in sacks of meal and sugar, glass demijohns, and oak kegs.

The storekeeper brought five hundred pounds of sugar.

"Howdy, Mis' Colton. Reckon you never figgered you'd be 'shinin'."

"No."

"But you couldn't git you no better place fer it."

Her square face brightened.

"That's jest what Trax says."

That night she approached him.

"Trax, all these here men knowin' what you're doin' — reckon it's safe?"

"They got no reason to say nothin'. The only reason anybody'd turn anybody else up was if he'd done somethin' to him. Then they'd git at him that-a-way. Git his still, see? Git him tore up. That way they'd git him."

She made no further comment. Her silence made its way through the wall of his egotism.

"You don't talk as much as you did, Matt. Else I got used to it."

"I was alone so long, honey. Seemed like I had to git caught up."

But the spring warmth was no longer so loosening to the tongue. The alien life the man was bringing in chilled the exuberance that had made her voluble.

"I'm fixin' to learn you to make the whiskey, Matt."

She stared at him.

"Less help we have, knowin' how much I got an' where 'tis, better it suits me, see?"

She said finally, "I kin learn."

The work seemed strange, when all her folk had farmed and timbered. But her closest contact with Trax was over the sour, seething mash. When they walked together back of the house, down to the running branch, their bodies pushing side by side through the low palmettos, they were a unit. Except to curse her briefly when she was clumsy, he was good-natured at his work. Crouching by the fire burning under the copper drum, the slow dripping from the coils of the distillate the only sound except for small woods life, she felt themselves man and wife. At other times his lovely body and unlovely spirit both evaded her.

He was ready to sell his wares. He drove to the village and to neighboring towns and cities, inviting friends and acquaintances to have a drink from one of the gallon jugs under the rear seat of the borrowed car. They pronounced it good 'shine. To the favored few financially able to indulge themselves he gave a drink of the " aged " liquor. Accustomed to the water-clear, scalding rawness of fresh 'shine, they agreed gravely that no better whiskey ever came in from Cuba. He let it be known that both brands would be available at any time, day or night, at the old Terry house four miles south of the village. He made a profound impression. Most bootleggers sold stuff whose origin and maker were unknown. Most 'shiners had always made it, or drifted into it aimlessly. Trax brought a pomp and ceremony to the local business.

Men found their way out the deep-rutted road. They left their cars among the pines and stumbled through the hammock to the house. They gathered in the big room Trax had recognized as suitable for his purposes. The long trenchered table old man Terry had sliced from red bay held the china pitcher of " corn " and the jelly glasses from which they drank. Their bird-dogs and hounds padded across the piazza and lay before the fire. Trax drank with them, keying their gatherings to hilarity. He was a convivial host. Sometimes Blaine brought along his guitar, and Trax clapped his hands and beat his feet on the floor as the old man picked the strings. But he was uneasy when a quarrel developed. Then he moved, white-faced among the men, urging someone else to stop it.

At first the woman tried to meet them hospitably. When, deep in the hammock at the still, she heard the vibration of a motor, she hurried up to the house to greet the guests. She smoothed back the gray hair from her worn face and presented her middle-aged bulk in a clean apron. If there was one man alone, Trax introduced her casually, insolently:

" This is my old woman."

When a group of men came together, he ignored her. She stood in the doorway, smiling vaguely. He continued his talk as though she were not there. Sometimes one of the group, embarrassed, acknowledged her presence.

" How do, ma'am."

For the most part they took their cue from Trax and did not

see her. Once, on her withdrawal to the kitchen, a stranger had followed for a match.

" Don't you mind workin' way out here in the woods? "

But she decided that Trax was too delicate to want his wife mixing with men who came to drink. At night he sometimes invited her into the big room with conspicuous courtesy. That was when one or two women had come with the men. Her dignity established the place as one where they might safely come. She sat miserably in their midst while they made banal jokes and drank from the thick glasses. They were intruders. Their laughter was alien among the pine trees. She stayed at the still most of the time. The labor was heavy and exacting. The run must be made when the mash was ready, whether it was day or night. It was better for Trax to stay at the house to take care of the customers.

In the early fall he was ready to expand. Matt was alone, scrubbing the floors between runs of whiskey. She heard a powerful car throbbing down the dirt road. It blew a horn constantly in a minor key. Men usually came into this place silently. She went to the piazza, wet brush in hand. With the autumnal drying of foliage, the road was discernible. The scent of wild vanilla filled the flatwoods. She drew in the sweetness, craning her neck to see.

A large blue sedan of expensive make swerved and rounded into the tracks other cars had made to the house. Trax was driving. He swung past the twin live oaks and into the sandy yard. He slammed the door behind him as he stepped out. He had bought the car with the remainder of Matt's three thousand and most of the summer's profits. He was ready to flash across his old haunts, a big operator from the interior.

" I kin sell that hundred gallons of aged stuff now fer what it's worth."

He nodded wisely. He sauntered into the house, humming under his breath.

" Hi-diddy-um-tum — " He was vibrant with an expectancy in which she had no part.

She heard him curse because the floor was wet. The cat crossed his path. He lifted it by the tail and slid it along the slippery boards. The animal came to her on the piazza. She drew it into her lap and sat on her haunches a long time, stroking the smooth hard head.

❦ ❦ ❦

Life was a bad dream. Trax was away a week at a time. He hired the two Lantry boys to take his place. Matt worked with them, for the boys unwatched would let the mash ferment too long. Trax returned to the flatwoods only for fresh supplies of liquor and of clean clothes. It pleased him to dress in blues that harmonized not too subtly with the blue sedan. He wore light-blue shirts and a red necktie that was a challenging fire under the dark insolent face. Matt spent hours each week washing and ironing the blue shirts. She protested his increasing absences.

"Trax, you jest ain't here at all. I hardly got the heart fer makin' the runs, an' you gone."

He smiled.

"Any time it don't suit you, I kin move my outfit to the east coast."

He laid the threat across her like a whip.

The young Lantrys too saw Trax glamorously. They talked of him to Matt as they mixed the mash, fired, and kept their vigils. This seemed all she had these days of the man: talk of him with the boys beside the still. She was frustrated, filled, not with resentment, but with despair. Yet she could not put her finger on the injustice. She flailed herself with his words.

"Any time you don't like it, I kin move."

She waited on Trax's old customers as best she could, running up the slight incline from the still-site to the house when she heard a car. Her strong body was exhausted at the end of the week. Yet when she had finished her elaborate baking on Saturday night she built up a roaring fire in the front room, hung the hot water kettle close to it for his bath, and sat down to wait for him.

Sometimes she sat by the fire almost all night. Sometimes he did not come at all. Men learned they could get a drink at Colton's any hour of the night on Saturday. When the square dance at Trimtree's was done, they came out to the flatwoods at two or three o'clock in the morning. The woman was always awake. They stepped up on the piazza and saw her through the window. She sat brooding by the fire, the striped cat curled in her lap. Around her bony shoulders she hugged the corduroy hunting jacket Trax had worn when he came to her.

She existed for the Saturday nights when the throb of the blue sedan came close, the Sunday mornings when he slept late and arose, sulky, for a lavish breakfast and dinner. Then he was gone again, and she was waving after him down the road. She thought that her love and knowledge of him had been always nothing but this watching through the pine trees as he went away.

The village saw more of him. Occasionally he loitered there a day to show off before he headed for the coast. At times he returned in the middle of the week and picked up fifteen or twenty gallons cached at Blaine's and did not go out to the flatwoods at all. On these occasions he had invariably a girl or woman with him; cheap pretty things whose lightness brought them no more than their shoddy clothes. The storekeeper, delivering meal and sugar to Matt, lingered one day. The still needed her, but she could not with courtesy dismiss him. At last he drew courage.

" Mis' Matt, dogged if I don't hate to complain on Trax to you, but folks thinks you don't know how he's a-doin' you. You're workin' like a dog, an' he ain't never home."

" I know."

" You work at 'shinin', somethin' you nor your folks never done — not that it ain't all right — an' Trax off in that big fine car spendin' the money fast as he turns it over."

" I know."

" The Klan talks some o' givin' him down the country fer it."

" 'Tain't nobody's business but his an' mine."

" Mis' Matt " — he scuffled in the sand — " I promised I'd speak of it. D'you know Trax has got him women goin' round with him? "

" No. I didn't know that."

" Ev'ybody figgered you didn't know that." He mopped his forehead. " The day you an' Trax was married, I was fixin' to tell you 'twa'n't nothin' but your money an' place he wanted to git him set up."

" That's my business, too," she said stonily.

He dropped his eyes before the cold face and moved to his truck. She called after him defiantly:

" What else did I have he'd want anyway! "

She went into the house. She understood the quality of her betrayal. The injustice was clear. It was only this: Trax had taken what he had not wanted. If he had said, " Give me the money and, for the time, the house," it would have been pleasant to give, solely because he wanted. This was the humiliation: that she had been thrown in on the deal, like an old mare traded in with a farm.

The Lantry boys called unanswered from the palmettos.

She had known. There was no need of pretense. There was no difference between today and yesterday. There was only the dissipation of a haze, as though a sheet had been lifted from a dead body, so that, instead of knowing, she saw.

❧ ❧ ❧

The man came home late Saturday afternoon. Startled, Matt heard the purr of the motor and hurried to the house from the still. She thought the woman with him had come for liquor. She came to meet them, wiping her hands on her brown gingham apron. Trax walked ahead of his companion, carrying his own shiny patent leather bag and a smaller shabby one. As they came into the house, she saw that it was not a woman, but a girl.

The girl was close on his heels, like a dog. She was painted crudely, as with a haphazard conception of how it should be done. Stiff blond curls were bunched under a tilted hat. A flimsy silk dress hung loosely on an immature frame. Cheap silk stockings bagged on thin legs. She rocked, rather than walked, on incredibly spiked heels. Her shoes absorbed Matt's attention. They were pumps of blue kid, the precise blue of the sedan.

" I mean, things got hot fer me on the east coast." Trax was voluble. " Used that coastal highway oncet too often. First thing I knowed, down below New Smyrna, I seed a feller at a garage give the high sign, an' I'm lookin' into the end of a .45." He flushed. " I jest did git away. It'll pay me to work this territory a whiles, till they git where they don't pay me no mind over there agin."

The girl was watching Matt with solemn blue eyes. Beside the gray bulk of the older woman, she was like a small gaudy doll. Trax indicated her to Matt with his thumb.

"Elly here'll be stayin' at the house a while."

He picked up the shabby bag and started up the stairs.

"Long as you an' me is usin' the downstairs, Matt, she kin sleep upstairs in that back room got a bed in it."

She pushed past the girl and caught him by the sleeve.

"Trax! What's this gal?"

"Ain't no harm to her." He laughed comfortably. He tweaked a wisp of her gray hair.

"She's jest a little gal young un," he said blandly, "'s got no place to go."

He drew the girl after him. The woman stared at the high-heeled blue slippers clicking on every step.

❦ ❦ ❦

A warm winter rain thrummed on the roof. The light rush of water sank muffled into the moss that padded the shingles. The sharpest sound was a gurgling in the gutter over the rain barrel. There had been no visible rising of the sun. Only the gray daylight had protracted itself, so that it was no longer dawn, but day. Matt sat close to the kitchen stove, her bulk shadowy in the dimness. Now and then she opened the door of the firebox to push in a stick of pine, and the light of the flames flickered over her drawn face.

She could not tell how much of the night she had sat crouched by the range. She had lain long hours unsleeping, while Trax breathed regularly beside her. When the rain began, she left the bed and dressed by the fresh-kindled fire. Her mouth was dry; yet every few minutes an uncontrollable chill shook her body. It would be easy to walk up the unused stairs, down the dusty hall to the back room with the rough pine bed in it, to open the door and look in, to see if anyone was there. Yet if she continued to sit by the fire, moving back the coffee pot when it boiled, surely Trax would come to the kitchen alone, and she would know that yesterday no woman had come home with him. Through the long days her distraught mind had been busy with imaginings. They might easily have materialized, for a moment, in a painted girl, small and very young, in blue kid slippers.

Trax was moving about. She put the frying pan on the stove, sliced bacon into it, stirred up cornmeal into a pone with soda and salt and water. Trax called someone. He came into the kitchen, warmed his hands at the stove. He poured water into the wash basin and soused his face in it. Matt set the coffee pot on the table. The girl pushed open the door a little way and came through. She came to the table uncertainly, as though she expected to be ordered away. Matt did not speak.

Trax said, " How's my gal? "

The girl brought her wide eyes to him and took a few steps to his chair.

" Where your shoes, honey? "

She looked down at her stockinged feet.

" I gotta be keerful of 'em."

He laughed indulgently.

" You kin have more when them's gone. Matt, give the young un somethin' to eat."

The thought struck the woman like the warning whir of a rattler that if she looked at the girl in this moment she would be compelled to lift her in her hands and drop her like a scorpion on the hot stove. She thought, " I cain't do sich as that." She kept her back turned until the impulse passed and she could control her trembling. Her body was of metal and wood. It moved of itself, in jerks. A stiff wooden head creaked above a frame so heavy it seemed immovable. Her stomach weighed her down. Her ample breasts hurt her ribs, as though they were of lead. She thought, " I got to settle this now."

She said aloud slowly, " I'll not wait on her, nor no other woman."

The girl twisted one foot over the other.

She said, " I ain't hungry."

Trax stood up. His mouth was thin. He said to Matt, " You'll wait on her, old lady, or you'll git along without my comp'ny."

She thought, " I got to settle it. I got to say it."

But she could not speak.

The girl repeated eagerly, " I ain't a bit hungry."

Trax picked up a plate from the table. He held it out to his wife.

She thought, " Anyway, cornbread an' bacon's got nothin' to do with it."

She dished out meat and bread. Trax held out a cup. She filled it with coffee. The man sat down complacently. The girl sat beside him and pecked at the food. Her eyes were lowered. Between mouthfuls, she twisted her fingers in her lap or leaned over to inspect her unshod feet.

Matt thought, " Remindin' me."

The paint had been rubbed from the round face. The hair was yellow, like allamanda blooms. The artificial curls that had protruded from the pert hat had flattened out during the damp night, and hung in loose waves on the slim neck. She wore the blue silk dress in which she had arrived.

Trax said, " You eat up good, Elly. May be night 'fore we git back to eat again." He turned to Matt. " Lantry boys been doin' all right? "

" They been doin' all right. Them's good boys. I heerd 'em come in a hour back. But they needs watchin' right on. They'll let the mash go too long, spite of everything, if I ain't right on top of 'em."

She hardened herself.

" You jest as good to stay home an' do the work yourself. I ain't goin' near the outfit."

" They kin make out by theirselves," he said easily.

He rose from the table, picking his teeth.

" Come on, Elly."

The girl turned her large eyes to the older woman, as though she were the logical recipient of her confession.

" I forgot to wash my hands an' face," she said.

Trax spoke curtly.

" Well, do it now, an' be quick."

He poured warm water in the basin for her and stood behind her, waiting. She washed slowly, with neat, small motions, like a cat. Trax handed her the clean end of the towel. They went upstairs together. Trax's voice was low and muffled. It dripped through the ceiling like thick syrup. Suddenly Matt heard the girl laugh.

She thought, " I figgered all thet owl-face didn't let on no more'n she meant it to."

In a few minutes they came down again. Trax called from the front room:

" Best to cook dinner tonight, Matt. We're like not to git back at noon."

They ran from the porch through the rain.

She walked after them. She was in time to see them step in the blue sedan. The high-heeled slippers flickered across the running-board. The car roared through the live oaks, down the tracks among the pines. Matt closed her eyes against the sight of it.

She thought, " Maybe she takened her satchel an' I jest didn't see it. Maybe she ain't comin' back."

She forced herself to go to the upstairs bedroom. The drumming on the roof sounded close and louder. The bed was awkwardly made. The shabby handbag stood open in a hickory rocker, exposing its sparse contents. A sound startled her. The cat had followed, and was sniffing the unfamiliar garments in the chair. The woman gathered the animal in her arms. They were alone together in the house, desolate and lonely in the rain-drenched flatwoods.

She thought of the Lantry boys under the palmettos. They were careless when they were cold and wet. They might not put the last five hundred pounds of sugar under cover. Shivering in the drizzle, they might use muddy water from the bank of the branch, instead of going a few yards upstream where it ran deep and clear. She threw Trax's corduroy jacket about her and went down the incline behind the house to oversee the work.

She had decided not to cook anything for the evening. But when the mist lifted in late afternoon, and the sun struck slantwise through the wet dark trees, she left the Lantry boys to finish and went to the house. She fried ham and baked soda biscuits and sweet potatoes. The meal was ready and waiting and she stirred up a quick ginger cake and put it in the oven.

She said aloud, desperately, " Might be he'll be back alone."

Yet when the dark gathered the bare house into its loneliness, as she had gathered the cat, and she lighted kerosene lamps in the long front room and a fire, the man and girl came together as she had known they would. Where she had felt only despair, suddenly she was able to hate. She picked up her anger like a stone and hurled it after the blue heels.

"Go eat your dinner."

She spoke to them as she would to Negro field hands. Trax stared at her. He herded Elly nervously ahead of him, as though to protect her from an obscure violence. Matt watched them, standing solidly on big feet. She had not been whole. She had charred herself against the man's youth and beauty. Her hate was healthful. It waked her from a drugged sleep, and she stirred faculties hurt and long unused.

She sat by the clay fireplace in the front room while the pair ate. They spoke in whispers, shot through by the sudden laugh of the girl. It was a single high sound, like the one note of the thrush. Hearing it, Matt twisted her mouth. When the casual clatter of plates subsided, she went to the kitchen and began scraping the dishes to wash them. Trax sat warily in his place. The girl made an effort to hand Matt odds and ends from the table. The woman ignored her.

Trax said to Elly, "Le's go by the fire."

Matt cleaned up the kitchen and fed the cat. She stroked its arching back as it chewed sideways on scraps of meat and potato. She took off her apron, listened at the open door for sounds from the Lantrys, bolted the door, and walked to the front room to sit stiff and defiant by the blazing pine fire. The girl sat with thin legs tucked under her chair. She looked from the man to the woman and back again. Trax stretched and yawned.

He said, "Guess I'll go down back an' give the boys a hand. I ain't any too sure they run one batch soon enough. I got to keep up my stuff. I got high-class trade. Ain't I, Elly?" He touched her face with his finger as he passed her.

The woman and the girl sat silently after his going. The cat padded in and sat between them.

The girl called timidly: "Kitty!"

Matt turned savagely.

"Keep your hands off him."

The girl laced her fingers and studied the animal.

"Do he scratch?"

Matt did not answer. She loosened her gray hair and combed it by the fire with a side-comb, plaiting it into two thin braids over her shoulders. Inside the childish hairdressing her face was bony and haggard. She went into the adjoining bedroom, undressed and got into bed. She lay reared up on one elbow, straining for every sound. The fire popped and crackled. Once the juice oozed from a pine log faster than it could burn. It made a sizzling, like boiling fat. A chair scraped and Elly went up to the back bedroom. Her high heels clicked overhead. Matt thought with satisfaction that the girl had no light. She was floundering around in the dark in the unfamiliar house.

In a little while the front door opened and closed softly. Matt heard Trax creak cautiously up the stairs to the back room.

Trax was sleeping away the bright March morning. Matt made no effort to be silent about her washing. She dipped noisily into the rain barrel. When the soft water was gone she drew from the well, rattling galvanized buckets. Elly sat on the bottom step of the rear stoop, scuffling her bare toes in the sand. She wore the blue silk dress. Beside her was a handful of her own garments in need of washing, a pair of silk stockings and two or three pieces of underwear. Matt passed in front of her to go to the clothes line.

Elly said, "Trax give me this dress."

The woman did not seem to hear her.

Elly continued. "Reckon it'll wash? It's spotted."

Matt did not answer. She hung flour-sacking towels on the line. The girl picked up her small pile, looked uncertainly at the tub of soapsuds, laid down the clothes. She went to the tub and began rubbing on the first garment she drew from the suds. It was one of Matt's gingham aprons. She rubbed with energy, and Matt towered over her before she noticed that the woman had left the line.

"Take your dirty hands out o' my tub."

The girl drew back, dripping suds from her thin arms. She turned her hands back and forth.

"They ain't dirty," she protested.

Matt laughed shortly. "Mighty simple, ain't you?"

An obscure doubt brushed her, like a dove that wavers to a perch and is gone again without lighting.

"Who do you figger I am?"

The girl faced her across the wash-tub. She said gravely, "The lady lives in Trax's house."

"Trax's house? Well, he lives in mine. Never heerd tell o' no sich thing as his wife, eh?"

The girl hesitated. "Trax jest said the old woman."

Matt breathed heavily. The girl took her silence and her questions for a mark of interest.

"Trax said you'd romp on me," she offered confidentially, "but you ain't." She wrapped one bare leg around the other. "I been romped on," she went on brightly. "Pa romped on me reg'lar."

"You got you folks then!"

"Yessum, but I don't know where he is. He run a blacksmith shop an' garage offen the hard road, but he closed up an' goed to Georgia with a lady. Then I lived with another lady down the road a piece. Trax sold her liquor; that's how come him to know me. She moved off, an' he takened me with him from there. Now I'm gonna live with him," she finished, adding with studied tact " — and you."

Trax came yawning to the rear stoop in time to see Matt walk toward the girl. Elly stared uncomprehending. He jumped to the sand and caught the woman's muscular arms from behind.

"Don't you touch her." He cracked his familiar whip over her. "You hurt that gal young un an' you've seed the last o' me."

The woman shook free from him in the strength of her rage.

"You git out o' here before I hurts her an' you, too. You take yer gal young un an' git."

He adjusted his mind slowly. Inconceivably, he had gone too far. Bringing the girl to the flatwoods had been dangerously brazen. It was done now. He understood that his hold on this place had become suddenly precarious. He had the car and he could move the still. Yet the layout suited his needs too exactly to be relinquished. He could not give it up. If the gray-headed woman was done with her infatuation, he was in trouble.

He said boldly, "I got no idee o' goin'. Me an' Elly be here right on."

She said, "I kin break ary one o' you in two with my hands."

"Not me, you cain't. Leave me tell you, ol' woman, I'm too

quick fer you. An' if you hurt Elly" — his dark face nodded at her — "if you crack down on her — with them big hands o' yourn — if you got any notion o' knifin'" — he paused for emphasis — "I'll git you sent to the chair, or up fer life — an' I'll be here in these flatwoods — in this house — right on."

He pushed the girl ahead of him and walked into the house, lighting a cigarette. He said over his shoulder, thickly between puffs, "An' that'd suit me jest fine."

She turned blindly to the wash-tub. She soaped the blue shirts without seeing them, rubbing them up and down automatically. Her life that had run like the flatwoods road, straight and untraveled, was now a maze, doubling back on itself darkly, twisted with confusion. The man stood with his neat trap at the end of every path; the girl with her yellow hair and big eyes, at the beginning.

She thought, "I got to settle it."

❧ ❧ ❧

Trax and Elly came and went like a pair of bright birds. The blue kid slippers, scuffed by the sand, flashed in and out of the old house. Matt watched the comings and goings heavily, standing solidly on the hand-hewn pine-board floors.

She did not go near the still. Her absence did not make the difference she had imagined. The Lantrys had the work well in hand. Trax paid their wages, and their product was satisfactory. Often she did not hear them come to their work through the pines and past the hammock. A northwest wind sometimes brought the scent of the mash to her nose. The storekeeper brought in sugar and meal by a lower trail, and she seldom saw him. Trax was selling all his liquor at a high urban price, and local patronage dwindled away. The woods were quiet day and night.

Then Trax and Elly were back again, talking of hotels and highways, of new business, the talk pierced through now and again by the girl's single-noted laughter. She eyed Matt gravely, but the woman felt that the girl, oddly, had no fear. Trax was insolent, as always, his eyes narrow and his ways wary. Matt cut down on the table. She cooked scarcely enough for the three to eat. Elly ate with her catlike slowness, taking twice as long at her meager plate as the others. Matt took to rising and clearing the table as soon as she and Trax had finished. She picked up the plates casually, as though unaware that the third one still showed half its food uneaten. Trax did not seem to notice. The girl sometimes looked hungrily after the vanishing portion. She made no protest. Once Matt found her in the kitchen between meals, eating cold cornbread. Trax backed her up in her curt order to Elly to keep out.

It enraged Matt to see Elly feed the cat. Elly saved bits from her sparse helpings and held them under the table when she thought herself unobserved. Occasionally when the girl held the animal in her lap, and Matt ignored it, Trax stroked him too, because it was Elly who held him. Matt knew they sometimes had food in Elly's room at night. She began to hear a soft padding up the stairs and on the bare floor overhead, and knew the cat went up to join them. In the morning he was smug, washing his whiskers enigmatically. His desertion was intolerable. She shut him out at night. He wailed for hours at the door, accustomed to sleeping snugly inside the house.

❦ ❦ ❦

Suddenly Trax was not taking Elly with him any more. The village had become accustomed to the grave childish face beside him when it disappeared. Casually he left her behind with Matt in the flatwoods. He drove away one morning and did not come back that night or the next.

Matt took it for a taunt. It seemed to her that he was daring her to trap herself. Elly watched the road anxiously the first day. She accepted, hours before Matt, his solitary departure. At their first breakfast alone together, she said hesitantly:

"I had a idee Trax was fixin' to go off alone."

Matt thought, "The fool don't know enough to keep quiet about it."

After the second day, Elly devoted herself to exploring outside the house. Trax had kept her close to him, and the hammock had been only a cluster of shrubs and great trees through which they came and went. The Spanish moss was hazed with green by the early spring, and she discovered that the gray strands were alive with infinitesimal rosy blossoms. Matt saw her sitting at the far edge of the hammock, pulling the stuff apart.

The woman thought, " She better git herself out o' my sight."

Elly roamed through the pines as far as the road, staring up and down its silent winding, then scampered back toward the house like an alarmed squirrel. She walked stealthily to the palmettos where the Lantrys worked the still, and watched them for hours, unseen. Except when Matt stared directly at her, her round-eyed gravity lifted into a certain lightness, as though she felt newly free to move about in the sunlight. She seemed content.

On a rainy afternoon Matt, ironing in the kitchen, heard a steady snipping from the front room. She stole to the door and peered through a crack. Elly was cutting pictures from an old magazine and making an arrangement of rooms and figures of men and women and children. She was talking to herself and occasionally to them. The cat was curled in her lap, shifting lazily as she moved forward or back.

Their meals together were silent. Matt became aware at dinner one day that the pink oleanders in a jelly glass were not of her picking and placing. She had always a spray of flowers or greenery on the table. Because Elly had brought in the blooms, she snatched them from the water and stuffed them in the stove.

She allowed the girl a minimum of food. Once when she took away the plates before Elly had fairly begun, the girl reached after her desperately and said " Matt! " Again, when Matt moved from the table, leaving a plate of biscuits behind, Elly pounced on the largest and crammed it into her mouth. She began to laugh, poking in the crumbs.

She said, " You ain't romped on me yet."

Matt decided that Trax had put Elly up to goading her. She spoke for the first time in days.

" Don't you let Trax put no notions in your head. I got no idee o' rompin' on you. That ain't what I'm fixin' to do."

For the most part, the girl was uncomplaining and strangely satisfied. The immature body, however, was becoming rapidly emaciated.

Trax was gone two weeks. He came in for an afternoon and loaded up with twenty gallon-jugs concealed under the large rear seat, and went hurriedly away. He called to the two women who stood watching on the piazza.

"Got a order."

Matt nodded grimly after him. She thought, "You got you one more chance, too, if you on'y knowed it." She turned to observe the girl beside her. There was apparent on the young face a faint wistfulness and no surprise. Matt thought, "She's got her orders jest to set tight."

Trax came home for the following week-end. He slept most of the time and was sulky. He paid no more attention to Elly than to the older woman. At no time in the two days or nights did he go to the upstairs room. When he was about, Elly followed him a few steps. Then, as he continued to ignore her, she dropped behind and took up her own simple affairs. Matt told herself that if he left this time without the girl, she was ready. On Monday morning, after loading, he went alone to the car.

She said carelessly, "I might take a notion to go some'eres or do somethin'. When you comin' back this time?"

He laughed insolently. "Steppin' out, Matt?" He was sure of himself. He was too quick for her. Whatever futilities she was planning, it would surprise her most to return on the day he named.

"Be back Sat'day."

He drove off smiling.

❦ ❦ ❦

Matt was nervous all week. On Saturday morning she surprised the Lantry boys by appearing at the still. They had come and gone without contact with her for some weeks.

She said, "Boys, I jest got word the Pro-hi's is comin' lookin' fer Trax's outfit. Now I ain't quick as you-all, an' I want each one o' you should go down the road a good piece an' stay there all day, watchin', one to the north an' 'tother to the south. I'll tend the outfit, an' if I hears a whistle I'll know what it means an' it'll give me time to smash the jugs an' git to the house."

The boys were in instant alarm.

"Must be somebody's turned Trax up," they said.

Matt said, "Mighty likely. Somebody's likely got it in fer him. Trax hisself done told me a long ways back, if anybody had it in fer a man, that was the way they'd git at him."

They nodded in agreement.

"That's about it, Mis' Matt. Git him tore up an' git at him that-a-way."

They hid several demijohns in nearby cover and hurried anxiously the two ways of the road. They reported later in the village that they heard no sound for an hour or so. Toward noon their straining ears caught the crash of an axe on metal. There was the high thin splintering of glass. The isolated crashes settled into a steady shattering of wood and iron and copper. A column of smoke began to rise from the vicinity of the still. The Lantry to the south skirted the road through the pines and joined his brother. They cut through the woods to the village and announced that the Prohi's had come in from the west and were tearing up Colton's outfit. The word went out to avoid the flatwoods road.

The Lantrys were waiting for Trax when he came through in late afternoon. They flagged him down. They drove with him as far as their own place, telling him what they knew.

"When we lit out we could hear 'em maulin' on the barrels an' purely see the smoke. Things is tore up an' burnt up all right."

They conjectured who, of his numerous enemies, might have betrayed him. He drove at a spring-breaking clip over the root-filled ruts of the sand road. His face was black and frightened. When he let the boys out of the car he had said nothing about the week's wages. They looked at each other.

One said, "How 'bout us gittin' ten dollars, anyway, Trax?"

"That's it. I ain't got it. I on'y got five myself. I was fixin' to turn over this lot quick."

"We hid out 'bout twenty gallons, if they ain't found it," they informed him eagerly. He listened tensely to a description of the location and was gone.

He drove into the yard and stopped the car in gear with a jerk. No one was in sight. He ran back of the house to the palmettos. A ring of fire had blackened palms and oaks and myrtle for a hundred feet around. A smoldering pile of bricks and barrel hoops and twisted metal in the center marked the site of the still. He began a frenzied search for the hidden jugs.

Matt peered from a window in the front room. She ordered Elly upstairs.

"You stay there till I tell you different."

The woman hurried into the yard with a jug of kerosene and a handful of papers. The sedan was twenty-five feet from the house, but the direction of the wind was safe. She soaked the hood and seats of the car with oil and piled papers on the floor. She tied a bundle of oil-soaked paper on the end of her longest clothes prop; touched a match to it. She lowered the pole to the machine. The oil caught fire. When the blaze reached the gas tank, the explosion disintegrated an already charring mass.

Trax heard the muffled roar up the incline behind him. The demijohns were where the Lantry boys had indicated. They were broken. He left the stench of overturned mash and spilled alcohol and ran to the house. He could not for a moment comprehend that the twisting mass of metal and flame was the blue sedan.

Matt stood on the rear stoop. He looked at her in bewilderment. His stare dropped from her straggling gray hair down the length of her frame. Her apron was smudged and torn. Her hands were black and raw. He came back to her implacable cold eyes. He choked.

"You done it yourself!"

He burst into spasmodic curses, then broke off, overcome by their futility. The sweat ran into his eyes. He wiped it out and gaped about him in loose-mouthed confusion. He shuffled a few feet to the stoop and sank down on the bottom step. The woman looked down at him.

"Better git goin'."

He rose, swaying.

"You ol' . . . "

His obscenities fell away from her as rain washed from the weathered shingles of the old house. She towered over him. The tall house towered over him. He was as alien as on the bright day when he had first come hunting here.

He plunged up the steps toward her, his head low between his shoulders.

"Better git back."

His outstretched fists dropped at his sides. The fingers fell open. The woman lifted the shotgun.

"Better git — "

He shook his head, unbelieving. His eyes clung to the dark cavities of the pitted steel. He moved one foot slowly to the next step.

The woman aimed carefully at the shoe, as though it were some strange reptile creeping into the house. She fired a trifle to the left, so that the pattern of the double-ought buckshot shell sprayed in a close mass into the sand. One pellet clipped through the leather, and a drop of blood sank placidly into the pine step. The man stared fascinated. His hand jerked to his mouth, like a wooden toy moved by strings. He stifled a sound, or tried to make one. The woman could not tell. He lifted a face dry with fear and backed down the steps.

It was necessary to walk widely to the side to avoid the heat of the burned car. He threw out his hands hopelessly and hesitated. The sun slanted orange and gold through the hammock. Beyond, there were already shadows among the dark pines. It would be twilight before he could be out of the flatwoods. He found voice.

"Matt," he whined, "how'll I git to town?"

The woman wiped her streaked face with a corner of her apron.

"Reckon you'll have to git there on foot, Mister — the way you come in the first place."

She turned her back and went into the house. The girl had come down the stairs and was flattened against a wall. Her face was brushed with a desperate knowledge. Matt jerked her head at the open front door.

"All right. I'm thu. You kin go on with him now."

"Matt — "

"Go on. Git."

The girl did not move. Matt pushed her headlong to the door. Elly took hold of the big arm with both hands, drawing back, and Matt struck her away. She went confusedly down the steps. Trax was leaving the hammock. He struck wildly through the pines. The girl took a few steps after him, then turned toward the woman watching from the doorway. Matt called loudly:

"Go on. Git."

The man had reached the road and was plunging along it to the north. The girl ran three or four paces in his direction, then stopped again, like a stray dog or cat that would not be driven away. She hesitated at the edge of the hammock. The small uncertain figure was visible between the twin oaks beyond the high porch. Matt turned into the house and closed the door.

She was strong and whole. She was fixed, deep-rooted as the pine trees. They leaned a little, bent by an ancient storm. Nothing more could move them.

The car in the yard had settled into a smoking heap. The acrid smell of burned rubber and paint filled the house. Matt closed the north window to keep out the stench. The glass rattled in its frame. The air was gusty and the spring night would be cold. There were swift movements and rattlings among the oak boughs above the roof, as though small creatures were pattering across the floor of the wind.

Matt shivered and kindled a fire in the front room. She looked about for the cat. The noise and disorder of the day had driven him to distant hunting grounds and he had not yet ventured to return. She drew close to the fire in her rocker and held her smudged hands to the blaze.

She thought, "I've lit a bait o' fires today."

That was over and done with. There would be no more 'shining among the palmettos; no more coming and going of folk; no more Trax and his owl-faced girl. She was very tired. Her square frame relaxed in its exhaustion. She leaned back her head and drowsed deeply in her chair.

When she wakened, the fire had burned to ashes. The moon rode high over the flatwoods, with clouds scurrying underneath. The room was silver, then black, as the moonlight came and went. The chill wind sucked through the pines. There was another sound; the sobbing of a lighter breath. Suddenly Matt knew the girl was still there.

She rose in a plunge from the rocker. She wasn't done with them yet. . . . She opened the door a few inches and listened. The muffled sound was unmistakable. It was the choked gasping of a child that has cried itself breathless. It came from the edge of the hammock. Where the pines began she could distinguish a huddle on the ground that was neither stump nor bushes. She closed the door.

Trax was gone — and Elly was here.

He had flung away and left her behind. She was discarded, as Matt had been long discarded. He was through with Elly, too. For the first time the woman was able to conceive of them separately. And the one was gone, and the other was here. She groped her way stupefied to the kitchen, lighted a kerosene lamp, and made a fire in the range. She wanted a scalding pot of tea to stop her shivering. She split a cold biscuit and fried it and sat down with her plate and teacup. She breathed hard, and ate and drank mechanically.

" He was done with her a long ways back."

He had driven off alone in the blue sedan, not to infuriate, but because there was nothing else to do with the girl. Matt chewed her biscuit slowly. She laughed grimly.

" I give him too much credit fer smartness."

A flash of anger stirred her, like a spurt of flame from an old fire, that Elly should be now at the edge of the hammock.

" Trax wa'n't man enough to take off his mess with him."

She sipped her cooling tea.

She remembered grudgingly the girl's contentment. The shadow of the man, passing away, left clear the picture of a child, pulling moss apart and cutting paper dolls. Rage at Trax possessed her.

" I'd orter hided him fer takin' sech a young un along his low-down way."

In a burst of fury she conceded the girl's youth. Elly was too young . . .

" I'd orter been hided. Me an' Trax together."

Matt rose from the table and gathered up the few dishes. She stopped in the act. She looked at her hands as though their knotty strength were strange to her.

" Snatchin' off a young un's rations . . ."

She leaned heavily on the table, pondering. Emptiness filled the house — a living presence — appalling — still.

She strode abruptly out the door and through the hammock to the pines. The moon had swung toward its setting and the rays lay long under the trees. The girl lay crouched against a broad mottled trunk.

Matt said, "You kin come on back."

The emaciated figure wavered from the ground on spindling legs. It tried to crowd close to the warmth of the woman's body. As they moved toward the house, the girl stumbled in the run-over slippers.

Matt said, "Here. Gimme them crazy shoes."

Elly stopped and took them from her bare feet. The woman put them in her apron pockets. She went ahead of the girl into the front room and bent down to kindle a fire.

— From *When the Whippoorwill,* Charles Scribner's Sons, 1940. Reprinted by permission.

BIOGRAPHICAL SKETCHES

Richmond Croom Beatty

Richmond Croom Beatty was born in Shawnee, Oklahoma, January 6, 1905. In 1907 his family returned to Alabama, settling in Birmingham. He was educated in the public schools of this city and at Birmingham-Southern College, where he was graduated A.B. in 1926. He received his M.A. and Ph.D. degrees from Vanderbilt University in 1928 and 1930. Since then he has taught at State Teachers College, Memphis (1930–1935), the University of Alabama (1935–1937), and Vanderbilt University, where he is at present Associate Professor of English.

He has contributed to such scholarly and critical magazines as *Forum, Yale Review, American Review, PMLA, Philological Quarterly*, and *American Literature*. He has also edited *English Dramas* (with E. W. Parks, 1935) and *William Byrd's Natural History of Virginia* (with William Mulloy, 1940). His biographies include *William Byrd of Westover* (1932), *Bayard Taylor* (1936), and *Lord Macaulay* (1938). He is at present, as a Guggenheim Fellow, completing a life of James Russell Lowell.

Roark Bradford

Mr. Bradford was born in Lauderdale County, Tennessee, August 21, 1896. He is descended from a line of Virginians who trace their ancestry to Governor William Bradford of Massachusetts. His early education was received at home and in the public schools of Tennessee and Arkansas. He was graduated in advance of his class from the University of California in 1917 in order that he might attend a training school for the coast artillery. Between 1920 and

1926 he worked on various newspapers in Georgia and Louisiana. He makes his home in the historic Old French Quarter of New Orleans.

Mr. Bradford's Negro stories were fairly well known before the publication of *Ol' Man Adam an' His Chillun* (1928), but his work was more widely recognized after Marc Connelly turned this book into dramatic form in *The Green Pastures*, which won the Pulitzer Prize for drama in 1930. *Ol' King David and the Philistine Boys* (1930) is a continuation of *Ol' Man Adam*. Other works by Mr. Bradford are *This Side of Jordan* (1929), *How Come Christmas* (1930), *John Henry* (1931), *Kingdom Coming* (1933), *Let the Band Play Dixie* (1934; short stories), and *The Three-Headed Angel* (1937). As a musical drama with Paul Robeson in the title rôle, *John Henry* had a brief run in New York during the season 1939–1940. Mr. Bradford has contributed short stories to numerous magazines.

Cleanth Brooks, Jr.

Mr. Brooks was born in Kentucky, October 16, 1906, but was reared in Tennessee. He attended Vanderbilt University, receiving his A.B. in 1928. After taking an M.A. at Tulane in 1929 he attended Oxford as a Rhodes Scholar, where he received his B.A. in 1932. Mr. Brooks is at present Associate Professor of English at Louisiana State University and associate editor of the *Southern Review*.

He has published essays in *Who Owns America*, *Virginia Quarterly Review*, *Southern Review*, and *A Southern Treasury of Life and Literature*, and is the author of the two books, *The Relation of the Alabama-Georgia Dialect to the Provincial Dialects of Great Britain* (1935) and *Modern Poetry and the Tradition* (1939). He has also edited several textbooks, including *An Approach to Literature* (with R. P. Warren and others) and *Understanding Poetry* (also with R. P. Warren).

Erskine Caldwell

Erskine Caldwell was born near White Oak, Georgia, December 17, 1903. During his childhood his father's appointments as a Presbyterian minister were often changed and his schooling was constantly interrupted. He attended Erskine College, the University of Virginia, and the University of Pennsylvania. While living in many parts of the South and North, in towns and large cities, and working as mill laborer, cotton picker, hack driver, book reviewer, stage hand, professional football player, cook, and waiter, he became intimately acquainted with the poor whites and other underprivileged groups about whom he writes. Many of his works, particularly the novels *Tobacco Road* (1932) and *God's Little Acre* (1933), treat of economic conditions in the South. In his effort to reveal what he considers the whole truth, his works have often run afoul of the censors. *Tobacco Road,* dramatized by Jack Kirkland and produced in 1933, is still enjoying (in 1940) a record-breaking continuous run in New York City and has been applauded in nearly every city in the country. In 1938 Mr. Caldwell lectured at the New School for Social Research on "Southern Tenant Farmers." His other works include *Journeyman* (1935; a novel), *Kneel to the Rising Sun and Other Stories* (1935), *Southways* (1938; short stories), books of social criticism, and a book of travel. He makes his home in Mount Vernon, Maine, but frequently travels in other parts of the country.

Clarence Elmore Cason

Clarence Cason was born in Ragland, Alabama, December 20, 1898. He was educated in the public schools of Talladega, Alabama, and at the University of Alabama and the University of Wisconsin. During the World War he was an instructor in aerial machine gunnery in France. He was an instructor at the University of Wisconsin and the University of Minnesota, and was head of the Department of Journalism at the University of Alabama. He died on May 8, 1935.

Professor Cason published articles, poems, and stories, principally about problems in the South, in many journals and magazines. His editorials appeared in many prominent newspapers, among them the New York *Times*, the Washington *Times*, the Louisville *Courier-Journal*, the *Christian Science Monitor*, and the Baltimore *Sun*. In 1935 his essays on the South were collected and published under the title *90° in the Shade*.

Brainard Cheney

Brainard Cheney was born in Fitzgerald, Georgia, June 3, 1900, and spent his boyhood in Lumber City, a town in the same vicinity. He attended college at The Citadel, the University of Georgia, and Vanderbilt University. Since 1925 he has engaged in newspaper work as a political commentator for the Nashville *Banner*.

His first published work outside the field of journalism was his Houghton Mifflin Prize Novel *Lightwood*, which appeared in 1939. The setting of this volume is the piney-woods country of Georgia. Mr. Cheney is at work at present on a second novel with a similar background.

Virginius Dabney

Virginius Dabney was born on the campus of the University of Virginia, February 8, 1901. He was also educated at this university, taking his A.B. in 1920 and his M.A. the following year. After a term spent as teacher of French, Mr. Dabney turned to journalism. He served as a reporter for the Richmond *Times Dispatch*, and then as capitol reporter for the *News Leader*. He returned to the *Times Dispatch* as chief editorial writer, his present position. He has won honors for "distinguished editorial writing," and in 1934 he spent six months in central Europe on a grant from the Oberlaender Trust. He has contributed frequently to magazines. *Liberalism in the South* appeared in 1932.

Donald Davidson

Mr. Davidson was born in Campbellsville, Tennessee, August 18, 1893, and was educated in his native state. He received his A.B. and

M.A. degrees at Vanderbilt University in 1917 and 1922 respectively. During the World War he served as a first lieutenant in the American Expeditionary Force. Since 1920 he has been a member of the Vanderbilt faculty, where he is now Professor of English.

Mr. Davidson has been an important figure in both the Fugitive and Agrarian groups of writers. His poetry includes *An Outland Piper* (1924), *The Tall Men* (1927), and *Lee in the Mountains and Other Poems* (1938). He has written frequently for *Forum, Southern Review, American Review,* and other magazines; and during the years 1927–1930 he edited a book page for newspapers in Nashville, Memphis, and Knoxville that was regarded by many as containing the finest body of critical reviews ever printed in the South. His latest volumes include a collection of essays, *The Attack on Leviathan* (1938), and a widely used textbook, *American Composition and Rhetoric* (1939).

Ward Allison Dorrance

Mr. Dorrance was born in Jefferson City, Missouri, April 30, 1904. He was reared by a grandparent who had served under General Lee, and is entirely Southern in his ancestry. He attended the University of Missouri, being graduated A.B. in 1926. After a year of study at the Sorbonne he returned to his Alma Mater, where he took his doctorate in 1935. At present he is Associate Professor of French at this university.

Mr. Dorrance has evinced a great interest in the Indian and folk traditions of the Ozark region. His books include: *The Survival of French in the Old District of Sainte Genevieve* (1935), *Three Ozark Streams* (1937), *We're from Missouri* (1938), and *Where the Rivers Meet* (1939). He has been awarded a Guggenheim fellowship for 1940–1941.

William Faulkner

William Faulkner was born in New Albany, Mississippi, September 25, 1897. Many of his ancestors were prominent in Southern politics; one of them, Colonel William Falkner [sic], wrote the popular novel, *The White Rose of Memphis*. Mr. Faulkner left the University of Mississippi after two years to join the Canadian (later, the British) flying corps. On his return to this country he attended college, worked as painter and carpenter, served as postmaster at the University of Mississippi, and wrote poems, articles, and fiction. When he was writing his first novel, *Soldiers' Pay*, and composing sketches for the New Orleans *Times-Picayune*, he roomed with Sherwood Anderson. He has visited New York and Hollywood several times and has written for the films, but he prefers the quiet of his large old house in Oxford, Mississippi.

Among his early novels, which did not sell well, are *Soldiers' Pay* (1926), *Sartoris* (1929), and *The Sound and the Fury* (1929). When *Sanctuary* was rejected by the publisher, he began the novel *As I Lay Dying* (1930) while earning his living as a coal shoveler in a power plant. After the publication of *Sanctuary* in 1931, Mr. Faulkner's novels and stories enjoyed a wide popularity. His later novels include *Light in August* (1932), *Absalom, Absalom!* (1936), *The Unvanquished* (1938), *The Wild Palms* (1939), and *The Hamlet* (1940). His short stories, published in numerous magazines, have been collected in *These Thirteen* (1931) and *Doctor Martino and Other Stories* (1934). He has published several volumes of poetry.

Caroline Gordon

Caroline Gordon was born in Todd County, Kentucky, October 6, 1895. She was graduated from Bethany College in West Virginia, and taught briefly in the high school at Clarksville, Tennessee, before turning to journalism. In 1924 she married Allen Tate. After living seven years in New York and in France (Miss Gordon was a Guggenheim Fellow for a year) the Tates moved to their home "Benfolly" in Clarksville, Tennessee. While still maintaining "Benfolly" as a residence, they have lived in Memphis and in Greensboro, North Carolina, where Mrs. Tate gave courses in short story writing. Their winter residence is now at Princeton.

Caroline Gordon has written many short stories that have won recognition in the better known collections. Her work has appeared chiefly in *Scribner's* and the *Southern Review*. She is also the author of four novels: *Penhally* (1931), *Aleck Maury, Sportsman* (1934), *None Shall Look Back* (1937), and *The Garden of Adonis* (1937).

Gerald White Johnson

Mr. Johnson was born in Riverton, North Carolina, August 6, 1890. He was graduated from Wake Forest College in 1911, and after service in France during the World War, he studied at the University of Toulouse, France. He has received honorary degrees from two colleges and a university. Until 1926 he was associated with several newspapers in North Carolina; since that year he has been an editorial writer for the Baltimore *Evening Sun*.

Mr. Johnson has contributed to numerous periodicals. Among his books are: *The Undefeated* (1926), *What Is News?* (1926), *Andrew Jackson: An Epic in Homespun* (1927), *Randolph of Roanoke* (1929), *The Secession of the Southern States* (1933), *The Sunpapers of Baltimore* (1937; in collaboration), *The Wasted Land* (1937), *American Way* (1938; in collaboration), and *America's Silver Age: the Statecraft of Clay-Webster-Calhoun* (1939).

Andrew Nelson Lytle

Andrew Lytle was born in Murfreesboro, Tennessee, December 26, 1902. He attended Sewanee Military Academy and later Vanderbilt University, where he received his B.A. in 1925. During the years 1927–1928 he was a student of George Pierce Baker in the School of the Drama at Yale.

Mr. Lytle has written stories and essays for the *Southern Review*, *Virginia Quarterly Review*, *Who Owns America*, *I'll Take My Stand*, and other publications. He has also written several plays and directed others frequently. For a year (1929) he acted professionally in New York. His books include *Bedford Forrest and His Critter Company* (1931) and a novel, *The Long Night* (1936). As a Guggenheim Fellow (1940–1941), he is completing another novel based upon the character of DeSoto.

George Marion O'Donnell

George Marion O'Donnell was born January 21, 1914, at Midnight Plantation, Midnight, Mississippi. He attended high school in Belzoni, Mississippi. During the years 1932–1934 he was a student at the State Teachers College, Memphis, Tennessee. In 1935 he entered the junior class at Vanderbilt University and was graduated A.B. in 1936; he received his M.A. in 1937. The two years following this period of study he ran a plantation in the Delta. In 1939 he returned to Vanderbilt as Fellow in Creative Writing.

Mr. O'Donnell has published in numerous critical and literary magazines, including the *Southern Review, Kenyon Review, Virginia Quarterly Review, Sewanee Review,* and *Poetry*. He was also a contributor to *Who Owns America*. At present he is at work on the first of a series of novels dealing with the development of the Delta region.

Frank Lawrence Owsley

Frank Lawrence Owsley was born in McGehee (a family name), Montgomery County, Alabama, January 20, 1890. He attended school at Wetumpka High School, entering the Alabama Polytechnic Institute, at Auburn, as an advanced undergraduate in 1909. Two years later he received his B.S. degree from this school, and a year later his M.S. Dr. Owsley took his M.A. at the University of Chicago in 1917 and his Ph.D. from the same institution in 1924. He taught at Birmingham-Southern College for several years before coming to Vanderbilt University in 1922, where he is at present Professor of History. He has held a Guggenheim fellowship.

Dr. Owsley is universally recognized as a foremost Southern historian. He contributed to *I'll Take My Stand* and to *Who Owns America,* and has written frequently for such publications as the *Southern Review, Virginia Quarterly Review, American Review, Mississippi Valley Historical Magazine,* and *Journal of Southern History*. He also contributed a monograph to the collection of *Essays in Honor of William E. Dodd*. His books include *States Rights in the Confederacy* (1925) and *King Cotton Diplomacy*

(1931). Recently he has been directing a number of revolutionary graduate studies at Vanderbilt University involving a reëxamination of the social structure of the Old South, and has published articles on this subject. For the year 1940 he is serving as President of the Southern Historical Association.

Edd Winfield Parks

Edd Winfield Parks was born in Newbern, Tennessee, in 1906. He was educated at the University of Tennessee, at Occidental College, and at Harvard University, from which he was graduated A.B. in 1928. After a year's teaching Mr. Parks entered Vanderbilt University, where he taught and studied for several years, receiving his M.A. from this institution in 1929 and his Ph.D. in 1933. Afterwards he served as head of the Department of English at Cumberland University. Since 1935 he has been teaching at the University of Georgia, where he is at present Associate Professor of English. He has also taught for several summers at Duke University.

Dr. Parks has written numerous critical articles and reviews for such magazines as the *Virginia Quarterly*, *Southern Review*, *New Republic*, *American Review*, *Sewanee Review*, and for *Culture in the South*. He has also edited *The Great Critics* (with J. H. Smith, 1932), *English Dramas* (with R. C. Beatty, 1935), *Sut Lovingood Travels with Old Abe Lincoln* (1937) and *Southern Poets* (for the American Writers Series, 1938). His books include *Segments of Southern Thought* (1939) — a collection of essays on Southern figures — and *Charles Egbert Craddock*, a biography, scheduled for publication in the autumn of 1940.

Julia Peterkin

Julia Peterkin was born in Laurens County, South Carolina, October 31, 1880. She received her bachelor's and master's degrees from Converse College before she was seventeen. After several years of teaching in a country school, she married and became mistress of Lang Syne Plantation near Fort Motte, South Carolina. Until recently Mrs. Peterkin helped manage the large plantation, and often served as doctor or adviser to several hundred Negroes and a few whites. In addition, she cultivated numerous hobbies — growing flowers, raising setters and turkeys, embroidering, planting fruits and vegetables, and studying music in Columbia, forty miles away.

After hearing Mrs. Peterkin speak of her vivid experiences on the plantation, her music teacher advised her to write stories. Her second novel, *Scarlet Sister Mary* (1928), which deals with the gullah Negro of South Carolina, won the Pulitzer award. It was later dramatized, Ethel Barrymore playing a leading rôle. Mrs. Peterkin still lives on her plantation. She is enthusiastic about outdoor life, is active in clubs, and has lectured at the Bread Loaf Writers' Conference. Other novels are *Black April* (1927) and *Bright Skin* (1932). Her short stories are collected in *Green Thursday* (1924). She has written essays and a study of Negro life, *Roll, Jordan, Roll* (1933).

John Crowe Ransom

John Crowe Ransom was born in Pulaski, Tennessee, April 30, 1888. The town is noted as the birthplace of Sam Davis and of the Ku Klux Klan, which Mr. Ransom's own great-uncle aided in organizing. Mr. Ransom received his A.B. degree from Vanderbilt University in 1909, and after teaching briefly in secondary schools in the South he was appointed a Rhodes Scholar. He took the " greats " or classical course at Oxford and received his B.A. in 1913. The following year he became a member of the English department at Vanderbilt, where he taught, with the exception of two years with the American Expeditionary Force and one year as a Guggenheim Fellow, until 1937. He is now Professor of Literature at Kenyon College, Gambier, Ohio, and editor of the *Kenyon Review*.

His writings have been numerous. His first three volumes were collections of poems which he produced during the decade 1917–1927. *Poems about God* appeared in 1919, to be followed by *Chills and Fever* in 1924 and *Two Gentlemen in Bonds* in 1927. During this period he was an important figure in the Fugitive Poets, who founded a poetry magazine in Nashville in 1922 which attracted wide attention both in this country and abroad. In 1930 his volume *God without Thunder*, an unorthodox defense of orthodoxy, indicated the beginning of a critical talent that has strengthened steadily and variously since. Mr. Ransom contributed important essays to the two Agrarian anthologies *I'll Take My Stand* and *Who Owns America*, and he has written frequently of late for the *Southern Review*, *American Review*, and his own Quarterly. His last book, *The World's Body*, a collection of essays about poetry, was published in 1938.

Marjorie Kinnan Rawlings

Marjorie (Kinnan) Rawlings was born in Washington, D. C., August 8, 1896. She attended the University of Wisconsin, where she was graduated A.B., with Phi Beta Kappa honors, in 1918. The next year she married Charles A. Rawlings. She spent the following decade doing newspaper work in New York City, Louisville, Kentucky, and Rochester, New York. Since 1928 she has lived on her orange grove in Hawthorn, Florida, and her most important literary work has been written against this Southern background.

Mrs. Rawlings' publications, in addition to many short stories, include *South Moon Under* (1933), *Golden Apples* (1935), and *The Yearling* (1938), which was awarded the Pulitzer Prize and enjoyed extensive popularity. A collection of her stories, *When the Whippoorwill* appeared in 1940.

Elizabeth Madox Roberts

Elizabeth Madox Roberts was born near Springfield, Kentucky, in 1886. She now lives in this region, known as the " Pigeon River country." Her ancestors were pioneers in Kentucky, and she spent her childhood in Kentucky and Colorado. In 1921, after making a brilliant record and winning prizes for essays and poetry, she was graduated from the University of Chicago. She went to New York, and after several years of painstaking work published her first novel, *The Time of Man* (1926), which was praised by the leading critics of this country and Europe. Other novels include *My Heart and My Flesh* (1927), *Jingling in the Wind* (1928), *The Great Meadow* (1930), *A Buried Treasure* (1931), *He Sent Forth a Raven* (1935), and *Black is My Truelove's Hair* (1938). A collection of short stories appeared in *The Haunted Mirror* (1932). She has published several volumes of poems.

Daniel Merritt Robison

Dr. Robison was born in Arrington, Williamson County, in middle Tennessee, September 30, 1893, and received his preparatory school education at the Battle Ground Academy in Franklin. During the years 1912–1915 he attended Vanderbilt University, dropping out at the end of his junior session to assume the office of county trustee of Williamson County, a position left vacant upon the death of his father. During the next year (1916–1917) he taught school at Peoples-Tucker High School in Springfield, Tennessee, resigning in order to enlist in the American Expeditionary Force. He was an officer in the army until his discharge in 1919, after which he returned to Vanderbilt, where he was graduated A.B. in 1920.

Dr. Robison's career for the next ten years was varied. He was employed by the International Shoe Company during the period 1920–1924, working in St. Louis and Illinois. For the next five years he was owner and editor of the Olney *Times*, a Democratic newspaper, published in Olney, Illinois. In the fall of 1929 he sold this journal and returned to Vanderbilt for graduate work. He was awarded his M.A. in History in 1930, and his Ph.D. in 1932. Thereafter he taught for four years at State Teachers College, Memphis, before being recalled to Vanderbilt, where he is at present Associate Professor of American History.

Dr. Robison has published articles in the *Journal of Southern History, Mississippi Historical Review, Tennessee Historical Magazine, Publications of the East Tennessee Historical Society,* and *Dictionary of National Biography*. He has also published a book, *Bob Taylor and the Agrarian Revolt in Tennessee* (1935). At present he is at work on a series of books dealing with the Whig tradition in the Solid South.

Wilbur Daniel Steele

Wilbur Daniel Steele was born in Greensboro, North Carolina, March 17, 1886. He was educated in Denver, where his father moved to become Professor of Bible Literature at the University of Denver. He attended art school at night during his undergraduate career, and on his graduation from the University of Denver he studied art in Boston, Paris, Florence, Venice, and New York. He wrote short stories while studying abroad, and though successful in his painting and etching, he decided to make writing his career. He has lived in Provincetown and Nantucket, Massachusetts, and in Charleston, South Carolina, and has traveled widely in Europe, Africa, and the United States.

Since 1919 Mr. Steele has won many prizes and contests for his short stories, which he has published in magazines and in the following collections: *Land's End and Other Stories* (1918), *The Shame Dance and Other Stories* (1923), *Urkey Island* (1926), *The Man Who Saw through Heaven and Other Stories* (1927), and *Tower of Sand and Other Stories* (1929). In recent years, however, he has devoted more of his time to plays than to short fiction. Among his novels are *Storm* (1914), *Isles of the Blest* (1924), and *Sound of Rowlocks* (1938).

Hudson Strode

Professor Strode was born in Cairo, Illinois, of Southern parents, on October 31, 1892. He received his schooling in Demopolis, Alabama, and was graduated from the University of Alabama (A.B.) and Columbia University (M.A.). He taught English at Syracuse University for two years, and since 1916 has been Professor of English at the University of Alabama.

He has published articles, poems, book reviews, and stories in numerous magazines and metropolitan newspapers, and has edited an anthology of lyric poetry, *Immortal Lyrics* (1938). His best known works, however, are books interpreting foreign countries: *The Story of Bermuda* (1932), *The Pageant of Cuba* (1935), and *South by Thunderbird* (1937). He is now at work on an interpretation of the Scandinavian countries and Finland.

Jesse Stuart

Jesse Stuart was born in the tiny settlement of W-Hollow, near Riverton, Kentucky, in 1907. He attended rural grammar schools and held odd jobs intermittently until 1922. After several years in high school at Greenup, he farmed, worked for a street carnival (until he was fired for letting girls ride the ferris wheel free), served at an army camp, and became a good blacksmith. He wrote poetry continually. Subsequently he entered Memorial University, Harrogate, Tennessee, and while there earned all of his expenses; he was graduated in three years. He taught school in the hills of Kentucky, spent a year at Vanderbilt University, and published a few poems in small magazines.

In 1933 the *American Mercury* published one of his poems, and since that time his verse and short stories have appeared regularly in many important magazines. His books include *Man with the Bull-Tongue Plow* (1932; poetry), *Head o' W-Hollow* (1936; short stories), *Beyond Dark Hills* (1938; autobiography), and *Trees of Heaven* (1940), a novel. For the last few years Mr. Stuart has farmed, served as principal of the Greenup County High School, and written verse and stories. He resides at Riverton, Kentucky.

Allen Tate

Allen Tate was born in Winchester, Clark County, Kentucky, November 19, 1899. He attended schools in Louisville, Nashville, and Washington, D. C., and was graduated A.B. *magna cum laude* at Vanderbilt University in 1922. He was one of the founders of the *Fugitive* and an important figure in the Agrarian movement. After several years' residence in New York, and in Europe as a Guggenheim Fellow, he taught at Southwestern University, in Memphis, and the Women's College of North Carolina at Greensboro. He has also lectured at Columbia and Harvard. At present he is Professor of Creative Writing at Princeton.

Mr. Tate is one of the most distinguished men of letters the South has produced. His works include two biographies, *Stonewall Jackson* (1928) and *Jefferson Davis* (1929), and several volumes of verse: *Mr. Pope and Other Poems* (1928), *Poems, 1928–1931* (1932), *The Mediterranean* (1936), and *Selected Poems* (1937). He has also written frequently for the *American Review, Southern Review, Yale Review, New Republic,* and other publications. A number of his essays appeared in 1936 under the title *Reactionary Essays in Poetry and Ideas.* His latest work is a novel, *The Fathers* (1938).

Floyd Tillery

Floyd Tillery was born near Opelika, Alabama, September 16, 1891. He was graduated from the University of Alabama in 1912. Mr. Tillery served as reporter on several newspapers in Alabama and taught for many years in private and public schools. During the World War he was stationed at an Officers' School of the United States Navy. After the war he did social welfare work in Birmingham, Alabama, for eight years. He has contributed articles and stories to such publications as *Forum, American Spectator* (Nathan-Boyd régime), *Christian Century, Nation, Your Life, Household,* and *Southern Literary Messenger.* Since 1936 Mr. Tillery has been an associate editor of the *Chattahoochee Valley Times* (Lanett, Alabama) and the West Point, Georgia, *News.* His address is West Point, Georgia.

Howell Vines

Howell Vines was born at Short Creek, Alabama, in 1900. He received his schooling in Jefferson County, Alabama, and attended the University of Alabama and Harvard. He has taught literature at Shorter College, Rice Institute, and the University of Richmond. Mr. Vines resides near Bessemer, Alabama.

"The Mustydines Was Ripe" is Mr. Vines' first short story; he published two novels previously: *A River Goes with Heaven* (1930) and *This Green Thicket World* (1934).

John Donald Wade

John Donald Wade was born in Marshallville, Georgia, September 28, 1892. He was graduated A.B. from the University of Georgia (1914), M.A. from Harvard (1915), and Ph.D. from Columbia (1924). He taught English at the University of Georgia in the years 1919–1925, and was Professor of English and American Literature at Vanderbilt University during 1928–1934. At present he holds a similar position at the University of Georgia, where he is also chairman of the Humanities Division.

Dr. Wade has written numerous essays for the *American Mercury*, *Virginia Quarterly Review*, and *Southern Review*; and for collections including *I'll Take My Stand*, *Who Owns America*, and *Culture in the South*. His books are *Augustus Baldwin Longstreet, a Study of the Development of Culture in the South* (1924) and *John Wesley* (1930). He was a Guggenheim Fellow in England during 1927, and the following year served as associate editor of the *Dictionary of National Biography*.

Robert Penn Warren

Robert Penn Warren was born in Guthrie, Kentucky, April 24, 1905. He was educated in the public schools of Kentucky and at Vanderbilt University, where he received his A.B. in 1925. Later he attended the University of California (M.A., 1927) and Yale University. He was named a Rhodes Scholar in 1928 and was graduated B.A. at Oxford in 1930. During this period he wrote for the Agrarian symposium, *I'll Take My Stand* (he had contributed frequently to the *Fugitive* while an undergraduate at Vanderbilt); and later one of his essays was included in *Who Owns America*. Other essays, stories, and poems have appeared frequently in *Scribner's*, *American Review*, *Virginia Quarterly Review*, *Southern Review*, *Poetry*, and other magazines.

Mr. Warren has taught English at Vanderbilt University, Southwestern University, and Louisiana State University. He is at present on leave of absence from Louisiana State University, as a Guggenheim Fellow. In addition to his regular academic duties he has served as associate editor of the *Southern Review* since its founding in 1935. His works include *John Brown, the Making of a Martyr* (1929), *Thirty-Six Poems* (1935), and *Night Rider*, a Houghton Mifflin Prize Novel (1939). He is an editor of several textbooks, including *An Approach to Literature, Understanding Poetry*, and *A Southern Harvest* (a collection of recent short stories by Southerners). During his present leave, Mr. Warren is completing a poetic drama, and he has another novel projected for the immediate future.

Walter Prescott Webb

Dr. Webb was born in Panola County, Texas, April 3, 1888. He received his bachelor's degree from his state university in 1915, his M.A. in 1920, and his Ph.D. in 1932. Meanwhile he had done further graduate work at the University of Chicago and the University of Wisconsin. He received a Guggenheim fellowship in 1932, and is at present Professor of History at the University of Texas.

Dr. Webb's books have proved of first-rate importance in the field of American history. *The Great Plains* — which was awarded the Loubat Prize by Columbia University — appeared in 1931. *The Texas Rangers*, a continuation of his regional studies, was brought out in 1935, to be followed by *Divided We Stand* — a brilliant defense of regionalism — in 1938. He also wrote, with E. L. Barker and W. E. Dodd, *The Growth of a Nation* (1928) and *The Story of Our Nation* (1929).

Thomas Wolfe

Thomas Wolfe was born in Asheville, North Carolina, October 3, 1900. He was graduated from the University of North Carolina and then attended the Harvard Graduate School for three years (A.M., 1922). In 1924 he became an instructor in English at New York University, resigning in 1930 to travel and study abroad on a Guggenheim fellowship. He died in Baltimore on September 15, 1938.

Wolfe wrote voluminously after his fourteenth year. Before his first novel, *Look Homeward, Angel,* appeared in 1929, he spent months in condensing and cutting the bulky manuscript. On his return from Europe in 1931, he brought with him about four hundred thousand words of material; in the same year he started a new book. An editor persuaded him to stop writing and begin the organization of his manuscripts for publication, which he did during 1934. *Of Time and the River,* a continuation of the plot of his first novel, appeared in 1935. Wolfe's short stories and sketches, some of which were collected in *From Death to Morning* (1935), were published in numerous magazines. *The Story of a Novel* (1936) describes his experiences as a writer. A posthumous novel, *The Web and the Rock,* appeared in 1939, and the last piece of longer fiction by Wolfe will be published sometime during 1940.

Wolfe's writing owes much of its richness to his excellent retentive memory, an insatiable desire for every kind of knowledge and experience, a lifelong habit of collecting facts and taking notes, and a deep love for the things of this earth. He admitted that his books are filled with incidents from his life, shaped to the purposes of the fictional context.

Stark Young

Stark Young was born in Como, Mississippi, October 11, 1881. He attended a private school and the University of Mississippi, from which he was graduated in 1901. He received his master's degree from Columbia in 1902. Mr. Young became a member of the faculty of the University of Mississippi in 1904, of the University of Texas in 1907, and of Amherst in 1915. He has been the dramatic critic on the New York *Times,* an editor of the *New Republic* and *Theatre Arts Monthly,* a director of plays (Lenormand's *The Failures* and O'Neill's *Welded*), and a lecturer. His novels are *Heaven Trees* (1926), *The Torches Flare* (1928), *River House* (1929), and *So Red the Rose* (1934). He published a collection of short stories, *The Street of the Islands,* in 1935. His other works include plays, poems, books about the theater, essays and sketches, a book of travel, textbooks, and translations. He resides in New York City.